D1482727

The Electromagnetodynamics of Fluids

The Electromagnetodynamics of Fluids

W. F. HUGHES AND F. J. YOUNG

Carnegie Institute of Technology

John Wiley & Sons, Inc., New York | London | Sydney

Library of Congress Catalog Card Number: 66-17631
Printed in the United States of America

Preface

In this book electrodynamics, thermodynamics, and fluid mechanics are integrated to yield a unified treatment of the foundations of magnetofluidmechanics, so important in the study of magnetohydrodynamics, plasma physics, and astrophysics. The first six chapters are devoted to explaining fundamental principles which are reinforced by many worked example problems. The remainder of the book is used to increase the reader's understanding and ability to apply these principles to actual physical problems with a realistic appreciation of the assumptions and the approximations involved. In pursuit of this goal much material of interest to the researcher is presented in the form of detailed analytical solutions and their graphical representation. The choice of the detailed examples was a difficult one because magnetofluidmechanics embraces such a wide range of phenomena. Although it is too much to expect that all of the examples presented here will prove to be important and useful, a rather wide range of applications of magnetofluidmechanics is covered.

This book is intended to be used both as a text for a two-semester graduate course and as a book for the professional engineer who wants to acquaint himself with this rapidly developing area. It is assumed that the students are advanced graduate students familiar with classical electricity and magnetism, thermodynamics, and fluid mechanics. However, since most students at this level are not familiar with the electrodynamics of moving media, the book begins with a discussion of special relativity and electrodynamics. Throughout the book the role of the electrodynamics of moving media is emphasized because it is the least understood and often the most important aspect of magnetofluidmechanics. Although the electrodynamics of moving media can be handled in most magnetohydrodynamic applications without recourse to special relativity, the relativistic development of electrodynamics is essential to the physical understanding of the subject and allows a more basic approach to problems in cosmical magnetofluidmechanics. It is noteworthy that the relativistic treatment of electrodynamics immediately resolves many paradoxes encountered in the literature concerning induced electromotive force and induced charge. Some of the examples the reader is asked to work are questions that keep recurring in the literature about once each decade. Problem 2-14 is such an example and is easily solved by the relativistic approach.

From our experience in the study and teaching of magnetofluidmechanics we find that students (and certain texts) are often confused by the role of the external circuit and its connection with the electric field. This confusion is the result of an effort to reduce magnetofluidmechanics to ordinary fluid mechanics by a wave of the hand and an assumption about the value of the electric field. In certain very simple one-dimensional configurations the electric field is not coupled with the equations of motion but even in so simple a case as the Hartmann problem the electric field depends upon the external circuit. In general, all of the electrodynamic field quantities are dependent upon the mechanical quantities and vice versa. Hence we have taken special care to integrate electrodynamics with fluid mechanics and thermodynamics.

The two-semester course based on this book is a problem-solving course. Twelve to fifteen problems are solved by the students each semester. In class much effort is made to encourage students to apply limiting-case checks to their work. Although this may seem puerile to some advanced graduate students, it is essential in magnetofluidmechanics because of the often complex results. In many sections of this book limiting-case checks are applied in order to check with the results of classical fluid mechanics.

We wish to express our thanks to those who assisted us during the preparation of the manuscript. We greatly appreciate the help we received from our students, who made use of the preliminary versions of this book. We are grateful to Mr. David Klein, who helped to compute many of the graphs contained herein, and to Dr. R. A. Elco for many interesting discussions. And finally, we are particularly indebted to Mrs. K. P. Spence, who typed the manuscript.

The order of the authors' names for this book was determined by a toss of a coin.

Pittsburgh, Pennsylvania   W. F. HUGHES
March, 1966   F. J. YOUNG

Contents

The Electromagnetodynamics of Fluids

Introduction

1 ELECTROMAGNETIC-FLUID INTERACTIONS

The interaction of electromagnetic fields and fluids may be described, from a scientific point of view, simply by the proper application of the principles of the special theory of relativity. However, the application of these principles, over half a century old, to actual physical phenomena of engineering interest has only recently taken place. The study of these applications to a continuum has become known as magnetohydrodynamics or magnetofluidmechanics, and the application to a kinetic theory fluid model, plasma dynamics.

We prefer to think of magnetofluidmechanics (or MFD) as a special branch of a broader topic that should be treated as an integrated whole, namely, the interaction of electromagnetic fields and fluids, both gases and liquids, both from a macroscopic and microscopic point of view. This book is concerned with the basic principles of this interaction in a continuum and the practical application of these principles to fundamental processes in nature and to engineering devices.

Astrophysicists and geophysicists realized soon after the advent of special relativity theory that electromagnetic-fluid interactions were of great importance in stellar and planetary processes. However, the engineering application of these interactions is relatively new, and only during the past ten years or so has much attention been given to what we commonly speak of as MFD or MHD.

Our purpose is to present a reasonably basic treatment of electrodynamics of deformable media as a foundation for students in both the sciences and in engineering. We will then discuss some applications, which, because of space limitations, must represent only some of the topics of current interest. We have chosen to focus our attention on applications

1

of interest mainly to engineers, but certainly of some useful importance to students of geophysics and astronomy.

Perhaps the main impetus to the engineering approach to electromagnetic-fluid interaction studies has come from the concepts of the MHD direct conversion generator, ion propulsion, studies of radio propagation in the ionosphere, and, what is one of the most exciting dreams of this age, controlled nuclear fusion. Because we approach these problems from a unified viewpoint, we prefer not to use the designation MFD or MHD, but rather electromagnetic-fluid interaction dynamics. Later, we will discuss the MHD approximations, including many of the applications under these assumptions. A full understanding of the processes, however, requires a more general background of information than that which can be obtained by an immediate study of the MHD interactions.

Another point to be made is that plasma physics is really also a special case of the more general problem. However, we will limit ourselves to a continuum model of the fluid. The basic concepts of electrodynamics are equally applicable to plasma dynamics from a microscopic viewpoint, and in fact we believe that a thorough grounding in MHD is necessary for a full understanding and appreciation of modern plasma physics.

The word *plasma* was adopted by Langmuir in 1929 to designate an ionized gas with the following properties.

1. Completely ionized.
2. Electrically neutral.
3. The Debye length h is much smaller than any physical dimension.

The Debye length is roughly the distance by which the positive and negative charges are separated by thermal energy in the gas, or, equivalently, the distance over which the excess electric charge may be considered different from zero. Today the word plasma is used much more loosely and is generally applied to any gas which has some degree of ionization. Certainly, then, if the gas is dense enough, the continuum theory may be applied to plasmas. In the next section we point out that, indeed, the continuum or hydrodynamical approach is actually valid for individual component species of very rarefied gases that are highly ionized and in a strong magnetic field.

The designation MFD or MHD is commonly applied to the special branch (of one general interaction) in which the magnetic forces and energy dominate the corresponding electrical quantities. The following is a list of a few of the applications of this theory in physics and engineering.

Astronomy and geophysics:
    Stellar and solar structure
    Interplanetary and interstellar matter

Planetary interiors (dynamo theory)
Solar storms and flares
Aurora theory
Radio propagation through the ionosphere
Interaction of interplanetary fluid (solar wind) and planetary magnetic
fields
Engineering:
MHD generator
Ion propulsion
MHD couplers and bearings
MHD pumps and meters
MHD boundary layer control of reentry vehicles
Radio propagation through ionized gases
Microwave diagnostics of ionized gases
Plasma jets
Fusion machines for power (not yet operative)

Some of these phenomena and devices must be treated by a microscopic
model (for example, kinetic theory), but at least the continuum model
gives useful information in nearly all cases and forms a sound starting
point for further work.

2 MACROSCOPIC AND MICROSCOPIC VIEWPOINT

As we have stated, we are concerned in this book with the macroscopic
treatment of a fluid. We will treat the fluid from a continuum point of
view and be concerned only with macroscopic quantities. The continuum
approach is valid for a wide variety of fluid behavior including gases in
the plasma regime. However, as the gas becomes rarefied, recourse must
be made to a microscopic approach. Although we may still be interested
in macroscopic quantities such as bulk pressure and velocity, a microscopic approach must be used to find the appropriate equations for the
macroscopic quantities.

Very often an exact statistical approach leads to equations for average
quantities that are the same as the classical ones such as the Navier-Stokes
equations. This is certainly true for a dense fluid under the continuum
model. But also, for example, in a plasma in an electromagnetic field an
exact treatment, beginning from the generalized Boltzmann equation,
leads in the case of a collisionless gas to equations, for each species of
particles, which are identical to the continuum equations. We will not
treat plasma dynamics from a statistical-mechanical or kinetic-theory
viewpoint and the reader may consult other references for details.

In dense gases, a continuum approach is valid and the macroscopic analyses discussed are meaningful. In any event, a well-grounded study of the macroscopic model is essential, we believe, for fully understanding plasma physics. Frequently, a simple hydrodynamical approach is quite adequate for a particular plasma problem, but unless one is well grounded in such basics as electrodynamics and continuum fluid mechanics, simplicity may be elusive.

In classical fluid mechanics the accuracy of the continuum assumption is indicated by the value of the Knudsen number K, the ratio of the mean free path L_f to the characteristic dimension L, of the problem. For $K \ll 1$ the continuum approach is valid, and for $K \gg 1$ free molecule (collisionless) flow theory is applicable and the particle distribution is approximately Maxwellian. For K of order unity the flow is very complex and recourse must be made to statistical mechanics.

In plasma dynamics (or rarefied magnetofluidmechanics) the Knudsen number is also an important parameter, but there are other parameters which must be considered in order to determine the character of the flow.

Particularly important is the ratio of the Larmor or gyro-radius L_l to the characteristic dimension L. Actually, each species of particle has its own gyro-radius in a magnetic field. If we denote the ion radius as L_{li} and the electron radius as L_{le}, we can define the Larmor numbers as L_{li}/L and L_{le}/L.* If $L_{li}/L \gg 1$ and $L_{le}/L \gg 1$ as well as $L_f/L \ll 1$, the continuum approximation is good. Physically these conditions indicate that the mean free path is much smaller than the characteristic dimension but that all Larmor radii are much larger. The particle distribution then is determined by collisions and equilibrium is rapidly established.

The statistical-mechanical treatment of a general plasma in an electric and magnetic field begins with the generalized Boltzmann transport equation, including electromagnetic terms, which in principle must be solved for the distribution functions for each species of particle that is not necessarily in thermodynamic equilibrium. Many approximate techniques have been evolved to obtain solutions, but we will not discuss them here. However, one very useful and important approach is to take moments of the Boltzmann equation. The first three moments correspond to the continuity, momentum, and energy equations for each species of particle in the plasma. The equations have a form similar to the equations of continuum mechanics for each species. The difficulty comes in evaluating the collision terms where the distribution function must be known along

---

* The Larmor or cyclotron or gyro-frequency of a particle is given by $|qB/m|$, where q is the charge, B the magnetic induction field, and m the mass of the particle. The radius L_l is given by $L_l = (m/qB)\sqrt{8kT/\pi m}$, where k is the Boltzmann constant and T the temperature.

with the detailed nature of the collision processes. In theory, the higher order moments form an infinite set of simultaneous dynamical equations for all transport properties of the plasma. For example, in order to provide closure for three or four moment equations, some assumption must be made about the collision processes. If collisions are assumed binary and elastic, a simple momentum exchange model can be used to approximate collisions in terms of a collision frequency, and closure can be effected for three moments. Essentially the distribution function is then Maxwellian. Such a multicomponent hydrodynamical model is widely used with considerable success in plasma dynamics. In fact, for a collisionless plasma the equations reduce exactly to ordinary hydro-dynamical forms (with electromagnetic effects) for each species. In this case the electromagnetic forces may dominate the collisions as we move into a denser regime, and the exact description of the collision phenomena may not always be as vital as in classical rarefied gasdynamics.

We can justify the continuum, homogeneous, isotropic fluid model. However, although each species in the multicomponent model satisfies nearly classical hydrodynamical equations, the electromagnetic effects cause complex couplings and anisotropies in macroscopic variables which cannot be predicted from a homogeneous macroscopic continuum approach, but the extension from the continuum model to the multicomponent model is not difficult.

3   CLASSIFICATION OF FLOW

It is useful to examine the complete range of flow types that are possible since the basic parameters L_f, L_{le}, and L_{li} are varied. Six arbitrary regions of flow have been made by Kantrowitz and Petschek (1957) and we will list them below to better define the continuum assumption. Here we are concerned only with the first two regions described. The classification is made on the assumption that an electromagnetic field is present and the gas is highly ionized. The magnetic field is assumed to be of sufficient strength so that the magnetic pressure $B^2/2\mu$ (B here is the magnetic induction and μ the magnetic permeability) is comparable to the mechanical pressure. If this is not the case, the flow classification must be different from the one described here and the effect of the Larmor radii may become of greater or lesser importance.

The regions of flow are listed in order of decreasing density:

1. *S*-Region. Here the macroscopic continuum model is valid and the electrical conductivity and transport properties are scalars (hence the designation *S*-region). The Knudsen number is small, $L_f/L \ll 1$, and the Larmor

radii are large. $L_{le}/L \gg 1$ and $L_{li}/L \gg 1$. Collisions dominate the particle interaction and the particle distribution is approximately Maxwellian.

2. *T*-Region. Here $L_f/L \ll 1$ and $L_{li}/L \gg 1$ but now $L_{le}/L \ll 1$. ($L_{le} < L_f, L_{li} > L_f$.) The electric force dominates in the Boltzmann equation. The fluid may still be considered a continuum since the larger ion Larmor radius insures collision domination for ions, making the transport properties the same as in the *S*-region. However, the electrons are governed principally by electric forces and therefore the electrical conductivity is no longer a scalar and must be considered a tensor; hence the designation *T*-region. Hall currents begin to become important.

3. *M*-Region. L_f/L is now not an important parameter and may be ≤ 1, but now both the ion and electron Larmor radii are less than the mean free path; $L_{le} < L_f$ and $L_{li} < L_f$, L_{li}/L and L_{le}/L may be $\gg 1$ or comparable to 1. The magnetic force dominates over the electric force and the value of L_f is not so important in determining the transport properties. Both magnetic and collision forces must be considered which makes this region difficult to analyze; however, the region is important because fusion reactors would operate here.

4. *E-M-Region*. Here $L_{li} < L_f$ and $L_f/L \gg 1$ ($L_{le} < L_f$ since $L_{le} < L_{li}$), but now $L_{li}/L \gg 1$. The ion Larmor radius becomes large compared to the characteristic dimension L (but L_{le} may be $\gtrless L$). The mean free path L_f is not so important but may be of the same order or larger than L. The main force is electromagnetic with collisions being negligible. The motion of individual particles is determined by the electromagnetic field. The collisionless multicomponent model is valid in this region.

5. *E*-Region. Here $L_{le}/L \gg 1$ and $L_f/L \gg 1$ (and hence $L_{li}/L \gg 1$ since $L_{le} \ll L_{li}$) and now $L_{le} < L_f$ so that the main force is the electric force. This is a region of very low density where some glow discharges operate.

6. If the Debye length is greater than L, there is no particle interaction and a single-particle Lagrangian approach seems preferred over a statistical fluid approach. This type of gas is not a plasma under the rigorous definition and is not of great interest to plasma physicists.

The flow regions S and T may be treated by ordinary continuum methods—magnetofluiddynamics. The T-region does require use of a tensor electrical conductivity, but may still be treated as in region S.

The regions E-M and E may be treated with precision by a multicomponent collisionless gas model.

Region M presents the most difficulty. Here both collisions and electromagnetic forces are important. To a good approximation, a simple collision model may be used to derive a multicomponent hydrodynamical model. The more exact treatment of region M requires a knowledge of the distribution function of the particles that are not necessarily in equilibrium. The flow of region M is a major problem of modern plasma physics.

The various regions of flow are shown graphically in Fig. I-1 after Kantrowitz and Petschek. This plot is based on the assumption that

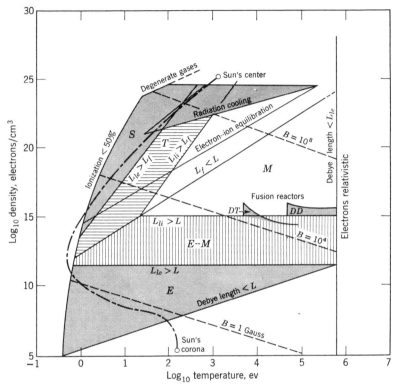

Figure I-1 Classification of regions of flow in magnetofluidmechanics according to ratios of critical lengths. (After Kantrowitz and Petschek, in *Magnetohydrodynamics*, edited by R. K. M. Landshoff, Stanford University Press, 1957.)

$P \sim B^2/2\mu$, that is, the magnetic pressure is of the same order as the mechanical pressure.

4   THE MACROSCOPIC CONTINUUM APPROACH AND TOPICS TO BE COVERED

As we have stated, this book is concerned only with the continuum approach to magnetofluidmechanics. A great many topics can be treated adequately by this approach and we believe that one must have a thorough grounding here before studying microscopic plasma dynamics. In fact, many plasma phenomena may be treated exactly by considering the continuum equations applied to individual species of the gas. Such a treatment is appropriate when the complex interaction terms become negligible. Because of space limitations we will not discuss such models here, but the extension to them from the homogeneous continuum is a simple matter.

The structure of this book is such that it can be divided naturally into three parts.

1. Introductory material to electrodynamics and fluid dynamics with emphasis on topics of special importance to magnetofluidmechanics: Chapters 1 through 4.

2. Basic concepts of MFD—thermodynamics, motion, applications, and qualitative nature of the interactions: Chapters 5 and 6.

3. Applications to various fluid flow systems and practical devices, and a study of wave motion—flow in channels, aerodynamics, etc.: Chapters 7 through 13.

We have tried to cover in detail the foundations of the subject and a selected group of fundamental applications. In limiting the material to what could be included in one book, many important topics were omitted. We have left out those topics which we think are of a more specialized nature and less well understood. Of particular importance are the following topics, not discussed, which the reader will find covered in the references listed at the end of the introduction.

Basic topics:
   Stability
   Turbulence (including pipe flow friction)
Some important applications:
   Dynamo problems of the Earth's interior
   Cosmical electrodynamics and stellar structure

All these may be treated by methods in this book and indeed form part of the basic principles of MFD. Furthermore, specific applications to detailed devices have not been possible, although the underlying principles have been discussed and the reader should be able to follow current research. For example, the MHD generator is discussed in terms of general channel flow and terminal characteristics. Propulsion devices are introduced by general traveling wave devices. It is hoped that new devices with engineering applications will be forthcoming and that this book will help provide the special groundwork necessary for such developments.

This book is intended to be used as a basic textbook for a one-year (two-semester) course in MHD and as a basic reference work in MHD. Certain details of the many special topics might well be omitted in certain types of courses. Many curves, mostly original, are presently in dimensionless form to illustrate basic processes and to serve as reference material. A few arbitrary, highly specialized problems have been included mainly to illustrate methods.

A few classical references follow which may serve as an introduction to magnetofluidmechanics in general and specifically to those special topics not treated.

REFERENCES

Alfvén, H., and C. Fälthammer, *Cosmical Electrodynamics* (2nd ed.), Oxford University Press, New York, 1963.

Batchelor, G. K., On the Spontaneous Magnetic Field in a Conducting Liquid in Turbulent Motion, *Proc. Roy. Soc. (London)*, Series A, **201**, p. 405, 1950.

Chandrasekhar, S., The Invariant Theory of Isotropic Turbulence in Magnetohydrodynamics, *Proc. Roy Soc. (London)*, Series A, **204**, p. 435, 1951.

Chandrasekhar, S., *Hydrodynamic and Hydromagnetic Stability*, Oxford University Press, New York, 1961.

Clauser, F. H., *Plasma Dynamics*, Addison-Wesley, Reading, Mass. 1960.

Cowling, T. G., *Magnetohydrodynamics*, Interscience, New York, 1957.

Denisse, J. F., and J. L. Delcroix, *Theory of Plasma Waves*, Interscience, New York, 1963.

Kantrowitz, A. R., and H. E. Petschek, An Introductory Discussion of Magnetohydrodynamics, in *Magnetohydrodynamics*, edited by R. K. M. Landshoff, Stanford University Press, Stanford, California, 1957.

Parker, E. N., Hydromagnetic Dynamo Models, *Astrophys. J.*, **122**, p. 293, 1955.

Spitzer, L., *Physics of Fully Ionized Gases*, Interscience, New York, 1956.

Stix, T. H., *The Theory of Plasma Waves*, McGraw-Hill, New York, 1962.

1

Principles of Special Relativity

1.1 INTRODUCTION

In the electromagnetodynamics of fluids, coupling among electromagnetic, fluid dynamic, and thermodynamic variables occurs. This coupling, besides being a result of electromagnetic body forces, is produced by media in relative motion. Although not mandatory, a brief consideration of the principles of special relativity greatly simplifies and facilitates the derivation and understanding of the equations and physical phenomena involved in any study where motion and electrodynamics are involved.

The values of the physical properties of various media are tabulated in handbooks, for example, conductivity of metals, dielectric permittivities of insulators and conductors, magnetic permeabilities of various materials, heat capacities, thermal conductivities, etc. In all cases the values of these properties are measured by an observer at rest with respect to the medium being tested. When there is relative motion between the observer and the medium, it is necessary to use the theory of special relativity to transform the material properties and fields from the coordinates of an observer at rest with respect to the medium to the coordinates of another observer. For example, in magnetohydrodynamics a liquid often flows in the presence of electric and magnetic fields, temperature gradients, pressure gradients, currents, and other physical disturbances. An observer riding along with the liquid can measure all its properties and all other interesting quantities, such as temperature, pressure, magnetic flux density, electric field, current density, and Poynting flux. Our job is to interpret those quantities as observers *not* at rest in the medium. The properties and quantities measured by the observer not at rest in the medium are, in general, *not the same* as those seen by the observer at rest in the medium. In the strictest sense, only when the relative motion between the observers is constant in time is the special theory of relativity applicable. However, for the accelerated cases usually met in existing devices, the special theory can be used with very little error. Only the special theory will be considered here, because it is adequate for macroscopic analyses and is much more tractable than the general theory of relativity. For the remainder of this text, it is convenient to denote the coordinate system of the observer at *rest* in the moving medium as the *rest*-frame coordinates, or simply as the rest frame. The coordinate systems of all other observers are called the laboratory-frame coordinates.

1.2   THE PHYSICAL BASIS FOR SPECIAL RELATIVITY

Well-known experiments by Michelson, Morley, de Sitter, and Alväger et al. have disclosed that the velocity of light is constant to all observers executing unaccelerated motion with respect to the light source. Although at different points in the development of the special theory of relativity the experimental results seemed unclear (Whittaker, 1951 and 1952), it is interesting to trace the historical development of the special theory, but it is not essential for the study of the electromagnetodynamics of fluids. Einstein (1905) recognized the experimental evidence and claimed for the special theory of relativity a general validity based on his principle of the constancy of the velocity of light in vacuo. This important principle may be stated as: the velocity of light in vacuo is the same to all observers regardless of the velocity of the light source relative to these observers. Consequently, it is easy to show that the time (denoted by t or t') is not the same to observers in relative motion. Consider the plane wave of light traveling in the x direction in Fig. 1.2-1. This plane wave of light was initiated at $t = t' = 0$ and $x = x' = 0$. This light wave is seen by two observers moving relative to each other in the x direction with speed V. Here the observer located at O uses coordinates x, y, z, and t and the observer at O' uses coordinates x', y', z', and t' and at $t = t' = 0$ the two coordinate systems coincide. To the observer at O the light reaches the station at $x = ct$ in time t. To the observer at O' the light reaches the corresponding station at $x' = ct'$ in time t', since by Einstein's principle the wave velocity in all unaccelerated coordinate systems is c. Therefore, $t'/t = x'/x$ and, since during the time interval under consideration the coordinate systems have separated, $x \neq x'$. Hence t cannot equal t'. The result that $t' \neq t$ may seem strange in view of our everyday experiences. This conclusion has been verified experimentally by measuring the decay times of unstable elementary particles moving slowly and moving at

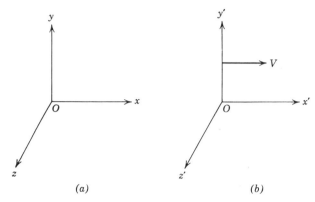

Figure 1.2-1   Coordinate system (*b*) is moving with respect to coordinate system (*a*) at a constant relative velocity *V* in the *x* direction.   Here (*a*) and (*b*) are called the *S* and *S'* of reference, respectively.

relativistic velocities (velocities which are comparable to *c*). Further consideration of a light wave originating from *O* and *O'*, along with Einstein's principle of special relativity, yields more relationships between *x*, *x'* and *t* and *t'*.   They are called the Lorentz transformations which were originally discovered (in a slightly less general form) by Lorentz from a study of Maxwell's equations (Lorentz, 1904 and 1923).   The Lorentz transformations are given by

$$x' = \beta(x - Vt) \qquad y' = y, \qquad \text{and} \quad z' = z \tag{1.2-1}$$

$$t' = \beta\left(t - \frac{Vx}{c^2}\right) \tag{1.2-2}$$

where

$$\beta = \left(1 - \frac{V^2}{c^2}\right)^{-\frac{1}{2}} \tag{1.2-3}$$

For $V^2 \ll c^2$, β becomes unity and (1.2-1) and (1.2-2) become the original Lorentz transformations.   When $\mathbf{V} = 0$, the Lorentz transformations reduce to the more intuitive Galilean transformations.   The inverse transformations are obtained simply by changing the sign on $\mathbf{V}$ and exchanging primed quantities for unprimed quantities.   The Lorentz transformations may be expressed in a more general vector form by using a linear vector operator α, which Silberstein (1914) called the longitudinal stretcher.   It is defined as

$$\alpha\mathbf{G} = \mathbf{G} + \frac{(\beta - 1)\mathbf{V}(\mathbf{V} \cdot \mathbf{G})}{|\mathbf{V}|^2} \tag{1.2-4}$$

where $\mathbf{G}$ is any vector and $\mathbf{V}$ is the velocity vector.   If $\mathbf{G}$ is expressed as

$\mathbf{G} = \mathbf{G}_\| + \mathbf{G}_\perp$ where $\mathbf{G}_\|$ and $\mathbf{G}_\perp$ are the components of $\mathbf{G}$ parallel and perpendicular to $\mathbf{V}$, then $\alpha\mathbf{G} = \beta\mathbf{G}_\| + \mathbf{G}_\perp$. Another easily derived property of the longitudinal stretcher is that $(\beta/\alpha)\mathbf{G} = \mathbf{G}_\| + \beta\mathbf{G}_\perp$. Letting $\mathbf{r}$ and $\mathbf{r}'$ be the position vectors in the S and S' coordinate systems, respectively, and using stretcher vector notation on (1.2-1) and (1.2-2) yields

$$\mathbf{r}' = \alpha\mathbf{r} - \beta\mathbf{V}t \quad \text{and} \quad t' = \beta\left(t - \frac{\mathbf{V}\cdot\mathbf{r}}{c^2}\right) \tag{1.2-5}$$

The Lorentz transformation in distance can be made to resemble a Galilean transformation if the vector $\mathbf{r}^\dagger$ is defined as $\mathbf{r}^\dagger = (\alpha/\beta)\mathbf{r}$. Then

$$\mathbf{r}' = \beta(\mathbf{r}^\dagger - \mathbf{V}t) \tag{1.2-6}$$

In (1.2-4), (1.2-5), and (1.2-6) no coordinate system is mentioned and these equations do not depend on taking the x axis as the direction of the velocity of coordinate separation.

1.3 KINEMATICS

To obtain a formula for the addition of velocities in the x direction, it is sufficient to calculate dx'/dt' in terms of dx/dt. From differentiation of (1.2-1) there results

$$\frac{dx'}{dt'} = \frac{(dx/dt) - V}{1 - (V/c^2)(dx/dt)} \tag{1.3-1}$$

or

$$\frac{dx}{dt} = \frac{(dx'/dt') + V}{1 + (V/c^2)(dx'/dt')} \tag{1.3-2}$$

Equation (1.3-2) is the Einstein formula for addition of velocities; V is the velocity of the S' frame with respect to the S frame; dx'/dt' is the velocity of a point seen by an observer riding in the S' frame; dx/dt is the velocity of the same point estimated by an observer in the S frame. Where $(V/c^2)(dx'/dt') \ll 1$ the velocities add in the ordinary way. If $(dx')/(dt') \to c$, then $(dx/dt) \to c$, indicating that both observers agree on the speed of light. A more general form can be obtained from differentiating (1.2-6) which yields

$$\frac{d\mathbf{r}'}{dt'} = \frac{(d\mathbf{r}^\dagger/dt) - \mathbf{V}}{1 - [\mathbf{V}\cdot(d\mathbf{r}/dt)]/c^2} \tag{1.3-3}$$

Equation (1.3-3) is not easy to appreciate physically in its present form. However, from the definitions of $\mathbf{r}^\dagger$ and the stretcher vector, (1.3-3) becomes

$$\mathbf{u'} = \frac{\mathbf{u}_\| - \mathbf{V} + \mathbf{u}_\perp/\beta}{1 - (\mathbf{V} \cdot \mathbf{u})/c^2} \tag{1.3-4}$$

Here $\mathbf{u'} = d\mathbf{r'}/dt'$, $\mathbf{u} = d\mathbf{r}/dt$, $\mathbf{u}_\|$ is the component of velocity parallel to $\mathbf{V}$ or $\mathbf{u}_\| = (\mathbf{u} \cdot \mathbf{V})/|\mathbf{V}|$, and $\mathbf{u}_\perp$ is the component of $\mathbf{u}$ perpendicular to $\mathbf{V}$. It is important to notice that the superposition of velocities is no longer valid since (1.3-4) is not a linear transformation. If $|\mathbf{V}| \ll c$, (1.3-4) reduces to the Newtonian form $\mathbf{u'} = \mathbf{u} - \mathbf{V}$. It is easy to show that $\mathbf{u'}^2 \to c^2$ when $\mathbf{V}^2 \to c^2$ in (1.3-4). This indicates that c is the upper limit for velocity. It can be further shown that it takes an infinite amount of energy to give a material particle the velocity of light with respect to a system in which it was originally at rest. An interesting feature of (1.3-4) is that as $|\mathbf{V}| \to c$ the motions perpendicular to $\mathbf{V}$ seen by the observer in the primed frame (called the S' frame) become small and vanish. This is easily explained physically because when $|\mathbf{V}| = c$, the parallel velocity of a point at rest in the S frame seen by the observer in the S' frame is c. Now if that point were moving perpendicular in the S frame and the observer in the S' frame could detect its motion, then light would have to travel at a velocity greater than c. Hence the observer in S' cannot see motions in S perpendicular to the relative motion between himself and the S frame when $|\mathbf{V}| = c$. For relative velocities slightly less than c the observer in S' sees perpendicular movements in S in "slow motion." From (1.3-4) it is clear that the "slow motion" exists regardless of the magnitude of $\mathbf{u}_\|$. For example, Equation (1.2-5) can be used to explain the phenomenon discovered by Fizeau in which running liquid changes the velocity of light. The velocity of light in still water is less than its velocity in air. From a nonrelativistic standpoint it would be expected that the velocity in running water would be equal to the vector sum of the velocity of the water and the velocity of light in still water. If c/n is the velocity of light in still water (n is the index of refraction of water) and V_w is the velocity of the water, and both velocities are directed in the same direction, then classically it would be expected that V_L, the velocity of light in running water, would be

$$V_L = \frac{c}{n} + V_w$$

Instead, Fizeau's experiment disclosed

$$V_L = \frac{c}{n} + V_w\left(1 - \frac{1}{n^2}\right) \tag{1.3-5}$$

This result can be obtained from (1.2-5) by letting $V = V_w$, $dx'/dt' = c/n$, $dx/dt = V_L$, and neglecting terms which vary as $1/c$.

By the differentiation of (1.3-1) with respect to t', a formula results for the acceleration seen by an observer in the primed coordinates viewing an accelerated object in the unprimed frame. There results

$$\frac{d^2x'}{dt'^2} = \frac{d^2x/dt^2}{\{\beta[1 - (V/c^2)(dx/dt)]\}^3} \tag{1.3-6}$$

From (1.3-6) it is apparent that a constant acceleration in one frame of reference does not appear to observers in other frames as a constant acceleration. The general formula for the transformation of accelerations is

$$\mathbf{a'} = \frac{\mathbf{a}^\dagger[1 - (\mathbf{V} \cdot \mathbf{u})/c^2] + (\mathbf{V} \cdot \mathbf{a})(\mathbf{u} - \mathbf{V})/c^2}{\beta[1 - (\mathbf{V} \cdot \mathbf{u})/c^2]^3} \tag{1.3-7}$$

where $\mathbf{a}$ is acceleration. When $|\mathbf{V}|/c \to 0$ (1.3-7) yields the Newtonian result $\mathbf{a'} = \mathbf{a}$. If, for example, a particle is at rest in the S frame, $\mathbf{u} = 0$ and the acceleration becomes

$$\mathbf{a'} = \frac{\mathbf{a}^\dagger - (\mathbf{V} \cdot \mathbf{a})\mathbf{V}/c^2}{\beta} \tag{1.3-8}$$

By the definitions of $\mathbf{a}^\dagger$ and the longitudinal stretcher (1.3-7) can be somewhat simplified. There results

$$\mathbf{a'}_y = \frac{\mathbf{a}_\| + \beta\{\mathbf{a}_\perp[1 - (\mathbf{V} \cdot \mathbf{u})/c^2] + \mathbf{u}_\perp(\mathbf{V} \cdot \mathbf{a})/c^2\}}{\{\beta[1 - (\mathbf{V} \cdot \mathbf{u})/c^2]\}^3} \tag{1.3-9}$$

1.4 LORENTZ CONTRACTION

Suppose a rod of length $L_0 = x_2 - x_1$ (to an observer at rest in the rest frame of the rod) is measured by an observer in another frame S'. (The length L_0 is commonly called the proper length of the rod.) Here the S' frame moves in the $+x$ direction with a velocity V with respect to the rest frame. The observer in the S' frame will observe a rod whose length is

$$x'_2 - x'_1 = \beta[x_2 - x_1 - V(t_2 - t_1)] \tag{1.4-1}$$

by (1.2-1). However, $t_2 - t_1$ is not known immediately, but $t'_2 - t'_1$ is known because in order to measure the rod, the observer in S' has to observe x'_2 and x'_1 simultaneously. Hence $t'_2 - t'_1$ must be zero. Then from (1.2-2)

$$t_2 - t_1 = \frac{\beta V}{c^2}(x'_2 - x'_1) \tag{1.4-2}$$

and upon the substitution of $t_2 - t_1$ into (1.4-1) there results

$$x'_2 - x'_1 = \frac{(x_2 - x_1)}{\beta} = L_0\sqrt{1 - V^2/c^2} \qquad (1.4\text{-}3)$$

Therefore a rod moving past an observer with a velocity V relative to the observer will be contracted provided the rod is parallel to the relative velocity vector. If the rod is perpendicular to the relative velocity vector, no contraction occurs, since $z' = z$ and $y' = y$.

The Lorentz contraction expressed by (1.4-3) can be more generally stated in vector form as

$$\mathbf{L}' = \frac{\mathbf{L_0}}{\alpha} \qquad (1.4\text{-}4)$$

The quantity $\sqrt{1 - |\mathbf{u}'|^2/c^2}$ is the Lorentz contraction factor for an object moving past an observer in S' with a relative velocity $\mathbf{u}'$. At times it is useful to express this factor in terms of the velocity of the object with respect to the S frame. This is accomplished by substituting $\mathbf{u}'$ from (1.3-4) into the Lorentz contraction factor. The result is

$$\sqrt{1 - |\mathbf{u}'|^2/c^2} = \frac{\sqrt{1 - |\mathbf{u}|^2/c^2}}{\beta[1 - (\mathbf{V} \cdot \mathbf{u})/c^2]} \qquad (1.4\text{-}5)$$

which reduces to the Lorentz contraction factor of (1.4-3) when the object is at rest in the S frame.

If the observer in the S' frame is passing by a sphere at rest in the S frame, it may seem obvious that the observer in S' actually sees or photographs an ellipsoid. This popular misinterpretation of the Lorentz contraction assumes that light quanta received by the retina have been emitted simultaneously by the sphere. Instead, the time at which these light quanta originate from an element of the surface of the sphere depends on the distance from the element to the retina. If it is assumed that the eye sees all the light quanta simultaneously, these light quanta could not have been emitted simultaneously from the sphere. Penrose (1959) showed that the appearance (to an observer in S') of a sphere at rest in S, no matter how the observer moves in S', is always such as to present a circular outline. The appearance of less symmetrical objects was investigated by Terrell (1959). He demonstrated that the visual appearance of an object is invariant (except for Doppler shifts in frequency). The Lorentz contraction is a real and measurable phenomenon but does not produce on the retina the distorted image one might expect. Good explanations of the effect are given by Weisskopf (1960) and Hagedorn (1964).

Consider the situation illustrated in Fig. 1.4-1 in which an observer in S' approaches a cube which is stationary in S. When the cube is very far away ($\phi \simeq 0$), the observer sees only its front side 1. As the observer proceeds toward the cube he sees side 1; he also sees side 2 which is shortened by perspective and he notices that the cube is rotating in a counterclockwise direction about its axis. The apparent rotation continues as ϕ increases and when $\phi = \phi_0 \simeq \sqrt{(c^2/V^2) - 1}$ the observer sees only side 2 which appears to be a square of length and width l. For $\phi > \phi_0$ sides 2 and 3 are visible and the apparent counterclockwise rotation of

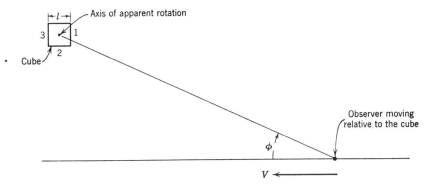

Figure 1.4-1 An observer and a cube in relative motion.

the cube continues as ϕ increases. When $\phi = \pi/2$ the observer sees side 2 which is shortened by perspective so that its dimensions are l by $l\sqrt{1 - V^2/c^2}$. For $\phi = \pi/2$ the apparent rotation is nearly 90° if V is nearly equal to c. As ϕ continues to increase beyond $\pi/2$, less and less of side 2 is visible and the observer sees only side 3, the backside. Hence, in special relativity, an observer moving at a great speed by an object sees an undistorted but rotating object.

1.5   THE TRANSFORMATION OF VOLUME AND AREA

Consider an elementary volume $dv_0 = dx\, dy\, dz$ fixed in the S frame of coordinates (rest frame). In S' this appears as

$$dv' = dx'\, dy\, dz = \frac{dv_0}{\beta} \tag{1.5-1}$$

because by (1.4-3) $dx' = dx/\beta$.

Surface areas whose normal vector is parallel to the relative motion will not be altered. Those having a normal vector perpendicular to the motion will be given by $dS'_\perp = \alpha/\beta\, dS_0$ by (1.4-3). Hence

$$dS' = \frac{\alpha}{\beta} dS_0 = dS_{0\parallel} + \frac{dS_{0\perp}}{\beta} \tag{1.5-2}$$

1.6 THE TRANSFORMATION OF PARTICLE DENSITY

If dN_0 is the total number of particles in an elementary rest frame volume dv_0, the particle density $n_0 = dN_0/dv_0$ may be transformed by using (1.4-3). Then

$$n' = \frac{dN_0}{dv_0}\frac{dv_0}{dv'} = \beta n_0 \qquad (1.6\text{-}1)$$

Hence an observer at rest in S' sees a greater particle density than does an observer in the rest frame S who is at rest with respect to the particles.

1.7 THE TRANSFORMATION OF MASS

As the bases for the mechanics of interesting particles, we use the laws of conservation of mass and momenta. In the absence of external forces these laws are stated mathematically as

$$\sum_{i=1}^{n} m_i = \text{const.} \qquad (1.7\text{-}1)$$

$$\sum_{i=1}^{n} m_i \mathbf{u}_i = \text{const.} \qquad (1.7\text{-}2)$$

In (1.7-1) the total mass of a system comprising n particles must remain constant as the particles interact. In (1.7-2) the components of momentum of the system of particles remain constant. These equations must hold in all sets of coordinates in uniform relative motion as they do in Newtonian mechanics. However, in special relativistic mechanics the transformation between coordinates is the Lorentz rather than the Galilean transformation. This complication manifests itself by causing the mass of a particle to depend upon its velocity.

Tolman (1912) considered a glancing transverse collision between two particles to derive the transformation of mass. The procedure is to apply the two conservation laws to the system of particles and then apply the Einstein formula for the addition of velocities. The result, regardless of the type of collision considered, is

$$m' = \frac{m_0}{\sqrt{1 - (|\mathbf{u}'|/c)^2}} \qquad (1.7\text{-}3)$$

where m' is the mass seen by an observer in S' and $\mathbf{u}'$ is the relative velocity of the particle to the observer in S'. m_0 is the rest mass of the particle.

If the S' frame of coordinates moves with respect to the S frame with relative velocity $\mathbf{V}$, the observer in the S frame will see a mass m. By combining (1.7-3) with (1.4-5) the transformation from m to m' is obtained. It is given by

$$m' = \beta\left(1 - \frac{\mathbf{V} \cdot \mathbf{u}}{c^2}\right)m \qquad (1.7\text{-}4)$$

and its time rate of change is

$$\frac{dm'}{dt'} = \frac{dm}{dt} - \frac{m\mathbf{V}(d\mathbf{u}/dt)}{c^2[1 - (\mathbf{V} \cdot \mathbf{u})/c^2]} \qquad (1.7\text{-}5)$$

1.8 THE TRANSFORMATION OF FORCE

Here we take Newton's second law to be: The summation of the forces exerted on a particle equals the time rate of change of the momentum of the particle. Since the mass is not constant, this becomes

$$\mathbf{F}' = \frac{d}{dt'}(m'\mathbf{u}') \qquad (1.8\text{-}1)$$

By the application of (1.4-5), (1.7-4), and (1.7-5), $\mathbf{F}'$ is expressed in terms of $\mathbf{F}$. The result is

$$\mathbf{F}' = \mathbf{F}_{\parallel} - \frac{\mathbf{V}(\mathbf{u} \cdot \mathbf{F}_{\perp})}{c^2 - \mathbf{V} \cdot \mathbf{u}} + \frac{\mathbf{F}_{\perp}}{\beta[1 - (\mathbf{V} \cdot \mathbf{u})/c^2]} \qquad (1.8\text{-}2)$$

which yields $F' = F$ when $|\mathbf{V}|^2 \ll c^2$. If a particle is at rest in the S frame, $\mathbf{u} = 0$ and (1.8-2) becomes

$$\mathbf{F}_{\parallel} = \mathbf{F}_{\parallel} + \frac{\mathbf{F}_{\perp}}{\beta} \qquad (1.8\text{-}3)$$

It is important to realize, since m' depends upon $\mathbf{u}'$, that in the mechanics of special relativity the acceleration resulting from a force is not necessarily in the same direction as the force.

1.9 POWER AND KINETIC ENERGY

In Newtonian mechanics, the power needed to move a particle is

$$P' = \mathbf{F}' \cdot \mathbf{u}' \qquad (1.9\text{-}1)$$

where P' is the power, $\mathbf{F}'$ the force supplying the power, and $\mathbf{u}'$ the velocity of the particle with respect to an observer at rest in S'. The particle obtains kinetic energy at the time rate of

$$\frac{dT'}{dt'} = P' = \mathbf{F}' \cdot \mathbf{u}' \tag{1.9-2}$$

where T' is the kinetic energy of the particle. By using (1.8-1) and (1.9-2), P' can be expressed as

$$P' = \frac{d}{dt'}\left(\frac{m_0 c^2}{\sqrt{1 - |\mathbf{u}'|^2/c^2}}\right) \tag{1.9-3}$$

The integration of (1.9-2) after the P' of (1.9-3) is introduced yields

$$T' = \frac{m_0 c^2}{\sqrt{1 - |\mathbf{u}'|^2/c^2}} + \text{const.} \tag{1.9-4}$$

Since the kinetic energy is zero when $\mathbf{u}' = 0$, const. $= -m_0 c^2$ and the kinetic energy becomes

$$T' = \frac{m_0 c^2}{\sqrt{1 - |\mathbf{u}'|^2/c^2}} - m_0 c^2 \tag{1.9-5}$$

For $|\mathbf{u}'|^2/c^2 \ll 1$ the kinetic energy is approximately

$$T' \cong m_0 c^2\left(\frac{1}{1 - |\mathbf{u}'|^2/2c^2} - 1\right) = \frac{m_0 \mathbf{u}'^2}{2} \tag{1.9-6}$$

which is the Newtonian kinetic energy. When $u' \to c$, the kinetic energy, just as did the mass, becomes unbounded showing that, in mechanics, c is a limiting velocity. The kinetic energy given in (1.9-5) can be expressed as

$$T' = (m' - m_0)c^2 \tag{1.9-7}$$

When a particle is brought to rest from a velocity of $\mathbf{u}'$, it decreases in mass by the amount $m' - m_0$ and loses the kinetic energy given by (1.9-7). This would suggest that associated with any mass m' is the energy $m'c^2$. Then the principle of conservation of mass implies the principle of conservation of energy. Hence it is postulated that the total energy E' associated with a mass m' is given by

$$E' = m'c^2 \tag{1.9-8}$$

Before the advent of nuclear weapons (1.9-8) was the most startling of the results of the special theory of relativity.

Associated with this energy is the momentum $\mathbf{p}'$ given by

$$\mathbf{p}' = \frac{E'}{c^2}\mathbf{u}' \tag{1.9-9}$$

1.10 THE TRANSFORMATIONS OF ENERGY, MOMENTUM, AND POWER

By the substitution of m' from (1.7-4) into (1.9-8) and by the definition of momentum, the transformation of energy from S to S' is given by

$$E' = \beta(E - \mathbf{V} \cdot \mathbf{p}) \qquad (1.10\text{-}1)$$

Similarly, the transformation of momentum is obtained using m' from (1.7-4) and $\mathbf{u}'$ from (1.3-3). It is

$$\mathbf{p}' = \beta\left(\mathbf{p}^{\dagger} - \frac{\mathbf{V}E}{c^2}\right) \qquad (1.10\text{-}2)$$

It is apparent, if $\mathbf{p}$ corresponds to $\mathbf{r}$, and E/c^2 corresponds to t, that momentum and energy transform according to the Lorentz transforms for distance and time. As a check on (1.10-2) and (1.8-2) the transformation of force can be obtained by differentiating (1.10-2) with respect to t'.

$$\frac{d'\mathbf{p}'}{dt'} = \frac{(d\mathbf{p}^{\dagger}/dt) - (\mathbf{V}/c^2)(dE/dt)}{1 - \mathbf{V} \cdot \mathbf{u}/c^2} \qquad (1.10\text{-}3)$$

or

$$\mathbf{F}' = \frac{\mathbf{F}^{\dagger} - (\mathbf{V}/c^2)(\mathbf{F} \cdot \mathbf{u})}{1 - (\mathbf{V} \cdot \mathbf{u})/c^2} \qquad (1.10\text{-}4)$$

This expression of $\mathbf{F}'$ in terms of $\mathbf{F}$ is equivalent to (1.8-2) and this derivation is much more direct than the previous one which yielded (1.8-2).

Differentiation of E' with respect to t' in (1.10-1) yields

$$P' = \frac{P - \mathbf{F} \cdot \mathbf{V}}{1 - (\mathbf{V} \cdot \mathbf{u})/c^2} \qquad (1.10\text{-}5)$$

which is the transformation formula for power. Here the observer in S' sees a particle moving in S. If $\mathbf{V} \cdot \mathbf{u} = 0$ the particle moves perpendicular to the relative motion between S and S', and the observer in S' must say the power he sees is the difference between power needed to propel the particle in the direction perpendicular to $\mathbf{V}$ and the power given up by the particle as it does work on the parallel component of the force. When $\mathbf{V} \cdot \mathbf{u} \neq 0$ the same thing happens, but is modified by the denominator of (1.10-5). This relationship is seen later in Chapter 2 where the transformation of Joulean power loss is derived.

1.11 THE DOPPLER SHIFT

A plane wave originating at the origin in the S frame propagates with velocity c in the $\mathbf{r}$ direction and has a frequency f according to an observer in S.

To the observer in S the wave is represented by $A \sin 2\pi f\,[t - (\mathbf{e} \cdot \mathbf{r})/c]$ where $\mathbf{e}$ is a unit vector in the direction of propagation. An observer in S' expresses the wave as $A' \sin 2\pi f\,'[t' - (\mathbf{e}' \cdot \mathbf{r}')/c]$. The Lorentz transforms of (1.2-5) and (1.2-6) are used to express $f(t - \mathbf{e} \cdot \mathbf{r}/c)$ in terms of primed quantities. The result is

$$f(t - \mathbf{e} \cdot \mathbf{r}/c) = f\beta\left[\left(1 - \frac{\mathbf{e} \cdot \mathbf{V}}{c}\right)t' - \left(\mathbf{e}^\dagger - \frac{\mathbf{V}}{c}\right) \cdot \frac{\mathbf{r}'}{c}\right] \qquad (1.11\text{-}1)$$

since $\mathbf{e} \cdot \mathbf{r}'^\dagger = \mathbf{e}^\dagger \cdot \mathbf{r}'$. The coefficient of t' in (1.11-1) is f' by definition. So from (1.11-1)

$$f' = \beta\left(1 - \frac{\mathbf{e} \cdot \mathbf{V}}{c}\right)f \qquad (1.11\text{-}2)$$

There are two interesting special cases to consider. The most easily observed, known as the radial Doppler effect, occurs when $\mathbf{e}$ and $\mathbf{V}$ are parallel. In this case

$$f' = \beta\left(1 - \frac{v}{c}\right)f = f\sqrt{\frac{c - V}{c + V}} \qquad (1.11\text{-}3)$$

which reduces to the nonrelativistic Doppler shift when $\beta \to 1$. The expression (1.11-3) has been accurately verified by Ives and Stilwell (1941). When $\mathbf{e}$ is perpendicular to $\mathbf{V}$, that is, the observer travels perpendicular to the direction of propagation, the transverse Doppler shift occurs. For the transverse case

$$f' = \beta f \qquad (1.11\text{-}4)$$

and the frequency shift is more difficult to observe than the radial Doppler shift.

By similar reasoning, we obtain from (1.11-1)

$$\mathbf{e}' = \frac{\mathbf{e}^\dagger - \mathbf{V}/c}{1 - \mathbf{e} \cdot \mathbf{V}/c} \qquad (1.11\text{-}5)$$

which is the transformation for the direction of propagation. By the definition of $\mathbf{e}^\dagger$ we obtain from (1.11-5)

$$\mathbf{e}' = \frac{(1 - V/c)\mathbf{e}_\| + \mathbf{e}_\perp/\beta}{1 - e_\| V/c} \qquad (1.11\text{-}6)$$

which means that the observer in S' sees a propagation vector pointing more toward the perpendicular to the relative velocity vector than does the observer in S. When $\mathbf{e}$ is parallel to $\mathbf{V}$,

$$\mathbf{e}' = \mathbf{e}_\| \qquad (1.11\text{-}7)$$

With transverse propagation, $\mathbf{e} \cdot \mathbf{V} = 0$ and (1.11-6) becomes

$$\mathbf{e}' = \mathbf{e}_\perp / \beta \qquad (1.11\text{-}8)$$

which is similar to the "slow motion" effect manifested in the perpendicular components of (1.3-4). However, when $V^2/c^2 \ll 1$ the propagation vectors are the same to all observers.

REFERENCES

Alväger, T., F. J. M. Farley, J. Kjellman, and I. Wallin, Test of the Second Postulate of Special Relativity in the GeV Region, *Physics Letters*, **12**, No. 3, pp. 260–262, 1964. This is the best terrestrial verification obtained before 1966.

Cullwick, E. G., *Electromagnetism and Relativity*, 2nd ed., Chapter 5, John Wiley, New York, 1959.

de Sitter, W., Constancy of the Velocity of Light, Konink. Akad. Wetensch. Amst., *Proc. of Sect. of Sci.*, **15**, p. 1297, 1913.

Eddington, A. S., *The Mathematical Theory of Relativity*, 2nd ed., Cambridge University Press, 1930.

Einstein, A., Zur Elektrodynamik bewegter Körper, *Ann. der Phys.*, **17**, p. 891, 1905.

Hagedorn, R., *Relativistic Kinematics*, W. A. Benjamin, New York, p. 54, 1964.

Ives, H. E., and G. R. Stilwell, An Experimental Study of the Rate of a Moving Atomic Clock, II, *J. Opt. Soc. Am.*, **31**, p. 369, 1941.

Lorentz, H. A., Electromagnetic Phenomena in a System Moving with Any Velocity Smaller Than That of Light, Konink, Akad. Wetensch. Amst., *Proc. of Sect. of Sci.*, **6**, Part 2, p. 809, 1904.

Lorentz, H. A., *Theory of Electrons and Its Applications to the Phenomena of Light and Radiant Heat*, G. E. Steckert and Co., 1923.

Michelson, A. A., The Relative Motion of the Earth and the Luminiferous Ether, *Am. J. Sci.*, **22**, p. 120, 1881.

Michelson, A. A., and E. W. Morley, On the Relative Motion of the Earth and the Luminiferous Aether, *Phil. Mag.*, **24**, No. 151, p. 449, 1887.

Møller, C., *The Theory of Relativity*, The Clarendon Press, Oxford, 1952.

Pauli, W., *Theory of Relativity* (translated), Section 35, Pergamon Press, London, 1958.

Penrose, R., The Apparent Shape of a Relativistically Moving Sphere, *Proc. Cambridge Phil. Soc.*, **55**, p. 137, 1959.

Silberstein, L., *Theory of Relativity*, pp. 124–125, 164, Macmillan, New York, 1914.

Terrell, J., Invisibility of the Lorentz Contraction, *Phys. Rev.*, **116**, p. 1041, 1959.

Tolman, R. C., Non-Newtonian Mechanics, The Mass of a Moving Body, *Phil. Mag.*, **23**, p. 375, 1912.

Tolman, R. C., *Relativity, Thermodynamics and Cosmology*, Oxford, 1934.

Weisskopf, V. F., The Visual Appearance of Rapidly Moving Objects, *Phys. Today*, **13**, No. 9, p. 24, 1960.

Whittaker, Sir Edmund, *A History of the Theories of Aether and Electricity*, Vols. 1 and 2, Thomas Nelson, London 1951, 1952.

2

The Electrodynamics of Moving Media

2.1 INTRODUCTION

It is the purpose of this chapter to study certain aspects of electrodynamics, involving moving media, which are usually not stressed in introductory electromagnetic field theory courses. A knowledge of Maxwell's equations for stationary media and vectors is assumed. The student who is well prepared in mathematics but unfamiliar with electrodynamics should consult one of the standard electrodynamics texts. Since the electromagnetodynamics of moving fluids involves the study of electromagnetic field quantities in various frames of reference, the Lorentz transformations in Chapter 1 are combined with Maxwell's electrodynamic equations to obtain the Maxwell-Lorentz transformations. These transformations relate the electromagnetic field quantities seen by observers in various frames of reference. The derivation of these transformations is not done in four-dimensional notation because the tensor notation tends to obscure the physical meaning of the results. However, a four-dimensional treatment is given in Appendix 2. Although many of the results of this treatment could have been obtained by combining a Galilean rather than a Lorentz transformation with Maxwell's equations, the Lorentz transform derivation is preferred because it allows for the correct treatment of space charge. Moreover, the use of Galilean transformations can lead to paradoxes even when the velocity of the medium, with respect to some observer, is very small compared to the speed of light. The Maxwell-Lorentz transformation is generally valid and not much more difficult than a Maxwell-Galilean transformation.

Electrodynamic phenomena of media in the rest frame are described by Maxwell's equations. These equations are based upon simple experiments also performed in the rest frame. In view of the results of the Lorentz transformations presented in Chapter 1, it may be stated that, in general, observers in relative motion do not obtain the same values for field quantities. However, this does not imply a different set of electrodynamic equations for every observer. From Maxwell's equations, each observer can solve propagation problems in free space and the results must be such that the velocity of light in free space to all observers is constant. Hence it has been found that Maxwell's equations are the same to all observers regardless of the relative velocities of their coordinate frames.

Consequently, Maxwell's equations are written in the coordinates of the laboratory and are transformed by the Lorentz transformations of (1.2-3) into rest frame coordinates. For the remainder of this text, the rest frame is denoted by primes and is the frame in which the moving media is at rest. The resulting equations are rearranged so that they have the same form in the rest as in the laboratory frame. Comparison of these two sets of Maxwell equations yields the Maxwell-Lorentz transformation (hereafter called the MLT) which relates the fields seen by observers in motion with respect to each other.

We will show that although the constitutive equations $D'_i = \epsilon_{ij}E'_j$, $B'_i = \mu_{ij}H'_j$, and $J'_i = \sigma_{ij}E'_j$ (here ϵ_{ij}, μ_{ij}, and σ_{ij} are the tensor permittivity, permeability, and conductivity as seen by an observer at rest in the medium) hold in the rest frame, for the observer in the laboratory frame (moving with respect to the medium) the situation is no longer so simple. To him, none of the fields can be related to their corresponding flux without including another kind of field quantity. For example, $\mathbf{D} = f(\mathbf{E}, \mathbf{B}, \mathbf{V})$, $\mathbf{B} = g(\mathbf{H}, \mathbf{D}, \mathbf{V})$, and $\mathbf{J} = h(\mathbf{E}, \mathbf{B}, \mathbf{V})$.

Hence great care must be exercised in the use of the constitutive equations in the laboratory frame. In this chapter some problems are considered which are most easily solved in the rest frame, because there the ordinary constitutive equations apply.

Since Maxwell's equations are the same to all observers, the problem of boundary conditions is easily solved once a particular frame of reference is chosen. It is important for the observer in the chosen frame of reference to apply the boundary conditions (without changing his frame of reference) regardless of the relative motion existing between the media.

In many devices a knowledge of the terminal voltage is very important. Terminal voltage and electromotive force are treated from Faraday's law and from the standpoint of special relativity. Here it is observed that the latter approach is the easiest to apply in many cases. However, the application of the special theory of relativity to calculating emf requires careful consideration of the relative motion between the observer and the circuit.

The concept of the Poynting vector, valid to all observers and extremely useful for energy consideration, will be examined. By means of the MLT, energy dissipated and stored as seen by the observer in the laboratory frame is written in terms of quantities seen by the rest frame observer. We shall see that energy dissipation and storage in the laboratory frame transform into energy dissipation, storage, and kinetic energy in the rest frame.

The terminal voltage of devices is related to the Poynting vector. This method allows the relatively easy calculation of terminal voltage provided the electric and magnetic fields are known on the closed surface of integration. This means of finding terminal voltage is very useful when eddy current effects cannot be neglected.

Finally, by using the Poynting vector and the MLT, we shall examine damping effects such as dielectric and magnetic hysteresis. Here we shall see that the hysteresis losses add directly to the Joulean losses.

2.2 MAXWELL'S EQUATIONS

Maxwell's equations in RMKS units are

$$\nabla \cdot \mathbf{D} = \rho_e \qquad \nabla' \cdot \mathbf{D}' = \rho'_e \qquad (2.2\text{-}1)$$

$$\nabla \cdot \mathbf{B} = 0 \qquad \nabla' \cdot \mathbf{B}' = 0 \qquad (2.2\text{-}2)$$

$$\nabla \times \mathbf{E} = -\frac{\partial \mathbf{B}}{\partial t} \qquad \nabla' \times \mathbf{E}' = -\frac{\partial \mathbf{B}'}{\partial t'} \qquad (2.2\text{-}3)$$

$$\nabla \times \mathbf{H} = \mathbf{J} + \frac{\partial \mathbf{D}}{\partial t} \qquad \nabla' \times \mathbf{H}' = \mathbf{J}' + \frac{\partial \mathbf{D}'}{\partial t'} \qquad (2.2\text{-}4)$$

To make the solution to any electrodynamic problem possible, three more equations are needed because there are seven unknowns in Maxwell's equations. These equations relate various quantities such as $\mathbf{J}$, $\mathbf{E}$, and $\mathbf{B}$ or $\mathbf{B}$, $\mathbf{H}$, and $\mathbf{D}$. They depend upon the medium and, in general, its relative motion and are called the constitutive equations. When the constitutive equations are written in the rest frame of the medium, they simplify so that $\mathbf{J}'$ and $\mathbf{D}'$ are functions of $\mathbf{E}'$, and $\mathbf{B}'$ is a function of $\mathbf{H}'$. For linear isotropic conducting media, Ohm's law holds (in the rest frame only)

$$\mathbf{J}' = \sigma \mathbf{E}' \qquad (2.2\text{-}5)$$

where $\mathbf{J}'$ is the conduction current density in amperes per meters^2, $\mathbf{E}'$ is the electric fields in volts per meter, and σ is the conductivity in (ohm meters)$^{-1}$. For linear isotropic dielectrics and magnetic materials, the constitutive equations are (in the rest frame only)

$$\mathbf{D}' = \epsilon \mathbf{E}' \tag{2.2-6}$$

and

$$\mathbf{B}' = \mu \mathbf{H}' \tag{2.2-7}$$

where $\mathbf{D}'$ is the electric flux density in volt-farads per meter or coulombs per meter, ϵ is the permittivity in farads per meter, $\mathbf{B}'$ is the magnetic flux density in webers per meters^2 or Teslas, $\mathbf{H}$ is the magnetic field in amperes per meter, and μ is the permeability in henrys per meter. Here ρ'_e is the charge unit volume in coulombs per meter^2.

Maxwell's equations can be expressed in integral form by applying Gauss's theorem to (2.2-1) and (2.2-2) and Stokes' theorem to (2.2-3) and (2.2-4). There results

$$\int_S \mathbf{D} \cdot d\mathbf{S} = \int_V \rho_e \, dV \tag{2.2-8}$$

and

$$\int_S \mathbf{B} \cdot d\mathbf{S} = 0 \tag{2.2-9}$$

Equations (2.2-1) and (2.2-8) indicate that electric flux originates and terminates on positive and negative charges. From (2.2-8) the electric flux emanating from a bounded volume equals the total charge in that volume. Equation (2.2-9) indicates that zero magnetic flux can be emanated from a bounded volume, a consequence of the absence of magnetic charges in nature. From the application of Stokes' theorem,

$$\oint \mathbf{E} \cdot d\mathbf{l} = -\int_S \frac{\partial \mathbf{B}}{\partial t} \cdot d\mathbf{S} \tag{2.2-10}$$

and

$$\oint \mathbf{H} \cdot d\mathbf{l} = \int_S \left(\mathbf{J} + \frac{\partial \mathbf{D}}{\partial t} \right) \cdot d\mathbf{S} \tag{2.2-11}$$

Equation (2.2-10) is Faraday's law which relates the voltage induced in a loop by a time-varying magnetic flux density passing through the surface formed by the loop. Equation (2.2-11) is Ampere's law which relates the scalar magnetic potential induced in a loop due to the current passing through the area formed by the loop (outside the current-carrying region $\nabla \times \mathbf{H} = 0$ and therefore $\mathbf{H} = -\nabla \psi$). For qualitative thinking and the establishing of boundary conditions, the integral form of Maxwell's equations is often superior to the point form, but in general the integral form yields quantitative results easily only when the geometry is very simple.

2.3 THE MAXWELL-LORENTZ TRANSFORMATION

In laboratory rectangular coordinates Maxwell's equations are

$$\frac{\partial D_x}{\partial x} + \frac{\partial D_y}{\partial y} + \frac{\partial D_z}{\partial z} = \rho_e \tag{2.3-1}$$

$$\frac{\partial B_x}{\partial x} + \frac{\partial B_y}{\partial y} + \frac{\partial B_z}{\partial z} = 0 \tag{2.3-2}$$

$$\frac{\partial E_z}{\partial y} - \frac{\partial E_y}{\partial z} = -\frac{\partial B_x}{\partial t} \tag{2.3-3}$$

$$\frac{\partial E_x}{\partial z} - \frac{\partial E_z}{\partial x} = -\frac{\partial B_y}{\partial t} \tag{2.3-4}$$

$$\frac{\partial E_y}{\partial x} - \frac{\partial E_x}{\partial y} = -\frac{\partial B_z}{\partial t} \tag{2.3-5}$$

$$\frac{\partial H_z}{\partial y} - \frac{\partial H_y}{\partial z} = J_x + \frac{\partial D_x}{\partial t} \tag{2.3-6}$$

$$\frac{\partial H_x}{\partial z} - \frac{\partial H_z}{\partial x} = J_y + \frac{\partial D_y}{\partial t} \tag{2.3-7}$$

$$\frac{\partial H_y}{\partial x} - \frac{\partial H_x}{\partial y} = J_z + \frac{\partial D_z}{\partial t} \tag{2.3-8}$$

Equations (2.3-1) through (2.3-8) inclusive are to be transformed in accordance with the Lorentz transform as established by (1.2-1) and (1.2-2). As a consequence of (1.2-1) and (1.2-2) or (1.2-5),

$$\frac{\partial}{\partial x} = \beta \left(\frac{\partial}{\partial x'} - \frac{V}{c^2} \frac{\partial}{\partial t'} \right) \tag{2.3-9}$$

and

$$\frac{\partial}{\partial t} = \beta \left(\frac{\partial}{\partial t'} - V \frac{\partial}{\partial x'} \right) \tag{2.3-10}$$

Substitution of (2.3-9) and (2.3-10) into Maxwell's equations yields

$$\beta \frac{\partial D_x}{\partial x'} + \frac{\partial D_y}{\partial y'} + \frac{\partial D_z}{\partial z'} = \rho_e + \frac{\beta V}{c^2} \frac{\partial D_x}{\partial t'} \tag{2.3-11}$$

$$\beta \frac{\partial B_x}{\partial x'} + \frac{\partial B_y}{\partial y'} + \frac{\partial B_z}{\partial z'} = \frac{\beta V}{c^2} \frac{\partial B_x}{\partial t'} \tag{2.3-12}$$

$$-\beta V \frac{\partial B_x}{\partial x'} + \frac{\partial E_z}{\partial y'} - \frac{\partial E_y}{\partial z'} = -\beta \frac{\partial B_x}{\partial t'} \tag{2.3-13}$$

$$\frac{\partial E_x}{\partial z'} - \beta \frac{\partial}{\partial x'}(E_z + VB_y) = -\beta \frac{\partial}{\partial t'}\left(B_y + \frac{V}{c^2} \cdot E_z\right) \tag{2.3-14}$$

$$\beta \frac{\partial}{\partial x'}(E_y - VB_z) - \frac{\partial E_x}{\partial y'} = -\beta \frac{\partial}{\partial t'}\left(B_z - \frac{V}{c^2} E_y\right) \tag{2.3-15}$$

$$\beta V \frac{\partial D_x}{\partial x'} + \frac{\partial H_z}{\partial y'} - \frac{\partial H_y}{\partial z'} = J_x + \beta \frac{\partial D_x}{\partial t'} \tag{2.3-16}$$

$$\frac{\partial H_x}{\partial z'} - \beta \frac{\partial}{\partial x'}(H_z - VD_y) = J_y + \beta \frac{\partial}{\partial t'}\left(D_y - \frac{V}{c^2} H_z\right) \tag{2.3-17}$$

$$\beta \frac{\partial}{\partial x'}(H_y + VD_z) - \frac{\partial H_x}{\partial y'} = J_z + \beta \frac{\partial}{\partial t'}\left(D_z + \frac{V}{c^2} H_y\right) \tag{2.3-18}$$

Equations (2.3-14), (2.3-15), (2.3-17), and (2.3-18) have the same form as (2.3-4), (2.3-5), (2.3-7), and (2.3-8), respectively. It would seem that the field quantities in the rest frame can be found in terms of the laboratory field quantities by forcing equations (2.3-14), (2.3-15), (2.3-17), and (2.3-18) to have the same form as (2.3-4), (2.3-5), (2.3-7), and (2.3-8). Then

$$E'_{x'} = E_x \tag{2.3-19}$$

$$E'_{z'} = \beta(E_z + VB_y) \tag{2.3-20}$$

$$B'_{y'} = \beta\left(B_y + \frac{V}{c^2} E_z\right) \tag{2.3-21}$$

$$E'_{y'} = \beta(E_y - VB_z) \tag{2.3-22}$$

$$B'_{z'} = \beta\left(B_z - \frac{V}{c^2} E_y\right) \tag{2.3-23}$$

$$H'_{x'} = H_x \tag{2.3-24}$$

$$H'_{z'} = \beta(H_z - VD_y) \tag{2.3-25}$$

$$J'_{y'} = J_y \tag{2.3-26}$$

$$D'_{y'} = \beta\left(D_y - \frac{V}{c^2} H_z\right) \tag{2.3-27}$$

$$H'_{y'} = \beta(H_y + VD_z) \tag{2.3-28}$$

$$J'_{z'} = J_z \tag{2.3-29}$$

$$D'_{z'} = \beta\left(D_z + \frac{V}{c^2} H_y\right) \tag{2.3-30}$$

Comparing the time derivative terms of (2.3-3) and (2.3-13), and (2.3-6) and (2.3-16), it seems reasonable to assume $B'_{x'} = aB_x$ and $D'_{x'} = bD_x$ where a and b are undetermined constants. Here a and b must be chosen so that (2.3-13) and (2.3-16) have the same form as (2.3-3) and (2.3-6). To express (2.3-12) and (2.3-13), for example, in rest frame field quantities, we use the inverse of relations (2.3-21) and (2.3-23) obtained by putting a negative sign in front of the velocities and interchanging primed with unprimed quantities. Then $B_y = \beta[B'_{y'} - (V/c^2)E'_{z'}]$ and

$$B_z = \beta[B'_{z'} + (V/c^2)E'_{y'}]$$

Under these substitutions (2.3-12) becomes

$$\frac{\beta}{a}\frac{\partial B'_{x'}}{\partial x'} + \beta\frac{\partial B'_{y'}}{\partial y'} - \frac{\beta V}{c^2}\frac{\partial E'_{z'}}{\partial y'} + \beta\frac{\partial B'_{z'}}{\partial z'} + \frac{\beta V}{c^2}\frac{\partial E'_{y'}}{\partial z'} = \frac{\beta V}{c^2 a}\frac{\partial B'_{x'}}{\partial t'} \quad (2.3\text{-}31)$$

and with the substitutions

$$E_z = \beta(E'_{z'} - VB'_{y'}) \quad \text{and} \quad E_y = \beta(E'_{y'} + VB'_{z'}) \quad (2.3\text{-}13)$$

becomes

$$-\frac{\beta V}{a}\frac{\partial B'_{x'}}{\partial x'} + \beta\frac{\partial E'_{z'}}{\partial y'} - \beta V\frac{\partial B'_{y'}}{\partial y'} - \beta\frac{\partial E'_{y'}}{\partial z'} - \beta V\frac{\partial B'_{z'}}{\partial z'} = -\frac{\beta}{a}\frac{\partial B'_{x'}}{\partial t'}$$

$$(2.3\text{-}32)$$

Multiply (2.3-31) by V and add it to (2.3-32) to obtain

$$\frac{\partial E'_{z'}}{\partial y'} - \frac{\partial E'_{y'}}{\partial z'} = -\frac{1}{a}\frac{\partial B'_{x'}}{\partial t'} \quad (2.3\text{-}33)$$

Next multiply (2.3-31) by V and subtract from it (2.3-32) to obtain

$$2\beta V\left(\frac{1}{a}\frac{\partial B'_{x'}}{\partial x'} + \frac{\partial B'_{y'}}{\partial y'} + \frac{\partial B'_{z'}}{\partial z'}\right)$$

$$+ \beta\left(1 + \frac{V^2}{c^2}\right)\left(-\frac{\partial E'_{z'}}{\partial y'} + \frac{\partial E'_{y'}}{\partial z'} - \frac{1}{a}\frac{\partial B'_{x'}}{\partial t'}\right) = 0 \quad (2.3\text{-}34)$$

But from (2.3-33) the second term of (2.3-34) is zero, so that (2.3-34) becomes

$$\frac{1}{a}\frac{\partial B'_{x'}}{\partial x'} + \frac{\partial B'_{y'}}{\partial y'} + \frac{\partial B'_{z'}}{\partial z'} = 0 \quad (2.3\text{-}35)$$

If $a = 1$, equations (2.3-34) and (2.3-33) assume the same form as (2.3-1) and (2.3-3), and we tentatively conclude that $B'_{x'} = B_x$. Substituting the inverse relationships for D_x, D_y, and D_z in (2.3-11) and (2.3-16), we have

$$\frac{\beta}{b}\frac{\partial D'_{x'}}{\partial x'} + \beta\frac{\partial D'_{y'}}{\partial y'} + \beta\frac{\partial D'_{z'}}{\partial z'} + \frac{\beta V}{c^2}\frac{\partial H'_{z'}}{\partial y'} - \frac{\beta V}{c^2}\frac{\partial H'_{y'}}{\partial z'} = \rho_e + \frac{\beta V}{c^2 b}\frac{\partial D'_{x'}}{\partial t'}$$

$$(2.3\text{-}36)$$

and

$$\frac{\beta V}{b}\frac{\partial D'_{x'}}{\partial x'} + \beta V\frac{\partial D'_{y'}}{\partial y'} + \beta V\frac{\partial D'_{z'}}{\partial z'} + \beta\frac{\partial H'_{z'}}{\partial y'} - \beta\frac{\partial H'_{y'}}{\partial z'} = J_x + \frac{\beta}{b}\frac{\partial D'_{x'}}{\partial t'}$$

(2.3-37)

Multiplying (2.3-36) by V and subtracting from (2.3-37) yields

$$\frac{\partial H'_{z'}}{\partial y'} - \frac{\partial H'_{y'}}{\partial z'} = \beta(J_x - \rho_e V) + \frac{1}{b}\frac{\partial D'_{x'}}{\partial t'}$$

(2.3-38)

which indicates that in addition to $b = 1$

$$J'_{x'} = \beta(J_x - \rho_e V)$$

(2.3-39)

Multiplying (2.3-36) by V and adding it to (2.3-37) yields

$$2\beta V\left(\frac{1}{b}\frac{\partial D'_{x'}}{\partial x'} + \frac{\partial D'_{y'}}{\partial y'} + \frac{\partial D'_{z'}}{\partial z'}\right) + \beta\left(1 + \frac{V^2}{c^2}\right)\left(\frac{\partial H'_{z'}}{\partial y'} - \frac{\partial H'_{y'}}{\partial z'}\right)$$

$$= J_x + \rho_e V + \frac{\beta}{b}\left(1 + \frac{V^2}{c^2}\right)\frac{\partial D'_{x'}}{\partial t'} \quad (2.3\text{-}40)$$

As $b = 1$, (2.3-40) combined with (2.3-38) results in

$$\frac{\partial D'_{x'}}{\partial x'} + \frac{\partial D'_{y'}}{\partial y'} + \frac{\partial D'_{z'}}{\partial z'} = \beta\left(\rho_e - \frac{V}{c^2}J_x\right)$$

(2.3-41)

Hence

$$\rho'_e = \beta\left(\rho_e - \frac{V}{c^2}J_x\right)$$

(2.3-42)

Equation (2.3-42) is the last of a set of transformations which make Maxwell's equations the same in the laboratory and rest frames. Under these transformations, commonly called the Maxwell-Lorentz transformations, and the Lorentz transformations for coordinates, Maxwell's equations are invariant. To summarize the MLT in vector form,

$$\mathbf{E}'_\perp = \beta(\mathbf{E} + \mathbf{V} \times \mathbf{B})_\perp \qquad \mathbf{E}'_\| = \mathbf{E}_\| \tag{2.3-43}$$

$$\mathbf{D}'_\perp = \beta\left(\mathbf{D} + \frac{\mathbf{V} \times \mathbf{H}}{c^2}\right)_\perp \qquad \mathbf{D}'_\| = \mathbf{D}_\| \tag{2.3-44}$$

$$\mathbf{H}'_\perp = \beta(\mathbf{H} - \mathbf{V} \times \mathbf{D})_\perp \qquad \mathbf{H}'_\| = \mathbf{H}_\| \tag{2.3-45}$$

$$\mathbf{B}'_\perp = \beta\left(\mathbf{B} - \frac{\mathbf{V} \times \mathbf{E}}{c^2}\right)_\perp \qquad \mathbf{B}'_\| = \mathbf{B}_\| \tag{2.3-46}$$

$$\mathbf{J}'_\perp = \mathbf{J}_\perp \qquad \mathbf{J}'_\| = \beta(\mathbf{J} - \rho_e\mathbf{V})_\| \tag{2.3-47}$$

$$\rho'_e = \beta\left(\rho_e - \frac{\mathbf{V}\cdot\mathbf{J}}{c^2}\right) \tag{2.3-48}$$

where $\beta = (1 - V^2/c^2)^{-\frac{1}{2}}$ and the subscripts $\perp$ and $\parallel$ denote the components perpendicular and parallel to the relative velocity between observers. In these expressions, the primed observer is moving with respect to the unprimed observer with velocity $\mathbf{V}$ and is riding along with the medium. The inverse MLT can be obtained by interchanging the primed and unprimed field quantities and substituting $-\mathbf{V}$ for $\mathbf{V}$. These relations can be obtained directly by using the vector form of (2.3-9) and (2.3-10).

It is important to realize that the MLT just derived is valid only when the frames are unaccelerated. For acceleration usually obtained in the laboratory or in magnetohydrodynamic devices, however, (2.3-43) through (2.3-48) are good approximations to the truth. Moreover, in the derivation of these equations no constitutive medium is mentioned and therefore the MLT is valid for the most general kind of medium. When we introduce the longitudinal stretcher operator of Chapter 1, equations (2.3-43) through (2.3-48) can be written as

$$\begin{bmatrix} \mathbf{E'} \\ \mathbf{H'} \end{bmatrix} = \beta \left\{ \begin{bmatrix} \dfrac{\mathbf{E}}{\alpha} \\ \dfrac{\mathbf{H}}{\alpha} \end{bmatrix} + \mathbf{V} \times \begin{bmatrix} \mathbf{B} \\ -\mathbf{D} \end{bmatrix} \right\} \tag{2.3-49}$$

$$\begin{bmatrix} \mathbf{D'} \\ \mathbf{B'} \end{bmatrix} = \beta \left\{ \begin{bmatrix} \dfrac{\mathbf{D}}{\alpha} \\ \dfrac{\mathbf{B}}{\alpha} \end{bmatrix} + \dfrac{\mathbf{V}}{c^2} \times \begin{bmatrix} \mathbf{H} \\ -\mathbf{E} \end{bmatrix} \right\} \tag{2.3-50}$$

$$\mathbf{J'} = \alpha(\mathbf{J} - \rho_e \mathbf{V}) \tag{2.3-51}$$

$$\rho'_e = \beta\left(\rho_e - \frac{\mathbf{V} \cdot \mathbf{J}}{c^2} \right) \tag{2.3-52}$$

where the operator α is defined by $\alpha\mathbf{G} = \beta\mathbf{G}_{\parallel} + \mathbf{G}_{\perp}$. When $V^2 \ll c^2$, β and α become unity, and the MLT of (2.3-49), (2.3-50), (2.3-51), and (2.3-52) simplify greatly. For $V^2 \ll c^2$, the MLT becomes

$$\begin{bmatrix} \mathbf{E'} \\ \mathbf{D'} \\ \mathbf{B'} \\ \mathbf{H'} \end{bmatrix} = \begin{bmatrix} \mathbf{E} \\ \mathbf{D} \\ \mathbf{B} \\ \mathbf{H} \end{bmatrix} + \mathbf{V} \times \begin{bmatrix} \mathbf{B} \\ \mathbf{H}/c^2 \\ -\mathbf{E}/c^2 \\ -\mathbf{D} \end{bmatrix} \tag{2.3-53}$$

$$\mathbf{J'} = \mathbf{J} - \rho_e \mathbf{V} \tag{2.3-54}$$

$$\rho'_e = \rho_e - \frac{\mathbf{V} \cdot \mathbf{J}}{c^2} \tag{2.}$$

In (2.3-55) we have retained the term of order V/c because if ρ_e is zero, $\mathbf{V} \cdot \mathbf{J}/c^2$ is the only term left and cannot be discarded without causing $\nabla' \cdot \mathbf{D}' = \rho'_e$ to be invalid. The act of neglecting $\mathbf{V} \cdot \mathbf{J}/c^2$ is a fruitful source of paradoxes and should be executed carefully.

2.4 THE CONSTITUTIVE EQUATIONS

So far it has not been important to say that S' or S is the laboratory frame of coordinates. At this point the choice is arbitrary but necessary, for the constitutive equations hold in only the rest frame. For convenience, S' is chosen to be the rest frame and S the laboratory frame. Unless otherwise specified, this notation is used in the remainder of the text.

In the electrodynamic phenomena of moving conducting media, Ohm's law is important. A general statement of this law valid in only the rest frame is $J'_i = \sigma_{ji}E'_j$, where the cartesian tensor summation convention that $J'_i = \sum_{j=1}^{3} \sigma_{ji}E'_j$ for $i = 1, 2, 3$ is used. Substituting for J'_i and E'_i from (2.3-49) and (2.3-51), respectively, into Ohm's law yields

$$J_i = \frac{\beta}{\alpha}\left\{\sigma_{ji}\left[\frac{E_j}{\alpha} + (\mathbf{V} \times \mathbf{B})_j\right]\right\} + \rho_e V_i \qquad (2.4\text{-}1)$$

Here it is important not to confuse the order of the operators, since $(1/\alpha)[\sigma_{ji}(E_j/\alpha)] \neq \sigma_{ji}(E_j/\alpha^2)$. Hence Ohm's law, which is relatively simple in the rest frame, becomes rather complicated in the laboratory frame. When $V^2 \ll c^2$, (2.4-1) becomes

$$J_i = \sigma_{ji}[E_j + (\mathbf{V} \times \mathbf{B})_j] + \rho_e V_i \qquad (2.4\text{-}2)$$

which is valid for any anisotropic, nonlinear (for σ_{ji} might be a function of $\mathbf{E}$ and $\mathbf{B}$) medium traveling at a velocity which is small compared to the speed of light. Often in magnetohydrodynamics ρ_e is negligible and the medium is such that $\sigma_{ij} = \delta_{ij}\sigma$. Then the medium is isotropic (mercury is an example) and Ohm's law in the laboratory frame becomes

$$\mathbf{J} = \sigma[\mathbf{E} + (\mathbf{V} \times \mathbf{B})] \qquad (2.4\text{-}3)$$

Numerous authors take Equation (2.4-3) as a fundamental principle, but it is really a result of the Maxwell-Lorentz transformations and a very special case of the general formulation (2.4-1). Ohm's law written in the laboratory frame may be the only relationship which produces coupling between Maxwell's equations and the momentum equations of the medium.

Consider the constitutive equations $D'_i = \epsilon_{ji}E'_j$ and $B'_i = \mu_{ji}H_j$ which are valid in only the rest frame of the medium. The primed quantities in these relationships are replaced by using (2.3-49) and (2.3-50). The result is

$$\frac{D_i}{\alpha} + \left(\frac{\mathbf{V} \times \mathbf{H}}{c^2}\right)_i = \epsilon_{ji}\left(\frac{E_j}{\alpha}\right) + \epsilon_{ji}(\mathbf{V} \times \mathbf{B})_j \tag{2.4-4}$$

$$\frac{B_i}{\alpha} - \left(\frac{\mathbf{V} \times \mathbf{E}}{c^2}\right)_i = \mu_{ji}\left(\frac{H_j}{\alpha}\right) - \mu_{ji}(\mathbf{V} \times \mathbf{D})_j \tag{2.4-5}$$

Equations (2.4-4) and (2.4-5) together with (2.3-49) and (2.3-50) yield six equations in eight unknowns: $\mathbf{E}$, $\mathbf{D}$, $\mathbf{B}$, $\mathbf{H}$, $\mathbf{E}'$, $\mathbf{D}'$, $\mathbf{B}'$, and $\mathbf{H}'$. Any one of these unknowns can be expressed in terms of any other two. This means that $\mathbf{D}$ cannot be expressed as a function of $\mathbf{E}$ only but must also depend upon another field quantity. For example, if a relationship between $\mathbf{D}$, $\mathbf{E}$, and $\mathbf{B}$ is required, $\mathbf{H}$ is obtained from (2.4-5) and substituted into (2.4-4) to yield

$$D_i = \left(\frac{1}{\alpha} - \frac{\alpha V^2}{c^2}\right)^{-1}\left\{\epsilon_{ji}\left(\frac{E_j}{\alpha}\right) + \frac{\mathbf{V}}{c^4} \times \alpha[\mu_{jk}^{-1}(\mathbf{V} \times \mathbf{E})_j]\right.$$
$$\left. + \epsilon_{ji}(\mathbf{V} \times \mathbf{B})_j - \frac{\mathbf{V}}{c^2} \times \alpha\left[\mu_{jk}^{-1}\left(\frac{B_j}{\alpha}\right)\right]\right\}_i \tag{2.4-6}$$

Here μ_{jk}^{-1} is the inverse of μ_{jk}. A similar expression (2.4-6) for $\mathbf{B}$ in terms of $\mathbf{H}$ and $\mathbf{D}$ is derived by solving (2.4-4) for $\mathbf{E}$ and substituting $\mathbf{E}$ into (2.4-5). The result is

$$B_i = \left(\frac{1}{\alpha} - \frac{\alpha V^2}{c^2}\right)^{-1}\left\{\mu_{ji}\left(\frac{H_j}{\alpha}\right) + \frac{\mathbf{V}}{c^4} \times \alpha[\epsilon_{jk}^{-1}(\mathbf{V} \times \mathbf{E})_j]\right.$$
$$\left. - \mu_{ji}(\mathbf{V} \times \mathbf{D})_j + \frac{\mathbf{V}}{c^2} \times \alpha\left[\epsilon_{jk}^{-1}\left(\frac{D_j}{\alpha}\right)\right]\right\}_i \tag{2.4-7}$$

When $V^2 \ll c^2$ the expressions just presented become

$$D_i = \epsilon_{ji}E_j + \epsilon_{ji}(\mathbf{V} \times \mathbf{B})_j - \left\{\frac{\mathbf{V}}{c^2} \times [\mu_{jk}^{-1}(B_j)]\right\}_i \tag{2.4-8}$$

and

$$B_i = \mu_{ji}H_j - \mu_{ji}(\mathbf{V} \times \mathbf{D})_j + \left\{\frac{\mathbf{V}}{c^2} \times [\epsilon_{jk}^{-1}(D_j)]\right\}_i \tag{2.4-9}$$

which are obtained by neglecting terms involving V^2/c^2. The right-hand members of (2.4-8) and (2.4-9) must be retained because they contain μ_{jk}^{-1} and ϵ_{jk}^{-1} factors which can be rather large. The necessity of including these terms is more apparent for an isotropic medium. In that case

$$\mathbf{D} = \epsilon\left[\mathbf{E} + \left(1 - \frac{1}{\kappa\kappa_m}\right)\mathbf{V} \times \mathbf{B}\right] \tag{2.4-10}$$

and

$$B = \mu\left[H - \left(1 - \frac{1}{\kappa\kappa_m}\right)V \times D\right] \qquad (2.4\text{-}11)$$

where $\kappa_m = \mu/\mu_0$ and $\kappa = \epsilon/\epsilon_0$. In a classical experiment by Wilson and Wilson (2.4-10) was verified. In their experiment $E = 0$, and since they used a material in which $\kappa = 6$ and $\kappa_m = 3$, (2.4-10) yielded $D = 17V \times H/c^2$; had they neglected the right-hand member of (2.4-9) the result would have been $D = 18V \times H/c^2$.

To complete our discussion of the constitutive equations, we will determine the MLT's for the polarization and magnetization vectors. By the definition of M, the magnetization vector, $B' = \mu_0(H' + M')$ or $B = \mu_0(H + M)$ and B' and H' can be replaced in terms of B and H by using (2.3-49) and (2.3-50). Then

$$\frac{\beta}{\alpha}(B - \mu_0 H) + \mu_0\beta V \times (D - \epsilon_0 E) = \mu_0 M' \qquad (2.4\text{-}12)$$

which is easily simplified as $D = \epsilon_0 E + P$ (here P is the dielectric polarization vector). The result is

$$M' = \beta\left(\frac{M}{\alpha} + V \times P\right) \qquad (2.4\text{-}13)$$

and similarly,

$$P' = \beta\left(\frac{P}{\alpha} - \frac{V \times M}{c^2}\right) \qquad (2.4\text{-}14)$$

From (2.4-13) and (2.4-14) it is clear that a medium which is either a nonmagnetic dielectric or a nonpolarizable magnetic material in its rest frame may appear to an observer in the laboratory frame as magnetic or polarizable, respectively.

Example 2.1 *Current-carrying wire in relative motion.* A wire carrying a direct current i' is shown in Fig. E2.1-1. To an observer sitting on the

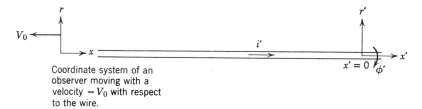

Coordinate system of an
observer moving with a
velocity $-V_0$ with respect
to the wire.

Figure E2.1-1 A coordinate system moving with respect to a wire.

wire the current is i' and the magnetic field outside the wire is $\mathbf{B}' = \hat{\phi}(\mu_0 i'/2\pi r')$. What fields would an observer traveling in the $-x'$ direction with a velocity V_0 see? Would he think the current in the wire differs from i'?

SOLUTION. The fields seen by the moving observer are given by the MLT. In the air, from (2.3-43), $\mathbf{E}_\perp = \beta(\mathbf{E}' - \mathbf{V} \times \mathbf{B}')_\perp$. In this case $\mathbf{E}'_\perp = 0$ and because (2.3-43) is valid for motion positive in the $+x$ direction $\mathbf{V} \times \mathbf{B}' = -\hat{r}(\mu_0 V_0 i'/2\pi r)$. Hence

$$\mathbf{E}_\perp = \hat{r}\, \frac{\beta V_0 i' \mu_0}{2\pi r} \quad \text{and} \quad E_\parallel = \hat{x}\, \frac{i'}{\sigma A} \tag{E2.1-1}$$

From (2.3-46)

$$\mathbf{B}_\perp = \beta \mathbf{B}'_\perp = \hat{\phi}\, \frac{\beta i' \mu_0}{2\pi r} \quad \text{and} \quad B_\parallel = 0 \tag{E2.1-2}$$

The $\mathbf{D}$ and $\mathbf{H}$ fields are no problem because the same constitutive equation holds for either observer in free space. Then $\mathbf{D} = \epsilon_0 \mathbf{E}$ and $\mathbf{H} = \mathbf{B}/\mu_0$. From expression (E2.1-2) it is clear that the moving observer sees a radial electric field not seen by an observer on the wire and that the moving observer sees a circumferential magnetic flux density which is modified by the factor β. The moving observer might attribute the electric field to a net charge accumulated in and/or on the wire provided he did know he was moving. This is given by

$$\rho_{ew} = \frac{\mu_0 \epsilon_0 \beta V_0 i'}{A} \quad \text{(coulombs per meter)} \tag{E2.1-3}$$

And he would think the current in the wire is

$$i = \beta i' \tag{E2.1-4}$$

At velocities usually encountered $\beta \simeq 1$; thus the most interesting result occurring at velocities much less than c is the observation of charge on the wire seen by the moving observer. It is interesting to compute the fields inside the wire. To the observer on the wire the electric field in the wire is

$$\mathbf{E}'_w = \hat{x}'\, \frac{i'}{\sigma A} \tag{E2.1-5}$$

where A is the cross-sectional area of the wire and σ its conductivity. By Ampere's circuital law, (2.2-11), the magnetic flux density in the wire is

$$\mathbf{B}'_w = \hat{\phi}\, \frac{\mu_w i' r}{2A} \tag{E2.1-6}$$

Here μ_w is the permeability of the wire in its rest frame. The observer moving in the $-x'$ direction with velocity V_0 observes fields given by (2.3-43) through (2.3-48) and (2.4-1) which are

$$\mathbf{E}_w = \hat{r}\frac{\mu_w\beta V_0 i' r}{2A} + \hat{x}\,\frac{i'}{\sigma A} \tag{E2.1-7}$$

and

$$\mathbf{B}_w = \hat{\phi}\frac{\beta\mu_w i' r}{2A} \tag{E2.1-8}$$

In addition, the MLT may be applied to the current density and charge in the wire. By (2.3-51)

$$\mathbf{J}_w = \hat{x}'\beta \mathbf{J}'_w = \hat{x}'\beta\frac{i'}{A} \tag{E2.1-9}$$

From (2.3-48) since $\rho'_{ew} = 0$

$$\rho_{ew} = \frac{\beta V_0 i'}{c^2 A} \tag{E2.1-10}$$

Equation (E2.1-9) is consistent with the earlier result of (E2.1-4) which gives an equation for the current seen by the moving observer in the wire.

To check (E2.1-10), the equation for the space charge seen in the wire by the moving observer, D_{rw} is calculated from (E2.1-10) and compared to D_{rw} computed from the constitutive equation (2.4-10). To calculate D_{rw} from (E2.1-10) it is convenient to use Gauss's law as given by (2.2-8). Then

$$D_{rw}2\pi rl = \frac{\beta V_0 i' \pi r^2 l}{c^2 A} \tag{E2.1-11}$$

Here l is the length of the wire in the x' direction. Therefore,

$$D_{rw} = \frac{\beta V_0 i' r}{2c^2 A} \tag{E2.1-12}$$

The substitution of $\mathbf{E}_w$ from (E2.1-7) and $\mathbf{B}_w$ from (E2.1-8) into (2.4-6) yields

$$D_{rw} = \beta^2\epsilon_w\left[\left(1 - \frac{\epsilon_0\mu_0 V_0^2}{\epsilon_w\mu_w c^2}\right)\frac{\mu_w\beta V_0 i' r}{2A} - \left(1 - \frac{\epsilon_0\mu_0}{\epsilon_w\mu_w}\right)\frac{\beta\mu_w i' r V_0}{2Ac^2}\right] = \frac{\beta i' r V_0}{2Ac^2}$$

The two methods yield the same value for D_{rw}. In summary, the fields seen by the moving observers are

$$\mathbf{D} = \hat{r}\,\frac{\beta V_0 i'}{2\pi c^2 r} + \hat{x}\,\frac{\epsilon_0 i'}{\sigma A} \qquad \mathbf{D}_w = \hat{r}\,\frac{\beta V_0 i' r}{2c^2 A} + \hat{x}\,\frac{\epsilon_w i'}{\sigma A}$$

$$\mathbf{E} = \hat{r}\,\frac{\beta V_0 i' \mu_0}{2\pi r} + \hat{x}\,\frac{i'}{\sigma A} \qquad \mathbf{E}_w = \hat{r}\,\frac{\mu_w \beta V_0 i' r}{2A} + \hat{x}\,\frac{i'}{\sigma A}$$

$$\mathbf{B} = \hat{\phi}\,\frac{\mu_0 \beta i'}{2\pi r} \qquad \mathbf{B}_w = \hat{\phi}\,\frac{\mu_w \beta i' r}{2A}$$

$$\mathbf{H} = \hat{\phi}\,\frac{\beta i'}{2\pi r} \qquad \mathbf{H}_w = \hat{\phi}\,\frac{\beta i' r}{2A}$$ (E2.1-13)

$$\mathbf{J} = 0 \qquad \mathbf{J}_w = \hat{x}\,\frac{\beta i'}{A}$$

$$\rho_e = 0 \qquad \rho_{ew} = \frac{V_0 \beta i'}{c^2 A}$$

and those seen by the observer in the rest frame of the wire are

$$\mathbf{D}' = \hat{x}\,\frac{\epsilon_0 i'}{\sigma A} \qquad \mathbf{D}'_w = \hat{x}\,\frac{\epsilon_w i'}{\sigma A}$$

$$\mathbf{E}' = \hat{x}\,\frac{i'}{\sigma A} \qquad \mathbf{E}'_w = \hat{x}\,\frac{i'}{\sigma A}$$

$$\mathbf{B}' = \hat{\phi}\,\frac{\mu_0 i'}{2\pi r} \qquad \mathbf{B}'_w = \hat{\phi}\,\frac{\mu_w i' r}{2A}$$ (E2.1-14)

$$\mathbf{H}' = \hat{\phi}\,\frac{i'}{2\pi r} \qquad \mathbf{H}'_w = \hat{\phi}\,\frac{i' r}{2A}$$

$$\mathbf{J}' = 0 \qquad \mathbf{J}'_w = \frac{i'}{A}$$

$$\rho'_e = 0 \qquad \rho'_{ew} = 0$$

To the moving observer the wire has an anisotropic permittivity and conductivity. It contains a positive space charge per unit length of magnitude $\beta V_0 i'/c^2$. When $\beta \to 1$, commonly called the magnetohydrodynamic approximation, the moving- and rest-frame observers see different values of electric field and electric flux density, but see the same values of magnetic field, magnetic flux density, and current density. Any differences in the latter quantities might be called high velocity relativistic effects, whereas the other differences, including the appearance of ρ_{ew}, are low velocity relativistic effects.

We shall encounter the example later when voltage, resistance, power, and Poynting vector transformations are discussed.

Example 2.2 *A TEM transmission line in relative motion.*   In Example 2.1 we dealt with a direct-current situation and found that an observer in relative motion with respect to the wire saw different fields from those seen by the observer in the rest frame of the wire. In this example, the same problem is worked for the alternating-current case of TEM transmission

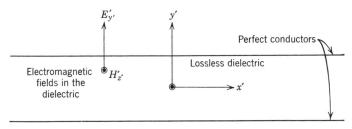

Figure E2.2-1   TEM propagation in the rest frame of the dielectric. Above the plane is medium 1 with properties μ_0 and ϵ_0.

between parallel ideal conducting slabs. We want to determine how the fields appear to an observer moving in the $-x$ direction (see Fig. E2.2-1) with a magnitude of velocity of V_0 with respect to the transmission line.

First the fields must be found in the rest frame. Assuming a TEM (transverse electromagnetic) mode, there will be only two components of field, $E'_{y'}$ and $H'_{z'}$. Here we assume variations of the form $F'(x', y', z')e^{j\omega't'}$. The Maxwell equations become

$$\frac{dE'_{y'}}{dx'} = -j\omega'\mu H'_{z'} \tag{E2.2-1}$$

$$\frac{dH'_{z'}}{dx'} = -j\omega'\epsilon E'_{y'} \tag{E2.2-2}$$

It is important to realize that Maxwell's equations, when written in any medium except free space, are simplest in the rest frame; otherwise they become tangled by the constitutive equations (2.4-10) and (2.4-11). Combining (E2.2-1) with (E2.2-2) produces

$$\frac{d^2\begin{bmatrix}E'_{y'}\\H'_{z'}\end{bmatrix}}{dx'^2} + \omega'^2\mu\epsilon\begin{bmatrix}E'_{y'}\\H'_{z'}\end{bmatrix} = 0 \tag{E2.2-3}$$

The solution for the electric field is

$$E'_{y'} = E'_0 e^{-jx'\omega'\sqrt{\mu\epsilon}} \tag{E2.2-4}$$

and from (E2.2-1)

$$H'_{z'} = E'_0 \sqrt{\frac{\epsilon}{\mu}}\, e^{-jx'\omega'\sqrt{\mu\epsilon}} \tag{E2.2-5}$$

where E'_0 is a constant and $\sqrt{\mu/\epsilon}$ is the intrinsic impedance of the dielectric as seen by an observer in the rest frame. Before transforming the electric and magnetic field intensity into the quantities seen by the moving observer, time must be introduced into (E2.2-4) and (E2.2-5). Then

$$E'_{y'}(x', t') = E'_0 \exp\left[j\omega'(t' - x'\sqrt{\mu\epsilon})\right] \tag{E2.2-6}$$

$$H'_{z'}(x', t') = E'_0 \sqrt{\frac{\epsilon}{\mu}} \exp\left[j\omega'(t' - x'\sqrt{\mu\epsilon})\right] \tag{E2.2-7}$$

To find out what the moving observer sees, all the primed quantities in (E2.2-6) and (E2.2-7) must be transformed by the Lorentz and Maxwell-Lorentz transformations. By (2.3-43)

$$E_0 = \beta(1 + V_0\sqrt{\mu\epsilon})E'_0 \tag{E2.2-8}$$

and by (2.3-45)

$$H_0 = \beta\sqrt{\frac{\epsilon}{\mu}}(1 + V_0\sqrt{\mu\epsilon})E'_0 \tag{E2.2-9}$$

It is not really necessary to use (2.3-45) to transform the magnitude of the $H'_{z'}$ field because (E2.2-7) relates H'_0 to E'_0. The quantity $\omega'(t' - x'\sqrt{\mu\epsilon})$ is transformed by the use of (1.2-1) and (1.2-2) to yield

$$\omega'(t' - x'\sqrt{\mu\epsilon}) = \beta\omega'\left[(1 + V_0\sqrt{\mu\epsilon})t - \left(\frac{V_0^2}{c^2} + V_0\sqrt{\mu\epsilon}\right)\frac{x}{V_0}\right] \tag{E2.2-10}$$

In accordance with (1.11-3) $\omega = \beta\omega'(1 + V_0\sqrt{\mu\epsilon})$ and the transformed fields seen by the moving observer become

$$E_y(x, t) = \beta(1 + V_0\sqrt{\mu\epsilon})E'_0 \exp\left\{j\omega\left[t - \frac{V_0^2/c^2 + V\sqrt{\mu\epsilon}}{V_0(1 + V_0\sqrt{\mu\epsilon})}x\right]\right\} \tag{E2.2-11}$$

$$H_z(x, t) = \beta\sqrt{\frac{\epsilon}{\mu}}(1 + V_0\sqrt{\mu\epsilon})E'_0 \exp\left\{j\omega\left[t - \frac{V_0^2/c^2 + V_0\sqrt{\mu\epsilon}}{V_0(1 + V_0\sqrt{\mu\epsilon})}x\right]\right\}$$

$$\tag{E2.2-12}$$

By the use of (2.3-44) and (2.3-46) $D_y(x, t)$ and $B_z(x, t)$ are found. The results are

$$D_y(x, t) = \beta\epsilon\left(1 + \frac{V_0}{c^2\sqrt{\mu\epsilon}}\right)E'_0 \exp\left\{j\omega\left[t - \frac{V_0^2/c^2 + V_0\sqrt{\mu\epsilon}}{V_0(1 + V_0\sqrt{\mu\epsilon})}x\right]\right\}$$

(E2.2-13)

$$B_z(x, t) = \beta\sqrt{\mu\epsilon}\left(1 + \frac{V_0}{c^2\sqrt{\mu\epsilon}}\right)E'_0 \exp\left\{j\omega\left[t - \frac{V_0^2/c^2 + V_0\sqrt{\mu\epsilon}}{V_0(1 + V_0\sqrt{\mu\epsilon})}x\right]\right\}$$

(E2.2-14)

The results just derived can be obtained from the relationships of Problem 1 at the end of the chapter. Before examining the physical significance of the magnitudes of the fields seen by the moving observer, we should note that in addition to seeing the Doppler shift frequency, the moving observer sees a different phase velocity V_p. This velocity, which is the reciprocal of the coefficient of x, is

$$V_p = \frac{1 + V_0\sqrt{\mu\epsilon}}{V_0/c^2 + \sqrt{\mu\epsilon}}$$

(E2.2-15)

Since V'_p, the phase velocity to the observer in the rest frame, is given by $V'_p = (\mu\epsilon)^{-1/2}$, (E2.2-15) becomes

$$V_p = \frac{V_0 + V'_p}{1 + V_0V'_p/c^2}$$

(E2.2-16)

which is true for all values of $V_0 < c$. This expression could have been obtained directly from (1.3-2). Where $V_0^2 \ll c^2$, V_p simplifies to

$$V_p \simeq (V_0 + V'_p)\left(1 - \frac{V_0V'_p}{c^2}\right) \simeq V'_p + V_0\left(1 - \frac{V_p'^2}{c^2}\right)$$ (E2.2-17)

The term $1 - V_p'^2/c^2$ is known as the Fresnel dragging coefficient. Non-relativistic theories such as the Lorentz electron theory yielded this result only when the medium was nonmagnetic. The form of the Fresnel dragging coefficient derived here in (E2.2-17) was verified by M. and H. A. Wilson (1913) in an experiment suggested by Einstein and Laub. Inspection of (E2.2-11), (E2.2-12), (E2.2-13), and (E2.2-14) indicates that for $V_0^2 \ll c^2$ the moving observer sees a significantly different magnitude for the **E** and **H** fields from that of the observer stationed on the medium. To both observers, the **D** and **B** fields are the same. This result is consistent with the MLT'S of (2.3-44) and (2.3-46), for if $V_0^2 \ll c^2$ the flux densities will be the same to both observers.

Inspection of (E2.2-11) and (E2.2-12) shows that $E_y = 0$ and $H_z = 0$ if $V_0 = -V'_p$ with speed $(\mu\epsilon)^{-1/2}$. This produces an interesting limiting case for checking the results. Since the observer is traveling at the phase velocity in the direction of electromagnetic wave propagation, we would expect him to say $\omega = 0$. This, indeed, is a result of this analysis. But why does this observer see electric displacement and magnetic induction but no electric or magnetic field? To those unaccustomed to problems of the electrodynamics of moving media this could be explained only by infinite permittivity and permeability. However, the constitutive equations (2.4-10) and (2.4-11) indicate that, although $\mathbf{E}_\perp$ and $\mathbf{H}_\perp$ are zero, $\mathbf{D}_\perp$ and $\mathbf{B}_\perp$ need not be zero. This is also indicated clearly in the electric and magnetic polarization equations (2.4-14) and (2.4-13). So when $V_0 = -\hat{x}V'_p$, $D_y = P_y$ and $B_z = \mu_0 M_z$. This can be shown by using (2.4-14) and (2.4-13) to find P_y and M_z, respectively.

2.5 BOUNDARY CONDITIONS

The boundary conditions used with Maxwell's equations are derived from these equations. Since the equations are the same to all observers, the boundary conditions are also the same. Figure 2.5-1 shows the

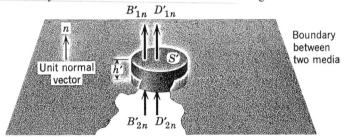

Figure 2.5-1 Illustration for the flux density boundary conditions. Medium 2 with properties ϵ_2 and μ_2 is below the plane.

boundary between two different media. A pillbox-shaped volume is placed so that part of it is in medium 1 and part in medium 2. The area of its broad surface is S' and its thickness h'. By the application of Gauss's theorem, (2.2-8),

$$\delta' + (\mathbf{n} \cdot \mathbf{D}'_1)\, \Delta S' - (\mathbf{n} \cdot \mathbf{D}'_2)\, \Delta S' = \rho'_e\, \Delta S' h' \qquad (2.5\text{-}1)$$

Here δ' is the flux which leaks from the lateral sides of the pill box ($\delta' \to 0$ as $h' \to 0$). Taking the limit as $h' \to 0$ yields

$$\mathbf{n} \cdot (\mathbf{D}'_1 - \mathbf{D}'_2) = \rho'_s \qquad (2.5\text{-}2)$$

where $\rho'_s = \lim\limits_{h' \to 0} \rho'_e h'$, the surface charge in coulombs per meter^2. A similar treatment for the magnetic flux density results in

$$\mathbf{n} \cdot (\mathbf{B}'_1 - \mathbf{B}'_2) = 0 \qquad (2.5\text{-}3)$$

Thus the electric flux density normal to a boundary between two media suffers a discontinuity equal to the surface charge located at the boundary. Since there is no free magnetic charge, the normal components of magnetic flux density are continuous at the boundary. It is important to notice that these conditions are not influenced by relative motion between the

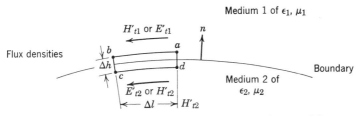

Figure 2.5-2 Illustration for the field intensity boundary conditions.

media involved. It is necessary to apply the boundary conditions to quantities seen by the same observer regardless of his motion or the relative motions of the media.

To derive the boundary conditions on the tangential components of the field intensities, consider (2.2-11) and Fig. 2.5-2. In this figure the flux densities D' and B' and the current density J' are normal to the area enclosed by the path of integration. If Ampere's law, (2.2-11) is applied to the circuit $abcda$,

$$H'_{t1}\,\Delta l' - H'_{t2}\,\Delta l' + \int_b^c \mathbf{H} \cdot d\mathbf{l} + \int_d^a \mathbf{H} \cdot d\mathbf{l} = \left(J' + \frac{\partial D'}{\partial t'}\right)\Delta h'\,\Delta l'$$

$$(2.5\text{-}4)$$

When $\Delta h' = 0$ with $\Delta l'$ fixed

$$H'_{t1} - H'_{t2} = \lim_{\Delta h' \to 0}\left(J' + \frac{\partial D'}{\partial t'}\right)\Delta h' \qquad (2.5\text{-}5)$$

The right-hand number of (2.5-5) approaches zero as long as $J' + \partial D'/\partial t'$ remains finite. However, in certain cases, usually involving perfect conductors or possibly high permittivity dielectrics, $\lim\limits_{\Delta h' \to 0}\left(J' + \dfrac{\partial D'}{\partial t'}\right)\Delta h'$ remains finite. Then the tangential component of magnetic field intensity produces a discontinuity at the boundary equal to the total current per unit length contained in a current sheet. If $\mathscr{J}' = \lim\limits_{\Delta h' \to 0}\left(J' + \dfrac{\partial D'}{\partial t'}\right)\Delta h'$

the boundary condition becomes

$$\mathbf{n} \times (\mathbf{H}'_1 - \mathbf{H}'_2) = \mathscr{I}' \tag{2.5-6}$$

Similarly, from (2.2-10) the boundary conditions on the electric field are obtained. In this case

$$\mathbf{n} \times (\mathbf{E}'_1 - \mathbf{E}'_2) = Ш' \tag{2.5-7}$$

where $Ш' = \lim\limits_{\Delta h' \to 0} -\dfrac{\partial B'}{\partial t'} \Delta h'$. Usually, $Ш' = 0$ except at the Bloch wall comprising the boundary between magnetic domains.

The boundary conditions for the tangential components of field intensities have now been derived and we can see that the tangential components are continuous across boundaries, provided there are no disturbances such as current sheets or magnetic domains. In studying magnetohydrodynamics, current sheets may result when certain configurations are idealized by assuming perfectly conducting boundaries; usually, however, $Ш' = 0$ and the appropriate condition on the electric field intensity is

$$\mathbf{n} \times (\mathbf{E}'_1 - \mathbf{E}'_2) = 0 \tag{2.5-8}$$

Example 2.3   To illustrate the use of MLT's and the role of the boundary conditions let us consider a lossy ferromagnetic dielectric slab traveling with velocity V_0 through a uniform magnetic field normal to the slab (See Figs. E2.3-1 and E2.3-2.)   We want to calculate the fields and charge

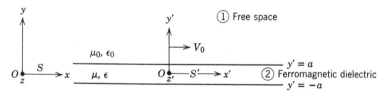

Figure E2.3-1   A lossy ferromagnetic dielectric slab moving at a velocity V_0 with respect to the xyz coordinate system.

distributions seen by an observer in the laboratory frame. Let the subscripts 1 and 2 denote free space and lossy ferromagnetic dielectric, respectively.   Maxwell's equations written for the observer in frame S in Figs. E2.3-1 and E2.3-2 are

$$\frac{dB_y}{dy} = 0 \tag{E2.3-1}$$

from $\nabla \cdot \mathbf{B} = 0$, and

$$\frac{dD_y}{dy} = \rho_e \tag{E2.3-2}$$

from $\nabla \cdot \mathbf{D} = \rho_e$ (here no space charge is assumed to exist in the rest frame) and from

$$\nabla \times \mathbf{E} = -\frac{\partial \mathbf{B}}{\partial t} \qquad \frac{d\mathbf{E}_z}{dy} = 0 \qquad \text{(E2.3-3)}$$

These equations are valid in both media. From the equation $\nabla \times \mathbf{H} = \mathbf{J}$

$$-\frac{dH_{x1}}{dy} = 0 \qquad \text{(E2.3-4)}$$

$$-\frac{dH_{x2}}{dy} = J_{z2} \qquad \text{(E2.3-5)}$$

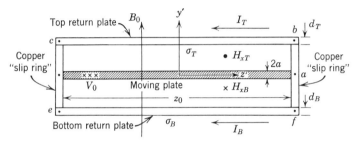

Figure E2.3-2   The moving slab and the electrical return circuit in which $z_0 \gg 2a$.

From (2.3-47) $J_{z2} = J'_{z2} = \sigma E'_{z2}$ and from (2.3-43) E'_{z2} is found, so that (E2.3-5) becomes

$$-\frac{dH_{x2}}{dy} = \sigma(E_{z2} + V_0 B_{y2}) \qquad \text{(E2.3-6)}$$

So far it can be concluded that B_{y1}, B_{y2}, H_{y1}, H_{y2}, D_{y1}, D_{y2}, E_{z1}, E_{z2}, and H_{x1} are constants. H_{x2} can be easily found from (E2.3-6). It is given by

$$H_{x2} = C_1 - \sigma(E_{z2} + V_0 B_0)y \qquad y \geq 0 \qquad \text{(E2.3-7)}$$

where C_1 is a constant, and by boundary condition (2.5-3), $B_0 = B_{y1} = B_{y2} =$ the applied magnetic field. By using boundary condition (2.5-6),

$$H_{x1} = C_1 - \sigma(E_{z2} + V_0 B_0)a \qquad \text{(E2.3-8)}$$

where a is the half-width of the ferromagnetic slab. At this point in our analysis we know B_{y1}, H_{y1}, B_{y2} and we know H_{x1} in terms of C_1 and E_{z2}. By boundary condition (2.5-8), $E_{z1} = E_{z2}$. So clearly C_1 and E_{z2} must be found. Let $J'_{z2} = J_0$ which depends upon the breadth of the ferromagnetic dielectric in the z direction and the method of electrical loading. Then

$$E_{z1} = E_{z2} = \frac{J_0}{\sigma} - V_0 B_0 \qquad \text{(E2.3-9)}$$

Figure E2.3-2 is a side view of the moving plate and its external connections. Here we assume the plate is so thin compared to the other dimensions that the assumption of a one-dimensional geometry is valid, and therefore end effects near the "slip rings" can be neglected. Let the top return circuit have a resistance per unit length of R_T and the bottom circuit R_B. Here $R_T = (\sigma_T d_T x_0)^{-1}$ and $R_B = (\sigma_B d_B x_0)^{-1}$, where x_0 is the length of the configuration in the x direction. The total current flowing is

$$I_0 = 2ax_0 J_0 \qquad (E2.3\text{-}10)$$

The current divides so that the current in the top and bottom return circuits is

$$I_T = \frac{2ax_0 J_0 (\sigma_B \, d_B)^{-1}}{(\sigma_T \, d_T)^{-1} + (\sigma_B \, d_B)^{-1}} \quad \text{and} \quad I_B = \frac{2ax_0 J_0 (\sigma_T \, d_T)^{-1}}{(\sigma_T \, d_T)^{-1} + (\sigma_B \, d_B)^{-1}}$$

$$(E2.3\text{-}11)$$

by Kirchhoff's voltage and current laws. Then

$$\mathbf{E}_T = -\hat{z} \, \frac{2aJ_0}{\sigma_T \, d_T + \sigma_B \, d_B} \qquad (E2.3\text{-}12)$$

and

$$\mathbf{E}_B = -\hat{z} \, \frac{2aJ_0}{\sigma_T \, d_T + \sigma_B \, d_B} \qquad (E2.3\text{-}13)$$

Since Kirchhoff's laws are compatible with Maxwell's equations, (E2.3-12) and (E2.3-13) can be checked by the application of $\oint \mathbf{E} \cdot d\mathbf{l} = 0$. Then

$$\int_{cb} \mathbf{E} \cdot d\mathbf{l} + \int_{fe} \mathbf{E} \cdot d\mathbf{l} = 0$$

This is clearly true since $\mathbf{E}_T = \mathbf{E}_B$ and the path elements are of opposite sign. Integration along path $dabcd$ yields E_{z2} in terms of J_0. Performing the line integral yields

$$E_{z2} = \frac{-2aJ_0}{\sigma_T \, d_T + \sigma_B \, d_B} \qquad (E2.3\text{-}14)$$

If this value of E_{z2} is substituted into (E2.3-9), J_0 can be determined. This results in

$$J_0 = \sigma V_0 B_0 \left(1 + \frac{2a\sigma}{\sigma_T \, d_T + \sigma_B \, d_B} \right)^{-1} \qquad (E2.3\text{-}15)$$

and

$$E_{z2} = \frac{-2a\sigma V_0 B_0}{\sigma_T \, d_T + \sigma_B \, d_B + 2a\sigma} \qquad (E2.3\text{-}16)$$

It is interesting to note that if either σ_T or σ_B is infinite, $J_0 = \sigma V_0 B_0$ and $E_{z2} = 0$. This is called the short-circuit case. When $\sigma_T = \sigma_B = 0$, $J_0 = 0$

and $E_{z2} = -V_0 B_0$ as would be expected from (E2.3-9). This is called the open-circuit case. In the general case the currents are

$$I_T = \frac{2 a x_0 \sigma_T \, d_T \sigma V_0 B_0}{\sigma_T \, d_T + \sigma_B \, d_B + 2 a \sigma} \qquad \text{(E2.3-17)}$$

$$I_B = \frac{2 a x_0 \sigma_B \, d_B \sigma V_0 B_0}{\sigma_T \, d_T + \sigma_B \, d_B + 2 a \sigma} \qquad \text{(E2.3-18)}$$

To determine C_1 consider $\oint \mathbf{H} \cdot d\mathbf{l} = \int_S \mathbf{J} \cdot d\mathbf{S}$ around a path that includes the ferromagnetic dielectric sheet and the bottom return circuit. Then

$$H_{x1}(y = a) = \frac{-2 a \sigma_T \, d_T \sigma V_0 B_0}{\sigma_T \, d_T + \sigma_B \, d_B + 2 a \sigma} \qquad \text{(E2.3-19)}$$

This result is easily checked. If $\sigma_B \to \infty$, the moving plate and the bottom return circuit comprise a solenoid outside of which the magnetic field is zero. So at $y = a$ it is to be expected that $H_{x1} = 0$. If $\sigma_T = \infty$, then $H_{x1}(y = a) = -2 a \sigma V_0 B_0$, because the plane $y = a$ is now contained inside a solenoid. Equation (E2.3-19) is adequate in both cases. By using (E2.3-8) it is seen that

$$C_1 = \frac{a \sigma V_0 B_0 (\sigma_B \, d_B - \sigma_T \, d_T)}{\sigma_T \, d_T + \sigma_B \, d_B + 2 a \sigma} \qquad \text{(E2.3-20)}$$

Substitution of C_1 into (E2.3-7) yields

$$H_{x2} = \frac{(\sigma_B \, d_B - \sigma_T \, d_T) a - (\sigma_B \, d_B + \sigma_T \, d_T) y}{\sigma_T \, d_T + \sigma_B \, d_B + 2 a \sigma} \cdot \sigma V_0 B_0 \qquad \text{(E2.3-21)}$$

To complete the solution for the observer in the laboratory frame H_{y1}, H_{y2}, D_{z1}, and D_{z2} must be found. Clearly, $H_{y1} = B_0/\mu_0$ and $D_{z1} = \epsilon_0 E_{z1}$. The electric displacement in the ferromagnetic dielectric is obtained from (2.4-10)

$$D_{z2} = \frac{\beta^2 \epsilon V_0 B_0 \left[\left(1 - \dfrac{\epsilon_0 \mu_0}{\epsilon \mu} \right) (\sigma_T \, d_T + \sigma_B \, d_B) - \dfrac{2 a \sigma \epsilon_0 \mu_0}{\beta^2 \epsilon \mu} \right]}{\sigma_T \, d_T + \sigma_B \, d_B + 2 a \sigma} \qquad \text{(E2.3-22)}$$

Here we note that there exists a value of load resistance which will make $D_{z2} = 0$ even though $E_{z2} \neq 0$. It is easily shown from (2.4-4) and (2.4-5) that

$$H_{y2} = \frac{\beta^2}{\mu} \left[(1 - \epsilon \mu V_0^2) B_0 + \left(\frac{1}{c^2} - \epsilon \mu \right) V_0 E_{z2} \right] \qquad \text{(E2.3-23)}$$

so that

$$H_{y2} = \frac{\beta^2 B_0}{\mu}\left[1 - \epsilon\mu V_0^2 - \frac{(1/c^2 - \epsilon\mu)2a\sigma V_0^2}{\sigma_T d_T + \sigma_B d_B + 2a\sigma}\right] \quad \text{(E2.3-24)}$$

In this example we can see that the return path for the current has an important effect on the field distributions. When $V_0^2 \ll c^2$, $H_{y2} \rightarrow \dfrac{B_0}{\mu}$; but D_{z2} does not become ϵE_{z2}. This may seem curious because the MLT for $\mathbf{D}$ has a V_0/c^2 in it but the MLT for $\mathbf{H}$ has not. However, if (2.3-44) is rewritten as $\mathbf{D}_\perp = \beta(\mathbf{D}' - \mathbf{V} \times \mu\epsilon\mathbf{H}')_\perp = \epsilon\beta(\mathbf{E}' - \mathbf{V} \times \mathbf{B})_\perp$, then it is clear that $\mathbf{D}_\perp$ should not necessarily approach $\epsilon\mathbf{E}'_\perp$ when $V^2 \ll c^2$.

Example 2.4   In the next section we shall study induced electromotive force, but first we shall look at a filament moving through a magnetic field. Consider a filament of finite length along the z' axis of the S' frame. In the S frame, which is the laboratory frame by our assumed convention, a large magnet produces a uniform magnetic field $\mathbf{B} = \hat{y}B_0$. Hence the observer in the laboratory frame sees a filament parallel to the z axis but traveling in the x direction through a uniform constant magnetic field with a velocity $\mathbf{V} = \hat{x}V$. We want to find the fields, seen by an observer riding in S', in the filament and in the air around the filament. Two cases are considered: (a) The filament is a nonmagnetic conductor, and (b) the filament is a dielectric insulator.

Nonmagnetic Conducting Filament

In the laboratory frame the electric field $\mathbf{E}$ is taken as zero. (The value of $\mathbf{E}$ is zero if no external field is applied with capacitor plates, etc.) Then as the filament begins to move, an observer on the filament in S' would say that his local electric field $\mathbf{E}'$ is given by $\mathbf{E}' = \mathbf{V} \times \mathbf{B}$. However, an electric field cannot exist in a conductor, and in a relaxation time the charge builds up at the ends of the filament so that the electric field (seen in the filament) due to the charge exactly balances out the $\mathbf{V} \times \mathbf{B}$ field due to motion. Then $\mathbf{E}' = 0$ in the filament and the observer in S says the field in the filament is $-\mathbf{V} \times \mathbf{B}$. He attributes this field to the charge on the ends of the filament. (The charge is the same in both frames of reference since $\mathbf{J} = 0$.) The observer in S' will see an $\mathbf{E}'$ field of $\mathbf{E}'_0 = \hat{z}VB_0$ in free space.

In the wire frame $(x'y'z')$ the wire will appear to have an $\mathbf{H}'$ field $\mathbf{H}' = \mathbf{B}'/\mu_0$ (assuming a nonmagnetic material). The value of $\mathbf{B}'_0$ and $\mathbf{B}_0$ are related by $\mathbf{B}'_\perp = \beta(\mathbf{B} - \mathbf{V} \times \mathbf{E}/c^2)$ and here $\mathbf{B}'_0 \simeq \mathbf{B}_0$ for nonrelativistic velocities, which we are assuming. In the laboratory frame in accordance with (2.4-13)

$$M = M' - V \times P = -V \times P \qquad \text{(E2.4-1)}$$

But $P' = 0$ since $E' = 0$ in the wire and hence by (2.4-14)

$$P = \frac{V \times M}{c^2} = -\frac{V \times (V \times P)}{c^2}$$

and hence

$$P = 0 \qquad \text{(E2.4-2)}$$

neglecting relativistic quantities of order V^2/c^2 and using $c^2 = (\mu_0 \epsilon_0)^{-1}$. Similarly, the magnetization can be written:

$$M = M' - \frac{V \times (V \times M)}{c^2} = M' = 0 \qquad \text{(E2.4-3)}$$

Dielectric Nonconducting Filament

In this case, as previously, when the filament begins to move, the observer in the filament sees an electric field $V \times B$ in the filament and in the space around it. However, in the dielectric no charge can flow so that this electric field remains in the filament. Hence $E' = VB_0\hat{z}$. In the laboratory frame, the electric field remains zero in all space and the filament.

The polarization in the filament (in the rest frame of the filament) is $P' = (\kappa - 1)\epsilon_0 E'$ since $E = 0$. Also $M' = 0$ since the filament is nonmagnetic. Hence in the laboratory frame:

$$M = -V \times P = -V \times P' = -(\kappa - 1)\epsilon_0 V$$

$$\times (V \times B) = \hat{y}(\kappa - 1)\frac{V^2}{c^2} H_0 \qquad \text{(E2.4-4)}$$

$$P = P' + \frac{V \times M'}{c^2} = P' = \epsilon_0(\kappa - 1)E' \qquad \text{(E2.4-5)}$$

and we see that M in the laboratory is zero to nonrelativistic order, and P is the same as P'.

The behavior of the conductor in the first of the above cases is the basis for the principle of electromagnetic induction. The free charge which rushes out to the ends of the filament will generate a voltage if the ends are attached to a meter (fixed in the laboratory) by rails or slider contacts, which are also fixed in the laboratory; we will discuss this problem later in detail.

2.6 INDUCED ELECTROMOTIVE FORCE

Induced electromotive force is bound to be of interest in any problem involving a medium moving through electromagnetic fields. Since the invention of the dynamo, the study of induced electromotive force has been a fertile source of confusion resulting in many controversies in the literature.

In the study of magnetohydrodynamic devices, terminal voltage and load current are usually the easiest quantities to measure experimentally. Because these quantities are related to the induced electromotive force (emf), it is important to understand the calculation of emf. The following sections demonstrate that no confusion arises provided proper account is taken of the relative motion between conductors and observers. It will be shown that such concepts as "motional emf" and "transformer emf" are meaningless unless the motion of the observer is specified. The special relativistic formulation used in this book renders meaningless the argument about the "seat" or source of the emf, because for each observer there exist seats of emf determined by the relative motion between each observer and the circuit.

No Relative Motion

In a particular problem, when the observers and media are at rest it is easy to define the induced electromotive force. It must satisfy two conditions: (1) that it be a measure of how nonconservative the electric field is, and (2) that it satisfy Kirchhoff's voltage law. The last consideration makes the emf useful in calculating circuit quantities. The definition that satisfies these criteria is

$$e = \oint \mathbf{E} \cdot d\mathbf{l} \qquad (2.6\text{-}1)$$

because

$$\sum_i I_i R_i = \sum_i \left[\int_i \mathbf{J} \cdot d\mathbf{S} \left(\int_i \mathbf{E} \cdot d\mathbf{l} \Big/ \int_i \mathbf{J} \cdot d\mathbf{A} \right) \right]$$

The field vector $\mathbf{E}$, measured in a reference system stationary with respect to the rigid circuit, must satisfy (2.2-3). An expression for the emf about any prescribed path may be found by integrating both sides of (2.2-3) over any two-sided surface $\mathbf{S}$ bounded by the path about which the emf is to be calculated. Then by Stokes' theorem

$$\int_\mathbf{S} \mathbf{\nabla} \times \mathbf{E} \cdot d\mathbf{S} = \oint \mathbf{E} \cdot d\mathbf{l} = - \int_S \frac{\partial \mathbf{B}}{\partial t} \cdot d\mathbf{S} \qquad (2.6\text{-}2)$$

or

$$e = -\frac{\partial}{\partial t}\int_{\mathrm{s}} \mathbf{B}\cdot d\mathbf{S}$$

Here the time derivative is exchanged with the integration because the surface $\mathbf{S}$ is independent of time. The surface integral $\int_{S} \mathbf{B}\cdot d\mathbf{S}$ is by definition equal to the magnetic flux ϕ linking the prescribed path. Thus the equation becomes the familiar form of Faraday's law

$$e = -\frac{\partial\phi}{\partial t} \tag{2.6-3}$$

Here ϕ is the total flux linking the path, including that resulting from any current in the circuit itself. The emf has been defined for a mathematical

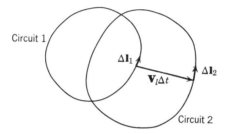

Figure 2.6-1   A nonrigid circuit.

line forming a closed path and not a closed conductor; for if a conductor contains eddy currents, the emfs evaluated about different paths are not generally equal. The emf about a conducting circuit containing finite-sized conductors is independent of the path through the conductors only if there are no eddy currents.

Because the Maxwell-Lorentz transformations have not been used, it might seem that Equation (2.6-3) is applicable to rigid currents and only to rigid currents. However, it can be extended to include a class of moving circuits. Consider the moving circuit shown in Fig. (2.6-1). During the time interval Δt this circuit changes its shape and position from that of circuit 1 to that of circuit 2. Let $\Delta\mathbf{l}_i$ be an element of the path in circuit 1 that moves to a new position in circuit 2. The velocity of this path element is $\mathbf{V}_{li}$. Here it is our objective to find an expression for $d\phi/dt$ when circuit 1 changes to circuit 2. The fluxes enclosed by circuits 1 and 2 are, respectively,

$$\phi_1 = \int_1 \mathbf{B}(t)\cdot d\mathbf{S} \tag{2.6-4}$$

and

$$\phi_2 = \int_2 \mathbf{B}(t + \Delta t) \cdot d\mathbf{S} \tag{2.6-5}$$

The area swept out by $\Delta \mathbf{l}_i$ as it goes from position 1 to 2 is

$$\Delta \mathbf{S}_i = (\mathbf{V}_{li} \times \Delta \mathbf{l}_i) \, \Delta t \tag{2.6-6}$$

Then

$$\phi_2 = \int_1 \mathbf{B}(t + \Delta t) \cdot d\mathbf{S} + \sum_i \mathbf{B}(t + \Delta t) \cdot \Delta \mathbf{S}_i \tag{2.6-7}$$

The total rate of change of flux is

$$\lim_{\Delta t \to 0} \frac{\phi_2 - \phi_1}{\Delta t} = \lim_{\Delta t \to 0} \left\{ \int_1 \left[\frac{\mathbf{B}(t + \Delta t) - \mathbf{B}(t)}{\Delta t} \right]_n \cdot d\mathbf{S} + \sum_i \mathbf{B}(t + \Delta t) \cdot (\mathbf{V}_{li} \times \Delta \mathbf{l}_i) \right\} \tag{2.6-8}$$

Taking the limit gives

$$\frac{d\phi}{dt} = \int_S \frac{\partial \mathbf{B}}{\partial t} \cdot d\mathbf{S} + \oint \mathbf{B} \cdot \mathbf{V}_l \times d\mathbf{l} \tag{2.6-9}$$

where $\mathbf{V}_l$ is the velocity of the path element $d\mathbf{l}$ which coincides with the moving conductor. But as $\mathbf{B} \cdot \mathbf{V}_l \times d\mathbf{l} = -(\mathbf{V}_l \times \mathbf{B}) \cdot d\mathbf{l}$ (2.6-9) becomes

$$e = -\int_S \frac{\partial \mathbf{B}}{\partial t} \cdot d\mathbf{S} + \oint (\mathbf{V}_l \times \mathbf{B}) \cdot d\mathbf{l} \tag{2.6-10}$$

when it is combined with (2.6-3). It should be emphasized that (2.6-10) yields the induced emf if, and only if, the velocity of the path element is identical to the velocity of the moving conductor. Such a path may always be found and this formula applied if the path contains sliding contacts which move such that the path length between any two points fixed on the conductors is a continuous function of time. This restriction occurs because (2.6-10) is completely independent of the observer's frame of coordinates.

Relative Motion Present

We have seen how Faraday's law can be extended to apply to cases where relative motion exists. However, the resulting formula (2.6-10) has the restriction that the path element of integration moves along with the conductor. A definition of the emf about any closed metallic circuit whose various parts may be moving relative to each other and which may or may not contain sliding contacts must be developed. This definition must be consistent with Kirchhoff's law and the Joulean dissipation in the elements must be $I^2 R$. (Here it is assumed that $V^2 \ll c^2$ so that the

Joulean dissipation is the same to all observers.) The resistance used, which should be the resistance seen by the observer in the rest frame, is defined as $R_i = \int_i \mathbf{E}' \cdot d\mathbf{l} \Big/ \int_i \mathbf{J}' \cdot d\mathbf{A}$. The primes are dropped from l and A because $V^2 \ll c^2$. The summation of the IR drops about the closed path is

$$\sum_i I_i R_i = \sum_i \int_i \mathbf{E}' \cdot d\mathbf{l} = \oint \mathbf{E}' \cdot d\mathbf{l} \qquad (2.6\text{-}11)$$

It then seems reasonable to define the emf about any prescribed path in a conducting nonrigid circuit as $e = \oint \mathbf{E}' \cdot d\mathbf{l}$ where $\mathbf{E}'$ is the electric field strength evaluated at the element $d\mathbf{l}$ by an observer stationary with respect to the conductor at that point. Since $\mathbf{E}' = (\mathbf{E} + \mathbf{V} \times \mathbf{B})$ when $V^2 \ll c^2$, $\mathbf{E} = \mathbf{E}' - (\mathbf{V} \times \mathbf{B})$. This can be substituted into $\nabla \times \mathbf{E} = -\dfrac{\partial \mathbf{B}}{\partial t}$. Then

$$\nabla \times \mathbf{E}' = -\frac{\partial \mathbf{B}}{\partial t} + \nabla \times (\mathbf{V} \times \mathbf{B}) \qquad (2.6\text{-}12)$$

Integrating (2.6-12) over the surface enclosed by the path about which the emf is being evaluated and applying Stokes' theorem yields

$$e = \oint \mathbf{E}' \cdot d\mathbf{l} = -\int_S \frac{\partial \mathbf{B}}{\partial t} \cdot d\mathbf{S} + \oint (\mathbf{V} \times \mathbf{B}) \cdot d\mathbf{l} \qquad (2.6\text{-}13)$$

Here $\mathbf{B}$ is the magnetic field due to all causes; and as $V^2 \ll c^2$, $\mathbf{B}$ is the same to all observers, $\mathbf{V}$ is the velocity of the segment of the conductor at the point corresponding to $d\mathbf{l}$ relative to some given observer, and $\partial \mathbf{B}/\partial t$ is the vector time rate of change of $\mathbf{B}$. It is very important to notice that (1) $\mathbf{V}$ is the velocity of the conductor relative to some given observer and not the velocity of the path element $d\mathbf{l}$ and (2) in general, the partial derivative with respect to time cannot be moved outside the integral since the area is a function of time. Equation (2.6-13), like (2.6-10), is independent of the choice of position of the observer. When (2.6-10) is applicable, (2.6-13) is often easier to use because any path of integration may be used.

If the eddy currents (or any other currents in the circuit) are large enough to cause a redistribution of the magnetic field, (2.6-13) is valid provided that the resulting magnetic field is used. The field problem must then be solved before the emf or voltage calculation can begin. In principle, (2.6-13) applies when the effects of eddy currents are strong, but once the fields are known it is simpler to use other methods of calculating terminal voltage. The equations derived here are useful primarily because they avoid the field problem. Hence both formulas are most profitably applied only when negligible eddy currents and little armature reaction are present. They can be easily used without solving the field problem for finding induced emfs in filamentary circuits or in circuits where eddy currents are negligible. This condition prevails when the largest dimension normal to current flow is $L \leq \delta$. Here δ is the skin depth and $\delta = (2/\omega\mu_0\sigma)^{1/2}$.

In both (2.6-10) and (2.6-13) the expression for the emf contains a surface integral and must be calculated for a closed circuit. It is nevertheless possible to define a unique potential difference between the terminals of a generator, as in the case of rigid circuits, if these terminals and the external circuit lie within a region which to some observers is irrotational, and if this same observer sees no part of this external circuit moving through a magnetic field. If it is possible to connect these terminals with a rigid line so that there is no emf in any closed circuit formed by this line and in any permitted external circuit, then it is possible to define uniquely a terminal voltage which is equal to the emf minus the IR drop in the generator. Then

$$V_{AB} = e - \int_A^B \mathbf{E}' \cdot d\mathbf{l} \qquad (2.6\text{-}14)$$

in accordance with the convention that the line integral ($\oint \mathbf{E}' \cdot d\mathbf{l}$) is taken as positive in the direction going from the negative terminal A through the generator to the positive terminal B and that $\int_A^B \mathbf{E}' \cdot d\mathbf{l}$ is integrated from A to B through the generator. It is very important to use $\mathbf{E}'$ in the integral of (2.6-14). In other words, the integral must be evaluated by an observer at rest on the conductor in which the IR drop is being calculated. V_{AB} is the potential of terminal B with respect to terminal A.

Before investigating methods for calculating terminal voltage when eddy currents are important, we shall illustrate the application of (2.6-10), (2.6-13) and (2.6-14) in several examples.

Example 2.5   In the circuit of Fig. E2.5-1 a voltmeter of high internal resistance is connected to two long wires which parallel a conductor carrying a direct current i. The shorting bar which completes the circuit moves to the right with a velocity V. The problem is to calculate the

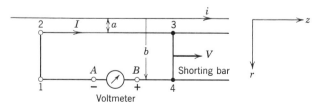

Figure E2.5-1   An elementary direct-current generator.

induced emf in the loop by using Faraday's law (2.6-10) and also (2.6-13), considering the viewpoints of various observers.

To all observers $\partial \mathbf{B}/\partial t = 0$ and (2.6-10) becomes

$$e = \oint (\mathbf{V}_l \times \mathbf{B}) \cdot d\mathbf{l} \qquad \text{(E2.5-1)}$$

According to our sign convention and consistent with the polarity assigned to the voltmeter, $d\mathbf{l}$ is positive in the clockwise direction. The shorting bar is moving through a steady magnetic field having a value

$$\mathbf{B} = \hat{\phi}\, \frac{\mu_0 i}{2r} \qquad \text{(E2.5-2)}$$

assuming that the current flowing in the loop induces a negligible magnetic field. If this assumption is not valid, the total field must be used. The line integral (E2.5-1) is zero everywhere except on the shorting bar; there $\mathbf{V}_l \times \mathbf{B}$ is in the negative radial direction and therefore

$$e = -\int_a^b \frac{V \mu_0 i}{2\pi} \frac{dr}{r} = -\frac{\mu_0 i V}{2\pi} \ln \frac{b}{a} \qquad \text{(E2.5-3)}$$

The calculation of the emf by (2.6-13) is identical with the above when the observer is at rest on the voltmeter because the velocity of the path element and the moving conductor are the same. To an observer stationary with respect to the shorting bar, the remainder of the loop moves in the negative z direction with speed V. Along conductors $\overline{14}$ and $\overline{23}$, $\mathbf{V} \times \mathbf{B}$ is perpendicular to $d\mathbf{l}$ and thus contributes nothing to the line integral. On the shorting bar, $V = 0$ and therefore the line integral is

$$e = \int_1^2 (\mathbf{V} \times \mathbf{B}) \cdot d\mathbf{l} \qquad \text{(E2.5-4)}$$

Here

$$\mathbf{V} \times \mathbf{B} = \hat{r}\, \frac{V \mu_0 i}{2\pi r} \quad \text{and} \quad (\mathbf{V} \times \mathbf{B}) \cdot d\mathbf{l} = -\frac{V \mu_0 i}{2\pi r}\, dr$$

Therefore

$$e = -\frac{\mu_0 i V}{2\pi} \ln \frac{b}{a}$$

which is the same value that the other observer obtained. Now consider the calculation of the emf to an observer having a velocity with respect to the voltmeter of $-\hat{z}V_0$, $V_0^2 \ll c^2$. Once again the conductor segments $\overline{14}$ and $\overline{23}$ do not contribute to the line integral. For segment $\overline{12}$, since

$\mathbf{V} \times \mathbf{B} = -\hat{r}V_0 B$, $d\mathbf{l} = -\hat{r} \, dr$, and $(\mathbf{V} \times \mathbf{B}) \cdot d\mathbf{l} = V_0 B \, dr$

$$\int_1^2 (\mathbf{V} \times \mathbf{B}) \cdot d\mathbf{l} = \frac{V_0 \mu_0 i}{2\pi} \ln \frac{b}{a} \qquad \text{(E2.5-5)}$$

and for segment $\overline{34}$

$$\int_3^4 (\mathbf{V} \times \mathbf{B}) \cdot d\mathbf{l} = \int_a^b -(V + V_0)B \, dr = -\frac{(V + V_0)\mu_0 i}{2\pi} \ln \frac{b}{a} \qquad \text{(E2.5-6)}$$

Then the emf seen by this observer is

$$e = \int_1^2 (\mathbf{V} \times \mathbf{B}) \cdot d\mathbf{l} + \int_3^4 (\mathbf{V} \times \mathbf{B}) \cdot d\mathbf{l} = -\frac{V\mu_0 i}{2\pi} \ln \frac{b}{a} \qquad \text{(E2.5-7)}$$

Clearly, great care must be exercised in speaking of the emf between two points. In the above example one observer claims that $\int(\mathbf{V} \times \mathbf{B}) \cdot d\mathbf{l} \neq 0$ over the shorting bar, but $\int(\mathbf{V} \times \mathbf{B}) \cdot d\mathbf{l} = 0$ over segment $\overline{12}$; a second observer claims it is zero over the sliding bar, but nonzero over segment $\overline{12}$; and a third observer says the line integral is not zero along either segment $\overline{12}$ or the sliding bar. As a consequence of Maxwell's equations, different observers must disagree as to the place where the emf is generated, but they will always agree on the value of the total emf about any closed circuit provided $V^2 \ll c^2$. It is not important to know the "seat" of the emfs, for it is only the total value of emf which is of any use.

If the voltmeter has an internal resistance R_v and the rest of the loop has a resistance R, (2.6-14) can be used to find the terminal voltage V_{AB}. In this case

$$V_{AB} = e - IR \qquad \text{(E.2.5-8)}$$

where I is positive in the clockwise direction. By Ohm's law $V_{AB} = R_v I$. Thus

$$V_{AB} = \frac{e}{1 + R/R_v} = \frac{-V\mu_0 i}{2\pi(1 + R/R_v)} \ln \frac{b}{a} \qquad \text{(E2.5-9)}$$

and

$$I = -\frac{V\mu_0 i}{2\pi(R + R_v)} \ln \frac{b}{a} \qquad \text{(E2.5-10)}$$

Here it is interesting to note that the ratio of the open-circuit voltage to the short-circuit current is equal to R, which is the internal resistance of the generator.

Example 2.6 Figure E2.6-1 represents a simple alternator comprising a loop of wire rotating in a uniform magnetic field. The induced emf is again easily found by using Faraday's law. In this problem it is convenient to use this law in the form of (2.6-2), which is equivalent to using (2.6-10), since the area of the coil is a constant. To an observer riding on the coil

$$\phi = -abB_0 \cos \omega t \qquad (E2.6-1)$$

assuming the coil to be in the xz plane when $t = 0$. Then

$$e = -\frac{\partial \phi}{\partial t} = -\omega abB_0 \sin \omega t \qquad (E2.6-2)$$

If (2.6-13) is used, there are two choices of observers, making the calculation of emf very easy. Of course, any choice of observer is valid and yields

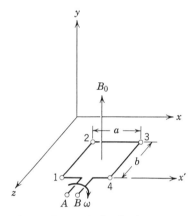

Figure E2.6-1   A simple alternator.

the same electromotive force. First, let the observer be fixed in the xyz coordinates. Then $\partial \mathbf{B}/\partial t = 0$ and (2.6-13) becomes

$$e = \oint (\mathbf{V} \times \mathbf{B}) \cdot d\mathbf{l} \qquad (E2.6-3)$$

Since terminal A is assumed to be negative, the path of integration should start at A and proceed toward terminal B. For segments $\overline{23}$ and $\overline{41}$, $\mathbf{V} \times \mathbf{B}$ is perpendicular to $d\mathbf{l}$. Thus

$$e = \int_1^2 (\mathbf{V} \times \mathbf{B}) \cdot d\mathbf{l} + \int_3^4 (\mathbf{V} \times \mathbf{B}) \cdot d\mathbf{l} \qquad (E2.6-4)$$

Over segment $\overline{12}$, $\mathbf{V} \times \mathbf{B} = (\hat{z}a\omega B_0/2) \sin \omega t$ and over segment $\overline{34}$, $\mathbf{V} \times \mathbf{B} = (-\hat{z}a\omega B_0/2) \sin (\pi - \omega t) = -(\hat{z}a/2)\omega B_0 \sin \omega t$. Taking account of the sign of $d\mathbf{l}$, (E2.6-4) becomes

$$e = -\omega ab B_0 \sin \omega t \qquad \text{(E2.6-5)}$$

Because $\partial \mathbf{B}/\partial t$ is zero, the observer on the xyz axes might call the emf just obtained a "motional electromotive force."

Now assume that the observer is stationary with respect to the coil. Then (2.6-13) becomes

$$e = -\int_S \frac{\partial \mathbf{B}}{\partial t} \cdot d\mathbf{S} \qquad \text{(E2.6-6)}$$

In the coordinate system which rotates with the coil, $\mathbf{B} = -\hat{x}' B_0 \sin \omega t + \hat{y}' B_0 \cos \omega t$. Then

$$\frac{\partial \mathbf{B}}{\partial t} \cdot d\mathbf{S} = \omega B_0(-\hat{x}' \cos \omega t - \hat{y}' \sin \omega t) \cdot \hat{y}' \, dS \qquad \text{(E2.6-7)}$$

$$= -\omega B_0 \sin \omega t \, dS$$

Therefore

$$e = -\omega ab B_0 \sin \omega t \qquad \text{(E2.6-8)}$$

The observer riding on the coil would call this "transformer emf" because to him $\oint (\mathbf{V} \times \mathbf{B}) \cdot d\mathbf{l} = 0$. This example demonstrates that the commonly used terms motional and transformer emf are meaningless unless the observer is specified. In general, it is not always possible to choose an observer that sees either a purely motional or transformer emf.

Example 2.7   *The Faraday disc generator.*   In Examples 2.5 and 2.6 it was easy to apply Faraday's law to calculate the emf. Depending upon the observer chosen, calculation by means of (2.6-13) was at least as difficult and sometimes much more difficult. In the Faraday disc generator, Faraday's law applies but its application is rather subtle.

Referring to Figs. E2.7-1 and E2.7-2 and choosing an observer sitting on either a brush or the external circuit, let us again use (2.6-13). To this observer $\partial \mathbf{B}/\partial t = 0$, and since the external circuit has no velocity relative to the brushes, the electromotive force is given by

$$e = \int_1^2 (\mathbf{V} \times \mathbf{B}) \cdot d\mathbf{l} \qquad \text{(E2.7-1)}$$

where $\mathbf{V}$ is the velocity of the *disc* at any point along the path of integration. Since $\mathbf{V} = \hat{\phi} r\omega$, $\mathbf{V} \times \mathbf{B} = r\omega B_0$ and then

$$e = \omega B_0 \int_0^a r \, dr = \frac{\omega B_0 a^2}{2} \qquad \text{(E2.7-2)}$$

The question is how (2.6-10) (Faraday's law) can alternatively be used. In spite of the similarity of (2.6-13) and (2.6-10), (2.6-10) is restricted to

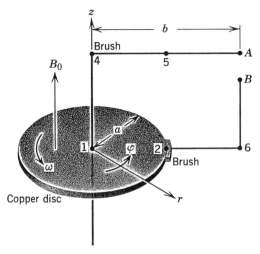

Figure E2.7-1 The Faraday disc generator.

paths of integration in which the velocity of the path element is identical to the conductor. Here path $\overline{12}$ is stationary with respect to the observer on the external circuit, but moves with respect to the Faraday disc. The path on which (2.6-10) is valid and identical to (2.6-13) is path $\overline{132}$ of Fig. E2.7-2. Here segment $\overline{13}$ rotates with the disc and segment $\overline{32}$ changes length as the disc rotates. By keeping the observer fixed on the external circuit,

$$e = \int_1^3 (\mathbf{V} \times \mathbf{B}) \cdot d\mathbf{l} + \int_3^2 (\mathbf{V} \times \mathbf{B}) \cdot d\mathbf{l} \qquad \text{(E2.7-3)}$$

and the conductor and path velocity are the same. On segment $\overline{23}$, $\mathbf{V} \times \mathbf{B}$ is perpendicular to $d\mathbf{l}$. Once again $e = \omega B_0 a^2 / 2$.

Now consider an observer riding on the disc. He sees the external circuit moving in the $-\varphi$ direction through a constant magnetic field.

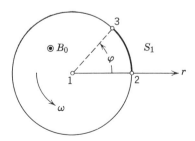

Figure E2.7-2 Top view of the previous figure.

Along segments $\overline{41}$, $\overline{12}$, and $\overline{6B}$ there are no contributions to the line integral. Thus

$$e = \int_A^4 (\mathbf{V} \times \mathbf{B}) \cdot d\mathbf{l} + \int_2^6 (\mathbf{V} \times \mathbf{B}) \cdot d\mathbf{l} \tag{E2.7-4}$$

Along segment $\overline{A4}$, $\mathbf{V} \times \mathbf{B} = -B_0 \omega \hat{r}$ and along segment $\overline{26}$, $\mathbf{V} \times \mathbf{B} = -\omega B_0 \hat{r}$. Therefore,

$$e = \omega B_0 \left(\int_b^0 r \, dr - \int_a^b r \, dr \right) = \frac{\omega B_0 a^2}{2} \tag{E2.7-5}$$

In this example we can see that when (2.6-13) is used to calculate the emf, the relative motion of the path of integration and the observer is irrelevant. However, the relative motion between the conductor at the path element and the observer is very important. Faraday's law is applied in such a manner that the conductor and path element move together. In other applications of Faraday's law it may be difficult to choose the proper path of integration; whereas the more general principle of (2.6-13) always applies and is valid for any choice of path.

Example 2.8   It is interesting to apply (2.6-13) to Example 2.3 because a complete field solution is available. From the field solution the terminal voltage V_T between the slip rings is

$$V_T = I_T R_T = I_B R_B = \frac{2az_0 V_0 B_0 \sigma}{\sigma_T \, d_T + \sigma_B \, d_B + 2a\sigma} \tag{E2.8-1}$$

by virtue of either (E2.3-17) or (E2.3-18). In order to apply (2.6-13), let the observer be fixed on the top plate. Then as $\partial \mathbf{B}/\partial t = 0$, $e = z_0 V_0 B_0$ where z_0 is the distance between the electrodes. By (2.6-14)

$$V_T = V_{da} = e - \int_{-z_0/2}^{z_0/2} (E_{z2} + V_0 B_0) \, dz \tag{E2.8-2}$$

because $E'_{z2} = E_{z2} + V_0 B_0$. Then $V_T = -E_{z2} z_0 = I_T R_T$ which agrees with (E2.8-1). However, if the field solution were not known, the determination of V_T still would be simple. Since $V_T = e - iR$ and $iR = I_0 z_0 / 2\sigma a x_0$,

$$V_T = z_0 V_0 B_0 - \frac{I_0 z_0}{2\sigma a x_0} \tag{E2.8-3}$$

The current I_0 divides between the top and bottom plate such that $I_T = I_0 R_B/(R_T + R_B)$ and $V_T/R_T = I_T$. Therefore

$$I_0 = \frac{V_T (R_T + R_B)}{R_B R_T} \tag{E2.8-4}$$

Accordingly, the substitution of I_0 from (E2.8-4) into (E2.8-3) yields

$$V_T = z_0 V_0 B_0 - \frac{V_T(R_T + R_B)z_0}{(2\sigma a x_0 R_B R_T)} \qquad (E2.8\text{-}5)$$

or

$$V_T = \frac{2\sigma a z_0 V_0 B_0}{(z_0/x_0)(1/R_B + 1/R_T) + 2\sigma a} \qquad (E2.8\text{-}6)$$

where $R_B^{-1} = \sigma_B d_B x_0/z_0$ and $R_T^{-1} = \sigma_T d_T x_0/z_0$. Hence Equation (E2.8-6) yields the same terminal voltage as (E2.8-1). Here the calculation of terminal voltage has been accomplished without knowing or obtaining the field solution.

Example 2.9 In the examples considered so far, the emf has been the same for all observers and paths of integration. This emf has been equal to the terminal voltage indicated by an ideal voltmeter.

If the Faraday disc of Example 2.7 has an alternating applied magnetic field, eddy currents play a major role even if their influence on the applied field is small. Let the applied magnetic field be $\mathbf{B} = \hat{z} B_M \sin \beta t$, the geometry be given by Figs. E2.7-1 and E2.7-2; assume the disc is made of a poor conductor so that the induced $\mathbf{B}$ field is negligible compared to the applied field. Using Faraday's law and taking path $A541326BA$, ϕ is easily evaluated. In Fig. E2.7-2 ϕ is the flux normal to the area $\overline{123}$, (hereafter called S_1) and increases with time, since path element $\overline{13}$ rides with the conductor with angular velocity ω. Then

$$\phi = -\frac{B_M a^2 \omega t}{2} \sin \beta t \qquad (E2.9\text{-}1)$$

since the area vector enclosed by path $A541326BA$ points in the $-\hat{z}$ direction. By Faraday's law

$$e_1 = -\frac{d\phi}{dt} = \frac{B_M a^2 \omega}{2} \sin \beta t + \frac{B_M a^2 \beta \omega t}{2} \cos \beta t \qquad (E2.9\text{-}2)$$

Equation (2.6-13), with the observer riding on the external circuit and the same path of integration, yields

$$e_2 = -\int_{S_1} \frac{\partial \mathbf{B}}{\partial t} \cdot d\mathbf{S} + \int_1^3 (\mathbf{V} \times \mathbf{B}) \cdot d\mathbf{l} \qquad (E2.9\text{-}3)$$

The line integral is the same as in Example 2.7, Equation (E2.7-3), except that B_0 is replaced by $B_M \sin \omega t$. Now the surface integral must be evaluated. The element of area is $d\mathbf{S} = -\hat{z} r \, dr \, d\varphi$ and $\partial \mathbf{B}/\partial t = \hat{z} \beta B_M \cos \beta t$.

Thus

$$-\int_{S_1} \frac{\partial \mathbf{B}}{\partial t} \cdot d\mathbf{S} = \int_0^a \int_0^{\omega t} \beta B_M \, r \cos \beta t \, dr \, d\varphi = \frac{a^2 \beta B_M \omega t}{2} \cos \beta t$$

$$(E2.9\text{-}4)$$

Therefore, the emf is given by

$$e_2 = \frac{\omega a^2 B_M}{2} \sin \beta t + \frac{\beta a^2 B_M \omega t}{2} \cos \beta t \qquad (E2.9\text{-}5)$$

The fact that the same emf has been obtained by (2.6-13) and Faraday's law is no surprise, because for path $A541326BA$ the two methods of calculation are equivalent. The resulting emf is alternating and its amplitude increases with time; if the terminal voltage does the same thing, we will have made quite a discovery. Keeping the same observer, apply (2.6-13) along path $A541326BA$. Here the surface integral vanishes and

$$e_3 = \int_1^2 (\mathbf{V} \times \mathbf{B}) \cdot d\mathbf{l} = \frac{\omega a^2 B_M}{2} \sin \beta t \qquad (E2.9\text{-}6)$$

This calculation yields a different value of emf from that of the previous calculations and thus questions the validity of (E2.9-6) and (E2.9-5). However, there is no reason why the emfs about different paths have to be equal. In fact Kirchhoff's voltage law assures us that the emf about different paths is not the same. These results will disturb people who confuse the emf with the terminal voltage, which must be independent of the means of its calculation. In the previous examples the emf was equal to the terminal voltage provided the voltmeter did not draw any current; in this example eddy currents cause voltage drops that are not negligible. By symmetry, the eddy currents flow in concentric circles about the z axis; the observer who chooses the radial path $\overline{12}$ finds that the eddy current J_φ is perpendicular to his path. Since $V_{AB} = e_3 - \int_A^B \mathbf{E}' \cdot d\mathbf{l}$ and $\mathbf{E}' \cdot d\mathbf{l} = (J_\varphi/\sigma)\hat{\varphi} \cdot \hat{r} \, dr = 0$, $V_{AB} = (\omega a^2 B_M/2) \sin \beta t$. For observers whose paths of integration include segment $\overline{32}$, the second term of (2.6-14) is not zero. To evaluate $\int_3^2 \mathbf{E}' \cdot d\mathbf{l}$ apply Faraday's law to path $\overline{232}$. Assuming E'_φ does not vary with φ

$$E'_\varphi 2\pi r = -\beta \pi r^2 B_M \cos \beta t$$

or

$$E'_\varphi = -\frac{r \beta B_M}{2} \cos \beta t \qquad (E2.9\text{-}7)$$

Then

$$\int_3^2 \mathbf{E}' \cdot d\mathbf{l} = \frac{a^2 \beta B_M \omega t}{2} \cos \beta t \qquad (E2.9\text{-}8)$$

The observer choosing path $A541326BA$ obtains a terminal voltage

$$V_{AB} = e_1 - \int_3^2 \mathbf{E}' \cdot d\mathbf{l} = \frac{\omega a^2 B_M}{2} \sin \beta t \qquad (E2.9\text{-}9)$$

and hence all three observers agree on the terminal voltage.

Example 2.10   In Fig. E2.10-1 a glass plate located in the xz plane moves in the x direction with velocity V through a magnetic field H_{0z}. The problem is to find the emf induced by the motion of the plate. Here we

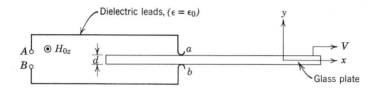

Figure E2.10-1   A simple generator.

assume the plate is very thin but has such length and breadth as to justify calling it an infinite sheet. We must calculate the electric fields seen by an observer riding in the plate and then evaluate $\int \mathbf{E}' \cdot d\mathbf{l}'$. Let the subscripts 0 and 1 denote free-space and glass-plate variables, respectively. By the continuity of the tangential components of magnetic field in the rest frame of the glass plate, it is easy to show that

$$H_{1z} = H_{0z}. \qquad (E2.10\text{-}1)$$

Assuming that no surface charge (real charge, not polarization charge) rests on the surface of the glass, the normal component of electric displacement is continuous. Thus

$$D'_{1y} = D'_{0y} \qquad (E2.10\text{-}2)$$

and from (2.3-50)

$$D'_{0y} = \frac{-\beta H_0 V}{c^2} = -\beta \epsilon_0 B_0 V \qquad (E2.10.3)$$

since $D_{0y} = 0$. Therefore

$$E'_{1y} = \frac{D'_{1y}}{\epsilon} = -\frac{\epsilon_0}{\epsilon} \beta V B_0 \qquad (E2.10\text{-}4)$$

since the normal component of $\mathbf{D}$ is continuous, and

$$E'_{0y} = -\beta B_0 V \qquad (E2.10\text{-}5)$$

Remembering the filaments connecting the brushes to A and B are not conductors, the rise in potential from A to B can now be calculated as

$$\Phi'_T = -\int_A^B \mathbf{E}' \cdot d\mathbf{l} = \beta B_0 V d\left(1 - \frac{\epsilon_0}{\epsilon}\right) \qquad \text{(E2.10-6)}$$

It is interesting to obtain D_{1y}. Since H_{1z} is given by (E2.10-1)

$$D_{1y} = 0 \qquad \text{(E2.10-7)}$$

by using (2.3-44). The electric displacement differs for different observers. By (2.3-43)

$$E_{1y} = \beta(E'_{1y} + VB'_{1z}) = \beta^2 VB_0\left(1 - \frac{\epsilon_0}{\epsilon}\right) \qquad \text{(E2.10-8)}$$

According to an observer riding on the external circuit, the rise in potential from A to B is

$$\Phi_T = -\int_A^B E_{1y}\, dy = \beta^2 VB_0\, d\left(1 - \frac{\epsilon_0}{\epsilon}\right) \qquad \text{(E2.10-9)}$$

Thus $\Phi_T = \beta\Phi'_T$, indicating that only at very high velocities do different observers see different values of potential. The emf can be calculated by using (2.6-13) and assuming $\beta \simeq 1$. Then

$$e = \oint (\mathbf{V} \times \mathbf{B}) \cdot d\mathbf{l} \qquad \text{(E2.10-10)}$$

where the observer is stationary with respect to the external circuit. The emf becomes $e = VB_0\, d$. The terminal voltage is given by

$$V_T = e - \int_A^B \mathbf{E}'_1 \cdot d\mathbf{l} = B_0 V d\left(1 - \frac{\epsilon_0}{\epsilon}\right) \qquad \text{(E2.10-11)}$$

which is the same as the potentials previously calculated provided $\beta \simeq 1$. This is no cause for alarm, because (2.6-13), from which (E2.10-11) is obtained, is based on the assumption that $\beta = 1$.

In this example, the internal potential drop in the generator cannot be neglected, as the generator is a dielectric rather than a conductor. It is interesting to note that the motional field $\mathbf{V} \times \mathbf{B}$ does not polarize the dielectric in the same way as would a static electric field.

2.7 THE SCALAR AND VECTOR POTENTIAL

Because the magnetic induction $\mathbf{B}'$ is solenoidal, let

$$\mathbf{B}' = \nabla' \times \mathbf{A}' \qquad (2.7\text{-}1)$$

From Maxwell's equation $\nabla' \times \mathbf{E}' = -\partial \mathbf{B}'/\partial t'$, $\nabla' \times (\mathbf{E}' + \partial \mathbf{A}'/\partial t') = 0$. Therefore a scalar potential may be introduced to yield

$$\mathbf{E}' = -\nabla'\Phi' - \frac{\partial \mathbf{A}'}{\partial t'} \qquad (2.7\text{-}2)$$

where Φ is the scalar potential. Upon the substitution of $\mathbf{B}'$ from (2.7-1) and $\mathbf{E}'$ from (2.7-2) into $\nabla' \times \mathbf{H}' = \mathbf{J}' + \partial \mathbf{D}'/\partial t'$, there results

$$-[\nabla'(\ln \mu)] \times (\nabla' \times \mathbf{A}') + \nabla'\nabla' \cdot \mathbf{A}' - \nabla'^2\mathbf{A}'$$

$$= \mu \mathbf{J}' - \mu \frac{\partial}{\partial t'}\left[\epsilon'\left(\nabla'\Phi + \frac{\partial \mathbf{A}}{\partial t'}\right)\right] \quad (2.7\text{-}3)$$

which is good for any medium. According to a theorem due to Helmholtz, a vector function is completely defined if its divergence and curl are known. The expression just derived simplifies somewhat if $\nabla' \cdot \mathbf{A}'$ is chosen such that

$$\nabla'\nabla' \cdot \mathbf{A}' = -\mu \frac{\partial}{\partial t'}(\epsilon\nabla'\Phi') \qquad (2.7\text{-}4)$$

Under the assumption of (2.7-4), (2.7-3) becomes

$$\nabla'^2\mathbf{A}' + [\nabla'(\ln \mu)] \times (\nabla' \times \mathbf{A}') - \mu \frac{\partial}{\partial t'}\left(\epsilon \frac{\partial \mathbf{A}'}{\partial t'}\right) = -\mu \mathbf{J}' \quad (2.7\text{-}5)$$

which is a nonlinear equation if μ is a function of $\mathbf{H}'$. Since $\mathbf{A}'$ depends upon the current distribution, Φ' should be related to the charge distribution through $\nabla' \cdot \mathbf{D}' = \rho'_e$. Substituting E' from (2.7-2) into the divergence equation gives

$$\nabla' \cdot \epsilon\left(\nabla'\Phi' + \frac{\partial \mathbf{A}'}{\partial t'}\right) = -\rho'_e \qquad (2.7\text{-}6)$$

The variable $\mathbf{A}'$ can be eliminated by solving (2.7-6) and (2.7-4) simultaneously. If the medium is linear and isotropic, and μ and ϵ do not vary with time, (2.7-4) becomes

$$\nabla' \cdot \mathbf{A}' = -\mu\epsilon \frac{\partial \Phi'}{\partial t'} + C \qquad (2.7\text{-}7)$$

where C is an arbitrary constant. (2.7-5) and (2.7-6) become

$$\nabla'^2 \mathbf{A}' - \mu\epsilon \frac{\partial^2 \mathbf{A}'}{\partial t'^2} = -\mu\mathbf{J}' \tag{2.7-8}$$

and

$$\nabla'^2 \Phi' + \frac{\partial}{\partial t'} \nabla' \cdot \mathbf{A}' = -\frac{\rho'_e}{\epsilon} \tag{2.7-9}$$

If $\nabla' \cdot \mathbf{A}'$ from (2.7-7) is substituted into (2.7-9), there results

$$\nabla'^2 \Phi' - \mu\epsilon \frac{\partial^2 \Phi'}{\partial t'^2} = -\frac{\rho'_e}{\epsilon} \tag{2.7-10}$$

This equation allows Φ' to be calculated from the charge distribution and (2.7-8) allows the vector potential to be calculated from the current distribution. To describe completely $\mathbf{A}'$, however, (2.7-7) must be evaluated. The magnetic induction $\mathbf{B}'$ is given by $\mathbf{B}' = \nabla' \times \mathbf{A}'$ and

$$\frac{\partial \mathbf{E}'}{\partial t'} = -\frac{\partial^2 \mathbf{A}'}{\partial t'^2} + \frac{1}{\mu\epsilon} \nabla'\nabla' \cdot \mathbf{A}' \tag{2.7-11}$$

since by (2.7-4) $\nabla'\nabla' \cdot \mathbf{A}' = -\mu\epsilon\nabla'(\partial\Phi'/\partial t')$. In the time-varying case, the fields can be calculated in an isotropic, linear, constant medium from the vector potential. This is true because the charge density is related to the current density by $\nabla' \cdot \nabla' \times \mathbf{H}' = \nabla' \cdot \mathbf{J}' + \partial\rho'_e/\partial t' = 0$. Where there is no time variation, since ρ'_e and $\mathbf{J}'$ are not related, $\mathbf{A}'$ and Φ' are independent and both (2.7-8) and (2.7-10) must be solved. The general solutions of these equations are

$$\mathbf{A}' = \frac{\mu}{4\pi} \int_{\text{vol}} \frac{\mathbf{J}'(t' - |\mathbf{r}'|\sqrt{\mu\epsilon})}{|\mathbf{r}'|} \, dV' \tag{2.7-12}$$

and

$$\Phi' = \frac{1}{4\pi\epsilon} \int_{\text{vol}} \frac{\rho'_e(t' - |\mathbf{r}'|\sqrt{\mu\epsilon})}{|\mathbf{r}'|} \, dV' \tag{2.7-13}$$

where $|\mathbf{r}'|$ is the distance from the current or charge to the point where the potential is being evaluated, and dV' is the element of volume in the source region. Here we integrate over the volume of the source region at a slightly earlier time $t' - |\mathbf{r}'|\sqrt{\mu\epsilon}$ to allow time for changes in the volume to propagate from the source to the observer through the distance $|\mathbf{r}'|$. These relations are valid in the rest frame only because they depend on the constitutive equations $\mathbf{B}' = \mu\mathbf{H}'$ and $\mathbf{D}' = \epsilon\mathbf{E}'$ valid in the rest frame only. $\mathbf{A}'$ and Φ' are sometimes called retarded potentials. The values of $\mathbf{J}'$ and ρ'_e must include image currents and charges so that we can account for the influence of material media.

Since Φ' and $\mathbf{A}'$ are the scalar and vector potentials in the rest frame, it may be shown that

$$\Phi = \beta(\Phi' + \mathbf{V} \cdot \mathbf{A}') \tag{2.7-14}$$

and

$$\mathbf{A}_{\parallel} = \beta\left(\mathbf{A}'_{\parallel} + \frac{\mathbf{V}}{c^2}\Phi'\right) \qquad \mathbf{A}_{\perp} = \mathbf{A}'_{\perp} \tag{2.7-15}$$

by the method used to obtain the Maxwell-Lorentz transformations. In Example 2.10 the potential transformed in accordance with (2.7-14). Since $\mathbf{A}' = 0$, $\Phi = \beta\Phi'$, which is apparent when (E2.10-6) and (E2.10-9) are compared.

Example 2.11 In Fig. E2.11-1 the $x'y'z'$ frame of coordinates is attached to the capacitor plates. An observer in the xyz frame of coordinates moves

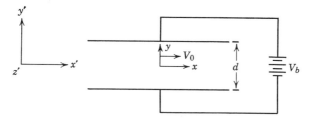

Figure E2.11-1   A parallel plate capacitor.

with a velocity V_0 relative to the capacitor plates. The scalar potential between the plates is

$$\Phi' = \frac{V_b}{d}y' \tag{E2.11-1}$$

and

$$\mathbf{A}' = 0$$

Then by (2.7-14) $\Phi = \beta V_b y/d$ and by (2.7-15)

$$\mathbf{A} = \frac{-\hat{x}\beta V_0 V_b y}{c^2 d} \tag{E2.11-2}$$

Since $\mathbf{B} = \nabla \times \mathbf{A}$, $\mathbf{B} = -\hat{z}(\partial A_x/\partial y) = +\hat{z}\beta V_0 V_b/c^2 d$. This is physically meaningful because to the observer in the xyz frame the charges on the capacitor plates move so that this observer sees a counterclockwise circulating current which produces a magnetic field in the z direction.

2.8 THE POYNTING VECTOR

By combining Maxwell's equations and integrating over a closed volume in the rest frame of the medium, an expression relating the instantaneous rate of flow of energy through the boundary surface to interior power loss and time rates of energy storage is obtained. The derivation, easily done, results in

$$\int_{S'} (\mathbf{E}' \times \mathbf{H}') \cdot d\mathbf{S}' = -\int_{\text{vol}} \left(\mathbf{H}' \cdot \frac{\partial \mathbf{B}'}{\partial t'} + \mathbf{E}' \cdot \frac{\partial \mathbf{D}'}{\partial t'} + \mathbf{J}' \cdot \mathbf{E}' \right) dV' \quad (2.8\text{-}1)$$

In the rest frame $\mathbf{J}' \cdot \mathbf{E}'$ is the power loss per unit volume due to Joulean heating. The term $\mathbf{H}' \cdot \partial \mathbf{B}'/\partial t' + \mathbf{E}' \cdot \partial \mathbf{D}'/\partial t'$ represents the time rate of increase of electromagnetic energy per unit volume; if the material has hysteresis, this term also includes the damping power loss per unit volume. Since the Poynting vector is derived from Maxwell's equations valid in either S' or S, the Poynting theorem is also valid in S and is written as

$$\int_{S} (\mathbf{E} \times \mathbf{H}) \cdot d\mathbf{S} = -\int_{\text{vol}} \left(\mathbf{H} \cdot \frac{\partial \mathbf{B}}{\partial t} + \mathbf{E} \cdot \frac{\partial \mathbf{D}}{\partial t} + \mathbf{J} \cdot \mathbf{E} \right) dV \quad (2.8\text{-}2)$$

However, in the S or laboratory frame of coordinates the right-hand side of (2.8-2) requires a different interpretation from that of the right-hand member of (2.8-1). To obtain the correct interpretation, we express the S frame quantities in terms of S' frame quantities. When we make use of the longitudinal stretcher operator defined in (1.2-4) and the Maxwell-Lorentz transformations on $\mathbf{E}$ and $\mathbf{J}$, it is easy to obtain

$$\mathbf{J} \cdot \mathbf{E} = \beta [\mathbf{J}' \cdot \mathbf{E}' + \mathbf{V} \cdot (\rho'_e \mathbf{E}' + \mathbf{J}' \times \mathbf{B}')] \quad (2.8\text{-}3)$$

By (1.5-1) $dV = dV'/\beta$ and thus

$$\int_{\text{vol}} \mathbf{J} \cdot \mathbf{E} \, dV = \int_{\text{vol}'} [\mathbf{J}' \cdot \mathbf{E}' + \mathbf{V} \cdot (\rho'_e \mathbf{E}' + \mathbf{J}' \times \mathbf{B}')] \, dV' \quad (2.8\text{-}4)$$

Here $\int_{\text{vol}'} \mathbf{J}' \cdot \mathbf{E}' \, dV'$ is the total Joulean power loss in the volume V' because Ohm's law holds only in the rest frame, and the remaining part of the volume integral represents the total power supplied by the electromagnetic body forces acting on the medium. If the electromagnetic force density is taken to be $\rho'_e \mathbf{E}' + \mathbf{J}' \times \mathbf{B}'$ (here forces due to striction effects and nonhomogeneous dielectric effects are not included), (2.8-4) agrees with the inverse of (1.10-5), a rather general result, which relates power in S to power in S'.

Rather than transform $\mathbf{H} \cdot \partial \mathbf{B}/\partial t + \mathbf{E} \cdot \partial \mathbf{D}/\partial t$ directly, we choose to transform $\int_{S} (\mathbf{E} \times \mathbf{J}) \cdot d\mathbf{S}$. Then, by (2.8-2)

$$\int_{\text{vol}} \left(\mathbf{H} \cdot \frac{\partial \mathbf{B}}{\partial t} + \mathbf{E} \cdot \frac{\partial \mathbf{D}}{\partial t} \right) dV = -\int_{S} (\mathbf{E} \times \mathbf{H}) \cdot d\mathbf{S} - \int_{\text{vol}} \mathbf{J} \cdot \mathbf{E} \, dV \quad (2.8\text{-}5)$$

By the inverse of (2.3-49)

$$\mathbf{E} \times \mathbf{H} = \beta^2 \left[\frac{\mathbf{E}'}{\alpha} \times \frac{\mathbf{H}'}{\alpha} + \frac{\mathbf{H}'}{\alpha} \times (\mathbf{V} \times \mathbf{B}') \right.$$

$$\left. + \frac{\mathbf{E}'}{\alpha} \times (\mathbf{V} \times \mathbf{D}') - (\mathbf{V} \times \mathbf{B}') \times (\mathbf{V} \times \mathbf{D}') \right]$$

which can be simplified by using the vector identities $(\mathbf{A} \times \mathbf{B}) \times (\mathbf{A} \times \mathbf{C}) = [\mathbf{A} \cdot (\mathbf{B} \times \mathbf{C})]\mathbf{A}$ and $\mathbf{A} \times (\mathbf{B} \times \mathbf{C}) = \mathbf{B}(\mathbf{A} \cdot \mathbf{C}) - \mathbf{C}(\mathbf{A} \cdot \mathbf{B})$. Accordingly $\mathbf{E} \times \mathbf{H}$ becomes

$$\mathbf{E} \times \mathbf{H} = \beta^2 \left\{ \frac{\mathbf{E}'}{\alpha} \times \frac{\mathbf{H}'}{\alpha} + \mathbf{V} \left[\frac{\mathbf{H}'}{\alpha} \cdot \mathbf{B}' + \frac{\mathbf{E}'}{\alpha} \cdot \mathbf{D}' \right] - \mathbf{B}' \left(\mathbf{V} \cdot \frac{\mathbf{H}'}{\alpha} \right) \right.$$

$$\left. - \mathbf{D}' \left(\mathbf{V} \cdot \frac{\mathbf{E}'}{\alpha} \right) + \mathbf{V}[\mathbf{V} \cdot (\mathbf{D}' \times \mathbf{B}')] \right\} \quad (2.8\text{-}6)$$

Here it is useful to recognize that for $|\mathbf{V}|^2 \ll c^2$, $\beta = 1$ and can be dropped from our calculations; however, we could not have made this assumption at the beginning of the derivation without losing the last term of (2.8-6). Then

$$\int_{\text{vol}} \left(\mathbf{H} \cdot \frac{\partial \mathbf{B}}{\partial t} + \mathbf{E} \cdot \frac{\partial \mathbf{D}}{\partial t} \right) dV$$

$$= -\int_S [\mathbf{E}' \times \mathbf{H}' + \mathbf{V}(\mathbf{H}' \cdot \mathbf{B}' + \mathbf{E}' \cdot \mathbf{D}' + \mathbf{V} \cdot \mathbf{D}' \times \mathbf{B}')$$

$$- \mathbf{B}'(\mathbf{V} \cdot \mathbf{H}') - \mathbf{D}'(\mathbf{V} \cdot \mathbf{E}')] \cdot d\mathbf{S} - \int_{\text{vol}} \mathbf{J} \cdot \mathbf{E} \, dV \quad (2.8\text{-}7)$$

This result can be simplified by using (2.8-1) to express $\int_S \mathbf{E}' \times \mathbf{H}' \cdot d\mathbf{S}$ and (2.8-4) to express $\int_{\text{vol}} \mathbf{J} \cdot \mathbf{E} \, dV$. The result is

$$\int_{\text{vol}} \left(\mathbf{H} \cdot \frac{\partial \mathbf{B}}{\partial t} + \mathbf{E} \cdot \frac{\partial \mathbf{D}}{\partial t} \right) dV$$

$$= \int_{\text{vol}} \left[\mathbf{H}' \cdot \frac{\partial \mathbf{B}'}{\partial t'} + \mathbf{E}' \cdot \frac{\partial \mathbf{D}'}{\partial t'} - \mathbf{V} \cdot (\rho'_e \mathbf{E}' + \mathbf{J}' \times \mathbf{B}') \right] dV$$

$$- \int_S \{ \mathbf{V}[\mathbf{H}' \cdot \mathbf{B}' + \mathbf{E}' \cdot \mathbf{D}' + \mathbf{V} \cdot (\mathbf{D}' \times \mathbf{B}')] - \mathbf{B}'(\mathbf{V} \cdot \mathbf{H}') - \mathbf{D}'(\mathbf{V} \cdot \mathbf{E}') \} \cdot d\mathbf{S}$$

$$(2.8\text{-}8)$$

which indicates that the time rate increase of energy stored in the control volume (calculated by an observer in S) is related not only to the time rate of increase of energy stored in S' but also to the body forces and/or surface stresses seen by the observer in S'. Clearly, the right-hand part of (2.8-8) involves the electromagnetic body force density $\rho'_e \mathbf{E}' + \mathbf{J}' \times \mathbf{B}'$ and the electromagnetic momentum $\mathbf{D}' \times \mathbf{B}'$. The surface integral of (2.8-8) can be converted into a volume integral by taking the divergence of its integrand. After a lengthy vector calculation, (2.8-8) can be converted to

$$\int_{\text{vol}} \left(\mathbf{H} \cdot \frac{\partial \mathbf{B}}{\partial t} + \mathbf{E} \cdot \frac{\partial \mathbf{D}}{\partial t} \right) dV$$

$$= \int_{\text{vol}} \left[\mathbf{H}' \cdot \frac{d^- \mathbf{B}'}{dt'} + \mathbf{E}' \cdot \frac{d^- \mathbf{D}'}{dt'} + \frac{\mathbf{V} \cdot d^-}{dt'} (\mathbf{D}' \times \mathbf{B}') \right] dV$$

$$- \int_{\text{vol}} [(\mathbf{H}' \cdot \mathbf{B}') \, \nabla' \cdot \mathbf{V} - \mathbf{H}' \cdot (\mathbf{B}' \cdot \nabla')\mathbf{V} + (\mathbf{E}' \cdot \mathbf{D}') \, \nabla' \cdot \mathbf{V}$$

$$- \mathbf{E}' \cdot (\mathbf{D}' \cdot \nabla')\mathbf{V} + (\mathbf{D}' \times \mathbf{B}') \cdot (\mathbf{V} \cdot \nabla')\mathbf{V}] \, dV \qquad (2.8\text{-}9)$$

where

$$\frac{d^-}{dt'} = \frac{\partial}{\partial t'} - \mathbf{V} \cdot \nabla'$$

This result has no simple interpretation. However, the inverse of (2.8-9) can be stated more simply in terms of the material derivative $D/Dt = \partial/\partial t + \mathbf{V} \cdot \nabla$ as

$$\int_{\text{vol}} \left(\mathbf{H}' \cdot \frac{\partial \mathbf{B}'}{\partial t'} + \mathbf{E}' \cdot \frac{\partial \mathbf{D}'}{\partial t'} \right) dV$$

$$= \int_{\text{vol}} \left\{ \mathbf{H} \cdot \frac{D\mathbf{B}}{Dt} + \mathbf{E} \cdot \frac{D\mathbf{D}}{Dt} - \mathbf{V} \cdot \frac{D}{Dt} (\mathbf{D} \times \mathbf{B}) \right.$$

$$+ [(\mathbf{H} \cdot \mathbf{B}) + (\mathbf{E} \cdot \mathbf{D}) - \mathbf{V} \cdot (\mathbf{D} \times \mathbf{B})] \nabla \cdot \mathbf{V}$$

$$\left. - [\mathbf{H} \cdot (\mathbf{B} \cdot \nabla) + \mathbf{E} \cdot (\mathbf{D} \cdot \nabla) + (\mathbf{D} \times \mathbf{B}) \cdot (\mathbf{V} \cdot \nabla)]\mathbf{V} \right\} dV \quad (2.8\text{-}10)$$

The material obeys the continuity equation $\partial \rho / \partial t + \nabla \cdot (\rho \mathbf{V}) = 0$ (ρ is mass density), which expresses the law of conservation of matter. From the continuity equation it follows that $\nabla \cdot \mathbf{V} = \rho(D/Dt)(1/\rho)$. Hence (2.8-10) can be expressed as

$$\int_{\text{vol}} \left(\mathbf{H}' \cdot \frac{\partial \mathbf{B}'}{\partial t'} + \mathbf{E}' \cdot \frac{\partial \mathbf{D}'}{\partial t'} \right) dV$$

$$= \int_{\text{vol}} \left\{ \rho \left[\mathbf{H} \cdot \frac{D}{Dt} \left(\frac{\mathbf{B}}{\rho} \right) + \mathbf{E} \cdot \frac{D}{Dt} \left(\frac{\mathbf{D}}{\rho} \right) - \mathbf{V} \cdot \frac{D}{Dt} \left(\frac{\mathbf{D} \times \mathbf{B}}{\rho} \right) \right] \right.$$

$$\left. - [\mathbf{H} \cdot (\mathbf{B} \cdot \nabla) + \mathbf{E} \cdot (\mathbf{D} \cdot \nabla) + (\mathbf{D} \times \mathbf{B}) \cdot (\mathbf{V} \cdot \nabla)]\mathbf{V} \right\} dV \quad (2.8\text{-}11)$$

The first two terms on the right side of (2.8-11) represent the time rate of increase of energy stored in the electromagnetic field (assuming no hysteresis) due to density and time variations and convection. The third term is the time rate of decrease of energy due to work being done by the conversion of the electromagnetic momentum $\mathbf{D} \times \mathbf{B}$. From this term it should be clear that $(\rho_e\mathbf{E} + \mathbf{J} \times \mathbf{B})$ is not the only electromagnetic body force. The remaining three terms vanish if velocity is uniform. A similar expression was derived by B. T. Chu (1959) in a less complete calculation where electromagnetic momentum was not treated in a consistent manner. Although Equation (2.8-11) is not simple to interpret; it will be useful later when the energy equation for magnetohydrodynamics is derived.

The fields calculated in Examples 2.1 and 2.3 satisfy Equation (2.8-3). In Example 2.1 there is no body force, so that $\mathbf{J} \cdot \mathbf{E} = \mathbf{J}' \cdot \mathbf{E}'$, and in Example 2.3 the body force could be calculated directly from (2.8-4).

2.9 TERMINAL VOLTAGE RELATED TO THE POYNTING VECTOR

The voltage rise from terminal 1 to 2 in Fig. 2.9-1 is defined as

$$V_{12} = -\int_1^2 \mathbf{E} \cdot d\mathbf{l}$$

or by (2.7-2)

$$V_{12} = \Phi_2 - \Phi_1 + \int_1^2 \frac{\partial \mathbf{A}}{\partial t} \cdot d\mathbf{l} \tag{2.9-1}$$

Here $\int_1^2 (\partial \mathbf{A}/\partial t) \cdot d\mathbf{l}$ is not independent of the path of integration. If the magnetic induction normal to the surface is zero for all values of t, or if $\mathbf{E} \gg \partial \mathbf{A}/\partial t$, the voltage rise is $V_{12} = V_T = \Phi_2 - \Phi_1$. Here V_T is the terminal voltage which is independent of the position of the voltmeter leads as long as they are located on the plane S_0. Expressing the time rate of energy flow through the surface yields

$$\int_S (\mathbf{E} \times \mathbf{H}) \cdot d\mathbf{S} = -\int_S \left[\left(\nabla\Phi + \frac{\partial \mathbf{A}}{\partial t}\right) \times \mathbf{H}\right] \cdot d\mathbf{S} \tag{2.9-2}$$

Now, if $\partial \mathbf{A}/\partial t \ll \nabla\Phi$, (2.9-2) becomes

$$\int_S (\mathbf{E} \times \mathbf{H}) \cdot d\mathbf{S} = -\int_{\text{vol}} \nabla \cdot [\nabla \times (\Phi\mathbf{H})] \, dV + \int_S \Phi \nabla \times \mathbf{H} \cdot d\mathbf{S} \tag{2.9-3}$$

Since $\nabla \cdot [\nabla \times (\Phi \mathbf{H})] \equiv 0$ Equation (2.9-3) becomes

$$\int_S (\mathbf{E} \times \mathbf{H}) \cdot d\mathbf{S} = \int_S \Phi\left(\mathbf{J} + \frac{\partial \mathbf{D}}{\partial t}\right) \cdot d\mathbf{S} \qquad (2.9\text{-}4)$$

Now if the displacement current density $\partial \mathbf{D}/\partial t$ is negligible, the right-hand part of (2.9-4) becomes $\int_{Sc_1} \Phi \mathbf{J} \cdot d\mathbf{S} + \int_{Sc_2} \Phi \mathbf{J} \cdot d\mathbf{S}$ where Sc_1 and Sc_2 are the cross sections of conductors 1 and 2, respectively. Assuming the

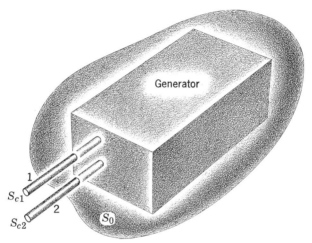

Figure 2.9-1 A closed surface S surrounding a generator. Here S_0 is a plane (part of S) which is perpendicular to the leads.

potential is constant throughout each conductor, and that

$$\int_{Sc_1} \mathbf{J}_1 \cdot d\mathbf{S} = -\int_{Sc_2} \mathbf{J}_2 \cdot d\mathbf{S}$$

$$\int_S (\mathbf{E} \times \mathbf{H}) \cdot d\mathbf{S} = (\Phi_2 - \Phi_1)\int_{Sc_2} \mathbf{J} \cdot d\mathbf{S} = V_T i \qquad (2.9\text{-}5)$$

The expression of (2.9-5) relates the instantaneous time rate of energy flow into a pair of terminals to the instantaneous power leaving the generator. Equation (2.9-5) is valid to any observer agreeing that $\partial \mathbf{A}/\partial t \ll \nabla \Phi$ and that $\partial \mathbf{D}/\partial t \ll \mathbf{J}$. These restrictions may seem severe but are the same ones in effect when we speak of the terminal voltage of a transformer or alternating-current generator. In these cases the alternating fields in the vicinity are finite but small enough that $\partial \mathbf{A}/\partial t \ll \nabla \Phi$.

Example 2.12   We now apply Equation (2.9-5) to recalculate the terminal voltage obtained by other means in previous examples. Consider Example

2.3. Here $\mathbf{E} \times \mathbf{H}$ is integrated over the surfaces in the xz planes of Fig. E2.3-2, which are located just underneath and above the top and bottom return circuits, respectively. The integration of $\mathbf{E} \times \mathbf{H}$ over the surface in the yz and xy planes yields nothing, because $\mathbf{E} \times \mathbf{H}$ is in the y direction. When applying (2.9-5) care must be taken to integrate over a closed surface. By Ampere's circuital law

$$H_{xT} - H_{xB} = \frac{I_0}{x_0} \tag{E2.12-1}$$

and assuming no applied field in the x direction, $H_{xT} = -H_{xB}$. Then

$$H_{xT} = \frac{I_0}{(2x_0)} \tag{E2.12-2}$$

and H_{xT} and H_{xB} are directed as indicated in Fig. E2.3-2. Underneath the top plate

$$\int_S (\mathbf{E} \times \mathbf{H}) \cdot d\mathbf{S} = -\hat{y} \left(\frac{-2a\sigma V_0 B_0}{\sigma_T d_T + \sigma_B d_B + 2a\sigma} \right) \frac{I_0}{2x_0} \cdot x_0 z_0$$

$$= \hat{y} \frac{a\sigma V_0 B_0 z_0 I_0}{\sigma_T d_T + \sigma_B d_B + 2a\sigma}$$

and above the bottom plate an identical result is obtained. Then by (2.9-5)

$$V_T I_0 = \frac{2a\sigma V_0 B_0 z_0 I_0}{\sigma_T d_T + \sigma_B d_B + 2a\sigma}$$

or

$$V_T = \frac{2a\sigma V_0 B_0 z_0}{\sigma_T d_T + \sigma_B d_B + 2a\sigma} \tag{E2.12-3}$$

which agrees with the results of Example 2.8.

2.10 PHASOR NOTATION

Whenever a system described by linear equations is excited by sinusoidal driving functions, it is convenient to introduce phasor concepts. Consider the field quantity $\mathbf{F}(x, y, z, t) = [\mathbf{F}(x, y, z)_{\max}/\sqrt{2}] \cos \omega t$. Here $\mathbf{F}(x, y, z, t)$ is a time and space dependent vector. The other quantity $\mathbf{F}(x, y, z)_{\max}/\sqrt{2}$ is a vector which is independent of time. For sinusoidal cases, Maxwell's equations can be transformed to eliminate the time variation. Since $\cos \theta = (e^{j\theta} + e^{-j\theta})/2$ and $\sin \theta = (e^{j\theta} - e^{-j\theta})/2j$, it suffices to assume $\mathbf{F}(x, y, z, t) = \mathbf{F}(x, y, z)e^{j\omega t}$ rather than using the sum of sines and cosines, because the solution for the actual input is composed of $e^{j\omega t}$ factors and their complex conjugates; hence all of the information needed to obtain the desired solution is contained in the solution corresponding to the term $e^{j\omega t}$. It is very important to linearize the equations before this transformation is made. In this book, we define the phasor-vector $\mathbf{F}(x, y, z) = \mathbf{F}(x, y, z)_{\max}/\sqrt{2}$ so that we may deal with root mean square quantities. The phasor-vectors, like complex numbers, obey the usual rules of addition, subtraction, multiplication, and division. However, the ordinary product of phasor-vectors has no useful meaning. It is more useful to consider products of the form $\mathbf{F}(x, y, z)\mathbf{G}^*(x, y, z)$. Here the asterisk denotes the complex conjugate. For example,

$$\langle \mathbf{F}(x, y, z, t)\mathbf{G}(x, y, z, t) \rangle = \frac{1}{T} \int_0^T \mathbf{F}(x, y, z, t)\mathbf{G}(x, y, z, t) \, dt$$

$$= \tfrac{1}{2}[\mathbf{F}(x, y, z)\mathbf{G}^*(x, y, z) + \mathbf{F}^*(x, y, z)\mathbf{G}(x, y, z)]$$

$$= \operatorname{Re} [\mathbf{F}(x, y, z)\mathbf{G}^*(x, y, z)] \tag{2.10-1}$$

where Re $\mathbf{F}$ means the real part of $\mathbf{F}$ and T is the period of the time-varying component. If the driving function of a given problem is a cosine function, the solution for the cosine driving function can be obtained from the solution which results when the cosine is replaced by $e^{j\omega t}$, and at any stage of the solution the actual time solution for the cosine driving function can be restored by taking the real part of $\mathbf{F}e^{j\omega t}$. Similarly, if the driving function is a sine function, the desired time variations are obtained by taking the imaginary part of the solution for $\mathbf{F}e^{j\omega t}$. In phasor-vector notation, Maxwell's equations become

$$\nabla \cdot \mathbf{D} = \rho_e \qquad\qquad \nabla' \cdot \mathbf{D}' = \rho'_e \tag{2.10-2}$$

$$\nabla \cdot \mathbf{B} = 0 \qquad\qquad \nabla' \cdot \mathbf{B}' = 0 \tag{2.10-3}$$

$$\nabla \times \mathbf{E} = -j\omega\mathbf{B} \quad \text{or} \quad \nabla' \times \mathbf{E}' = -j\omega\mathbf{B}' \tag{2.10-4}$$

$$\nabla \times \mathbf{H} = \mathbf{J} + j\omega\mathbf{D} \qquad \nabla' \times \mathbf{H}' = \mathbf{J} + j\omega'\mathbf{D}' \tag{2.10-5}$$

Here we use the same notation for phasor-vectors as formerly used for vectors. To do otherwise would be cumbersome, and it will be clear to the reader when these quantities are phasor-vectors.

2.11   THE COMPLEX POYNTING VECTOR

Using phasor-vector quantities in Maxwell's equations enables us to calculate the time average of the Poynting vector. It also allows us to study the effects of magnetic and dielectric losses. By taking the dot product of $\mathbf{H}^*$ with (2.10-4) there results

$$\mathbf{H}^* \cdot \nabla \times \mathbf{E} = -j\omega \mathbf{H}^* \cdot \mathbf{B} \qquad (2.11\text{-}1)$$

and dotting $\mathbf{E}$ into the complex conjugate of (2.10-5) yields

$$\mathbf{E} \cdot \nabla \times \mathbf{H}^* = \mathbf{E} \cdot \mathbf{J}^* - j\omega \mathbf{E} \cdot \mathbf{D}^* \qquad (2.11\text{-}2)$$

Combining (2.11-1) and (2.11-2) gives

$$\nabla \cdot (\mathbf{E} \times \mathbf{H}^*) = -j\omega \mathbf{H}^* \cdot \mathbf{B} + j\omega \mathbf{E} \cdot \mathbf{D}^* - \mathbf{E} \cdot \mathbf{J}^* \qquad (2.11\text{-}3)$$

When there are losses in the medium due to various damping mechanisms, the simplest way to describe approximately the resulting hysteresis loops is to assume they are elliptical. This is equivalent to saying $\epsilon = \epsilon' - j\epsilon''$ and $\mu = \mu' - j\mu''$. Then (2.11-3) written in the rest frame becomes

$$\nabla' \cdot (\mathbf{E}' \times \mathbf{H}'^*) = -\omega'\mu'' |\mathbf{H}'|^2 - \omega'\epsilon'' |\mathbf{E}'|^2 - \mathbf{E}' \cdot \mathbf{J}'^*$$
$$+ j\omega'(\epsilon' |\mathbf{E}'|^2 - \mu' |\mathbf{H}'|^2) \qquad (2.11\text{-}4)$$

Integrating this over the volume, applying Stokes' theorem to the left-hand member, and separating the real and imaginary parts yields

$$\text{Re}\int_S (\mathbf{E}' \times \mathbf{H}'^*) \cdot d\mathbf{S} = \int_{\text{vol}} (-\mathbf{E}' \cdot \mathbf{J}'^* - \epsilon''\omega' |\mathbf{E}'|^2 - \mu''\omega' |\mathbf{H}'|^2)\, dV$$
$$(2.11\text{-}5)$$

and

$$\text{Im}\int_S (\mathbf{E}' \times \mathbf{H}'^*) \cdot d\mathbf{S} = \int_{\text{vol}} j\omega'(\epsilon' |\mathbf{E}'|^2 - \mu' |\mathbf{H}'|^2)\, dV \qquad (2.11\text{-}6)$$

The term $-\text{Re}\int_S (\mathbf{E}' \times \mathbf{H}'^*) \cdot d\mathbf{S}$ represents the real part of the time rate of energy flow into a closed volume to supply power losses. The other term given by (2.11-6) is reactive time rate of energy flowing in and out of storage in the electromagnetic field. By means of the MLT, (2.11-5) can be transformed into laboratory coordinates. Then, assuming $|\mathbf{V}|^2 \ll c^2$,

$$\mathbf{J}'^* \cdot \mathbf{E}' = [\mathbf{J}^* \cdot \mathbf{E} - \mathbf{V} \cdot (\mathbf{J}^* \times \mathbf{B} + \rho_e^*\mathbf{E})] \qquad (2.11\text{-}7)$$

by virtue of (2.8-7). The term $\epsilon'' |\mathbf{E}'|^2 + \mu'' |\mathbf{H}'|^2$ must be transformed also. Here $|\mathbf{E}'|^2 = (\mathbf{E} + \mathbf{V} \times \mathbf{B})(\mathbf{E}^* + \mathbf{V} \times \mathbf{B}^*)$ and, if we use the vector identity $\mathbf{A} \cdot (\mathbf{B} \times \mathbf{C}) = -\mathbf{B} \cdot (\mathbf{A} \times \mathbf{C})$, it is easy to obtain

$$\omega'\epsilon'' |\mathbf{E}'|^2 = \omega\epsilon''\{|\mathbf{E}|^2 - \mathbf{V} \cdot [\mathbf{E}^* \times \mathbf{B} + \mathbf{E} \times \mathbf{B}^* + (\mathbf{V} \times \mathbf{B}) \times \mathbf{B}^*]\}$$
$$(2.11\text{-}8)$$

Similarly,

$$\omega'\mu'' |\mathbf{H}'|^2 = \omega\mu''\{|\mathbf{H}|^2 - \mathbf{V} \cdot [\mathbf{D}^* \times \mathbf{H} + \mathbf{D} \times \mathbf{H}^* + (\mathbf{V} \times \mathbf{D}) \times \mathbf{D}^*]\}$$

(2.11-9)

Here we substitute ω for ω' because we neglect the Doppler shift. Combining (2.11-5) with (2.11-7), (2.11-8), (2.8-3), and (2.11-9) yields

$$\mathbf{E}' \cdot \mathbf{J}'^* + \omega'(\epsilon'' |\mathbf{E}'|^2 + \mu'' |\mathbf{H}'|^2)$$

$$= \mathbf{E} \cdot \mathbf{J}^* + \omega(\epsilon'' |\mathbf{E}|^2 + \mu'' |\mathbf{H}|^2) - \mathbf{V} \cdot (\mathbf{J}^* \times \mathbf{B} + \rho_e^*\mathbf{E})$$

$$- \omega\mathbf{V} \cdot \{2 \operatorname{Re} [\epsilon''(\mathbf{E} \times \mathbf{B}) + \mu''(\mathbf{D} \times \mathbf{H})]$$

$$+ \epsilon''(\mathbf{V} \times \mathbf{B}) \times \mathbf{B}^* + \mu''(\mathbf{V} \times \mathbf{D}) \times \mathbf{D}^*\} \qquad (2.11\text{-}10)$$

observing that $\mathbf{E}^* \times \mathbf{B} + \mathbf{E} \times \mathbf{B}^* = 2 \operatorname{Re} (\mathbf{E} \times \mathbf{B})$. In this equation the real power density seen by a rest frame observer is expressed in terms of laboratory-frame quantities. The various terms of the right side of (2.11-10) can be interpreted physically. The first two terms represent the Joulean and damping losses present in the medium. The third term indicates a gain in power density resulting from the presence of the ordinary electromagnetic body forces. The remaining term has the form of a power-density gain which may be the result of electromagnetic momentum.

In this section it is important to observe from (2.11-5) how the hysteresis losses appear and how they add directly to the Joulean losses. In addition, Equation (2.11-10) produces terms similar to those of (2.8-3) as well as terms corresponding to some portion of the third term of (2.8-8).

PROBLEMS

1. Show that $\mathbf{D}_\perp = 1/(1 - \epsilon\mu V^2)[(\epsilon\mathbf{E}/\beta^2) + (\mu\epsilon - 1/c^2)\mathbf{V} \times \mathbf{H}]$ and derive a relationship for $\mathbf{B}_\perp$ in terms of $\mathbf{H}$ and $\mathbf{E}$.
2. Derive Equation (2.4-14).
3. A parallel plate capacitor has a battery connected to it and passes by an observer at velocity $\mathbf{V}_0$ with respect to the observer. Determine the fields seen by the observer.
4. Rework Example 2.2 for an observer moving in the $-y$ direction with a velocity V_0 relative to the dielectric material. Is there a frequency difference between observers? In what direction does the moving observer see propagation of electromagnetic waves? Does the moving observer see the same intrinsic impedance (ratio of $|E_y|/|H_z|$) as the rest-frame observer?
5. Find the fields in a waveguide of rectangular cross section in which the dielectric (assumed to be lossless and having a permeability μ) is moving with respect to the lossless waveguide walls. Consider both TE and TM modes and give the cutoff frequencies that result.
6. Rework Example 2.3 assuming that the applied magnetic field is $\mathbf{H} = \hat{z}H_0$. This field existed in medium 1 (free space) before the ferromagnetic dielectric

plate was introduced. Also find the fields seen by the observer riding on the plate. If there are no electrodes and return circuit, how much charge accumulates on the surface of the plate?

7. If the two large surfaces of a glass plate are plated with metal and shorted with a jumper stationary with respect to the magnet supplying H_z, what are the fields? Assuming $\sigma = 0$, what total charge would flow in this circuit after it was first closed? (See Fig. P2.7-1.)

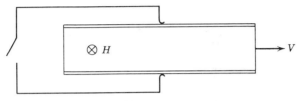

Figure P2.7-1   Glass plate of Problem 2.7.

8. Rework Problem 7 assuming a thin glass rod instead of a plate. (See Fig. P2.8-1.)

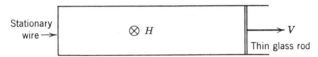

Figure P2.8-1   Configuration for Problem 2.8.

9. What is the charge distribution in the first case of Example 2.4? What are the fields in free space adjacent to the filament seen by the observer riding on the filament?

10. Redo Example 2.1, including all relativistic effects.

11. Rework Example 2.4 using a magnetic dielectric filament of circular cross section.

12. Find the fields around and in a magnetic dielectric sphere traveling through a uniform magnetic field.

13. In Fig. P2.13-1, a sliding brush rides on the secondary winding of the iron-cored circuit. The primary winding, being excited with direct current, supplies flux which links the secondary winding. In the secondary winding circuit there is a time rate of change of flux linkages. Is a voltage generated? Explain and defend your answer by referring to Equations (2.6-3), (2.6-10), and (2.6-13).

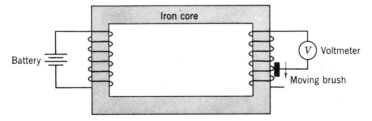

Figure P2.13-1   Configuration for Problem 2.13.

14. If the voltmeter in Fig. P2.14-1 is drawn away from the core so that the spring metal clips on the voltmeter always make contact either with each other or with the metal core, will there be a surge on the voltmeter?

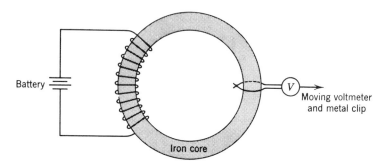

Figure P2.14-1   Circuit used in Problem 2.14.

15. If a circular cylinder of copper surrounds a current-carrying conductor as shown in Fig. P2.15-1 and has brushes on its inside and outside surfaces which are connected to a voltmeter, will there be an emf generated in the voltmeter loop if the copper cylinder is moving along the wire with velocity V relative to the voltmeter? Would it make any difference if the cylinder were iron instead of copper?

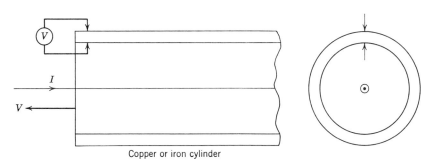

Copper or iron cylinder

Figure P2.15-1   Circuit of Problem 2.15.

16. In Fig. P2.16-1, a coil form is rotated by winding the wire on a reel. Will there be a voltmeter reading in the circuit of sketch (a)? sketch (b)?

17. Figure P2.17-1 contains two disc-shaped magnets which have a hole drilled along their axes. They are magnetized so that the flat surfaces of the discs are the magnetic poles. One disc is held fixed while the other rotates with an angular velocity Ω. Will there be a voltmeter reading?

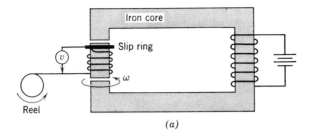

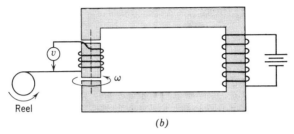

Figure P2.16-1   Circuit for Problem 2.16.

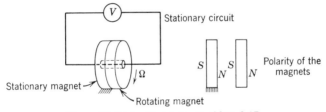

Figure P2.17-1   Sketch for Problem 2.17.

18. (a) A semi-infinite channel is made of very good conducting material. The channel is shorted at $x = 0$ and is fed by a current source at $x = -\infty$. The configuration is infinite in the z direction and is shown in Fig. P2.18-1. A semi-infinite dielectric magnetic slab moves with velocity $\hat{x}V$ relative to the conducting

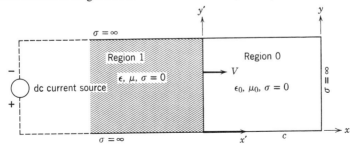

Figure P2.18-1   The configuration of Problem 2.18.

plates. The dielectric magnetic slab is nonconducting and is characterized by a μ and an ϵ. Show that the fields observed in the laboratory frame, being the rest frame of the conducting plates, are given by

$$H_z^0 = \frac{1 - V^2/c^2}{1 - \dfrac{V^2 \epsilon}{c^2 \epsilon_0}} \, \mathscr{J}$$

where $\mathscr{J}$ is the strength per unit width of the current source and

$$E_y^0 = 0, \qquad D_y^0 = 0, \qquad B_z^0 = \mu_0 H_z^0$$

$$E_y^1 = \frac{(\mu - \mu_0)VH_z^0}{1 - V^2/c}$$

$$D_y^1 = \frac{-\mu_0(\epsilon - \epsilon_0)VH_z^0}{1 - V^2/c^2}$$

$$B_z^1 = \frac{\mu(1 - V^2\mu/c^2\mu_0)H_z^0}{1 - V^2/c^2}$$

and

$$H_z^1 = \frac{1 - V^2\epsilon/c^2\epsilon_0}{1 - V^2/c^2} H_z^0$$

where the superscripts 1 and 0 refer to dielectric magnetic slab and free space respectively. (*b*) Rework the problem for a finite (in the x dimension) dielectric magnetic slab. (*c*) Rework (*a*) for the case of a conducting channel fed by a voltage source of strength V_b at $x = 0$ and open circuited at $x = -\infty$. *Hint:*

$$H_{0z} = \frac{\epsilon_0 V_b V(1 - \epsilon/\epsilon_0)}{d(1 - V^2\epsilon/c^2\epsilon_0)}$$

19. (*a*) The following question may shed some light on general relativity and Mach's principle. Consider two concentric spheres with equal and opposite charge constrained to remain uniformly distributed over their surfaces. When the spheres are at rest, there is no electric or magnetic field outside the outer sphere. When the spheres rotate with the same constant angular velocity about an axis through their center, there is again no electric field in the outer space region, but there is a magnetic field since the magnetic moment of each rotating sphere is proportional to the square of its radius. Calculate this magnetic field. What are the fields seen by an observer in arbitrary relative motion to the rotating spheres? Suppose that the spheres are stationary. Then, regardless of the motion of the observer, he should detect no field whatsoever. The covariance of Maxwell's equations implies that if both the electric and magnetic fields are zero in one frame of reference, they will remain zero in all reference frames. This is why, regardless of his frame of reference, the observer will find neither an electric nor a magnetic field since all the components of the electromagnetic field tensor are zero in one reference frame.

(*b*) According to Mach's principle, inertial effects are due to the distribution of mass in the universe. Hence, according to Mach's principle, if the universe contained only the two concentric spheres and an observer, there would be no way to find out whether or not the spheres were rotating. Einstein's general relativity does not give an unambiguous answer to the question of the possibility or impossibility of detecting the rotational motion of a single body in an otherwise empty universe. However, its answer tends toward the latter. A significant question is whether or not an observer could detect an electric or magnetic field from the concentric sphere system just described in an otherwise empty universe. The answer may seem obvious. If the spheres are at rest, regardless of the observer's motion he will detect no field. There is no energy density in the surrounding space associated with either field, so how could the observer's motion affect the situation? If the spheres are rotating, the observer will detect either a magnetic field or an electric field, or both, depending on the motion of his reference frame. Hence he could make an unambiguous conclusion regarding the rotation of the spheres. On the other hand, the question may not be so easy. The very reason why the observer can detect no field regardless of his motion when the spheres are stationary in the normal universe is apparently due to the presence of the distant masses. What happens when these masses are not present? Will it then be possible to detect rotation by this method? (Problem suggested by Mario Rabinowitz, Westinghouse Research Laboratories.)

REFERENCES

Arzeliès, H., *Milieux conducteurs ou polarisables en mouvement*, Paris, Gauthier-Villars, 1959.

Chu, B. T., Thermodynamics of Electrically Conducting Fluids, *Phys. Fluids*, **2**, p. 473, 1959.

Cullwick, E. G., *Electromagnetism and Relativity*, 2nd ed., Wiley, New York, 1959.

Jackson, J. D., *Classical Electrodynamics*, Wiley, New York, 1962.

Jouguet, M., *Électricite theorique*, Vols. II and III, Rédaction des élèves, École supérieure d'électricité de Paris, 1954, 1955.

Landau, L. D., and E. M. Lifshitz, *Electrodynamics of Continuous Media*, Addison-Wesley, Reading, Mass., 1960.

Landau, L. D., and E. M. Lifshitz, *Classical Theory of Fields*, Revised 2nd ed., Addison-Wesley, Reading, Mass., 1962.

Panofsky, W. K. H., and M. Phillips, *Classical Electricity and Magnetism*, Addison-Wesley, Reading, Mass., 1955. Beware of the missing primes in equation (4) of Section 9-4.

Skilling, H. H., *Electrical Engineering Circuits*, Chapters 3 and 4, Wiley, New York, 1957.

Sommerfeld, A., *Electrodynamics*, Academic Press, New York, 1952.

Wilson, H. A., and M. Wilson, Electric Effect of a Magnetic Insulator Rotating in a Magnetic Field, *Proc. Roy. Soc. Series A.*, **89**, p. 99, 1913.

3

The Electromagnetic Body Force

3.1 INTRODUCTION

Perhaps the most basic concept in electromagnetism is Coulomb's law for the force on a charged particle in an electric field. In fact, the electric field is defined in terms of the force on a charged test particle. The only interaction force between material particles (other than gravitational or nuclear) is given by the Coulomb force law. It states that the force on a charged particle is proportional to the product of the charge on the particle and the local electric field seen by the particle. In RMKS units:

$$\mathbf{F}' = q\mathbf{E}' \tag{3.1-1}$$

where the primes indicate that the quantities are measured in the rest frame of the particle. Equation (3.1-1) is a fundamental law and can be used even in relativistic mechanics since everything is computed in the local rest frame of the particle. (The charge on a particle is one of the basic invariants, as is c, the velocity of light, in relativity.)

All electromagnetic phenomena are based on Equation (3.1-1) which defines the electric field in the limit as the charge q becomes infinitesimal. In fact, the magnetic field is a macroscopic concept and can be defined in terms of the motion of charges, or current.

In this chapter we will discuss the force on charged particles and the body force in a fluid medium. Discussion of body force in a general solid is somewhat more complex, although the results for the fluid may be applied to certain types of simple solids.

3.2 THE LORENTZ FORCE ON A CHARGED PARTICLE

When a charged particle moves in the presence of arbitrary electric and magnetic fields, the resulting force is called the Lorentz force. (Note that we say moves "in the presence of" a field, not "through a field," because motion relative to a field is a meaningless concept. Only the motion of a particle relative to some observer is meaningful.) In the local rest frame of a charged particle the force is simply $\mathbf{F}' = q\mathbf{E}'$. Now if the particle moves with relative velocity $\mathbf{V}$ with respect to some observer who is arbitrarily fixed in the laboratory frame (see Fig. 3.2-1), the force $\mathbf{F}'$ is still $q\mathbf{E}'$. However, let us express $\mathbf{E}'$ in terms of the field quantities measured by the observer. From the Lorentz transformation on the electric

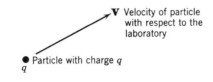

Figure 3.2-1 A charged particle in motion with respect to the laboratory frame of reference.

field $\mathbf{E}'_{\perp} = \beta(\mathbf{E} + \mathbf{V} \times \mathbf{B})_{\perp}$, $\mathbf{E}'_{\parallel} = \mathbf{E}_{\parallel}$, the force $\mathbf{F}'$ can be written:

$$\mathbf{F}'_{\perp} = q\beta(\mathbf{E} + \mathbf{V} \times \mathbf{B})_{\perp}$$
$$\mathbf{F}'_{\parallel} = q\mathbf{E}_{\parallel} \tag{3.2-1}$$

We know that the force on a particle transforms as

$$\mathbf{F}'_{\perp} = \beta\mathbf{F}_{\perp}$$
$$\mathbf{F}'_{\parallel} = \mathbf{F}_{\parallel} \tag{3.2-2}$$

where $\mathbf{F}$ is measured by the observer in the laboratory frame and $\mathbf{F}'$ is the force measured by an observer moving with the particle (in the rest frame). From (3.2-1),

$$\mathbf{F}_{\perp} = \frac{\mathbf{F}'_{\perp}}{\beta} = q(\mathbf{E} + \mathbf{V} \times \mathbf{B})_{\perp} \qquad \mathbf{F}_{\parallel} = q\mathbf{E}_{\parallel} \tag{3.2-3}$$

which is the Lorentz force law in the laboratory. Hence $\mathbf{F} = q(\mathbf{E} + \mathbf{V} \times \mathbf{B})$ is a covariant expression valid in any frame, where $\mathbf{V}$ is the velocity of the particle with respect to that frame, and $\mathbf{E}$ and $\mathbf{B}$ are the local fields seen by an observer in that frame. In the rest frame, of course, $\mathbf{V} = 0$ and we get simply $\mathbf{F}' = q\mathbf{E}'$.

For $|V|^2/c^2 \ll 1$, F' and F may be assumed equal because then:

$$F = F' = q(E + V \times B) = qE' \qquad (3.2\text{-}4)$$

This basic force law is the basis for all electromagnetic body force laws which are merely expressions of the Lorentz force suitably integrated in terms of macroscopic quantities. This integration is not simple and leads to ambiguities so that a more straightforward, if less basic, method of body force calculation begins immediately with macroscopic quantities.

Example 3.1 Consider a magnet at rest in the laboratory. In Fig. E3.1-1 a charged particle (of charge q) is suspended between the pole pieces of the

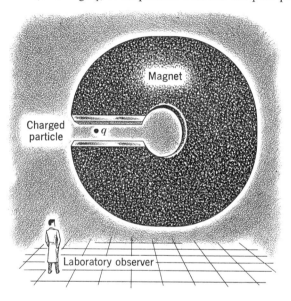

Figure E3.1-1 A magnet and charged particle suspended between the pole pieces. The particle and magnet undergo various relative motions.

magnet, or in the solenoid of an electromagnet. What is the force on the particle when it and the magnet are undergoing various relative motions? We will consider several cases (in the nonrelativistic approximation $|V|^2/c^2 \ll 1$.

(*a*) The magnet and particle are both at rest in the laboratory. There is no force on the particle since in the laboratory frame we take the background electric field to be zero.

(*b*) The magnet is at rest, but the particle is made to move with velocity V through the magnetic field between the pole pieces. The force on the particle is $q(\mathbf{V} \times \mathbf{B})$. In the laboratory frame $\mathbf{F} = q(\mathbf{E} + \mathbf{V} \times \mathbf{B})$ and $\mathbf{E}$ is zero. In the local rest frame of the particle, the electric field $\mathbf{E}'$ is $\mathbf{V} \times \mathbf{B}$ so that $\mathbf{F}' = q(\mathbf{V} \times \mathbf{B})$ and $\mathbf{F}' = \mathbf{F}$ to the nonrelativistic approximation.

(c) The magnet moves with velocity $\mathbf{V}$ with respect to the laboratory, and the particle (remaining between the pole pieces) moves along with the magnet at the same velocity. The observer in the laboratory says, of course, the force is $\mathbf{F} = q(\mathbf{E} + \mathbf{V} \times \mathbf{B})$. The velocity $\mathbf{V}$ is the velocity of the particle (in a magnetic field $\mathbf{B}$) with respect to the laboratory. The only question remaining is: What is $\mathbf{E}$ (between the pole pieces where the particle is located) as measured by the laboratory observer? We know that $\mathbf{E} = \mathbf{E}' - \mathbf{V} \times \mathbf{B}$, where $\mathbf{E}'$ is the electric field measured between the pole pieces by an observer riding with the magnet or particle. Now $\mathbf{E}'$ will have to be zero as we will show presently. Hence $\mathbf{E} = -\mathbf{V} \times \mathbf{B}$ between the pole pieces and $\mathbf{F} = 0$. If the particle moves along with the magnet, it feels no force.

(d) The magnet moves with velocity $\mathbf{V}_m$, but the particle remains stationary. What is the force on the particle while it remains between the pole pieces? After the magnet passes by, the force is clearly zero since $\mathbf{V} \times \mathbf{B}$ is zero and the background $\mathbf{E}$ in the laboratory is zero. If we say that $\mathbf{E}$ (measured by an observer on the magnet between the pole pieces) is zero, then $\mathbf{F} = q(\mathbf{E} + \mathbf{V}_p \times \mathbf{B})$. ($\mathbf{V}_p$ is the velocity of the particle relative to the laboratory and is zero.) $\mathbf{E}$ is $-\mathbf{V}_m \times \mathbf{B}$ so that $\mathbf{F} = -q\mathbf{V}_m \times \mathbf{B}$. Alternatively, $\mathbf{F} = q\mathbf{E}_p = -q\mathbf{V}_m \times \mathbf{B}$ since $\mathbf{E}_p$ (the field seen by the particle) is $\mathbf{E}$.

Hence if the magnet begins to move from rest, the particle will experience a force. The particle accelerates up to the velocity of the magnet and then continues to move at constant velocity with the magnet. A little thought shows that the path of the particle is curved until it reaches the velocity of the magnet.

We still must show that $\mathbf{E}'$, the local electric field between the pole pieces, is always zero. There are several ways of looking at this problem. If we say that the pole pieces are electrical conductors, then the electric field in them is zero and hence, by continuity of tangential electric field, it must be zero between the pole pieces. Actually, when the magnet begins to move, an electric field appears because the magnet is a body moving through a magnetic field (the fact that it generates the field itself is irrelevant) with respect to the laboratory frame in which the electric field is zero. As was explained in Chapter 2, free charge then appears on the extremities of the conductors, nullifying the electric field resulting from $\mathbf{V}_m \times \mathbf{B}$ and making the local electric field in the magnet (and hence between the pole pieces) zero. The electric field between the pole pieces then appears to the laboratory observer as $(-\mathbf{V}_m \times \mathbf{B})$.

Alternatively, we can explain the zero $\mathbf{E}'$ by regarding the magnetic source as a solenoid. If the current density in the solenoid is $\mathbf{J}'$, the current density as seen in the laboratory is $\mathbf{J}$, where $\mathbf{J}' \doteq (\mathbf{J} - \rho_e \mathbf{V})$. ρ_e is the charge density (in the conductor comprising the solenoid) as measured in the laboratory frame. Since the wire is a conductor, $\rho'_e = 0$ and hence $\rho_e = (\mathbf{V} \cdot \mathbf{J})/c^2$. Now it follows from $\nabla \times \mathbf{H} = \mathbf{J}$ (and we assume an air solenoid so that $\mathbf{B}' = \mathbf{B}$ and $\mathbf{H}' = \mathbf{H}$ nonrelativistically) that ρ_e can be expressed in terms of $\mathbf{B}$ as

$$\rho_e = \frac{\mathbf{V} \cdot (\nabla \times \mathbf{H})}{c^2} \tag{E3.1-1}$$

In the laboratory frame, then, $\mathbf{E}$ follows from $\nabla \cdot \mathbf{D} = \rho_e$ (assuming an air solenoid so that $\mathbf{B} = \mu_0 \mathbf{H}$ and $\mathbf{D} = \epsilon_0 \mathbf{E}$) as

$$\mathbf{E} = -\mathbf{V}_m \times \mathbf{B}. \tag{E3.1-2}$$

3.3 THE BODY FORCE AND ITS TRANSFORMATION

The electromagnetic body force results, ultimately, from the Coulomb force. However, on a macroscopic scale it is convenient to express the body force in material media in terms of the electromagnetic field quantities and properties of the material. There are various ways of expressing the body force directly in terms of the field quantities, or in terms of stresses due to electromagnetic effects. If we consider a control volume filled with some material, the total body force on the material can be found by integrating the body force density throughout the volume, or by integrating the stresses over the surface of the control volume. The two methods are equivalent and must give the same answer. The electromagnetic stress tensor will be defined so that it does satisfy this condition (see Section 3.5).

We denote the electromagnetic body force density as $\mathbf{f}_e$ (in RMKS units measured in Newtons per meter[3]). From Chapter 1 we know that the body force on a system $\mathbf{F}$ transforms as $\mathbf{F}'_\perp = \beta \mathbf{F}_\perp$, $\mathbf{F}'_\parallel = \mathbf{F}_\parallel$. We also know that an elemental volume δV transforms as $\delta V = (1/\beta)\,\delta V'$ (since $\delta V'$ is the volume measured in the rest frame) so that $\mathbf{f}_e$ which is $\mathbf{F}/\delta V$ transforms as

$$\mathbf{f}'_{e\perp} = \mathbf{f}_{e\perp}$$
$$\mathbf{f}'_{e\parallel} = (1/\beta)\mathbf{f}_{e\parallel} \tag{3.3-1}$$

which can be expressed simply as $\mathbf{f}_e = \alpha \mathbf{f}'_e$ where α is the stretcher operator. For most work in magnetohydrodynamics, of course, $V^2/c^2 \ll 1$ and $\mathbf{f}'_e = \mathbf{f}_e$ is accurate to the nonrelativistic approximation. Numerically, then, $\mathbf{f}_e$ calculated in either frame is the same to this approximation.

3.4   THE FORM OF THE BODY FORCE IN A FLUID

We can derive the body force density in a linear fluid from a virtual work analysis if we know the free energy density of the fluid-field system. This density variation is known at least for quasi-static processes, and a virtual work process can be performed. The variation in free energy F for an isothermal system can be written

$$\delta F|_T = \int_{\text{vol}} (\mathbf{H} \cdot \delta \mathbf{B} + \mathbf{E} \cdot \delta \mathbf{D})\, dV \qquad (3.4\text{-}1)$$

where V is the volume of the system. The detailed derivation of the body force density is a classical but lengthy procedure and will not be reproduced here. An excellent account is given in the work by Landau and Lifshitz listed in the references.

In a general anisotropic solid the force derivation is not so simple and is not discussed here. Isotropic, linear solids, however, can be treated exactly as fluids.

The general quasi-static body force density for linear media (including effects of charge and current interactions, inhomogeneities in the fields and dielectric and magnetic properties, and striction effects) can be written in the rest frame as

$$\mathbf{f}_e = \rho_e \mathbf{E} + \mathbf{J} \times \mathbf{B} - \frac{\epsilon_0}{2} E^2 \nabla \kappa - \frac{\mu_0}{2} H^2 \nabla \kappa_m$$

$$+ \frac{\epsilon_0}{2} \nabla \left(E^2 \frac{\partial \kappa}{\partial \rho} \cdot \rho \right) + \frac{\mu_0}{2} \nabla \left(H^2 \frac{\partial \kappa_m}{\partial \rho} \cdot \rho \right) \qquad (3.4\text{-}2)$$

Strictly speaking, this equation is valid only in the rest frame (the primes are left off for convenience but should be understood) because the constitutive equations have been implicitly used in the derivation. As we shall see, however, in magnetohydrodynamics where the first two terms constitute the only appreciable force this equation can be used in any coordinate system. That is, the term $\rho_e \mathbf{E} + \mathbf{J} \times \mathbf{B}$ is valid in any frame of reference. In practice, of course, we can calculate the force in the local rest frame, and numerically this force is the same in the laboratory frame to the nonrelativistic approximation. We will discuss forces in general moving media later from the point of view of the stress tensor.

Let us examine the character of each of the terms that appear in the body force expression (3.4-2).

1. $\rho_e \mathbf{E}$: This is the electric force present when there exists net space charge ρ_e. In metallic conductors ρ'_e is zero and the force $\rho_e \mathbf{E}$ will be

negligible compared to $\mathbf{J} \times \mathbf{B}$. Dielectrics may be charged and in some situations this force may become important. In conducting gases, space charge neutrality will usually prevail, but sometimes, as in wave motion, space charge may exist (for example, space charge waves) and the force must be included.

2. $\mathbf{J} \times \mathbf{B}$: The interaction force between the current and magnetic field is expressed by this term, which becomes the predominant force in magneto-fluidmechanics. In conducting gases, the only force is $\rho'_e \mathbf{E}'$; but $\mathbf{E}' = \mathbf{E} + \mathbf{V} \times \mathbf{B}$ so that we define current in terms of charge flux and express $\rho'_e \mathbf{E}'$ as $\rho_e \mathbf{E} + \mathbf{J} \times \mathbf{B}$. We see then that $\mathbf{J} \times \mathbf{B}$ will have meaning in both conducting liquids and gases.

3. $\left(-\dfrac{\epsilon_0}{2} E^2 \boldsymbol{\nabla}\kappa - \dfrac{\mu_0}{2} H^2 \boldsymbol{\nabla}\kappa_m \right)$: These forces are a result of inhomo-geneities in the dielectric constant or permeability. At an interface or free surface where sharp discontinuities in κ or κ_m can occur, delta function-type body forces can occur which correspond to surface stresses (thinking in terms of a stress-tensor formulation). Such forces might be compared to surface tension effects. (A discontinuity in mechanical pressure can exist across such an interface. In a static situation the mechanical pressure must balance the electromagnetic body forces.)

The force acts to pull the material with a higher value of κ or κ_m into the region of lower κ or κ_m.

4. $\left[\dfrac{\epsilon_0}{2} \boldsymbol{\nabla}\left(E^2 \dfrac{\partial \kappa}{\partial \rho} \cdot \rho \right) + \dfrac{\mu_0}{2} \boldsymbol{\nabla}\left(H^2 \dfrac{\partial \kappa_m}{\partial \rho} \cdot \rho \right) \right]$: These are the electrostric-tion and magnetostriction effects, and they occur if κ or κ_m are functions of the density ρ. Most substances exhibit some striction behavior, but in magnetofluidmechanics the effect is usually completely dominated by the $\mathbf{J} \times \mathbf{B}$ force. Striction forces are those usually referred to as resulting from inhomogeneities in the field quantities. As will be shown, the striction effects can be balanced by a state of mechanical hydrostatic compression.

Let us now look at an example.

Example 3.2   A capacitor is shown in Fig. E3.2-1. A dielectric slab essentially fills the space between the capacitor with a spacing h. The plates are of width l, and variations in the z direction are neglected. What is the force on the dielectric slab (when the total charge per unit length on the capacitor is Q) as a function of a, the distance of insertion of the slab in the x direction?

SOLUTION.   The plates are each at a uniform potential so that the $\mathbf{E}$ field between them is a constant E_1 (except where the field is E_2 in the small air gap between the slab and plate). The slab becomes polarized (but there is no real charge on the slab) so that the $\mathbf{D}$ field is the same in the air gap and slab. Hence if the dielectric constant of the slab is ϵ:

$$D_s = D_2 = \epsilon E_1 \qquad \text{(E3.2-1)}$$

Hence $D_1 = \epsilon_0 E_1$ and $E_2 = D_2/\epsilon_0 = \kappa E_1$. From conservation of charge, $\rho_{s1}(l - a) + \rho_{s2}a = Q$ where ρ_{s1} and ρ_{s2} are the surface charge densities as shown in Fig. E3.2-1. From $\nabla \cdot \mathbf{D} = \rho_e$, $E_1 = \rho_{s1}/\epsilon_0$ and $E_2 = \rho_{s2}/\epsilon_0$; hence $\rho_{s2} = \kappa \rho_{s1}$ and $E_1 = Q/\epsilon_0(l - a + \kappa a)$. The only force (neglecting any striction effects) is due to the change in κ at the surface A of the slab.

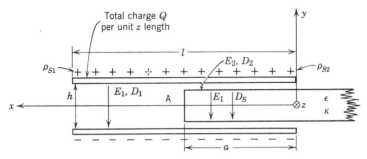

Figure E3.2-1   A capacitor with total charge Q with a dielectric slab inserted between the plates.

The force F_x in the x direction (per unit length out of the paper) is

$$F_x = \int_{-h/2}^{h/2} \int_{a-\delta}^{a+\delta} \frac{-\epsilon_0}{2} E_1{}^2 \, \nabla \kappa \, dx \, dy \qquad \text{(E3.2-2)}$$

where the integral is taken over the area A and through A from $x = a - \delta$ to $x = a + \delta$ to include the interface. The integral is

$$F_x = \frac{Q^2(\kappa - 1)h}{2\epsilon_0(l - a + \kappa a)^2} \qquad \text{(E3.2-3)}$$

3.5 THE STRESS TENSOR FORMULATION OF THE BODY FORCE

The formulation of the body force based on Coulomb interaction is an action at a distance theory. Equivalently, a field theoretic description can be formulated entirely in terms of field quantities. The body force may be completely specified by an electromagnetic stress tensor T_{ij}, and the body force density is simply related to the tensor divergence of the stress tensor.

Like the mechanical stress tensor, the stress tensor T_{ij} is an array of electromagnetic stresses. The equations of equilibrium state that, in static situations, the electromagnetic stress tensor, mechanical stress tensor, and any other body forces must add to zero. In dynamical situations, the electromagnetic stress tensor adds with the mechanical stress tensor in the dynamical equations. This is the case in fluid dynamics.

The sign convention on the stress tensor is shown in Fig. 3.5-1. On the positive surface, the first subscript indicates the normal axis of the surface on which the stress acts, and the second subscript indicates the direction of the stress. On the negative surface the stresses act in the opposite direction.

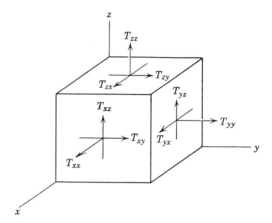

Figure 3.5-1   The sign convention for the stress tensor.

The total force acting on a control volume can be expressed as the integral of the stresses over the surface:

$$F_i = \int_A T_{ji}\, dA_j \tag{3.5-1}$$

and hence the body force density follows from Gauss's theorem as

$$f_{e_i} = \frac{\partial T_{ji}}{\partial x_j} \tag{3.5-2}$$

This expression is not quite correct, however, since electromagnetic fields possess momenta and the actual interaction force with matter must take this into account. The true interaction body force in a dynamical situation would then be

$$f_{e_i} = \frac{\partial T_{ji}}{\partial x_j} - \frac{\partial g_i}{\partial t} \tag{3.5-3}$$

where g_i is the momentum flux density associated with the electromagnetic field. This momentum is a very small quantity and, in practice, negligible. We will discuss the form of g_i later.

The Maxwell stress tensor T_{ij} is not a unique expression but must be chosen so that its tensor divergence gives the proper body force density (Equation (3.4-2)). Any arbitrary function, whose tensor divergence is zero, can be added to the stress tensor without changing the body force. It should be noted that the stresses are not necessarily real physical entities and that only the tensor divergence (or integral over a volume) is significant. Interpretation of the stress components as actual real stresses can lead to difficulties. If we remember that the electromagnetic body force is ultimately derived from Coulomb interaction, this last statement becomes clear. There is no molecular momentum transfer (as in mechanical viscosity) to generate real shear stresses such as those existing in the mechanical stress tensor.

A covariant expression valid in any frame of reference may be written for the stress tensor if striction effects are neglected. The Maxwell form is

$$T_{ij} = -\tfrac{1}{2}[\mathbf{D} \cdot \mathbf{E} + \mathbf{B} \cdot \mathbf{H}]\,\delta_{ij} + D_i E_j + B_i H_j \qquad (3.5\text{-}4)$$

In the rest frame, striction effects can easily be included in the following manner: (The constitutive equations are implied when writing the striction effects in this manner.)

$$T'_{ij} = -\frac{1}{2}\left(\mathbf{D}' \cdot \mathbf{E}' + \mathbf{B}' \cdot \mathbf{H}' - \rho E'^2 \frac{\partial \epsilon}{\partial \rho} - \rho H'^2 \frac{\partial \mu}{\partial \rho}\right)\delta_{ij}$$
$$+ D'_i E'_j + B'_i H'_j \qquad (3.5\text{-}5)$$

Using Maxwell's equation and assuming a linear isotropic medium, the divergence of (3.5-5) reduces to the following expression in the rest frame:

$$\frac{\partial T'_{ji}}{\partial x_j} = f'_{e_i} + \frac{\partial}{\partial t}(\mathbf{D}' \times \mathbf{B}')_i \qquad (3.5\text{-}6)$$

where f'_{e_i} is given by Equation (3.4-2). For media in which $\kappa = \kappa_m = 1$ (free space properties), the constitutive equations are valid in any frame of reference and Equation (3.5-6) would hold in any frame of reference. The striction terms would then be zero, as would any variations in μ or ϵ, so that the force would reduce to simply $\mathbf{f}_e = \rho_e \mathbf{E} + \mathbf{J} \times \mathbf{B}$ valid in any frame of reference.

In order to specify completely the body force, the momentum of the electromagnetic field must now be introduced. We know, for any frame, that $f_{e_i} = (\partial T_{ji}/\partial x_j) - (\partial g_i/\partial t)$. Two expressions are in common use for g_i. The Minkowski tensor is given by

$$g_i = (\mathbf{D} \times \mathbf{B})_i \qquad (3.5\text{-}7)$$

in any frame, and the Abraham tensor is written

$$g'_i = \frac{1}{c^2} (\mathbf{E}' \times \mathbf{H}')_i \qquad (3.5\text{-}8)$$

in the rest frame only. Since the Abraham tensor becomes more complicated in the general covariant expression, the Minkowski tensor is more frequently used, but the resulting four-dimensional energy momentum tensor is not symmetric (see Appendix 2) and hence cannot be correct in itself. Current thought seems to favor the Minkowski momentum and the introduction of an interaction momentum so that the net effect on the material media is as if the electromagnetic momentum were the Abraham value of $(1/c^2)(\mathbf{E} \times \mathbf{H})$. Depending on the momentum expression used, the body force is different. Using the Abraham value, an extra force is introduced into Equation (3.4-2) so that we obtain from (3.4-2) and (3.5-3) in the rest frame

$$
\begin{aligned}
f'_{e_i} &= \frac{\partial T'_{ji}}{\partial x_j} - \frac{\partial g'_i}{\partial t} \\
&= \left[\rho_e \mathbf{E}' + \mathbf{J}' \times \mathbf{B}' - \frac{\epsilon_0}{2} E'^2 \nabla \kappa - \frac{\mu_0}{2} H'^2 \nabla \kappa_m \right. \\
&\quad \left. + \frac{\epsilon_0}{2} \nabla \left(E'^2 \frac{\partial \kappa}{\partial \rho} \cdot \rho \right) + \frac{\mu_0}{2} \nabla \left(H'^2 \frac{\partial \kappa_m}{\partial \rho} \cdot \rho \right) \right]_i \\
&\quad + \frac{\partial}{\partial t} (\mathbf{D}' \times \mathbf{B}')_i - \frac{1}{c^2} \frac{\partial}{\partial t} (\mathbf{E}' \times \mathbf{H}')_i \quad (3.5\text{-}9)
\end{aligned}
$$

The use of the Minkowski tensor would lead, in the rest frame, to Equation (3.4-2).

The additional force $(1/c^2)(\kappa \kappa_m - 1)(\partial/\partial t)(\mathbf{E}' \times \mathbf{H}')$ (in the rest frame) is a very small quantity and to date has never been measured. Hence the exact form of the electromagnetic momentum is still subject to question.

From a practical standpoint, the question is an academic one, and the force is adequately given by expression (3.4-2) in the rest frame. For moving media (3.5-4) can be used (in the absence of striction) and leads to (in any frame):

$$\mathbf{f}_e = \rho_e \mathbf{E} + \mathbf{J} \times \mathbf{B} + \tfrac{1}{2}(D_k \nabla E_k - E_k \nabla D_k)$$

$$+ \tfrac{1}{2}(B_k \nabla H_k - H_k \nabla B_k) + \frac{\partial}{\partial t} (\mathbf{D} \times \mathbf{B}) - \frac{\partial \mathbf{g}}{\partial t} \quad (3.5\text{-}10)$$

If the Minkowski expression for $\mathbf{g}$ is used, the last two terms are identically zero. If the Abraham expression is used, there is a net force.

However, this force, if it exists, is so small that it can be neglected in all real problems; and we can write for moving media the covariant expression

$$\mathbf{f}_e = \rho_e \mathbf{E} + \mathbf{J} \times \mathbf{B} + \tfrac{1}{2}(D_k \nabla E_k - E_k \nabla D_k) + \tfrac{1}{2}(B_k \nabla H_k - H_k \nabla B_k)$$

$$(3.5\text{-}11)$$

If the constitutive equations can be written (in the rest frame), (3.5-11) reduces to (3.4-2) (without striction). In linear homogeneous material the last two terms of (3.5-11) are identically zero and we get simply the covariant expression

$$\mathbf{f}_e = \rho_e \mathbf{E} + \mathbf{J} \times \mathbf{B} \qquad (3.5\text{-}12)$$

3.6 THE STRESS TENSOR AND PRINCIPAL STRESSES

We may obtain a simple physical interpretation of the stress tensor by examining the principal stresses. If the coordinate axes are rotated, the stress components change, just as in elasticity theory. For a particular stress state, the individual values of the stress components depend on the orientation of the axes and are related by an orthogonal transformation. The principal axes and corresponding principal stresses are defined so that the shear stresses are all zero and only normal stresses exist in the direction of the principal axes.

The principal stresses and corresponding principal axes are found by diagonalizing the stress tensor. Hence, if we denote the principal stresses as λ and the principal axes as $\mathbf{A}$, we can write the following equations. The secular determinant is

$$|T_{ij} - \delta_{ij}\lambda| = 0 \qquad (3.6\text{-}1)$$

to be solved for the three roots of λ, and

$$[T_{ij} - \delta_{ij}\lambda][A_i] = 0 \qquad (3.6\text{-}2)$$

to be solved for the three corresponding vectors which define the principal axes.

Rather than trying to solve (3.6-1) and (3.6-2) in generality, it is easier to get a physical picture if the stress tensor is split into an electric and a magnetic part since the two parts are completely uncoupled. Thus we obtain a state of principal electric stresses and a state of principal magnetic stresses. The total stress state is then the linear superposition of the two and we can write

$$T_{ij} = T_{ij}^{\ e} + T_{ij}^{\ m} \qquad (3.6\text{-}3)$$

where $T_{ij}^{\ e}$ and $T_{ij}^{\ m}$ are the parts resulting from the electric and magnetic fields, respectively. The two sets of principal axes and stresses can be found by solving

$$|T_{ij}{}^e - \delta_{ij}\lambda^e| = 0$$

$$[T_{ij}{}^e - \delta_{ij}\lambda^e][A_i{}^e] = 0 \tag{3.6-4}$$

and

$$|T_{ij}{}^m - \delta_{ij}\lambda^m| = 0$$

$$[T_{ij}{}^m - \delta_{ij}\lambda^m][A_i{}^m] = 0 \tag{3.6-5}$$

Let us first examine the problem in any frame of reference and use Equation (3.5-4) for the stress tensor. (Later we can leave in striction effects and work in the rest frame.) Writing out the secular determinants we obtain

$$\begin{vmatrix} [\tfrac{1}{2}(D_xE_x - D_yE_y - D_zE_z) - \lambda^e] & D_yE_x & D_zE_x \\ D_xE_y & [\tfrac{1}{2}(D_yE_y - D_xE_x - D_zE_z) - \lambda^e] & D_zE_y \\ D_xE_z & D_yE_z & [\tfrac{1}{2}(D_zE_z - D_xE_x - D_yE_y) - \lambda^e] \end{vmatrix} = 0$$

$$\tag{3.6-6}$$

and a similar determinant for the magnetic part of the stress tensor with **D** and **E** replaced by **B** and **H**, respectively. (It may be noted here that although $T_{ij} + \tau_{ij}$, where τ_{ij} is the mechanical stress tensor, must be symmetric in any frame to satisfy equilibrium requirements, T_{ij} is not necessarily symmetric.) Regardless of the constitutive equations, the values of λ^e and λ^m are the following:

$$\lambda_1{}^e = \frac{\mathbf{E} \cdot \mathbf{D}}{2}$$

$$\lambda_2{}^e = \lambda_3{}^e = -\frac{\mathbf{E} \cdot \mathbf{D}}{2} \tag{3.6-7}$$

$$\lambda_1{}^m = \frac{\mathbf{H} \cdot \mathbf{B}}{2}$$

$$\lambda_2{}^m = \lambda_3{}^m = -\frac{\mathbf{H} \cdot \mathbf{B}}{2} \tag{3.6-8}$$

If **E** and **D** are colinear, and **B** and **H** are colinear, the principal axes are oriented as follows: $\lambda_1{}^e$ is a tension along the **E** vector, and $\lambda_2{}^e$ and $\lambda_3{}^e$ represent a compression normal to the **E** vector. $\lambda_1{}^m$ is a tension along the **H** vector and $\lambda_2{}^m$ and $\lambda_3{}^m$ represent a compression normal to the **H** line. However, in general these vectors are colinear only in the rest frame of isotropic media. In the laboratory frame, the vectors are not generally colinear (as can be seen by referring to the laboratory constitutive equations). In this general situation the principal axes cannot be given such a simple interpretation.

If we assume that $\mathbf{B} = \mu\mathbf{H}$ is valid in the laboratory frame, then $\mathbf{B}$ and $\mathbf{H}$ are colinear and the magnetic principal stress state is as outlined above. In most work in magnetofluidmechanics, as we shall see, the assumption that $\mathbf{B} = \mathbf{B}'$ and $\mathbf{H} = \mathbf{H}'$ allows us to write $\mathbf{B} = \mu\mathbf{H}$ in any frame and to interpret the magnetic principal stresses as we have. The $\mathbf{E}$ and $\mathbf{D}$ fields are not usually colinear in the laboratory frame.

The stress states given by (3.6-7) and (3.6-8) are states of tension along a principal axis and compression normal to that axis. The electric and magnetic stresses have different principal axes, of course, but the stress states may be added together in a linear fashion. As an alternative to the tension and compression interpretation, we can think of the stress states as pure hydrostatic compression of the value $\mathbf{E} \cdot \mathbf{D}/2 + \mathbf{H} \cdot \mathbf{B}/2$ superposed on a tension of $\mathbf{E} \cdot \mathbf{D}$ along $\mathbf{A}_1{}^e$, and a tension of $\mathbf{H} \cdot \mathbf{B}$ along $\mathbf{A}_1{}^m$. Only if $\mathbf{E}$ and $\mathbf{D}$ are colinear does $\mathbf{A}_1{}^e$ coincide with $\mathbf{E}$. In most physical situations, as we have pointed out, $\mathbf{B}$ and $\mathbf{H}$ are essentially colinear (if the medium is isotropic) and $\mathbf{A}_1{}^m$ is aligned with the $\mathbf{H}$ field.

We have now arrived at the popular statement: The net effect of the body force is to create an electromagnetic pressure plus a tension along the field lines. We have analyzed this statement and discussed its validity. Of course these electromagnetic stresses enter into dynamical equations exactly as mechanical stresses do, so that positive electromagnetic stresses or tensions can be balanced by mechanical pressure and vice versa. We must always keep in mind, however, that the divergence of the stress tensor is the only meaningful concept and that the stresses we have been discussing are not necessarily real entities. Confusion and paradoxes may result if we try to attach physical significance to the stresses themselves.

3.7 PRINCIPAL STRESSES INCLUDING STRICTION EFFECTS

In an isotropic medium the striction term can be included in the rest frame in a simple manner, and the stress tensor in the rest frame written as

$$T_{ij} = -\frac{1}{2}\left[\mathbf{D} \cdot \mathbf{E} + \mathbf{D} \cdot \mathbf{H} - \rho E^2 \frac{\partial \epsilon}{\partial \rho} - \rho H^2 \frac{\partial \mu}{\partial \rho}\right] \delta_{ij} + D_i E_j + B_i H_j$$

$$(3.7\text{-}1)$$

where $\frac{1}{2}[\rho E^2(\partial \epsilon/\partial \rho) + \rho H^2(\partial \rho/\partial \rho)]$ are the striction terms. (The primes are omitted but understood to apply in this section.) These terms correspond to electromagnetic hydrostatic tension (and hence in an equilibrium configuration can be balanced by mechanical pressure).

By following the method of the previous section, the principal stresses are

$$\lambda_1{}^e = \frac{\mathbf{D} \cdot \mathbf{E}}{2} + \tfrac{1}{2}\rho E^2 \frac{\partial \epsilon}{\partial \rho}$$

$$\lambda_2{}^e = \lambda_3{}^e = -\frac{\mathbf{D} \cdot \mathbf{E}}{2} + \tfrac{1}{2}\rho E^2 \frac{\partial \epsilon}{\partial \rho} \tag{3.7-2}$$

$$\lambda_1{}^m = \frac{\mathbf{H} \cdot \mathbf{B}}{2} + \tfrac{1}{2}\rho H^2 \frac{\partial \mu}{\partial \rho}$$

$$\lambda_2{}^m = \lambda_3{}^m = -\frac{\mathbf{H} \cdot \mathbf{B}}{2} + \tfrac{1}{2}\rho H^2 \frac{\partial \mu}{\partial \rho} \tag{3.7-3}$$

and, if we assume a linear medium, $\mathbf{D} \cdot \mathbf{E}/2$ and $\mathbf{H} \cdot \mathbf{B}/2$ can be replaced by $\epsilon_0 \kappa E^2/2$ and $\mu_0 \kappa_m H^2/2$, respectively. In this case, the principal axes are $\mathbf{A}_1{}^e$ and $\mathbf{A}_1{}^m$ along $\mathbf{E}$ and $\mathbf{H}$, respectively, $\mathbf{A}_2{}^e$ and $\mathbf{A}_3{}^e$ normal to $\mathbf{E}$, and $\mathbf{A}_2{}^m$ and $\mathbf{A}_3{}^m$ normal to $\mathbf{H}$.

3.8   FORCE DENSITY IN MAGNETOFLUIDMECHANICS

Although in most problems of fluid flow the dominant force is $\mathbf{J} \times \mathbf{B}$, in some instances other terms become important. In cases involving a dielectric fluid or the theory of plasma waves, for example, space change can become appreciable and the $\rho_e \mathbf{E}$ term may become important. In some situations, the other terms may also become important.

However, in magnetofluidmechanics, the body force is usually adequately represented by $(\rho_e \mathbf{E} + \mathbf{J} \times \mathbf{B})$. Thus we can write

$$\mathbf{f}'_e = \rho'_e \mathbf{E}' + \mathbf{J}' \times \mathbf{B}' \tag{3.8-1}$$

$$\mathbf{f}_e = \rho_e \mathbf{E} + \mathbf{J} \times \mathbf{B} \tag{3.8-2}$$

since this form of the body force is a covariant expression and valid in any frame of reference. This fact can readily be seen if $\mathbf{J}'$ is assumed zero. The general proof is left as an exercise.

Example 3.3   We now show that in the special case of $\mathbf{J}' = 0$ the expression $\mathbf{f}_e = \rho_e \mathbf{E} + \mathbf{J} \times \mathbf{B}$ is covariant. From the Lorentz transformations on ρ_e and $\mathbf{E}$ and $\mathbf{J}$ we have

$$\mathbf{f}'_e = \rho'_e \mathbf{E}' = \beta \left(\rho_e - \frac{\mathbf{V} \cdot \mathbf{J}}{c^2} \right) (\mathbf{E}_{\parallel} + \beta \mathbf{E}_{\perp} + \beta \mathbf{V} \times \mathbf{B}) \tag{E3.3-1}$$

Using the transformation $\mathbf{J}' = \beta(\mathbf{J} - \rho_e\mathbf{V})$, we obtain

$$\mathbf{f}'_e = \beta\rho_e\left(1 - \frac{V^2}{c^2}\right)(\mathbf{E}_\| + \beta\mathbf{E}_\perp) + \beta^2\mathbf{J}\left(1 - \frac{V^2}{c^2}\right) \times \mathbf{B}$$

$$= \frac{1}{\beta}\,\rho_e\mathbf{E}_\| + [\rho_e\mathbf{E} + \mathbf{J} \times \mathbf{B}]_\perp \qquad \text{(E3.3-2)}$$

Hence we check the transformation on $\mathbf{f}_e$ if we set $\mathbf{f}_e = \rho_e\mathbf{E} + \mathbf{J} \times \mathbf{B}$, since $\mathbf{f}'_{e\|} = (1/\beta)\mathbf{f}_{e\|}$ and $\mathbf{f}'_{e\perp} = \mathbf{f}_{e\perp}$.

3.9   FORMS OF THE STRESS TENSOR FOR REFERENCE

The stress tensor is written out explicitly in various forms for convenience and ready reference.

1. General covariant expression (neglecting striction):

$$\begin{bmatrix} \begin{bmatrix} \tfrac{1}{2}(D_xE_x - D_yE_y - D_zE_z) \\ +\tfrac{1}{2}(B_xH_x - B_yH_y - B_zH_z) \end{bmatrix} & (D_xE_y + B_xH_y) & (D_xE_z + B_xH_z) \\[2mm] (D_yE_x + B_yH_x) & \begin{bmatrix} \tfrac{1}{2}(D_yE_y - D_xE_x - D_zE_z) \\ +\tfrac{1}{2}(B_yH_y - B_xH_x - B_zH_z) \end{bmatrix} & (D_yE_z + B_yH_z) \\[2mm] (D_zE_x + B_zH_x) & (D_zE_y + B_zH_y) & \begin{bmatrix} \tfrac{1}{2}(D_zE_z - D_xE_x - D_yE_y) \\ +\tfrac{1}{2}(B_zH_z - B_xH_x - B_yH_y) \end{bmatrix} \end{bmatrix}$$

$$= -\tfrac{1}{2}(\mathbf{D}\cdot\mathbf{E} + \mathbf{B}\cdot\mathbf{H})\,\delta_{ij} + D_iE_j + B_iH_j \quad \text{(3.9-1)}$$

2. In the rest frame for linear isotropic media, including striction effects as shown on page 98.

3.10   SUMMARY

We have discussed the Lorentz force on a charged particle in a relativistic context. The form of the body force was stated in the rest frame, and a simplified form for use in magnetohydrodynamics was expressed in covariant form.

The stress tensor was introduced and discussed in covariant form; the electromagnetic momentum was discussed; and the rest frame formulation was given, including striction. The stress tensor was diagonalized and the principal stresses derived.

One important concept remains. In treating the stress and force problem in a relativistic fashion, we have retained three-dimensional language

$$
\begin{bmatrix}
\frac{1}{2}\epsilon(E_x^2 - E_y^2 - E_z^2) + \frac{1}{2}\rho E^2 \frac{\partial \epsilon}{\partial \rho} + \frac{1}{2}\mu(H_x^2 - H_y^2 - H_z^2) + \frac{1}{2}\rho H^2 \frac{\partial \mu}{\partial \rho} & (\epsilon E_x E_y + \mu H_x H_y) & (\epsilon E_x E_z + \mu H_x H_z) \\[1.2em]
(\epsilon E_x E_y + \mu H_x H_y) & \frac{1}{2}\epsilon(E_y^2 - E_x^2 - E_z^2) + \frac{1}{2}\rho E^2 \frac{\partial \epsilon}{\partial \rho} + \frac{1}{2}\mu(H_y^2 - H_x^2 - H_z^2) + \frac{1}{2}\rho H^2 \frac{\partial \mu}{\partial \rho} & (\epsilon E_y E_z + \mu H_y H_z) \\[1.2em]
(\epsilon E_x E_z + \mu H_x H_z) & (\epsilon E_y E_z + \mu H_y H_z) & \frac{1}{2}\epsilon(E_z^2 - E_x^2 - E_y^2) + \frac{1}{2}\rho E^2 \frac{\partial \epsilon}{\partial \rho} + \frac{1}{2}\mu(H_z^2 - H_x^2 - H_y^2) + \frac{1}{2}\rho H^2 \frac{\partial \mu}{\partial \rho}
\end{bmatrix}
$$

$$
= -\frac{1}{2}\left[(\mathbf{D}\cdot\mathbf{E} + \mathbf{B}\cdot\mathbf{H}) - \rho E^2 \frac{\partial \epsilon}{\partial \rho} - \rho H^2 \frac{\partial \mu}{\partial \rho}\right]\delta_{ij} + D_i E_j + B_i H_j \qquad (3.9\text{-}2)
$$

throughout. Another method of treatment is the four-dimensional, relativistic approach.

Actually, the stress tensor is only part of a four-dimensional, energy-momentum-stress tensor (or simply energy-momentum tensor, as it is called) which can be written in covariant form. This tensor must include the electrical and mechanical energy, momentum, and stress in the presence of material media. The three spatial components of the tensor divergence of this total electromagnetic-mechanical tensor represent the equations of motion, and the fourth component is the energy equation. The main difficulty with this approach is that the appropriate form is in question, and an exact, reliable formulation can only be effected for homogeneous, isotropic, linear material. However, this assumption is valid in most problems involving fluids, and a relativistic theory of fluid-electromagnetic interaction can be formulated from it. This problem is further discussed in Chapter 5, and a short account is given in Appendix 2. The reader should also consult the references for further details.

PROBLEMS

1. Derive Equation E3.1-2 in detail by the method outlined in the last paragraph of Example 3.1.

2. Discuss the derivation of E3.1-2 by considering a loop fixed in the laboratory and looking at the flux change through it as the magnet passes. (Using $\nabla \times \mathbf{E} = -(\partial \mathbf{B}/\partial t)$.)

3. Work Example 3.2 assuming the voltage across the capacitors is held constant.

4. A piece of magnetostrictive material is placed in a nonuniform magnetic field. Discuss the equilibrium configuration of the material. What are the stresses in it?

5. Rework Example 3.2 using the stress tensor. (*Hint:* Determine the stress tensor on the surface of the dielectric and integrate over the area.)

6. Prove that $T_{ij} + \tau_{ij}$ must be symmetric.

7. Derive the principal stresses and principal directions of the stress tensor in detail.

8. Show, generally, that $\mathbf{f}_e = \rho_e \mathbf{E} + \mathbf{J} \times \mathbf{B}$ is a covariant expression by using the Lorentz transformations on the field quantities and $\mathbf{f}_e$.

9. Discuss qualitatively the force on a linear magnetic rod inserted (*a*) in a solenoid and (*b*) in the field of a permanent magnet. Is there a force on such a material inserted in a homogeneous magnetic field? Is there a force on a nonmagnetic material such as brass or aluminum in a nonhomogeneous magnetic field? Suppose the brass is moved through the field. Is there a force? Does your answer to this last question depend on the homogeneity of the magnetic field?

10. A Ni alloy wire (magnetostrictive) is used as a high-frequency pressure probe, as shown in Fig. P3.10-1. The tip of the wire (*A*) is exposed to the fluid. The pressure wave in the fluid initiates a stress wave in the wire which travels along the wire and is absorbed by the damper *C*. The coil *B* picks up the signal generated by the stress wave. Such a device can also be used as a delay line for a signal fed in at A. Explain qualitatively the operation of this system, and relate the signal at B to the wire stresses and important parameters.

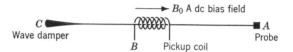

Figure P3.10-1   A magnetostrictive pressure probe.

11. What are the boundary conditions on the surface of an elastic solid in static equilibrium in an electromagnetic field? (*Hint:* The total stress tensor (mechanical plus electromagnetic) must be a constant. Hence the total tensor just inside the solid boundary must be equal to the electromagnetic tensor just outside the body.)

12. Find the force on the dielectric in Problem 18 of Chapter 2.

13. Under what conditions is T_{ij} not symmetric? If T_{ij} is symmetric in the rest frame, is it always symmetric in other frames?

REFERENCES

Abraham, M., and R. Becker, *The Classical Theory of Electricity and Magnetism*, Blackie and Sons, London, 1932.

Becker, R., and M. Abraham, *Theorie Der Electrizitat*, Vol. II, Teubner, Leipzig, 1933 (lithoprinted by J. W. Edwards, Ann. Arbor, Mich., 1945).

Hughes, W. F., Relativistic Magnetohydrodynamics and Irreversible Thermodynamics, *Proc. Cambridge Phil. Soc.*, **57**, p. 878, 1961.

Landau, L. D., and E. M. Lifshitz, *Electrodynamics of Continuous Media*, Sections 15, 34, Addison-Wesley, Reading, Mass., 1960.

Marx, G., and G. Györgyi, Der Energie-Impuls-Tensor Des Elektromagnetischen Feldes und Die Ponderamotorischen Kräfte in Dielektrika, *Acta. Phys. Hung*, **3**, p. 213, 1954.

Møller, C., *The Theory of Relativity*, Chapters V and VI, Oxford University Press, 1952.

Panofsky, W. K. H. and M. Phillips, *Classical Electricity and Magnetism*, Chapter 6 and Section 10.6, Addison-Wesley, Reading., Mass. 1955.

Pauli, W., *Theory of Relativity* (translated), Section 35, Pergamon Press, London, 1958.

Post, E. J., *Formal Structure of Electromagnetics*, North-Holland Publishing Co., Amsterdam, 1962.

Sommerfeld, A., *Electrodynamics*, Academic Press, New York, 1952.

Stratton, J. A., *Electromagnetic Theory*, McGraw-Hill, New York, 1941.

Toupin, R. A., The Elastic Dielectric, *J. Rat. Mech. Anal.*, **5**, p. 849, 1956.

4

The Fluid Equations—
Basic Ideas of Viscous Flow
in Magnetohydrodynamics

4.1 INTRODUCTION

We have been discussing, so far, the ·general electrodynamics of continuous media without reference to the specific physical properties of the medium, whether fluid or solid. We now wish to begin the study of fluids specifically. In this chapter we will review some of the basic ideas of continuum fluid mechanics and how they are modified by the presence of electromagnetic effects.

Electromagnetic body forces act on the fluid, and in turn the motion of the fluid in the presence of the electromagnetic field may generate an induced emf and alter the fields. In Chapters 2 and 3 we discussed the nature of the body force and the effect of relative motion of conductors in the presence of electromagnetic fields. Now we can begin to combine these basic concepts and discuss the motion of electrically conducting deformable media.

There are two basic approaches in fluid mechanics, the macroscopic continuum model and the kinetic theory or microscopic model. For the relatively high densities that occur under ordinary atmospheric conditions, the continuum model is adequate, and the fluid may be assumed to be a liquid or gas, homogeneous and isotropic in the mechanical and electromagnetic sense. Effects of anisotropy may be taken into account by using tensor constitutive equations (tensor electric conductivity, permeability, etc.), although such effects are usually not important in dense fluids. The Hall current may be considered in this way.

In general, electrically conducting liquids and gases have various dielectric constants (which may depend on frequency) but all conducting liquids have the permeability of free space (that is, μ_0). Hence care must be exercised in writing constitutive equations.

Rarefied gases cannot be treated adequately by the continuum model and a microscopic approach must be used. There are several possible models of varying degrees of accuracy which may be used. In general, the procedure is to reduce the general Boltzmann transport equation to an appropriate form for the problem under consideration. The solution to the transport equations is not easy and only certain simple situations can be treated exactly.

The simplest model of a rarefied gas is the multicomponent model consisting of electrons, neutrals, and various ionic species. Here the concepts of conductivity are no longer useful, and the equations of motion, along with the definition of current in terms of charged particle flux, make unnecessary the use of equations derived from Ohm's law (although a certain combination of the equations of motion is often referred to as Ohm's law for a plasma).

If we begin with the Boltzmann transport equation, the operational definitions of macroscopic thermodynamics become unnecessary, and the problem becomes one of determining the distribution function of the gas. All thermodynamic properties may be defined in terms of this function. In a sense, then, the basic equations of continuum gas mechanics (momentum, energy, continuity, and state) result from assumptions about the distribution function which allow the transport equation to reduce to these basic equations. This reduction is achieved by taking moments of the Boltzmann equation and making assumptions about collisions and distribution functions.

We now begin the study of continuum fluid mechanics, namely, classical macroscopic fluid mechanics and the interactions with electromagnetic fields.

4.2   THE FUNDAMENTAL EQUATIONS OF VISCOUS FLOW

If the fluid, either gas or liquid, is treated as a continuum, certain convenient models can be used in MHD to describe the fluid behavior. These models are no different from those used in conventional fluid mechanics. The only effect of the electromagnetic field is a coupling through the electromagnetic body force in the equation of motion and a more subtle coupling through the energy equation. The fluid equations of continuity and state are essentially unchanged. A complete discussion of the energy equation and thermodynamics is reserved for Chapter 5.

The classical Navier-Stokes equation of motion is derived by assuming a linear relationship between the stress tensor and strain rate tensor in the fluid. These equations of motion, with the addition of the electromagnetic body force, are used in MHD. Other fluid models (visco-elastic, etc.) are possible, and, in fact, purely elastic equations can be used for magnetoelasticity studies. In this section these basic fluid equations are discussed.

The equation of motion in terms of stress can be written

$$\rho\left(\frac{\partial V_i}{\partial t} + V_j\frac{\partial V_i}{\partial x_j}\right) = \frac{\partial}{\partial x_j}(\tau_{ji} + T_{ji}) - \frac{\partial g_i}{\partial t} - \rho\frac{\partial \psi}{\partial x_i} \qquad (4.2\text{-}1)$$

where τ_{ji} is the mechanical stress tensor, T_{ji} the electromagnetic stress tensor, and g_i the momentum of the electromagnetic field. ρ is the density of the fluid, and ψ is the gravitational potential.

Except for certain problems in rarefied gas dynamics and plasma dynamics, the fluid is isotropic and the normal stress components of the mechanical stress tensor (diagonal terms) are equal and are identified with the fluid mechanical (and thermodynamic) pressure. Hence the mechanical stress tensor can be separated into a pressure and viscous part as

$$\tau_{ij} = -P\delta_{ij} + \tau'_{ij} \qquad (4.2\text{-}2)$$

where τ'_{ij} is the viscous stress tensor. In anisotropic fluids P is sometimes defined as $-\frac{1}{3}(\tau_{11} + \tau_{22} + \tau_{33}) = -\frac{1}{3}\tau_{ii}$. The equation of motion can be written as

$$\rho\left(\frac{\partial V_i}{\partial t} + V_j\frac{\partial V_i}{\partial x_j}\right) = -\frac{\partial P}{\partial x_i} + \frac{\partial \tau_{ji}}{\partial x_j} + \frac{\partial T_{ji}}{\partial x_j} - \frac{\partial g_i}{\partial t} - \rho\frac{\partial \psi}{\partial x_i} \qquad (4.2\text{-}3)$$

The Navier-Stokes equations of motion in terms of velocity components may be written in general form in the following fashion for isotropic homogeneous fluids:

$$\rho\left(\frac{\partial V_i}{\partial t} + V_j\frac{\partial V_i}{\partial x_j}\right) = -\frac{\partial P}{\partial x_i} + \frac{\partial}{\partial x_i}\left\{\mu_f\left(\frac{\partial V_i}{\partial x_j} + \frac{\partial V_j}{\partial x_i} - \frac{2}{3}\delta_{ij}\frac{\partial V_k}{\partial x_k}\right)\right\}$$

$$+ \frac{\partial}{\partial x_i}\left(\zeta\frac{\partial V_k}{\partial x_k}\right) + f_{ei} - \rho\frac{\partial \psi}{\partial x_i} \qquad (4.2\text{-}4)$$

where $\mathbf{f}_e$ is the electromagnetic body force density $(\partial T_{ij}/\partial x_j - \partial g_i/\partial t)$ and

μ_f is the viscosity.* The pressure P is the ordinary mechanical pressure and does not contain any electromagnetic pressure which is accounted for in the body force term. The second coefficient of viscosity is denoted by ζ. (Some writers use a different second coefficient of viscosity, λ, which is related to the one used here by $(\lambda = \zeta - \frac{2}{3}\mu_f)$. ζ is zero for a monatomic gas.)

The second coefficient of viscosity comes about because of compressibility effects and in an incompressible fluid the term involving the second coefficient is zero since $\nabla \cdot V = 0$.

The most general form of the electromagnetic body force is given in Equation (3.5-2), but in most MHD work this body force can be represented simply by

$$\mathbf{f}_e = \rho_e \mathbf{E} + \mathbf{J} \times \mathbf{B} \qquad (4.2\text{-}5)$$

as indicated in Chapter 3.

The commonly used form of the equation of motion thus takes a simpler form under the assumption that the body force is adequately represented by Equation (4.2-5). This assumption is a good one because all liquid metals are virtually nonmagnetic, and the electric forces are usually negligible anyway.

Another point of interest is the fact that the second coefficient of viscosity is often assumed to have the value associated with a monatomic gas: $\zeta = 0$, or $\lambda = -\frac{2}{3}\mu_f$. Frequently this assumption is far from correct. In fact, in liquids (with compressibility included as in wave motion) the value of ζ may become many times that of μ_f (the ordinary viscosity).

Using the body force given in Equation (4.2-5), the equation of motion (4.2-4) can be written as follows:

$$\rho\left(\frac{\partial V_i}{\partial t} + V_j \frac{\partial V_i}{\partial x_j}\right) = -\frac{\partial P}{\partial x_i} + \frac{\partial}{\partial x_j}\left[\mu_f\left(\frac{\partial V_i}{\partial x_j} + \frac{\partial V_j}{\partial x_i} - \frac{2}{3}\delta_{ij}\frac{\partial V_k}{\partial x_k}\right)\right]$$

$$+ \frac{\partial}{\partial x_i}\left(\zeta \frac{\partial V_k}{\partial x_k}\right) - \rho\frac{\partial \psi}{\partial x_i} + \rho_e E_i + (\mathbf{J} \times \mathbf{B})_i \quad (4.2\text{-}6)$$

For an incompressible fluid, the term $\nabla \cdot V$ is zero and the equations can be simplified. Furthermore, the viscosity can be assumed quasi-constant to a high degree of accuracy and removed from the derivative. The incompressible equation of motion is then

$$\rho\left(\frac{\partial \mathbf{V}}{\partial t} + (\mathbf{V} \cdot \nabla \mathbf{V})\right) = -\nabla P + \mu_f \nabla^2 \mathbf{V} - \rho \nabla \psi + \rho_e \mathbf{E} + \mathbf{J} \times \mathbf{B} \quad (4.2\text{-}7)$$

---

* The symbol μ_f is used for viscosity and μ for magnetic permeability so that no confusion will arise.

Since the equation of continuity of the fluid is unaffected by electro-magnetic effects, it takes the same form as in ordinary fluid mechanics. Thus the general equation is

$$\frac{\partial \rho}{\partial t} + \nabla \cdot (\rho \mathbf{V}) = 0 \qquad (4.2\text{-}8)$$

For an incompressible fluid the density is constant and the equation is simply

$$\nabla \cdot \mathbf{V} = 0 \qquad (4.2\text{-}9)$$

The general form of the equation of state, necessary for a complete description of a gas is independent of electromagnetic effects to a high degree of accuracy. A perfect gas can be represented in the ordinary thermodynamical sense by

$$PV = n\bar{R}T \qquad (4.2\text{-}10)$$

where P is the thermodynamic pressure which is to be identified with the mechanical pressure, $\bar{R}$ is the universal gas constant, T is absolute temperature, V is volume, and n is the number of moles.

In the equation of state in the form of (4.2-10), as well as in the equation of motion, the pressure is to be interpreted as the thermodynamic pressure of the fluid. This pressure does not include radiation pressure or the normal components of the electromagnetic stress tensor, although these electromagnetic pressure terms may indeed give rise to a mechanical pressure in the fluid. The equation of motion expresses this balance. Since the radiation pressure and the hydrostatic components of the body force are manifestations of the electromagnetic body force, it seems artificial to include them in the pressure term and then later separate them out. In the absence of motion or gravity, the thermodynamic or mechanical pressure may be exactly balanced by the electromagnetic body force or pressure.

Some writers include the hydrostatic components of the body force in an arbitrarily defined total pressure. In this case the equation of state becomes more complicated. This inclusion is unnecessary, however, and we will leave the equation of state uncoupled (at least to the degree of accuracy used in all MHD work) from the electromagnetic effects.

It might be well to mention here that under certain conditions in the flow of gases (especially high speed rarefied flows), it is possible that the normal mechanical stress components will be unequal so that the mechanical pressure is anisotropic. When this situation occurs, the thermo-dynamic pressure used in the equation of state may be identified with the mean value of the mechanical pressure components.

4.3   FLOW UNDER THE ACTION OF ELECTROMAGNETIC BODY FORCES

We now have at our disposal enough basic knowledge to apply to an actual fluid and to begin the study of magnetofluidmechanics (MFD). Since we know the basic descriptive equations of MFD, the application to real problems should be a formality. However, a real physical situation is not always simple to describe in terms of a mathematical model; because of the many assumptions and special methods that may be applied to specific problems, there are many possible pitfalls between physical problems and mathematical models.

The need for critical examination is even more important in MFD than in ordinary fluid mechanics. One situation in which we must proceed with care is the extrapolation of the results of a two-dimensional mathematical model to three-dimensional situations. In some instances of boundary layer flow, for example, such extrapolation leads to completely erroneous results which might not be the case in conventional fluid mechanics.

In general, the electromagnetic body force affects the character of the flow, and the currents and fields themselves are determined by the fluid velocity (through the Lorentz transformations and hence in Ohm's law $\mathbf{J} = \sigma(\mathbf{E} + \mathbf{V} \times \mathbf{B}) = \sigma \mathbf{E}'$ and possibly in other field equations depending on the problem.) The fluid equations and Maxwell's equations are thus coupled and must be solved simultaneously. The details of these solutions are reserved for later chapters.

One important question arises: under what conditions does the electromagnetic body force induce or alter the motion of the fluid and under what conditions does it merely alter the static pressure in the fluid? Just as a gravitational field sets up a hydrostatic pressure field in a fluid (without necessarily inducing motion) so the electromagnetic body force does the same thing under certain conditions. Although the electromagnetic body force, unlike the gravity force, is usually nonconservative (rotational) and not derivable from a scalar potential function, under certain specific circumstances the electromagnetic body force may be at least approximately conservative and therefore derivable from a scalar potential function ϕ. The equation of motion then takes the form

$$\rho\left(\frac{\partial \mathbf{V}}{\partial t} + (\mathbf{V} \cdot \nabla)\mathbf{V}\right) = -\nabla(P + \phi) - \rho\,\nabla\psi + \nabla \cdot \tau \qquad (4.3\text{-}1)$$

where ψ is the gravitational potential. If a new pressure $P^* = P + \phi$ is defined, then the equation of motion is the same as when the electro-magnetic body force is omitted, and the fluid velocity or flow pattern can be changed only if the boundary conditions or velocity are different or if the boundary conditions on P^* are different from those on P. Certainly, if ϕ goes to zero at the boundary of a flow field, the electromagnetic body force should have no effect other than altering the pressure distribution in the fluid. We say the same thing when we state that a conservative force cannot induce vorticity in the fluid (from Kelvin's vortex theorem). In a stationary fluid, then, the application of an irrotational (conservative) body force does not necessarily induce motion but may merely change the static pressure distribution. It must be remembered, however, that a conservative electromagnetic body force is the exception and that usually this force is rotational and does alter the flow. This point is discussed in detail in Sections 11 and 12 of Chapter 6.

The coupling of electromagnetic effects to incompressible flow results in a fourth-order system of equations. If the part of the magnetic field induced by the fluid motion is negligible, or identically uncoupled, the system reduces to second order, as in ordinary fluid mechanics. Fully developed laminar viscous MFD flow between infinite parallel plates (with a magnetic field applied normal to the plates) is an example of a second-order system in which the induced magnetic field is uncoupled. (This problem is known as the Hartmann problem, after the Danish physicist Hartmann, and is discussed in Chapter 7.) In the development region of such flow, however, the induced magnetic field becomes coupled into the equations of motion and the system becomes fourth order.

Frequently in coupled systems the induced field is small and the fourth-order system can be reduced by approximation to a second-order system. (The magnetic Reynolds number is a measure of the induced field and is discussed in Chapter 6.) The flow field can then be calculated and the in-duced field subsequently determined, as will be illustrated in later chapters.

4.4 SOME COMMENTS ON BOUNDARY CONDITIONS

Boundary conditions on the electromagnetic field, discussed in Chapter 2, can be applied at a wall or interface. Their application is straight-forward, but it is well to remember that the boundary conditions on field quantities hold in any frame of reference for the field quantities measured in that frame. That is, the boundary conditions can be written in terms of laboratory quantities, or any other, if convenient. This fact follows directly from the covariance of the Maxwell equations. (See Chapter 6 for a further discussion.)

General theorems can be developed from these boundary conditions that are particularly useful for fluid flow in channels whose walls are insulators or perfect conductors (see Chapter 7).

Another important type of boundary condition occurs at infinity. In order to establish the value of, say, the electric field at infinity in unbounded (external) flow, a suitable base frame of reference must be chosen in which we know the condition at infinity. Usually this frame is the laboratory or Earth frame of reference in which the electric field at infinity $\mathbf{E}_\infty$ is zero. Then in the frame of any real object, moving with velocity $\mathbf{V}$ with respect to the laboratory, the electric field at infinity $\mathbf{E}'_\infty$ must have the value $\mathbf{E}'_\infty = \mathbf{V} \times \mathbf{B}$ where $\mathbf{B}$ is the magnetic field in the

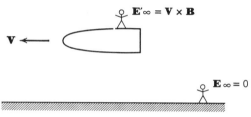

Figure 4.4-1   A reentry vehicle moving with respect to the Earth.

laboratory frame of reference. If no magnetic field is present, both $\mathbf{E}'_\infty$ and $\mathbf{E}_\infty$ are zero. Beginning with a base frame of reference, the proper condition in any reference frame can be established by the appropriate Lorentz transformation of the field quantity.

The above example is of importance in boundary layer theory in the Earth's atmosphere. In Fig. 4.4-1, a reentry vehicle having an ionized and hence electrically conducting boundary layer moves in the presence of the Earth's magnetic field. The boundary condition on $\mathbf{E}'$ (with respect to the vehicle) is $\mathbf{V} \times \mathbf{B}$ at large distances from the vehicle surface. (In the Earth's frame $\mathbf{E}_\infty = 0$.)

Now consider a vehicle stationary in a wind tunnel with fluid velocity $-\mathbf{V}$. The situation would ultimately be the same if the tunnel had insulating walls or were open circuited. The tunnel would act as a generator and at infinity (in the tunnel far from the vehicle) the value of $\mathbf{E}_\infty$ (with respect to the laboratory and vehicle) would be $\mathbf{V} \times \mathbf{B}$. In the local rest frame of the fluid, the value of the electric field at infinity would be zero.

4.5   TERMINAL VOLTAGE AND EQUIVALENT CIRCUITS

Any fluid flow field in MFD can be represented by an equivalent electrical circuit and thought of as an electrical machine (motor or generator). It is possible, therefore, to speak of terminal voltage in an MFD flow. This voltage can be defined between any two points, usually picked as the lead input points to electrodes, if they are present. In Chapter 7 when we discuss channel flow, these concepts can be made clear. In addition, a flow device has an open-circuit terminal voltage, a short-circuit current, and an internal impedance. Equivalent circuits may be constructed, then, with the parameters depending on the electromagnetic field and flow quantities. Such circuits will be constructed for various flow devices in later chapters.

If we think of the terminals of the flow device as fixed in the laboratory frame, we can then attach various external circuits to the equivalent flow circuit. Sometimes the complexity of the problem may preclude this simple model, and the entire field problem, fluid flow plus external circuit, will have to be solved simultaneously.

Let us now turn our attention to the terminal voltage and the derivation of a general, simplified expression for direct-current operation. In Chapter 2 the terminal voltage was defined as

$$V_{AB} = \oint \mathbf{E}' \cdot d\mathbf{l} - \int_A^B \mathbf{E}' \cdot d\mathbf{l} \qquad (4.5\text{-}1)$$

V_{AB} is the terminal voltage of terminal B with respect to terminal A. An infinite impedance voltmeter attached across the terminals AB would read this voltage, a positive V_{AB} indicating a positive B terminal. In the equation, $\mathbf{E}'$ is the local electrical field in the fluid as seen in the fluid rest frame (by an observer moving locally with the fluid), the integral from A to B is inside the fluid, the cyclic integral includes the external circuit, and the paths of both integrals are arbitrary. Equation (4.5-1) may be applied directly to all MFD problems, but a special form for steady (direct-current) operation is very useful. Expanding the equation by using the Lorentz transformations on $\mathbf{E}$ and Maxwell's equations, there results

$$V_{AB} = -\int_S \frac{\partial \mathbf{B}}{\partial t} \cdot d\mathbf{S} + \oint (\mathbf{V} \times \mathbf{B}) \cdot d\mathbf{l} - \int_A^B \mathbf{E} \cdot d\mathbf{l} - \int_A^B (\mathbf{V} \times \mathbf{B}) \cdot d\mathbf{l} \quad (4.5\text{-}2)$$

The integral from A to B is taken through the fluid between the terminals along an arbitrary path. $\mathbf{V}$ is the velocity of the fluid at any point along the path, and $\mathbf{E}$ is the electric field measured in the laboratory frame. (The paths are fixed in the laboratory frame and the fluid flows by.) The area S is that enclosed by the cyclic integral (Fig. 4.5-1).

Now in steady state, $\partial \mathbf{B}/\partial t = 0$ and since the terminals A and B are located in the laboratory frame of reference (as is the external circuit), the following identity must be true

$$-\int_A^B (\mathbf{V} \times \mathbf{B}) \cdot d\mathbf{l} + \oint (\mathbf{V} \times \mathbf{B}) \cdot d\mathbf{l} = \int_B^A (\mathbf{V} \times \mathbf{B}) \cdot d\mathbf{l} = 0 \quad (4.5\text{-}3)$$

where the integral from B to A is taken through the external circuit and hence must be zero, since the external circuit is at rest with respect to the laboratory frame. Combining Equations (4.5-2) and (4.5-3), we find that for flow in which the magnetic field is constant

$$V_{AB} = -\int_A^B \mathbf{E} \cdot d\mathbf{l} \qquad (4.5\text{-}4)$$

where the integral is taken through the fluid along an arbitrary path. If the value of the integral is positive, the voltage at terminal B (with respect

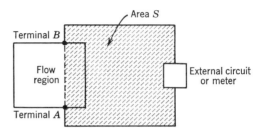

Figure 4.5-1   Terminals and external circuit of an MFD flow.

to terminal A) is positive. Strictly speaking, Equation (4.5-4) is valid for steady magnetic field problems and hence direct-current or steady flow operation.

4.6   FORMS OF THE BASIC EQUATIONS FOR REFERENCE

For reference, the equations of motion are now written out in detail. The material or substantial derivative is denoted as D/Dt. Equations (4.6-1) through (4.6-3) are for a general compressible fluid and Equations (4.6-4) through (4.6-7) are for an incompressible fluid. For a more comprehensive listing see (Hughes and Gaylord) referenced at the end of this chapter.

Cartesian Coordinates

$$\rho \frac{Du}{Dt} = -\frac{\partial P}{\partial x} + \frac{\partial}{\partial x}\left[2\mu_f \frac{\partial u}{\partial x} + (\zeta - \tfrac{2}{3}\mu_f)\,\nabla \cdot \mathbf{V}\right]$$

$$+ \frac{\partial}{\partial y}\left[\mu_f\left(\frac{\partial u}{\partial y} + \frac{\partial v}{\partial x}\right)\right] + \frac{\partial}{\partial z}\left[\mu_f\left(\frac{\partial w}{\partial x} + \frac{\partial u}{\partial z}\right)\right]$$

$$- \rho \frac{\partial \psi}{\partial x} + (\rho_e E_x + J_y B_z - J_z B_y)$$

$$\rho \frac{Dv}{Dt} = -\frac{\partial P}{\partial y} + \frac{\partial}{\partial y}\left[2\mu_f \frac{\partial v}{\partial y} + (\zeta - \tfrac{2}{3}\mu_f)\,\mathbf{\nabla}\cdot\mathbf{V}\right]$$

$$+ \frac{\partial}{\partial z}\left[\mu_f\left(\frac{\partial v}{\partial z} + \frac{\partial w}{\partial y}\right)\right] + \frac{\partial}{\partial x}\left[\mu_f\left(\frac{\partial u}{\partial y} + \frac{\partial v}{\partial x}\right)\right]$$

$$- \rho\frac{\partial \psi}{\partial y} + (\rho_e E_y + J_z B_x - J_x B_z)$$

$$\rho \frac{Dw}{Dt} = -\frac{\partial P}{\partial z} + \frac{\partial}{\partial z}\left[2\mu_f \frac{\partial w}{\partial z} + (\zeta - \tfrac{2}{3}\mu_f)\,\mathbf{\nabla}\cdot\mathbf{V}\right]$$

$$+ \frac{\partial}{\partial x}\left[\mu_f\left(\frac{\partial w}{\partial x} + \frac{\partial u}{\partial z}\right)\right] + \frac{\partial}{\partial y}\left[\mu_f\left(\frac{\partial v}{\partial z} + \frac{\partial w}{\partial y}\right)\right]$$

$$- \rho\frac{\partial \psi}{\partial z} + (\rho_e E_z + J_x B_y - J_y B_x)$$

$$\frac{D}{Dt} = u\frac{\partial}{\partial x} + v\frac{\partial}{\partial y} + w\frac{\partial}{\partial z} + \frac{\partial}{\partial t}$$

$$\mathbf{\nabla}\cdot\mathbf{V} = \frac{\partial u}{\partial x} + \frac{\partial v}{\partial y} + \frac{\partial w}{\partial z} \tag{4.6-1}$$

Cylindrical Coordinates

$$\rho\left(\frac{Dv_r}{Dt} - \frac{v_\theta^2}{r}\right)$$

$$= -\frac{\partial P}{\partial r} + \frac{\partial}{\partial r}\left[2\mu_f \frac{\partial v_r}{\partial r} + (\zeta - \tfrac{2}{3}\mu_f)\,\mathbf{\nabla}\cdot\mathbf{V}\right]$$

$$+ \frac{1}{r}\frac{\partial}{\partial \theta}\left[\mu_f\left(\frac{1}{r}\frac{\partial v_r}{\partial \theta} + \frac{\partial v_\theta}{\partial r} - \frac{v_\theta}{r}\right)\right]$$

$$+ \frac{\partial}{\partial z}\left[\mu_f\left(\frac{\partial v_r}{\partial z} + \frac{\partial v_z}{\partial r}\right)\right]$$

$$+ \frac{2\mu_f}{r}\left[\frac{\partial v_r}{\partial r} - \frac{1}{r}\frac{\partial v_\theta}{\partial \theta} - \frac{v_r}{r}\right] - \rho\frac{\partial \psi}{\partial r}$$

$$+ (\rho_e E_r + J_\theta B_z - J_z B_\theta)$$

$$\rho\left(\frac{Dv_\theta}{Dt} + \frac{v_r v_\theta}{r}\right) = -\frac{1}{r}\frac{\partial P}{\partial \theta} + \frac{1}{r}\frac{\partial}{\partial \theta}\left[\frac{2\mu_f}{r}\frac{\partial v_\theta}{\partial \theta} + (\zeta - \tfrac{2}{3}\mu_f)\,\mathbf{\nabla}\cdot\mathbf{V}\right]$$

$$+ \frac{\partial}{\partial z}\left[\mu_f\left(\frac{1}{r}\frac{\partial v_z}{\partial \theta} + \frac{\partial v_\theta}{\partial z}\right)\right] + \frac{\partial}{\partial r}\left[\mu_f\left(\frac{1}{r}\frac{\partial v_r}{\partial \theta} + \frac{\partial v_\theta}{\partial r} - \frac{v_\theta}{r}\right)\right]$$

$$+ \frac{2\mu_f}{r}\left(\frac{1}{r}\frac{\partial v_r}{\partial \theta} + \frac{\partial v_\theta}{\partial r} - \frac{v_\theta}{r}\right) - \rho\frac{1}{r}\frac{\partial \psi}{\partial \theta}$$

$$+ (\rho_e E_\theta + J_z B_r - J_r B_z)$$

$$\rho\frac{Dv_z}{Dt} = -\frac{\partial P}{\partial z} + \frac{\partial}{\partial z}\left[2\mu_f\frac{\partial v_z}{\partial z} + (\zeta - \tfrac{2}{3}\mu_f)\,\mathbf{\nabla}\cdot\mathbf{V}\right]$$

$$+ \frac{1}{r}\frac{\partial}{\partial r}\left[\mu_f r\left(\frac{\partial v_r}{\partial z} + \frac{\partial v_z}{\partial r}\right)\right] + \frac{1}{r}\frac{\partial}{\partial \theta}\left[\mu_f\left(\frac{1}{r}\frac{\partial v_z}{\partial \theta} + \frac{\partial v_\theta}{\partial z}\right)\right]$$

$$- \rho\frac{\partial \psi}{\partial z} + (\rho_e E_z + J_r B_\theta - J_\theta B_r)$$

$$\frac{D}{Dt} = \frac{\partial}{\partial t} + v_r\frac{\partial}{\partial r} + \frac{v_\theta}{r}\frac{\partial}{\partial \theta} + v_z\frac{\partial}{\partial z}$$

$$\mathbf{\nabla}\cdot\mathbf{V} = \frac{1}{r}\frac{\partial}{\partial r}(rv_r) + \frac{1}{r}\frac{\partial v_\theta}{\partial \theta} + \frac{\partial v_z}{\partial z} \tag{4.6-2}$$

Spherical Coordinates

$$\rho\left(\frac{Dv_r}{Dt} - \frac{v_\theta^2 + v_r^2}{r}\right) = -\frac{\partial P}{\partial r} + \frac{\partial}{\partial r}\left[2\mu_f\frac{\partial v_r}{\partial r} + (\zeta - \tfrac{2}{3}\mu_f)\,\mathbf{\nabla}\cdot\mathbf{V}\right]$$

$$+ \frac{1}{r}\frac{\partial}{\partial \theta}\left\{\mu_f\left[r\frac{\partial}{\partial r}\left(\frac{v_\theta}{r}\right) + \frac{1}{r}\frac{\partial v_r}{\partial \theta}\right]\right\}$$

$$+ \frac{1}{r\sin\theta}\frac{\partial}{\partial \varphi}\left\{\mu_f\left[\frac{1}{r\sin\theta}\frac{\partial v_r}{\partial \varphi} + r\frac{\partial}{\partial r}\left(\frac{v_\varphi}{r}\right)\right]\right\}$$

$$+ \frac{\mu_f}{r}\left[4\frac{\partial v_r}{\partial r} - \frac{2}{r}\frac{\partial v_\theta}{\partial \theta} - \frac{4v_r}{r} - \frac{2}{r\sin\theta}\cdot\frac{\partial v_\varphi}{\partial \varphi}\right.$$

$$\left. - \frac{2v_\theta\cot\theta}{r} + r\cot\theta\frac{\partial}{\partial r}\left(\frac{v_\theta}{r}\right) + \frac{\cot\theta}{r}\frac{\partial v_r}{\partial \theta}\right]$$

$$- \rho\frac{\partial \psi}{\partial r} + (\rho_e E_r + J_\theta B_\varphi - J_\varphi B_\theta)$$

$$\rho\left(\frac{Dv_\theta}{Dt} + \frac{v_r v_\theta}{r} - \frac{v_\varphi^2 \cot\theta}{r}\right)$$

$$= -\frac{1}{r}\frac{\partial P}{\partial\theta} + \frac{1}{r}\frac{\partial}{\partial\theta}\left[\frac{2\mu_f}{r}\frac{\partial v_\theta}{\partial\theta} + \frac{2}{r}\mu_f v_r + (\zeta - \tfrac{2}{3}\mu_f)\,\mathbf{\nabla\cdot V}\right]$$

$$+ \frac{1}{r\sin\theta}\frac{\partial}{\partial\varphi}\left\{\mu_f\left[\frac{\sin\theta}{r}\frac{\partial}{\partial\theta}\left(\frac{v_\varphi}{\sin\theta}\right) + \frac{1}{r\sin\theta}\frac{\partial v_\theta}{\partial\varphi}\right]\right\}$$

$$+ \frac{\partial}{\partial r}\left\{\mu_f\left[r\frac{\partial}{\partial r}\left(\frac{v_\theta}{r}\right) + \frac{1}{r}\frac{\partial v_r}{\partial\theta}\right]\right\}$$

$$+ \frac{\mu_f}{r}\left\{2\left(\frac{1}{r}\frac{\partial v_\theta}{\partial\theta} - \frac{1}{r\sin\theta}\frac{\partial v_\varphi}{\partial\varphi} - \frac{v_\theta\cot\theta}{r}\right)\cdot\cot\theta\right.$$

$$\left. + 3\left[r\frac{\partial}{\partial r}\left(\frac{v_\theta}{r}\right) + \frac{1}{r}\frac{\partial v_r}{\partial\theta}\right]\right\} - \rho\frac{1}{r}\frac{\partial\psi}{\partial\theta} + (\rho_e E_\theta + J_\varphi B_r - J_r B_\varphi)$$

$$\rho\left(\frac{Dv_\varphi}{Dt} + \frac{v_\varphi v_r}{r} + \frac{v_\theta v_\varphi\cot\theta}{r}\right)$$

$$= -\frac{1}{r\sin\theta}\frac{\partial P}{\partial\varphi} + \frac{1}{r\sin\theta}\frac{\partial}{\partial\varphi}$$

$$\times\left[\frac{2\mu_f}{r\sin\theta}\frac{\partial v_\varphi}{\partial\varphi} + \frac{2\mu_f v_r}{r} + \frac{2\mu_f v_\theta}{r}\cot\theta + (\zeta - \tfrac{2}{3}\mu_f)\,\mathbf{\nabla\cdot V}\right]$$

$$+ \frac{\partial}{\partial r}\left\{\mu_f\left[\frac{1}{r\sin\theta}\frac{\partial v_r}{\partial\varphi} + r\frac{\partial}{\partial r}\left(\frac{v_\varphi}{r}\right)\right]\right\}$$

$$+ \frac{1}{r}\frac{\partial}{\partial\theta}\left\{\mu_f\left[\frac{\sin\theta}{r}\frac{\partial}{\partial\theta}\left(\frac{v_\varphi}{\sin\theta}\right) + \frac{1}{r\sin\theta}\frac{\partial v_\theta}{\partial\varphi}\right]\right\}$$

$$+ \frac{\mu_f}{r}\left\{3\left[\frac{1}{r\sin\theta}\frac{\partial v_r}{\partial\varphi} + r\frac{\partial}{\partial r}\left(\frac{v_\varphi}{r}\right)\right]\right.$$

$$\left. + 2\cot\theta\left[\frac{\sin\theta}{r}\frac{\partial}{\partial\theta}\left(\frac{v_\varphi}{\sin\theta}\right) + \frac{1}{r\sin\theta}\frac{\partial v_\theta}{\partial\varphi}\right]\right\}$$

$$- \rho\frac{1}{r\sin\theta}\frac{\partial\psi}{\partial\varphi} + (\rho_e E_\varphi + J_r B_\theta - J_\theta B_r)$$

$$\frac{D}{Dt} = \frac{\partial}{\partial t} + v_r\frac{\partial}{\partial r} + \frac{v_\theta}{r}\frac{\partial}{\partial\theta} + \frac{v_\varphi}{\sin\theta}\frac{\partial}{\partial\varphi}$$

$$\mathbf{\nabla\cdot V} = \frac{1}{r^2}\frac{\partial}{\partial r}(r^2 v_r) + \frac{1}{r\sin\theta}\frac{\partial}{\partial\theta}(v_\theta\sin\theta) + \frac{1}{r\sin\theta}\frac{\partial v_\varphi}{\partial\varphi} \qquad (4.6\text{-}3)$$

Incompressible Fluid (viscosity assumed quasi-constant)

Vector

$$\rho\left[\frac{\partial \mathbf{V}}{\partial t} + (\mathbf{V} \cdot \nabla)\mathbf{V}\right] = -\nabla P + \mu_f \nabla^2 \mathbf{V} - \rho \nabla \psi + \rho_e \mathbf{E} + \mathbf{J} \times \mathbf{B} \quad (4.6\text{-}4)$$

Cartesian Coordinates

$$\rho\left(\frac{\partial u}{\partial t} + u\frac{\partial u}{\partial x} + v\frac{\partial u}{\partial y} + w\frac{\partial u}{\partial z}\right)$$

$$= -\frac{\partial P}{\partial x} + \mu_f\left(\frac{\partial^2 u}{\partial x^2} + \frac{\partial^2 u}{\partial y^2} + \frac{\partial^2 u}{\partial z^2}\right) - \rho\frac{\partial \psi}{\partial x} + \rho_e E_x + J_y B_z - J_z B_y$$

$$\rho\left(\frac{\partial v}{\partial t} + u\frac{\partial v}{\partial x} + v\frac{\partial v}{\partial y} + w\frac{\partial v}{\partial z}\right)$$

$$= -\frac{\partial P}{\partial y} + \mu_f\left(\frac{\partial^2 v}{\partial x^2} + \frac{\partial^2 v}{\partial y^2} + \frac{\partial^2 v}{\partial z^2}\right) - \rho\frac{\partial \psi}{\partial y} + \rho_e E_y + J_z B_x - J_x B_z$$

$$\rho\left(\frac{\partial w}{\partial t} + u\frac{\partial w}{\partial x} + v\frac{\partial w}{\partial y} + w\frac{\partial w}{\partial z}\right)$$

$$= -\frac{\partial P}{\partial z} + \mu_f\left(\frac{\partial^2 w}{\partial x^2} + \frac{\partial^2 w}{\partial y^2} + \frac{\partial^2 w}{\partial z^2}\right) - \rho\frac{\partial \psi}{\partial z} + \rho_e E_z + J_x B_y - J_y B_x$$

$$(4.6\text{-}5)$$

Cylindrical Coordinates

$$\rho\left(\frac{\partial v_r}{\partial t} + v_r\frac{\partial v_r}{\partial r} + \frac{v_\theta}{r}\frac{\partial v_r}{\partial \theta} + v_z\frac{\partial v_r}{\partial z} - \frac{v_\theta^2}{r}\right)$$

$$= -\frac{\partial P}{\partial r} + \mu_f\left(\frac{\partial^2 v_r}{\partial r^2} + \frac{1}{r}\frac{\partial v_r}{\partial r} + \frac{1}{r^2}\frac{\partial^2 v_r}{\partial \theta^2} + \frac{\partial^2 v_r}{\partial z^2} - \frac{v_r}{r^2} - \frac{2}{r^2}\frac{\partial v_\theta}{\partial \theta}\right)$$

$$- \rho\frac{\partial \psi}{\partial r} + \rho_e E_r + J_\theta B_z - J_z B_\theta$$

$$\rho\left(\frac{\partial v_\theta}{\partial t} + v_r\frac{\partial v_\theta}{\partial r} + \frac{v_\theta}{r}\frac{\partial v_\theta}{\partial \theta} + v_z\frac{\partial v_\theta}{\partial z} + \frac{v_r v_\theta}{r}\right)$$

$$= -\frac{1}{r}\frac{\partial P}{\partial \theta} + \mu_f\left(\frac{\partial^2 v_\theta}{\partial r^2} + \frac{1}{r}\frac{\partial v_\theta}{\partial r} + \frac{1}{r^2}\frac{\partial^2 v_\theta}{\partial \theta^2} + \frac{2}{r^2}\frac{\partial v_r}{\partial \theta} - \frac{v_\theta}{r^2} + \frac{\partial^2 v_\theta}{\partial z^2}\right)$$

$$- \frac{\rho}{r}\frac{\partial \psi}{\partial \theta} + \rho_e E_\theta + J_z B_r - J_r B_z$$

$$\rho\left(\frac{\partial v_z}{\partial t} + v_r\frac{\partial v_z}{\partial r} + \frac{v_\theta}{r}\frac{\partial v_z}{\partial \theta} + v_z\frac{\partial v_z}{\partial z}\right)$$

$$= -\frac{\partial P}{\partial z} + \mu_f\left(\frac{\partial^2 v_z}{\partial r^2} + \frac{1}{r}\frac{\partial v_z}{\partial r} + \frac{1}{r^2}\frac{\partial^2 v_z}{\partial \theta^2} + \frac{\partial^2 v_z}{\partial z^2}\right)$$

$$- \rho\frac{\partial \psi}{\partial z} + \rho_e E_z + J_r B_\theta - J_\theta B_r \qquad (4.6\text{-}6)$$

Spherical Coordinates

$$\rho\left(\frac{\partial v_r}{\partial t} + v_r\frac{\partial v_r}{\partial r} + \frac{v_\theta}{r}\frac{\partial v_r}{\partial r} + \frac{v_\varphi}{r\sin\theta}\frac{\partial v_r}{\partial \varphi} - \frac{v_\theta{}^2 + v_\varphi{}^2}{r}\right)$$

$$= -\frac{\partial P}{\partial r} + \mu_f\left[\frac{1}{r^2}\frac{\partial}{\partial r}\left(r^2\frac{\partial v_r}{\partial r}\right) + \frac{1}{r^2\sin\theta}\frac{\partial}{\partial \theta}\left(\sin\theta\frac{\partial v_r}{\partial \theta}\right)\right.$$

$$\left. + \frac{1}{r^2\sin^2\theta}\frac{\partial^2 v_r}{\partial \varphi^2} - \frac{2v_r}{r^2} - \frac{2}{r^2}\frac{\partial v_\theta}{\partial \theta} - \frac{2v_\theta\cot\theta}{r^2} - \frac{2}{r^2\sin\theta}\frac{\partial v_\varphi}{\partial \varphi}\right]$$

$$- \rho\frac{\partial \psi}{\partial r} + \rho_e E_r + J_\theta B_\varphi - J_\varphi B_\theta \quad ,$$

$$\rho\left(\frac{\partial v_\theta}{\partial t} + v_r\frac{\partial v_\theta}{\partial r} + \frac{v_\theta}{r}\frac{\partial v_\theta}{\partial \theta} + \frac{v_\varphi}{r\sin\theta}\frac{\partial v_\theta}{\partial \varphi} + \frac{v_r v_\theta - v_\varphi{}^2\cot\theta}{r}\right)$$

$$= -\frac{1}{r}\frac{\partial P}{\partial \theta} + \mu_f\left[\frac{1}{r^2}\frac{\partial}{\partial r}\left(r^2\frac{\partial v_\theta}{\partial r}\right) + \frac{1}{r^2\sin\theta}\frac{\partial}{\partial \theta}\left(\sin\theta\cdot\frac{\partial v_\theta}{\partial r}\right)\right.$$

$$\left. + \frac{1}{r^2\sin^2\theta}\frac{\partial^2 v_\theta}{\partial \varphi^2} + \frac{2}{r^2}\frac{\partial v_r}{\partial \theta} - \frac{v_\theta}{r^2\sin^2\theta} - \frac{2\cos\theta}{r^2\sin^2\theta}\frac{\partial v_\varphi}{\partial \varphi}\right]$$

$$- \frac{\rho}{r}\frac{\partial \psi}{\partial \theta} + \rho_e E_\theta + J_\varphi B_r - J_r B_\varphi$$

$$\rho\left(\frac{\partial v_\varphi}{\partial t} + v_r\frac{\partial v_\varphi}{\partial r} + \frac{v_\theta}{r}\frac{\partial v_\varphi}{\partial \theta} + \frac{v_\varphi}{r\sin\theta}\frac{\partial v_\varphi}{\partial \varphi} + \frac{v_\varphi v_r + v_\theta v_\varphi\cot\theta}{r}\right)$$

$$= -\frac{1}{r\sin\theta}\frac{\partial P}{\partial \varphi} + \mu_f\left[\frac{1}{r^2}\frac{\partial}{\partial r}\left(r^2\frac{\partial v_\varphi}{\partial r}\right) + \frac{1}{r^2\sin\theta}\frac{\partial}{\partial \theta}\left(\sin\theta\frac{\partial v_\varphi}{\partial \theta}\right)\right.$$

$$+ \frac{1}{r^2\sin^2\theta}\frac{\partial^2 v_\varphi}{\partial \varphi^2} - \frac{v_\varphi}{r^2\sin^2\theta} + \frac{2}{r^2\sin^2\theta}\frac{\partial v_r}{\partial \varphi}$$

$$\left. + \frac{2\cos\theta}{r^2\sin^2\theta}\cdot\frac{\partial v_\theta}{\partial \varphi}\right] - \frac{\rho}{r\sin\theta}\frac{\partial \psi}{\partial \varphi} + \rho_e E_\varphi + J_r B_\theta - J_\theta B_r \qquad (4.6\text{-}7)$$

4.7 STRAIN RATE TENSOR AND STRESS TENSOR RELATIONSHIPS FOR REFERENCE

The deformation rate tensor is written (in cartesian tensor notation) as $\partial V_i/\partial x_j$, where V_i is the velocity. The symmetric part of the deformation rate tensor is the strain rate tensor, and the antisymmetric part is the rotation tensor. If we denote the strain rate tensor as e_{ij} and the rotation tensor as ω_{ij}, the deformation rate tensor is $e_{ij} + \omega_{ij}$.

The rotation tensor can be related to the angular velocity Ω_j of an infinitesimal fluid element as: $\Omega_1 = \omega_{32}$, $\Omega_2 = \omega_{13}$, $\Omega_3 = \omega_{21}$.

In terms of velocity, then,

$$e_{ij} = e_{ji} = \tfrac{1}{2}\left(\frac{\partial V_i}{\partial x_j} + \frac{\partial V_j}{\partial x_i}\right) \tag{4.7-1}$$

$$\omega_{ij} = -\omega_{ji} = \tfrac{1}{2}\left(\frac{\partial V_i}{\partial x_j} - \frac{\partial V_j}{\partial x_i}\right) \tag{4.7-2}$$

The stress tensor τ_{ij}, which can be written $\tau_{ij} = -P\delta_{ij} + \tau'_{ij}$ (where τ'_{ij} is the viscous stress tensor), can be related to the deformation rate tensor in a homogeneous isotropic fluid by Equation (4.7-3). Here μ_f is the viscosity. Two definitions of the second coefficient of viscosity are in common use: λ is defined as $-\tfrac{2}{3}\mu_f$ for a monatomic gas, and ζ is defined as zero for a monatomic gas. Hence $\zeta = \lambda + \tfrac{2}{3}\mu_f$. τ'_{ij}, the viscous stress tensor, may include normal components if λ is not zero.

$$\begin{aligned}
\tau_{ij} &= -P\delta_{ij} + \tau'_{ij} = -P\delta_{ij} + 2\mu_f e_{ij} + \delta_{ij}\lambda\theta \\[4pt]
&= -P\delta_{ij} + \mu_f\left(\frac{\partial V_i}{\partial x_j} + \frac{\partial V_j}{\partial x_i}\right) + \lambda\delta_{ij}\frac{\partial V_k}{\partial x_k} \\[4pt]
&= -P\delta_{ij} + \mu_f\left(\frac{\partial V_i}{\partial x_j} + \frac{\partial V_j}{\partial x_i} - \frac{2}{3}\delta_{ij}\frac{\partial V_k}{\partial x_k}\right) + \zeta\delta_{ij}\frac{\partial V_k}{\partial x_k}
\end{aligned} \tag{4.7-3}$$

θ is the dilatation $\partial V_i/\partial x_i$ and is equal to the trace of the strain rate tensor.

REFERENCES

Aris, R., *Vectors, Tensors, and the Basic Equations of Fluid Mechanics*, Prentice-Hall, Englewood Cliffs, New Jersey, 1962.

Cowling, T. G., *Magnetohydrodynamics*, Interscience, New York, 1957.

Eringen, A. C., *Nonlinear Theory of Continuous Media*, McGraw-Hill, New York, 1962.

Ferraro, V. C. A., and C. Plumpton, *An Introduction to Magneto-Fluid Mechanics*, Oxford University Press, 1961.

Goldstein, S., *Modern Developments in Fluid Dynamics*, Vols. I and II, Oxford University Press, 1938.

Hughes, W. F., and E. W. Gaylord, *Basic Equations of Engineering Science*, Schaum Publishing Co., New York, 1964.

Lamb, H., *Hydrodynamics*, 6th ed., Cambridge University Press, 1932; Dover Publications, New York.

Landau, L. D., and E. M. Lifshitz, *Fluid Mechanics*, Addison-Wesley, Reading Mass., 1959.

Landau, L. D., and E. M. Lifshitz, *Electrodynamics of Continuous Media*, Addison-Wesley, Reading, Mass., 1960.

Pai, S. I., *Viscous Flow Theory*, Vols. I and II, Van Nostrand, New York, 1956.

Schlichting, H., *Boundary Layer Theory*, McGraw-Hill, New York, 1955.

Sommerfeld, A., *Mechanics of Deformable Media*, Academic Press, New York, 1950.

Thompson, W. B., *An Introduction to Plasma Physics*, Addison-Wesley, Reading, Mass., 1962.

5

The Fluid Equations—
Energy and Thermodynamics

5.1 INTRODUCTION

The coupling of the electromagnetic and mechanical effects into an energy equation is no easy task. An exact energy relationship involving only electromagnetic field quantities can be derived from Maxwell's equations. This relationship, known as Poynting's theorem, has been discussed in detail in Chapter 2 and will play an important part now as we turn to the development of the thermodynamics of conducting fluids in the presence of electromagnetic fields.

We know that many properties of material media are functions of the magnetic and electric fields. Specific heats and thermal conductivity are of primary concern here. Similarly, electromagnetic parameters such as permeability and permittivity may depend on temperature, pressure, etc. This secondary coupling of the equations can become rather complex.

Another type of secondary coupling, which has been extensively treated by the methods of irreversible thermodynamics, is the so-called effects of "coupled irreversibilities." Any potential gradient (electromagnetic, force, temperature, etc.) can give rise to fluxes that are associated not only with that particular gradient but with other potential gradients as well. A temperature gradient, for example, may give rise not only to a heat flux but also to an electrical current. A complete formulation of these coupled effects can be achieved for small departures from thermodynamic equilibrium by linearizing the equations coupling the forces and fluxes. The reciprocal theorem of Onsager makes possible the formulation of a fairly complete theory. We will not pursue this subject, however, since these irreversible coupling effects are usually negligible compared to the primary couplings of concern in MHD or plasma dynamics. The theory of irreversible thermodynamics has been extensively developed (including electromagnetic effects) by De Groot, Prigogine et al.

Before discussing the energy equation, one more point should be mentioned. This section is concerned with processes that are essentially nonrelativistic, that is, $|\mathbf{V}|^2/c^2 \ll 1$, and it begins with the classical equations of thermodynamics and fluid motion. However, a completely relativistic treatment can be made. We know that Maxwell's equations are covariant and hence any proper treatment of electromagnetic theory must be done in a relativistic fashion. The analysis in this book is based on that fact, although we often make low-speed approximations and avoid using four-dimensional notation. Since the Lorentz transformations for the electromagnetic field quantities are important even at low velocities (compared to light), a completely four-dimensional analysis is aesthetically pleasing. If we think of the electromagnetic field and fluid as forming a coupled system, we can express both the equation of motion and the energy equation in a single four-dimensional equation. This formulation, requiring the establishment of the energy-momentum tensor for a system of fluid and field quantities, is discussed in Appendix 2. There are unsettled questions concerning the correct form of this tensor, but under certain assumptions, which cover most problems in MHD, a consistent formulation, giving the proper equations for extremely high-speed relativistic flow, can be developed. (The references at the end of this chapter list some recent work on the relativistic approach to thermodynamics.)

5.2 THERMODYNAMICS OF INCOMPRESSIBLE FLUIDS

Before we discuss the thermodynamics of a general compressible fluid in the presence of an electromagnetic field, some useful results can be obtained if we confine ourselves to a fixed unit volume enclosing a fixed amount of fluid. We will be concerned then with a system of mass ρ which does not change volume and which does not undergo translation and we will be working in the rest frame of the fluid.

Poynting's theorem is the starting point for any thermodynamical analysis. In any frame of reference the theorem may be written for a *unit volume* as

$$-\nabla \cdot (\mathbf{E} \times \mathbf{H}) = \mathbf{E} \cdot \mathbf{J} + \mathbf{E} \cdot \frac{\partial \mathbf{D}}{\partial t} + \mathbf{H} \cdot \frac{\partial \mathbf{B}}{\partial t} \qquad (5.2\text{-}1)$$

which is a general relationship among electromagnetic field quantities and holds regardless of the process involved. Various thermodynamical interpretations are given to the terms in this equation. The left-hand term $-\nabla \cdot (\mathbf{E} \times \mathbf{H})$ is a flux into the unit control volume. Sometimes this flux is referred to as energy flux, but from a thermodynamical standpoint the idea of energy flux is not very satisfactory. It would be perhaps better to call this term a flux of work or heat, since at least part of this Poynting flux may represent heat. Indeed, the concept of radiation heat and the Stefan-Boltzmann law and the Wien displacement law may be based on a classical electromagnetic development.

The right-hand side of Equation (5.2-1), therefore, must represent a conversion of the heat or work or show how it is distributed between reversible work and irreversible dissipation. If the Poynting theorem is written in the rest frame the following interpretation can be given: $-\nabla' \cdot (\mathbf{E}' \times \mathbf{H}')$ is the flux term (into the control volume). The $\mathbf{E}' \cdot \mathbf{J}'$ term is the rate of Joulean dissipation (irreversible work done on the material media in the control volume). $\mathbf{E}' \cdot (\partial \mathbf{D}'/\partial t') + \mathbf{H}' \cdot (\partial \mathbf{B}'/\partial t')$ must be (in a linear incompressible media) the rate at which reversible work is done by the fields setting themselves up within the volume. If the medium is nonlinear, hysteresis losses, representing internal dissipation in the material, can occur in time-varying processes. If the material is lossy, the term $\mathbf{E}' \cdot (\partial \mathbf{D}'/\partial t') + \mathbf{H}' \cdot (\partial \mathbf{B}'/\partial t')$ must represent not only the reversible work but the hysteresis losses as well. The form of these losses in terms of complex permeability and permittivity is discussed in Section 5.9.

In the general frame of reference (laboratory frame), $-\nabla \cdot (\mathbf{E} \times \mathbf{H})$ is, again, the flux of work or heat. The right-hand terms are now somewhat different, however. In linear, homogeneous material the following interpretation can be given if the medium is incompressible so that striction effects can be neglected. The term $\mathbf{E} \cdot \mathbf{J}$ is exactly equal to $\mathbf{E}' \cdot \mathbf{J}'$, the rate of Joulean dissipation, plus an additional term

$$\mathbf{V} \cdot (\rho_e \mathbf{E} + \mathbf{J} \times \mathbf{B}),$$

which is precisely the rate at which work is done by the fields in translating the fluid through the control volume. (If the fluid were inhomogeneous, or striction effects were present, this last term would not fully account for this work.) $\mathbf{E} \cdot (\partial \mathbf{D}/\partial t) + \mathbf{H} \cdot (\partial \mathbf{B}/\partial t)$ is the rate then at which reversible work is done by the fields if the medium is linear so that there are no hysteresis losses. If the material is nonlinear, or is inhomogeneous, or if striction effects are present, $\mathbf{E}' \cdot \mathbf{J}'$ is still the Joulean dissipation rate, but $\mathbf{E} \cdot (\partial \mathbf{D}/\partial t) + \mathbf{H} \cdot (\partial \mathbf{B}/\partial t)$ must also include the work done by the additional body forces (due to inhomogeneities and striction) and the irreversible losses.

We see then that only in certain simple cases can the conventional interpretation be given to the terms in the Poynting theorem. To recapitulate, $-\nabla \cdot (\mathbf{E} \times \mathbf{H})$ *in any frame of reference* is the flux of heat and work. (The fact that this term is a covariant expression follows directly from the Poynting theorem, as will be discussed in Appendix 2.) $\mathbf{E}' \cdot \mathbf{J}'$ is always the Joulean dissipation rate (regardless of the form of Ohm's law). $\mathbf{E} \cdot \mathbf{J}$ is the Joulean dissipation rate plus the rate at which the forces $\rho_e \mathbf{E} + \mathbf{J} \times \mathbf{B}$ do work; $\mathbf{E} \cdot (\partial \mathbf{D}/\partial t) + \mathbf{H} \cdot (\partial \mathbf{B}/\partial t)$ is the rate of reversible work done by the fields (and rate of translation work done by striction forces and forces due to inhomogeneities in the fields) plus the irreversible dissipation rate due to losses in the material. In the rest frame, $\mathbf{E}' \cdot (\partial \mathbf{D}'/\partial t') + \mathbf{H}' \cdot (\partial \mathbf{B}'/\partial t')$ is the rate of reversible work plus losses.

If we confine ourselves to the *rest frame*, certain thermodynamic relationships can be written immediately. Remember, we are still working with an incompressible fluid so that the system of mass ρ occupies and remains fixed in the unit control volume. Hence $\mathbf{E}' \cdot \mathbf{J}'$ is the rate of Joulean dissipation (or irreversible work) and $\mathbf{E}' \cdot (\partial \mathbf{D}'/\partial t') + \mathbf{H}' \cdot (\partial \mathbf{B}'/\partial t')$ is the rate at which the fields do reversible work. We will confine ourselves to a *linear medium*, although ϵ and μ may be functions of ρ and the temperature T. The following thermodynamic relationships can then be written, where the subscript T denotes total thermodynamic properties, including mechanical and electromagnetic effects. A property without a subscript denotes a purely mechanical property; a subscript e denotes a property associated with the electromagnetic field; U, F, and s are the specific (per unit mass) internal energy, Helmholtz free energy, and entropy, respectively; and W_r is the reversible work done per unit mass on the fluid medium. The basic relationships are:

$$dU_T = T\, ds_T + dW_r \tag{5.2-2}$$

$$dF_T = -s_T\, dT + dW_r \tag{5.2-3}$$

$$F_T = U_T - Ts_T \tag{5.2-4}$$

The reversible work rate for an incompressible fluid per unit mass is given by

$$\frac{\partial W'_r}{\partial t'} = \left(\mathbf{E}' \cdot \frac{\partial \mathbf{D}'}{\partial t'} + \mathbf{H}' \cdot \frac{\partial \mathbf{B}'}{\partial t'}\right)\frac{1}{\rho} \tag{5.2-5}$$

for linear media. Hence we can write for unit volume

$$\rho\, dU'_T = \rho T\, ds'_T + \mathbf{E}' \cdot d\mathbf{D}' + \mathbf{H}' \cdot d\mathbf{B}' \tag{5.2-6}$$

$$\rho\, dF'_T = -\rho s'_T\, dT + \mathbf{E}' \cdot d\mathbf{D}' + \mathbf{H}' \cdot d\mathbf{B}' \tag{5.2-7}$$

We are still working in the rest frame, in order that integration may be performed later (hence the primes), and all properties include electrical as well as mechanical effects (hence the subscript T). From (5.2-6) and (5.2-7)

$$\mathbf{E}' = \rho\left(\frac{\partial U'_T}{\partial \mathbf{D}'}\right)_{s'_T, \rho, \mathbf{B}'} = \rho\left(\frac{\partial F'_T}{\partial \mathbf{D}'}\right)_{T, \rho, \mathbf{B}'} \qquad (5.2\text{-}8)$$

$$\mathbf{H}' = \rho\left(\frac{\partial U'_T}{\partial \mathbf{B}'}\right)_{s'_T, \rho, \mathbf{D}'} = \rho\left(\frac{\partial F'_T}{\partial \mathbf{B}'}\right)_{T, \rho, \mathbf{D}'} \qquad (5.2\text{-}9)$$

$$s'_T = -\left(\frac{\partial F'_T}{\partial T}\right)_{\rho, \mathbf{D}', \mathbf{B}'} \qquad (5.2\text{-}10)$$

By integrating the above three equations, we obtain explicit expressions for the internal energy, free energy, and entropy. In order to perform this integration, we must be in the rest frame so that the constitutive equations can be written in the following form:

$$\mathbf{D}' = \epsilon(\rho, T)\mathbf{E}' \qquad \mathbf{B}' = \mu(\rho, T)\mathbf{H}' \qquad (5.2\text{-}11)$$

It is assumed that the material is linear and isotropic so that ϵ and μ depend only on density ρ and temperature T. There results the following:

$$U'_T = U'_0(s'_T, \rho) + \frac{D'^2}{2\epsilon\rho} + \frac{B'^2}{2\mu\rho} \qquad (5.2\text{-}12)$$

$$F'_T = F'(T, \rho) + \frac{D'^2}{2\epsilon\rho} + \frac{B'^2}{2\mu\rho} \qquad (5.2\text{-}13)$$

$$s'_T = s'(T, \rho) + \frac{E'^2}{2\rho}\left(\frac{\partial\epsilon}{\partial T}\right)_\rho + \frac{H'^2}{2\rho}\left(\frac{\partial\mu}{\partial T}\right)_\rho \qquad (5.2\text{-}14)$$

$F'(T, \rho)$ and $s'(T, \rho)$ depend only on the mechanical quantities T and ρ. However, U'_0 depends on s'_T but can be evaluated in terms of F' from Equation (5.2-4). We thus obtain the following expression for the internal energy:

$$U'_T = U'(T, \rho) + \frac{D'^2}{2\epsilon\rho} + \frac{B'^2}{2\mu\rho} + \frac{TE'^2}{2\rho}\left(\frac{\partial\epsilon}{\partial T}\right)_\rho + \frac{TH'^2}{2\rho}\left(\frac{\partial\mu}{\partial T}\right)_\rho \quad (5.2\text{-}15)$$

The primes may be dropped from F', s' and U' since they are functions of mechanical properties which are the same in any frame of reference to the nonrelativistic approximation. It follows then that the specific enthalpy h'_T can be written as

$$h'_T = h'(T, \rho) + U'_e + P'_e\left(\frac{1}{\rho}\right) = h(T, \rho) + \frac{1}{\rho}\left[\frac{D'^2}{\epsilon}\left(1 + \frac{T}{2\epsilon}\frac{\partial\epsilon}{\partial T}\right.\right.$$
$$\left.\left. - \frac{\rho}{2\epsilon}\frac{\partial\epsilon}{\partial\rho}\right) + \frac{B'^2}{\mu}\left(1 + \frac{T}{2\mu}\frac{\partial\mu}{\partial T} - \frac{\rho}{2\mu}\frac{\partial\mu}{\partial\rho}\right)\right] \quad (5.2\text{-}16)$$

5.3   THERMODYNAMICS OF COMPRESSIBLE FLUIDS

Let us continue our discussion by examining compressible media in the rest frame. In the last section we obtained explicit expressions for the internal energy, entropy, and free energy. These expressions were obtained on a unit mass basis, and are properties of the fluid. Hence, they should be valid for compressible fluids as well. In fact equations (5.2-8) through (5.2-16) are still valid for compressible fluids. It is when we take differentials of the properties that we must be careful to include density variations. In order to complete the formulation of the thermodynamics for a system of unit mass of compressible fluid, it is necessary to obtain an expression for the reversible work done on unit mass of the fluid. We can obtain an expression for this reversible work in the following manner.

Equation (5.2-5) which is valid for unit mass of incompressible fluid (hence unit volume) must be modified to include the work of distortion done by the total stress tensor, and to account for the fact that the reversible work done in setting up the electromagnetic fields (as given by Equation [5.2-5]) must be modified to include the dilatation effect. The reversible work of distortion is the work done by the total pressure as the fluid mass contracts or expands (that is, dilatation work). The total stress tensor must include the mechanical stresses plus the electromagnetic stresses (since the sum of these two stresses enters into the dynamical equations). The total pressure P'_T can then be written as

$$P'_T = P + P'_e = P + \frac{\mathbf{E}' \cdot \mathbf{D}'}{2} + \frac{\mathbf{H}' \cdot \mathbf{B}'}{2} - \rho \frac{E'^2}{2}\left(\frac{\partial \epsilon}{\partial \rho}\right)_T - \rho \frac{H'^2}{2}\left(\frac{\partial \mu}{\partial \rho}\right)_T$$

$$(5.3-1)$$

in the rest frame of the fluid. (The rest frame is taken as a frame attached to the center of mass of the unit mass as it undergoes distortion.) Here P is the actual mechanical pressure (that enters into the gas law). $(\mathbf{E}' \cdot \mathbf{D}'/2) + (\mathbf{H}' \cdot \mathbf{B}'/2)$ is the ordinary electromagnetic pressure, and

$$-\left[\rho \frac{E'^2}{2}\left(\frac{\partial \epsilon}{\partial \rho}\right)_T + \rho \frac{H'^2}{2}\left(\frac{\partial \mu}{\partial \rho}\right)_T\right]$$

are the striction terms.

In order to determine the reversible work dW_r (accompanying a change of state), we must correct Equation (5.2-5) to account for dilatation. Let us look at Equation (5.2-3): $dF_T = -s_T\,dT + dW_r$. This is a general equation, valid for unit mass, and since we know the specific free energy and specific entropy, the differentials can be formed from Equations

(5.2-13) and (5.2-14) and the expression for the reversible work immediately obtained. When we take the derivatives, we must include density variations. Thus

$$s'_T dT = \left[s(T, \rho) + \frac{E'^2}{2\rho}\left(\frac{\partial \epsilon}{\partial T}\right)_\rho + \frac{H'^2}{2\rho}\left(\frac{\partial \mu}{\partial T}\right)_\rho \right] dT \qquad (5.3-2)$$

$$dF'_T = dF(T, \rho) - \frac{E'^2}{2\rho}\left(\frac{\partial \epsilon}{\partial T}\right)_\rho dT - \frac{H'^2}{2\rho}\left(\frac{\partial \mu}{\partial T}\right)_\rho dT + \frac{E'}{\rho} \cdot d\mathbf{D}'$$

$$+ \frac{\mathbf{H}'}{\rho} \cdot d\mathbf{B}' + \frac{\mathbf{E}' \cdot \mathbf{D}'}{2} d\left(\frac{1}{\rho}\right) + \frac{\mathbf{H}' \cdot \mathbf{B}'}{2} d\left(\frac{1}{\rho}\right) \qquad (5.3-3)$$

$$+ \rho \frac{E'^2}{2}\left(\frac{\partial \epsilon}{\partial \rho}\right)_T d\left(\frac{1}{\rho}\right) + \frac{\rho H'^2}{2}\left(\frac{\partial \mu}{\partial \rho}\right)_T d\left(\frac{1}{\rho}\right)$$

Combining the last two equations produces

$$dW'_r = dF + s\, dT - P'_e\, d\left(\frac{1}{\rho}\right) + \mathbf{E}' \cdot d\left(\frac{\mathbf{D}'}{\rho}\right) + \mathbf{H}' \cdot d\left(\frac{\mathbf{B}'}{\rho}\right) \qquad (5.3-4)$$

which is a general equation for the reversible work done per unit mass of compressible fluid.

The electromagnetic pressure P'_e is given by

$$P'_e = -\rho \frac{E'^2}{2}\left(\frac{\partial \epsilon}{\partial \rho}\right)_T - \frac{\rho H'^2}{2}\left(\frac{\partial \mu}{\partial \rho}\right)_T + \frac{\mathbf{E}' \cdot \mathbf{D}'}{2} + \frac{\mathbf{H}' \cdot \mathbf{B}'}{2} \qquad (5.3-5)$$

Now, $dF + s\, dT$ includes only mechanical quantities and hence must simply be $-Pd(1/\rho)$ where P is the mechanical pressure. Finally, then, we obtain the following form for the reversible work:

$$dW'_r = -P'_T\, d\left(\frac{1}{\rho}\right) + \mathbf{E}' \cdot d\left(\frac{\mathbf{D}'}{\rho}\right) + \mathbf{H}' \cdot d\left(\frac{\mathbf{B}'}{\rho}\right) \qquad (5.3-6)$$

which is valid in the rest frame for linear isotropic media.

This expression for the reversible work forms the starting point for the analysis of the energy equation in magnetohydrodynamics; from it, several thermodynamical relationships can be derived. Of particular interest are the following:

$$dF'_T = -s'_T\, dT - P'_T\, d\left(\frac{1}{\rho}\right) + \mathbf{E}' \cdot d\left(\frac{\mathbf{D}'}{\rho}\right) + \mathbf{H}' \cdot d\left(\frac{\mathbf{B}'}{\rho}\right) \qquad (5.3-7)$$

$$dU'_T = T\, ds'_T - P'_T\, d\left(\frac{1}{\rho}\right) + \mathbf{E}' \cdot d\left(\frac{\mathbf{D}'}{\rho}\right) + \mathbf{H}' \cdot d\left(\frac{\mathbf{B}'}{\rho}\right) \qquad (5.3-8)$$

It should be emphasized that all of the preceding development has been carried out in the rest frame (the constitutive equations have been used freely) for a linear and isotropic material. Implicit in the analysis has been the assumption that the properties can be separated into purely electromagnetic and purely mechanical parts. This assumption, implied in the integration of Equations (5.2-8) through (5.2-10) is a good one for essentially all work in MHD. The main coupling, due to an influence on the specific heats by the field quantities, is a very small effect and will not be treated here.

5.4 ENERGY EQUATION OF MAGNETOHYDRODYNAMICS

We now have enough basic information to develop a general energy equation for electrically conducting fluids in the presence of electromagnetic fields. Our analysis will be based on two important assumptions: We assume the fluid is linear, that is the constitutive equations are of the form $\mathbf{D}' = \epsilon(\rho, T)\mathbf{E}'$; $\mathbf{B}' = \mu(\rho, T)\mathbf{H}'$, and that the mechanical and electromagnetic parts of the thermodynamic properties are separable. These assumptions are the same ones used in the development of the thermodynamic relationships in the previous sections.

The energy equation, which is really a control-volume form of the first law of thermodynamics, will be derived in the rest frame of the fluid and then formally transformed, in a convenient manner, into the laboratory frame. Mathematically, this corresponds to a transformation to an Eulerian representation. We begin the analysis in the rest frame in order to make free use of the constitutive equations in their simple linear form, which can, of course, be applied only in the rest frame of the fluid. The conventional method of deriving the fluid energy equation in Eulerian coordinates is based on a control volume (in the laboratory frame) through which fluid is allowed to flow. A complete energy balance is then made by considering the total change in quantities due to convection and time rates of change. We will not use this approach here, but the end result will be the same as that of the laboratory-frame (or Eulerian coordinate) energy equation.

Many attempts have been made to formulate the energy equation directly in the laboratory frame, and indeed it can be done. But the calculations become tiresome and it does not appear to be the most straightforward method of obtaining the desired result. One notable attempt in this direction was made by Chu (1959)[*], but his analysis is

---

[*] B. T. Chu, Thermodynamics of Electrically Conducting Fluids, *Physics of Fluids*, Vol. 2, No. 5, 1959, p. 473. See also S. Goldstein, *Colorado Lectures on Fluid Mechanics*, Interscience, New York, 1960. Goldstein makes the same assertion as Chu about the Poynting flux, and indeed is given the credit by Chu for this method of approach.

based on the premise that the Poynting flux of energy is $\mathbf{E'} \times \mathbf{H'}$ in any frame of reference, a fact clearly in contradiction with the covariant nature of the Poynting theorem. Chu makes free use of the expressions we have derived here for the thermodynamic properties, but he implicitly assumes that they hold in any frame of reference. It must be remembered that the entire derivation of these quantities and of the reversible work was based on the constitutive equations as written in the rest frame. (This condition was used in order to integrate Equations (5.2-8), (5.2-9), and (5.2-10) to obtain the thermo-dynamic properties.)

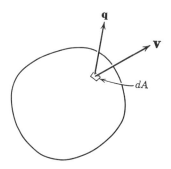

Figure 5.4-1 The control volume for the energy balance.

Consider a control volume in the rest frame (Fig. 5.4-1). The center of mass of the fluid within the control volume is fixed with respect to the control surface. Since we are in the rest frame, the fluid under-goes no rigid body motion, only distortion motion (shear and dilatation). Making an energy balance, we equate the rate of in-crease of the total internal energy in the control volume (accounting for convection effects brought about by dila-tation) to the sum of the rates at which (1) heat is transferred into the volume; (2) the surroundings do reversible work at the boundaries because of the dilatation; (3) the surroundings do irreversible shear work on the fluid; and (4) radiation flows into the control volume. This radiation term is given by the Poynting flux. This balance can be written as

$$\frac{\partial}{\partial t'} \int_{\text{vol}} \rho U'_T \, dV + \int_A \rho U'_T V_i \, dA_i = - \int_A q_i \, dA_i + \int_A V_i \tau_{ji} \, dA_j$$

$$+ \int_A V_i T'_{ji} \, dA_j - \int_A (\mathbf{E'} \times \mathbf{H'})_i \, dA_i \quad (5.4\text{-}1)$$

In (5.4-1), V_i is the fluid velocity taken positive out of the control volume; q_i is the heat flux vector, positive out of the control volume; and mechanical stress tensor is written τ_{ji}, the prime indicating rest-frame values is unnecessary since we are only interested in the distortion work which is independent of the translational motion.* τ'_{ji} was used in Chap-ter 4 to indicate the shear part of the mechanical stress tensor and we

---

* For a discussion of this point, see particularly R. Aris, *Vectors, Tensors, and the Basic Equations of Fluid Mechanics*, Prentice-Hall, Englewood Cliffs, N.J., 1962.

retain that notation here for consistency. (We do not have to specify the rest-frame mechanical stress tensor and need not reserve the prime for such specification.)

The radiation heat flux (as given by the Stefan-Boltzmann law) may be included either in the q_i heat flux vector or in the Poynting flux. We choose to include this heat radiation in the q_i terms, thus eliminating from the electromagnetic terms in the energy balance the electromagnetic field quantities associated with this type of radiation. Hence **E** and **H** will not contain the high-frequency components accompanying the radiant heat.

If we use Gauss's theorem, Equation (5.4-1) can be put into the following form:

$$\frac{\partial}{\partial t'}(\rho U'_T) + \frac{\partial}{\partial x'_i}(\rho U'_T V_i) = -\nabla' \cdot \mathbf{q}$$

$$+ \frac{\partial}{\partial x'_i}(\tau_{ji}V_j + T'_{ji}V_j) - \nabla' \cdot (\mathbf{E}' \times \mathbf{H}') \quad (5.4\text{-}2)$$

By combining Equation (5.4-2) with the continuity equation, $(\partial\rho/\partial t') + \rho\nabla' \cdot \mathbf{V} = 0$ (with the velocity set to zero since we are working in the rest frame), Equation (5.4-2) becomes

$$\rho\frac{\partial U'_T}{\partial t'} = -\nabla' \cdot \mathbf{q} + \frac{\partial}{\partial x'_i}(\tau_{ji}V_j + T'_{ji}V_j) - \nabla' \cdot (\mathbf{E}' \times \mathbf{H}') \quad (5.4\text{-}3)$$

The second term on the right-hand side can now be expanded in the following manner:

$$\frac{\partial}{\partial x'_i}(\tau_{ji}V_j + T'_{ji}V_j) = \tau_{ji}\frac{\partial V_j}{\partial x'_i} + T'_{ji}\frac{\partial V_j}{\partial x'_i}$$

$$= -P\,\nabla' \cdot \mathbf{V} + \tau'_{ji}\frac{\partial V_j}{\partial x'_i} - P'_e\nabla' \cdot \mathbf{V}$$

$$+ \mathbf{E}' \cdot (\mathbf{D}' \cdot \nabla')\mathbf{V} + \mathbf{H}' \cdot (\mathbf{B}' \cdot \nabla')\mathbf{V} \quad (5.4\text{-}4)$$

where we have used the fact that **V** is zero (but not its derivatives) and the electromagnetic stress tensor has been taken as

$$T'_{ij} = -P'_e\delta_{ij} + D'_iE'_j + B'_iH'_j \quad (5.4\text{-}5)$$

which is the form explained at length in Chapter 3.

We recognize $\tau'_{ji}(\partial V_j/\partial x'_i)$ as the mechanical dissipation function Φ, and the mechanical and electromagnetic pressures may be combined into the total pressure. In order to simplify the energy equation further, a useful identity may be developed from Equation (2.8-11). Under the conditions of our present analysis ($\mathbf{V} = 0$ and all field quantities have primes), Equation (2.8-11) becomes

$$\mathbf{H}' \cdot \frac{\partial \mathbf{B}'}{\partial t'} + \mathbf{E}' \cdot \frac{\partial \mathbf{D}'}{\partial t'} = \rho \mathbf{H}' \cdot \frac{\partial}{\partial t'}\left(\frac{\mathbf{B}'}{\rho}\right)$$

$$+ \rho \mathbf{E}' \cdot \frac{\partial}{\partial t'}\left(\frac{\mathbf{D}'}{\rho}\right) - \mathbf{H}' \cdot (\mathbf{B}' \cdot \boldsymbol{\nabla}')\mathbf{V} - \mathbf{E}' \cdot (\mathbf{D}' \cdot \boldsymbol{\nabla}')\mathbf{V} \quad (5.4\text{-}6)$$

Combining Equations (5.4-6), (5.4-4), and (5.4-3), we obtain

$$\rho \frac{\partial U'_T}{\partial t'} = -\boldsymbol{\nabla}' \cdot \mathbf{q} - P'_T \boldsymbol{\nabla}' \cdot \mathbf{V} + \Phi - \boldsymbol{\nabla}' \cdot (\mathbf{E}' \times \mathbf{H}')$$

$$- \mathbf{H}' \cdot \frac{\partial \mathbf{B}'}{\partial t'} - \mathbf{E}' \cdot \frac{\partial \mathbf{D}'}{\partial t'} + \rho \mathbf{H}' \cdot \frac{\partial}{\partial t'}\left(\frac{\mathbf{B}'}{\rho}\right) + \rho \mathbf{E}' \cdot \frac{\partial}{\partial t'}\left(\frac{\mathbf{D}'}{\rho}\right)$$

$$(5.4\text{-}7)$$

Now we add the terms $\boldsymbol{\nabla}' \cdot (\mathbf{E}' \times \mathbf{H}') + \mathbf{E}' \cdot \mathbf{J}' + \mathbf{H}' \cdot (\partial \mathbf{B}'/\partial t') + \mathbf{E}' \cdot (\partial \mathbf{D}'/\partial t') = 0$ (which are zero by Poynting's theorem) to the right-hand side of (5.4-7) and simplify:

$$\rho \frac{\partial U'_T}{\partial t'} = -\boldsymbol{\nabla}' \cdot \mathbf{q} + \Phi + \mathbf{E}' \cdot \mathbf{J}' - \rho P'_T \frac{\partial}{\partial t'}\left(\frac{1}{\rho}\right)$$

$$+ \rho \mathbf{H}' \cdot \frac{\partial}{\partial t'}\left(\frac{\mathbf{B}'}{\rho}\right) + \rho \mathbf{E}' \cdot \frac{\partial}{\partial t'}\left(\frac{\mathbf{D}'}{\rho}\right)$$

$$= -\boldsymbol{\nabla}' \cdot \mathbf{q} + \Phi + \mathbf{E}' \cdot \mathbf{J}' + \rho \frac{\partial W'_r}{\partial t'} \quad (5.4\text{-}8)$$

The partial derivatives with respect to time refer here and in Equations (5.4-9) through (5.4-11) to fixed spatial coordinates and should not be thought of as thermodynamical partial derivatives.

A much more useful form of the energy equation may be obtained by writing the internal energy term as

$$dU'_T = dW'_r + T \, ds'_T \quad (5.4\text{-}9)$$

The reversible work term then cancels out of Equation (5.4-8), leaving the following relationship in terms of entropy:

$$\rho T \frac{\partial s'_T}{\partial t'} = -\boldsymbol{\nabla}' \cdot \mathbf{q} + \Phi + \mathbf{E}' \cdot \mathbf{J}' \quad (5.4\text{-}10)$$

The most useful form of the energy equation, involving the mechanical internal energy explicitly, can be obtained from (5.4-10) by substituting

$dU = -Pd(1/\rho) + T\,ds$ (for the mechanical properties alone). The primes on the mechanical properties are unnecessary, remember. We then have

$$\rho\left(\frac{\partial U}{\partial t'} + T\frac{\partial s'_e}{\partial t'}\right) = -\rho P\frac{\partial}{\partial t'}\left(\frac{1}{\rho}\right) - \nabla'\cdot\mathbf{q} + \Phi + \mathbf{E}'\cdot\mathbf{J}'$$

$$= -P\,\nabla'\cdot\mathbf{V} - \nabla'\cdot\mathbf{q} + \Phi + \mathbf{E}'\cdot\mathbf{J}' \qquad (5.4\text{-}11)$$

s'_e is given explicitly by Equation (5.2-14).

Equation (5.4-11) is still written in the rest frame, however, and we are particularly interested in a laboratory-frame (or Eulerian coordinate) formulation since the equations of motion are written this way. Since we have already based our analysis on a control-volume approach, the transformation to laboratory coordinates is a formality. We merely transform the partial derivatives with respect to time to the material derivative. The other terms in the equation are invariant to such a transformation since they do not depend on rigid body motion. The transformation gives the following final equation in the laboratory-frame coordinates:

$$\rho\left[\frac{DU}{Dt} + T\frac{Ds'_e}{Dt}\right] = -P\,\nabla\cdot\mathbf{V} - \nabla\cdot\mathbf{q} + \Phi + \mathbf{E}'\cdot\mathbf{J}' \qquad (5.4\text{-}12)$$

The field quantities have been left in their rest-frame values since they have an easily interpreted physical significance.

Equation (5.4-12) tells us then how the mechanical internal energy is balanced by the work and heat terms and how it is related to the electromagnetic terms. The first term on the right-hand side is the work done by mechanical pressure on the fluid; the second term is the rate of influx of heat; the third term is the mechanical dissipation function; and the last term, $\mathbf{E}'\cdot\mathbf{J}'$, is the rate of Joulean dissipation. It should be noted that this term is written in a general fashion and is valid regardless of the form of Ohm's law. In fact, the same expression may be used in plasma dynamics where the generalized form of Ohm's law becomes extremely complex. If Ohm's law in the simple form $\mathbf{J}' = \sigma\mathbf{E}'$ holds, then the Joulean dissipation may be written J'^2/σ.

The rate of increase of electromagnetic entropy on the left-hand side of (5.4-12) is usually a very small quantity and in most MHD problems it can be neglected entirely. If it is neglected, the form of the energy equation becomes even simpler, having only mechanical terms on the left-hand side. The equation is then identical with the energy equation derived by Pai (1957) and others that is usually used in MHD.

The $-\nabla\cdot\mathbf{q}$ term may be split into a conduction and radiation part. If Fourier's law is applied we obtain: $-\nabla\cdot\mathbf{q} = -\nabla\cdot\mathbf{q}_r + \nabla\cdot(\kappa_T\nabla T)$, where $\mathbf{q}_r$ is the radiation heat flux and κ_T is the thermal conductivity. When combined with Fourier's law, the energy equation is

$$\rho\left(\frac{DU}{Dt} + T\frac{Ds'_e}{Dt}\right) = -P\,\mathbf{\nabla}\cdot\mathbf{V} - \mathbf{\nabla}\cdot\mathbf{q}_r + \mathbf{\nabla}\cdot(\kappa_T\,\mathbf{\nabla}T) + \Phi + \mathbf{E}'\cdot\mathbf{J}'$$

(5.4-13)

If κ_T is constant, the term $\mathbf{\nabla}\cdot(\kappa_T\mathbf{\nabla}T)$ may be written $\kappa_T\nabla^2 T$.

The two assumptions underlying our derivation and its final form, given by Equation (5.4-12), are (1) that the material is linear, and (2) that the mechanical and electromagnetic parts of the properties can be separated. The latter is equivalent to assuming that the mechanical specific heats have a negligible dependence on the electromagnetic fields, which is true except under extreme conditions, such as those that exist at cryogenic temperatures.

5.5 ENERGY EQUATION IN TERMS OF ENTHALPY

If we assume that the mechanical and electrical parts of the internal energy are separable, the specific enthalpy follows directly from the expression of internal energy in Equation (5.2-15) and the total pressure. We can express the enthalpy h'_T (per unit mass) as

$$h'_T = P'_T\frac{1}{\rho} + U'_T$$

(5.5-1)

where the mechanical part is

$$h = P\left(\frac{1}{\rho}\right) + U$$

(5.5-2)

and the electromagnetic part is

$$h'_e = P'_e\left(\frac{1}{\rho}\right) + U'_e = \frac{1}{\rho}\left[\frac{D'^2}{\epsilon}\left(1 + \frac{T}{2\epsilon}\frac{\partial\epsilon}{\partial T} - \frac{\rho}{2\epsilon}\frac{\partial\epsilon}{\partial\rho}\right)\right.$$
$$\left. + \frac{B'^2}{\mu}\left(1 + \frac{T}{2\mu}\frac{\partial\mu}{\partial T} - \frac{\rho}{2\mu}\frac{\partial\mu}{\partial\rho}\right)\right] \quad (5.5-3)$$

By combining the definition of the mechanical part of the enthalpy with the energy equation (5.4-12), we have

$$\rho\frac{Dh}{Dt} + \rho T\frac{Ds'_e}{Dt} = \frac{DP}{Dt} - \mathbf{\nabla}\cdot\mathbf{q} + \Phi + \mathbf{E}'\cdot\mathbf{J}'$$

(5.5-4)

which is the general expression valid for a compressible or incompressible fluid.

5.6 ENERGY EQUATION FOR A PERFECT GAS

For a perfect gas the energy equation may be simplified by expressing the mechanical part of the internal energy, or enthalpy, in terms of specific heats. From the definition of the mechanical specific heats (assuming no electromagnetic field dependence),

$$c_V = \frac{\partial U}{\partial T}\bigg|_V$$

$$c_P = \frac{\partial h}{\partial T}\bigg|_P$$

(5.6-1)

DU/Dt and Dh/Dt can be written as $c_V(DT/Dt)$ and $c_P(DT/Dt)$, respectively. Hence, the energy equation may be written in terms of c_V or c_P as

$$\rho c_V \frac{DT}{Dt} + \rho \frac{Ds'_e}{Dt} = -P\,\nabla \cdot \mathbf{V} - \nabla \cdot \mathbf{q} + \Phi + \mathbf{E'} \cdot \mathbf{J'} \quad (5.6\text{-}2)$$

or

$$\rho c_P \frac{DT}{Dt} + \rho \frac{Ds'_e}{Dt} = \frac{DP}{Dt} - \nabla \cdot \mathbf{q} + \Phi + \mathbf{E'} \cdot \mathbf{J'} \quad (5.6\text{-}3)$$

It should be noted that the specific heats appear outside the derivative, even though they may be functions of temperature. This fact follows from the definition of the specific heats.

5.7 ENERGY EQUATION IN TERMS OF ENTROPY

The energy relationship in terms of entropy has already been derived in the rest frame (Equation 5.4-10). A convenient form of this equation is obtained by transforming to laboratory coordinates, which entails only changing the derivative to the material derivative. We obtain

$$\rho T\left(\frac{Ds}{Dt} + \frac{Ds'_e}{Dt}\right) = \rho T \frac{Ds'_T}{Dt} = -\nabla \cdot \mathbf{q} + \Phi + \mathbf{E'} \cdot \mathbf{J'}$$

$$\rho T \frac{Ds}{Dt} = \frac{Dh}{Dt} - \frac{DP}{Dt}$$

(5.7-1)

as the desired result. This equation is of great importance in developing the thermodynamics of irreversible processes, which will now be discussed.

5.8   THE SECOND LAW AND IRREVERSIBLE THERMODYNAMICS

The second law of thermodynamics can be written for a control volume in the laboratory frame as

$$\frac{Q}{T} = -\int_A \frac{\mathbf{q}}{T} \cdot d\mathbf{A} \leq \frac{\partial}{\partial t} \int_{\text{vol}} \rho s'_T \, dV + \int_A \rho s'_T \mathbf{V} \cdot d\mathbf{A} \qquad (5.8\text{-}1)$$

If the rate of total entropy production per unit volume Σ_T is introduced, an equality can be made, and Equation (5.8-1) becomes

$$\int_{\text{vol}} \Sigma_T \, dV - \int_A \frac{\mathbf{q}}{T} \cdot d\mathbf{A} = \frac{\partial}{\partial t} \int_{\text{vol}} \rho s'_T \, dV + \int_A \rho s'_T \mathbf{V} \cdot d\mathbf{A} \qquad (5.8\text{-}2)$$

By virtue of Gauss's theorem, the above equation becomes

$$\Sigma_T - \nabla \cdot \left(\frac{\mathbf{q}}{T}\right) = \rho \frac{D's_T}{Dt} \qquad (5.8\text{-}3)$$

By combining the above equation and the energy equation (5.7-1), we can express the entropy production rate in the following form:

$$\Sigma_T = \frac{\mathbf{E'} \cdot \mathbf{J'}}{T} + \frac{\Phi}{T} + \mathbf{q} \cdot \nabla\left(\frac{1}{T}\right) \qquad (5.8\text{-}4)$$

which is a general expression for linear isotropic media. By separating the conduction and radiation heat and introducing Fourier's law but allowing a variable κ_T, we obtain

$$\Sigma_T = \frac{\mathbf{E'} \cdot \mathbf{J'}}{T} + \frac{\Phi}{T} + \frac{\kappa_T(\nabla T \cdot \nabla T)}{T^2} + \mathbf{q}_r \cdot \nabla\left(\frac{1}{T}\right) \qquad (5.8\text{-}5)$$

The above expression for the dissipation due to the presence of the electromagnetic field $\mathbf{E'} \cdot \mathbf{J'}$ is perfectly general, but if Ohm's law holds in the simple isotropic form, $\mathbf{E'} \cdot \mathbf{J'}$ can be written as J'^2/σ. A useful form of Equation (5.8-5) is the following, which is applicable to media in which Ohm's law holds and in which radition heat transfer is negligible.

$$\Sigma_T = \frac{J'^2}{T\sigma} + \frac{\Phi}{T} + \frac{\kappa_T(\nabla T \cdot \nabla T)}{T^2} \qquad (5.8\text{-}6)$$

5.9   EXTENSION TO DISPERSIVE AND NONLINEAR MEDIA

If ϵ and μ are functions of the field quantities, the medium is no longer linear and may undergo hysteresis losses. No simple interpretation of the right-hand side of Poynting's theorem (Equation 5.2-1) is possible, although the Poynting flux $\mathbf{E} \times \mathbf{H}$ still has the same physical interpretation. If we consider an alternating process of frequency ω so that the field quantities can be represented in phasor notation, an expression can be derived for the hysteresis losses. The dielectric constant ϵ and permeability μ may be written as complex quantities and the Poynting theorem separated into real and imaginary parts. This type of analysis has been carried out in Chapter 2 and will not be repeated here. The final result (for the losses in the rest frame) is

$$\frac{\omega}{2} (\epsilon'' E'^2 + \mu'' H'^2) \tag{5.9-1}$$

where ϵ'' and μ'' are the imaginary parts of the dielectric constant and permeability, respectively. In the above equation the field quantities are peak values. In terms of root mean square values $|\bar{\mathbf{E}}'|$ and $|\bar{\mathbf{H}}'|$, the expression becomes

$$\omega(\epsilon'' \bar{E}'^2 + \mu'' \bar{H}'^2) \tag{5.9-2}$$

This expression then represents the dissipation due to internal losses. Although the sign on the real part of ϵ and μ may in fact be negative, the imaginary part must always be positive so that the loss or dissipation term is always positive. The necessity of this condition is a direct consequence of the second law of thermodynamics.

The expression for the total entropy production per unit volume (Equation 5.8-4) may be modified by the inclusion of the hysteresis losses. Hence

$$\Sigma'_T = \frac{\mathbf{E}' \cdot \mathbf{J}'}{T} + \frac{\Phi}{T} + \mathbf{q} \cdot \nabla\left(\frac{1}{T}\right) + \frac{\omega(\epsilon'' E'^2 + \mu'' H'^2)}{2T} \tag{5.9-3}$$

where the time average of all terms is understood (except $\epsilon'' E'^2$ and $\mu'' H'^2$, which are peak values), and T is assumed constant.

These losses are zero for absolutely linear media, but in reality all material is slightly nonlinear and hence may undergo some hysteresis losses. In MHD this loss is negligible, especially since the material is linear. For all practical purposes the values of ϵ'' and μ'' are negligible compared to the real parts of ϵ and μ. If, however, the imaginary parts, and hence the losses, are appreciable, no simple formulation of the internal energy and derivation of the energy equation can be given. In fact, the internal energy cannot be defined in a rational thermodynamical sense.

If ϵ and μ depend on frequency, which must be the case if ϵ'' and μ'' are not zero, the material is said to be dispersive, and for values of ϵ'' and μ''

which are small compared to the real parts of ϵ and μ, a rational thermodynamical analysis may be carried out with dispersion taken into account. An analysis of material with very small ϵ'' and μ'' (called "transparent" material) can be made for incompressible media, but we shall not pursue the subject further here since it is not of primary concern in magnetohydrodynamics or fluid flow. The reader is referred to Chapter IX, Sections 58–64, of the excellent account by Landau and Lifshitz listed in the references.

It may now be obvious that the stress tensor discussed in Chapter 3 is valid, strictly speaking, for media where there is no dispersion and where ϵ and μ are real quantities which do not depend on the field quantities. An energy method must be used to derive the forces and stresses, and such energy methods cannot be formulated in a rigorous manner for complex materials. The general, time average stress tensor for dispersive nonlinear media is still open to question.

5.10 THE MECHANICAL ENERGY EQUATION AND COMBINATION WITH THE THERMODYNAMICAL RELATIONSHIPS

Various other forms of the energy equation can be derived by combining the energy equation with the equation of motion.

A purely mechanical energy equation can be derived by forming the scalar product of the velocity vector and the equation of motion. Such an equation, merely expressing the balance between kinetic and potential energy and the work done by forces causing rigid body motion, can be written as

$$\rho\left(V_i \frac{\partial V_i}{\partial t} + V_i V_j \frac{\partial V_i}{\partial x_j}\right) = V_i\left(\frac{\partial \tau_{ji}}{\partial x_j} + \frac{T_{ji}}{\partial x_j} - \frac{\partial g_i}{\partial t}\right) - V_i \rho \frac{\partial \psi}{\partial x_i} \quad (5.10\text{-}1)$$

or, assuming that the gravitational potential ψ is independent of time, as

$$\rho \frac{D}{Dt}\left(\frac{V^2}{2} + \psi\right) = -V_i \frac{\partial P}{\partial x_i} + V_i \frac{\partial \tau'_{ji}}{\partial x_j} + \mathbf{V} \cdot \mathbf{f}_e$$

$$= V_i \frac{\partial \tau_{ji}}{\partial x_j} + \mathbf{V} \cdot \mathbf{f}_e \quad (5.10\text{-}2)$$

where τ'_{ji} is the mechanical viscous stress tensor, and $\mathbf{f}_e$ is the electromagnetic body force per unit volume.

Equation (5.10-2), the mechanical energy equation, may be combined with the energy equation (5.4-12). This total energy balance equation is often useful and can be written as

$$\rho \frac{D}{Dt}\left(\frac{V^2}{2} + \psi + U\right) + \rho T \frac{Ds'_e}{Dt} = -V_i \frac{\partial P_i}{\partial x_i} + V_i \frac{\partial \tau'_{ji}}{\partial x_j} + \mathbf{V} \cdot \mathbf{f}_e$$

$$-\nabla \cdot \mathbf{q} + \mathbf{E}' \cdot \mathbf{J}' + \Phi - P\nabla \cdot \mathbf{V}$$

(5.10-3)

The total mechanical stress tensor $\tau_{ij} = -P\delta_{ij} + \tau'_{ij}$ may be introduced and the above relationship cast into the form

$$\rho \frac{D}{Dt}\left(\frac{V^2}{2} + \psi + U\right) = \frac{\partial}{\partial x_j}(V_i \tau_{ji}) - \nabla \cdot \mathbf{q} + \mathbf{E}' \cdot \mathbf{J}' + \mathbf{V} \cdot \mathbf{f}_e - \rho T \frac{Ds'_e}{Dt}$$

(5.10-4)

It is often useful to introduce the total mechanical enthalpy h_0 (per unit mass) as $h_0 = (P/\rho) + U + (V^2/2)$, which is sometimes called the stagnation enthalpy. Introducing this definition into Equation (5.10-3), we have

$$\rho \frac{D}{Dt}(h_0 + \psi) = \frac{\partial P}{\partial t} + V_i \frac{\partial \tau'_{ji}}{\partial x_j} + \mathbf{V} \cdot \mathbf{f}_e - \nabla \cdot \mathbf{q} + \Phi + \mathbf{E}' \cdot \mathbf{J}' - \rho T \frac{Ds'_e}{Dt}$$

(5.10-5)

The term $\partial \tau'_{ji}/\partial x_j$ may of course be expressed in terms of strain rate and is merely the viscous force term that occurs in the equation of motion. Equation (5.10-5) can be expressed in various simplified forms by introducing Fourier's law, Ohm's law, and detailed rate relationships. Let us recall that if the body force is represented as $\rho_e \mathbf{E} + \mathbf{J} \times \mathbf{B}$, the sum of terms $\mathbf{E}' \cdot \mathbf{J}' + \mathbf{V} \cdot \mathbf{f}_e$ is simply $\mathbf{E} \cdot \mathbf{J}$. Equation (5.10-5) may be written then as

$$\rho \frac{D}{Dt}(h_0 + \psi) = \frac{\partial P}{\partial t} + V_i \frac{\partial \tau'_{ji}}{\partial x_j} - \nabla \cdot \mathbf{q} + \Phi + \mathbf{E} \cdot \mathbf{J} - \rho T \frac{Ds'_e}{Dt}$$

(5.10-6)

If we neglect the electromagnetic entropy term on the right-hand side and introduce Fourier's law with a constant thermal conductivity κ_T, the equation becomes

$$\rho \frac{D}{Dt}(h_0 + \psi) = \frac{\partial P}{\partial t} + V_i \frac{\partial \tau'_{ji}}{\partial x_j} + \kappa_T \nabla^2 T + \Phi + \mathbf{E} \cdot \mathbf{J} \quad (5.10-7)$$

If the fluid is inviscid, we obtain

$$\rho \frac{D}{Dt}(h_0 + \psi) = \frac{\partial P}{\partial t} + \kappa_T \mathbf{\nabla}^2 T + \mathbf{E} \cdot \mathbf{J} \tag{5.10-8}$$

which is a very useful relationship and one that we will use extensively in the development of magnetohydrodynamic compressible flow.

5.11 FORMS OF THE DISSIPATION FUNCTION FOR REFERENCE

The mechanical dissipation function Φ may be written in various coordinate systems as follows (λ is here a second coefficient of viscosity as defined in Chapter 4):

Cartesian

$$\Phi = 2\mu_f\left[\left(\frac{\partial u}{\partial x}\right)^2 + \left(\frac{\partial v}{\partial y}\right)^2 + \left(\frac{\partial w}{\partial z}\right)^2 + \frac{1}{2}\left(\frac{\partial u}{\partial y} + \frac{\partial v}{\partial x}\right)^2 + \frac{1}{2}\left(\frac{\partial v}{\partial z} + \frac{\partial w}{\partial y}\right)^2\right.$$
$$\left. + \frac{1}{2}\left(\frac{\partial w}{\partial x} + \frac{\partial u}{\partial z}\right)^2\right] + \lambda\left(\frac{\partial u}{\partial x} + \frac{\partial v}{\partial y} + \frac{\partial w}{\partial z}\right)^2 \tag{5.11-1}$$

where u, v, and w are the components of 'velocity in the x, y, and z directions, respectively.

Cylindrical

$$\Phi = 2\mu_f\left[\left(\frac{\partial v_r}{\partial r}\right)^2 + \left(\frac{1}{r}\frac{\partial v_\theta}{\partial \theta} + \frac{v_r}{r}\right)^2 + \left(\frac{\partial u_z}{\partial z}\right)^2 \frac{1}{2}\left(\frac{1}{r}\frac{\partial v_z}{\partial \theta} + \frac{\partial v_\theta}{\partial z}\right)^2\right.$$
$$\left. + \frac{1}{2}\left(\frac{\partial v_r}{\partial z} + \frac{\partial v_z}{\partial r}\right)^2 + \frac{1}{2}\left(\frac{1}{r}\frac{\partial v_r}{\partial \theta} + \frac{\partial v_\theta}{\partial r} - \frac{v_\theta}{r}\right)^2\right]$$
$$+ \lambda\left(\frac{\partial v_r}{\partial r} + \frac{1}{r}\frac{\partial v_\theta}{\partial \theta} + \frac{v_r}{r} + \frac{\partial v_z}{\partial z}\right)^2 \tag{5.11-2}$$

Spherical

$$\Phi = 2\mu_f\left\{\left(\frac{\partial v_r}{\partial r}\right)^2 + \left(\frac{1}{r}\frac{\partial v_\theta}{\partial \theta} + \frac{v_r}{r}\right)^2 + \left(\frac{1}{r\sin\theta}\frac{\partial v_\varphi}{\partial \varphi} + \frac{v_r}{r} + \frac{v_\theta\cot\theta}{r}\right)^2\right.$$
$$+ \frac{1}{2}\left(\frac{\sin\theta}{r}\frac{\partial}{\partial \theta}\left(\frac{v_\varphi}{\sin\theta}\right) + \frac{1}{r\sin\theta}\frac{\partial v_\theta}{\partial \varphi}\right)^2$$
$$\left. + \frac{1}{2}\left[\frac{1}{r\sin\theta}\frac{\partial v_r}{\partial \varphi} + r\frac{\partial}{\partial r}\left(\frac{v_\varphi}{r}\right)\right]^2 + \frac{1}{2}\left(r\frac{\partial}{\partial r}\left(\frac{v_\theta}{r}\right) + \frac{1}{r}\frac{\partial v_r}{\partial \theta}\right)^2\right\}$$
$$+ \lambda\left(\frac{\partial v_r}{\partial r} + \frac{1}{r}\frac{\partial v}{\partial \theta} + 2\frac{v_r}{r} + \frac{1}{r\sin\theta}\frac{\partial v_\varphi}{\partial \varphi} + \frac{v_\theta\cot\theta}{r}\right) \tag{5.11-3}$$

PROBLEMS

1. The thermocouple engine is a device which utilizes the emf generated by a thermocouple to power a direct-current motor. We desire an expression for the maximum efficiency of such a heat engine operating in the steady state. Assume the open-circuit emf of the thermocouple is proportional to the temperature difference across the couple and that the only heat supplied by the high-temperature source is heat conducted along the thermocouple wires which is proportional to the temperature difference between the hot and cold reservoirs. Fig. P5.1-1 shows a sketch of the device.

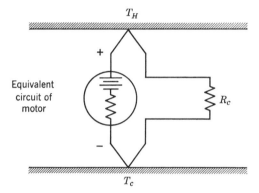

Figure P5.1-1

2. The conventional scheme of converting heat energy into electrical is first to convert the heat energy into mechanical energy (for example, with a steam engine) and then converting the mechanical energy into electrical energy with a generator. A vast improvement over this scheme, if practically possible, would be to convert heat energy directly into electrical energy. One such direct conversion device consists of a paramagnetic substance surrounded by an electrical coil. The cycle that has been proposed to study the feasibility of this paramagnetic direct conversion device involves the following processes:

  1. Rev. isothermal magnetization of the material during which the magnetic intensity H increases from 0 to 4×10^6 amp/m at a temperature of 30°C.

  2. Isentropic magnetization of the material to a temperature of 100°C.

  3. Rev. isothermal decrease of the magnetic intensity.

  4. Isentropic demagnetization of the material during which the temperature of the substance returns to its original value.

Calculate the electrical energy produced and the net heat transferred per unit volume of material during a cycle. What do you think may be the practical limitations of this direct conversion device?

3. An interesting method has been proposed to convert *thermal energy into electric energy* delivered to a load, avoiding the conventional methods in which thermal energy is converted first into mechanical (boilers and turbines) and then into electrical (alternators, etc.) energy. The method is based on the use of capacitors with certain special dielectrics, whose permittivity ϵ *varies with*

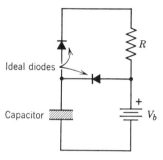

Figure P5.3-1

temperature. (This means that, with a given **E** field, the polarization is temperature dependent.) The scheme proposed is shown in Fig. P5.3-1. The relative permittivity $\kappa = \epsilon/\epsilon_0$ is plotted in Fig. P5.3-2 for a certain material of this kind (namely a Barium strontium titanate). The idea is to *heat and cool cyclically the capacitor* with the purpose of supplying electric power to the load resistor R (such as a bank of light bulbs or a motor or what not). You are asked to investigate the function of the battery V_b in the following types of operation:

A-1. The system is initially at rest with the capacitor at 50°C. A jet of warm air heats it up to 130° and the circuit is allowed to come to steady state.

A-2. Starting from the 130°C steady state above, the capacitor is cooled back to 50°C by a jet of cold air.

B-1. The system is initially at rest with the capacitor at 135°C. A jet of hot air heats it up to 150°C and the circuit is allowed to come to steady state.

B-2. Starting from the 150°C steady state above, the capacitor is cooled back to 135°C.

More specifically, consider a numerical situation in which the area of the condenser plates is 4.35×10^{-2} m² and the thickness of the dielectric is 2.16×10^{-4} m. The voltage of the battery is 200 volts. The load resistor is 100 ohms. The diodes can be considered as ideal (that is, they act either as an open or a closed switch). *Calculate the energy supplied by the battery in each of the four situations described.*

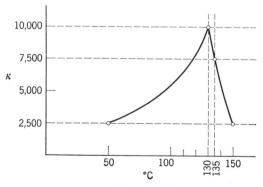

Figure P5.3-2

REFERENCES

Callen, H. B., The Application of Onsager's Reciprocal Relations to Thermoelectric, Thermomagnetic, and Galvanomagnetic Effects, *Phys. Rev.*, **73**, p. 1349, 1948, and **85**, p. 16, 1952.

Chu, B. T., Thermodynamics of Electrically Conducting Fluids, *Phys. Fluids*, **2**, September-October, p. 473, 1959.

Goldstein, S., *Colorado Lectures on Fluid Mechanics*, Interscience, New York, 1960.

Hughes, W. F., Relativistic Magnetohydrodynamics and Irreversible Thermodynamics, *Proc. Cambridge Phil. Soc.*, **57**, p. 878, 1961.

Kluitenberg, G. A., and P. Mazur, Relativistic Thermodynamics of Irreversible Processes (in five parts), *Physica*, **19**, Part 1, p. 689, 1953; **19**, Part 2, p. 1079, 1953.

Kluitenberg, G. A., and S. R. De Groot, Relativistic Thermodynamics of Irreversible Processes, *Physica*, **20**, Part 3, p. 199, 1954; **21**, Part 4, p. 148, 1955; **21**, Part 5, p. 169, 1955.

Landau, L. D., and E. M. Lifshitz, *Electrodynamics of Continuous Media*, Addison-Wesley, Reading, Mass., 1960.

Mazur, P., and S. R. De Groot, On Onsager's Relations in a Magnetic Field, *Physica*, **19**, p. 961, 1953.

Mazur, P., and S. R. De Groot, On Pressure and Ponderomotive Force in a Dielectric, *Physica*, **22**, p. 657, 1956.

Mazur, P., and I. Prigogine, Thermodynamique des effets thermomagnétique et galvanomagnétique, *J. Phys. et le Radium*, **12**, p. 616, 1951.

Møller, C., *Theory of Relativity*, Oxford, 1952.

Pai, S. I., Energy Equation of Magneto-Gas-Dynamics, *Phys. Rev.*, **105**, No. 5, p. 1424, 1957.

Pham Mau Quan, Étude électromagnétique et thermodynamique d'un fluide relativiste chargé, *J. Rational Mechanics and Analysis*, **5**, p. 472, 1956.

6

The Fluid Equations—
Magnetohydrodynamic
Approximations, Equations,
and Parameters

6.1 INTRODUCTION

Magnetohydrodynamics or magnetogasdynamics has come to mean the study of the flow of electrically conducting fluids in the presence of a magnetic field under certain special assumptions. In this book we are concerned, generally, with a broader class of flows and are interested in the most general type of electromagnetic-fluid interaction (which we have called magnetofluidmechanics). Various specialized classes of flow have developed, such as MHD, MGD, electrohydrodynamics, etc., but these distinctions will not be formally treated in this book, except as they arise as the natural consequences of physical assumptions in individual problems. In this chapter, however, we will discuss the assumptions that are usually made in what is known as "magnetohydrodynamics," some of the important parameters which characterize electromagnetic-fluid interaction and flow, and the character of some of the basic equations.

6.2 THE GENERAL MAGNETOFLUIDMECHANIC PROBLEM

Most fluid flow (compressible or incompressible) which undergoes an interaction with a magnetic field is of a nature that allows the so-called MHD or MGD approximations. These approximations are discussed in the next section. In this section, we wish to write (making as few assumptions as possible) the complete general equations for a flowing fluid interacting with a magnetic and electric field. Later these basic equations can be used extensively for large classes of problems which do not fit into the so-called MHD or MGD approximation. We will draw upon the equations developed in Chapters 4 and 5 and the principles of electrodynamics developed in Chapter 2.

The Maxwell equations in RMKS units (in general form) are

$$\nabla \cdot \mathbf{D} = \rho_e \tag{6.2-1}$$

$$\nabla \cdot \mathbf{B} = 0 \tag{6.2-2}$$

$$\nabla \times \mathbf{E} = -\frac{\partial \mathbf{B}}{\partial t} \tag{6.2-3}$$

$$\nabla \times \mathbf{H} = \mathbf{J} + \frac{\partial \mathbf{D}}{\partial t} \tag{6.2-4}$$

which hold in any frame of reference, either the rest frame (local frame of reference at rest with respect to the fluid) or the laboratory frame. (When we say the equations hold in a given frame we mean that they hold for an observer in that frame using his own coordinate system and measuring the field quantities with respect to his frame.) In addition to Maxwell's equations, the current conservation equation (valid in any frame)

$$\nabla \cdot \mathbf{J} + \frac{\partial \rho_e}{\partial t} = 0 \tag{6.2-5}$$

may be used. But it is not independent of Maxwell's equations and follows directly from (6.2-1) and (6.2-4).

The constitutive equations must be used in one form or another. If a linear medium is assumed, we can write in the rest frame

$$\mathbf{D}' = \epsilon \mathbf{E}' = \epsilon_0 \kappa \mathbf{E}' = \epsilon_0 (1 + \chi) \mathbf{E}' = \epsilon_0 \mathbf{E}' + \mathbf{P}' \tag{6.2-6}$$

$$\mathbf{B}' = \mu \mathbf{H} = \mu_0 \kappa_m \mathbf{H}' = \mu_0 (1 + \chi_m) \mathbf{H}' = \mu_0 (\mathbf{H}' + \mathbf{M}') \tag{6.2-7}$$

In the laboratory frame these become

$$\mathbf{D} = \epsilon_0 \mathbf{E} + \mathbf{P} = \epsilon[\mathbf{E} + \mathbf{V} \times \mathbf{B}] - \frac{1}{c^2} \mathbf{V} \times \mathbf{H} \tag{6.2-8}$$

$$\mathbf{B} = \mu_0 (\mathbf{H} + \mathbf{M}) = \mu[\mathbf{H} - \mathbf{V} \times \mathbf{D}] + \frac{1}{c^2} \mathbf{V} \times \mathbf{E} \tag{6.2-9}$$

For most materials (solids or fluids) of interest in the study of motion and electromagnetic interaction, the magnetic permeability is that of free space, that is, μ_0. This assumption is generally valid for all conducting liquids: liquid metals, gases, and solutions. In some gases (plasmas in particular), the permittivity (dielectric constant) must be taken as ϵ_0 (as for free space). This condition is not satisfied for liquid metals, or even liquid salt solutions, however, and ϵ may even be a complex function of frequency. The assumption that $\epsilon = \epsilon_0$ (which is sometimes made) can lead to completely erroneous results. For conductors in which $\epsilon \neq \epsilon_0$ (virtually all nongases), Equation (6.2-6) or (6.2-8) may be used for linear material. In materials in which μ and ϵ both have their free space value of μ_0 and ϵ_0, the constitutive equations (6.2-8) and (6.2-9) reduce to the rest-frame form even in the laboratory frame; thus

$$D = \epsilon_0 E \qquad (6.2\text{-}10)$$
$$B = \mu_0 H \qquad (6.2\text{-}11)$$

These last two equations are valid for plasmas.

As will be seen, in most MHD problems (as part of the MHD approximation), the magnetic field B is essentially the same in each frame and $B = B'$. Here the constitutive equation (6.2-11) may be used (that is, $B = \mu_0 H$ for liquid metals and gases) even if $\epsilon \neq \epsilon_0$. It must be emphasized that (6.2-10) is not true in general and must never be used for liquids. Only in certain plasma models may (6.2-10) be used meaningfully.

The correct boundary conditions at media interfaces on the field quantities have been discussed in Chapter 2. They can be stated as the ordinary boundary conditions of electromagnetic field theory, if the field quantities are measured consistently in one given frame of reference which does not move with respect to the interface. That is, an observer in the rest or laboratory frame may apply the boundary conditions (at the interface) to the field quantities which he measures (if he does not move normal to the interface). This fact follows immediately from the covariant character of Maxwell's equations. At an interface then

$$E_1 \times n = E_2 \times n$$
$$E'_1 \times n = E'_2 \times n \qquad (6.2\text{-}12)$$

$$D_1 \cdot n = D_2 \cdot n + \rho_s$$
$$D'_1 \cdot n = D'_2 \cdot n + \rho'_s \qquad (6.2\text{-}13)$$

$$B_1 \cdot n = B_2 \cdot n$$
$$B'_1 \cdot n = B'_2 \cdot n \qquad (6.2\text{-}14)$$

$$H_1 \times n = H_2 \times n + \mathscr{I}$$
$$H'_1 \times n = H'_2 \times n + \mathscr{I}' \qquad (6.2\text{-}15)$$

where subscript 1 refers to medium 1 and subscript 2 to medium 2. (Primed and unprimed quantities refer to the rest frame and laboratory frame, respectively.) The unit normal vector **n** points from medium 2 into medium 1. $\mathscr{I}$ is the current sheet density at the interface. ρ_s is the true charge layer density at the interface. The field quantities must be used as stated and if the constitutive equations are used, they must be used in an appropriate form. If the observer moves with respect to the interface (in a direction normal to the interface), it is a simple matter to transform all the field quantities of Equations (6.2-12) through (6.2-15) to the appropriate moving frame.

The fluid equations of motion have been discussed in Chapter 4. The most general form of the body force may be used, but for most problems, where striction effects and inhomogeneity effects can be neglected, the body force is adequately represented simply by $\mathbf{J} \times \mathbf{B} + \rho_e \mathbf{E}$. The equation of state (which is necessary for gas flow) has been discussed in Chapter 4, and the energy equation has been discussed in Chapter 5.

These equations, along with the appropriate Lorentz transformations, can be used to solve rather general problems in magnetofluidmechanics, either steady state or alternating current, high or low frequency. We adopt the attitude in this book that one should start with these basic equations and simplify them, according to the appropriate physical assumptions, for any particular problem. (An important point to remember is that the equation of motion and energy equation are valid only for nonrelativistic velocities, as opposed to the Maxwell equations, which are generally valid.) Consequently, it would be inconsistent to retain the exact relativistic form of the Lorentz transformations. Some confusion has arisen as to what constitutes the low velocity (nonrelativistic) approximation for these transformations. The only approximation that is generally valid is to set $\sqrt{1 - (|\mathbf{V}|^2/c^2)}$ to unity. Other assumptions, such as $\rho'_e = \rho_e$, are not generally valid, even at low velocities, contrary to usage by some early workers in the field. Consistent with the nonrelativistic approximation (but still valid otherwise), the Lorentz transformations take the form

$$\mathbf{E}' = \mathbf{E} + \mathbf{V} \times \mathbf{B} \tag{6.2-16}$$

$$\mathbf{D}' = \mathbf{D} + \frac{\mathbf{V} \times \mathbf{H}}{c^2} \qquad \mathbf{P}' = \mathbf{P} - \frac{\mathbf{V} \times \mathbf{M}}{c^2} \tag{6.2-17}$$

$$\mathbf{B}' = \mathbf{B} - \frac{\mathbf{V} \times \mathbf{E}}{c^2} \qquad \mathbf{M}' = \mathbf{M} + \mathbf{V} \times \mathbf{P} \tag{6.2-18}$$

$$\mathbf{H}' = \mathbf{H} - \mathbf{V} \times \mathbf{D} \tag{6.2-19}$$

$$\mathbf{J} = \mathbf{J}' + \rho'_e \mathbf{V} \tag{6.2-20}$$

$$\rho_e = \rho'_e + \frac{\mathbf{V} \cdot \mathbf{J}}{c^2} \tag{6.2-21}$$

All terms (except $\sqrt{1 - (|V|^2/c^2)}$ must be retained in the transformations for ρ_e and $\mathbf{J}$ (even under the MHD approximation, as will be shown), or paradoxical results may be obtained.)

If the equation $\nabla \cdot \mathbf{D} = \rho_e$ is used, the assumption that $\rho'_e = 0$ in the rest frame (for conductors) does not allow one to say that $\rho_e = 0$ (in the laboratory frame) and hence one cannot write $\nabla \cdot \mathbf{D} = 0$ in the laboratory frame. (The Faraday disc problem was an example which illustrated this point.) If $\nabla \cdot \mathbf{D} = \rho_e$ and Equation (6.2-21) for the charge density transformation are used, it is seen that even though $\rho'_e = 0$ in the rest frame, ρ_e in the laboratory frame is not necessarily zero. This confusion is usually avoided by using the current conservation equation (6.2-5). In the MHD approximation then, $\nabla \cdot \mathbf{J} = 0$, but in high-frequency situations the full equation $\nabla \cdot \mathbf{J} + (\partial \rho_e/\partial t) = 0$ must be used. This current conservation equation obviates the use of $\nabla \cdot \mathbf{D} = \rho_e$ which becomes redundant.

With these observations on ρ_e and $\mathbf{J}$ in mind, we turn to the MHD approximation.

6.3   THE MHD APPROXIMATION

In addition to the nonrelativistic approximation, certain additional simplifications can be made for flow which is quasi-steady (steady or low-frequency oscillatory), and in which the electric field is of the order of magnitude of the induced quantity $\mathbf{V} \times \mathbf{B}$. This type of flow is usually referred to as MHD (magnetohydrodynamic) or MGD (magnetogas-dynamic) flow and is a special case of the more general magnetofluid-mechanics treated in this book. The following assumptions are made under the MHD approximation:

1. $|V|^2 \ll c^2$. This is in keeping with the nonrelativistic Newtonian form of the equations of motion and allows the $\sqrt{1 - (V^2/c^2)}$ factor to be taken as unity.

2. The electric fields are assumed to be of order $\mathbf{V} \times \mathbf{B}$, that is, of the order of magnitude of the induced effects. This assumption is equivalent to assuming that the induced magnetic field is much smaller than the externally applied magnetic field. It can be shown then that the Lorentz transformation for the B field is simply

$$\mathbf{B} = \mathbf{B}' \qquad (6.3\text{-}1)$$

The magnetic field is then the same in all frames of reference and we make no distinction between $\mathbf{B}$ and $\mathbf{B}'$. This conclusion can be seen by the following order of magnitude argument: In general,

$$\mathbf{B}' = \mathbf{B} - \frac{\mathbf{V} \times \mathbf{E}}{c^2}$$

Then if $\mathbf{E} \approx 0(\mathbf{V} \times \mathbf{B})$, it follows that $\mathbf{B}' = \mathbf{B} + 0(|\mathbf{V}|^2 \mathbf{B}/c^2)$ and since $|\mathbf{V}|^2 \ll c^2$, $\mathbf{B}' = \mathbf{B}$. However, merely because $\mathbf{B} = \mathbf{B}'$ we cannot always assume that $\mathbf{H}' = \mathbf{H}$. In the MHD approximation it usually is assumed that $\mathbf{H} = \mathbf{H}'$, so that the constitutive equation is simply $\mathbf{B} = \mu \mathbf{H}$ (for any $\mathbf{H}$) in the laboratory frame. (Remember that $\mathbf{B} = \mu_0 \mathbf{H}$ and $\mathbf{D} = \epsilon_0 \mathbf{E}$ in any frame if, and only if, the permeability and permittivity are μ_0 and ϵ_0, respectively.)

Let us examine the conditions under which it may be assumed that $\mathbf{H} = \mathbf{H}'$. From the Lorentz transformation, $\mathbf{H}' = \mathbf{H} - \mathbf{V} \times \mathbf{D}$ (for $V^2/c^2 \ll 1$), and using the constitutive equation for $\mathbf{D}$, we have

$$\mathbf{H}' = \mathbf{H} - \mathbf{V} \times \left[\epsilon(\mathbf{E} + \mathbf{V} \times \mathbf{B}) - \frac{1}{c^2}(\mathbf{V} \times \mathbf{H}) \right]$$

and hence

$$\mathbf{H}' = \mathbf{H} - 0(\epsilon V^2 \mathbf{B}) - 0\left(\frac{V^2}{c^2} \mathbf{H} \right) \approx \mathbf{H} - 0(\epsilon \mu V^2 \mathbf{H}) - 0\left(\frac{V^2}{c^2} \mathbf{H} \right)$$

but $\epsilon \mu = \kappa \kappa_m/c^2$, so that $\mathbf{H} = \mathbf{H}'$ is a valid assumption if $V^2 \kappa \kappa_m/c^2 \ll 1$ and $\mathbf{E} \approx 0(\mathbf{V} \times \mathbf{B})$. This assumption is valid, certainly for all gases (since $\kappa = \kappa_m = 1$) and conductors. (Some dielectrics might have extremely high values of κ.) Most ordinary materials, however, have κ of order 1 to 10^6 so that $\mathbf{H} = \mathbf{H}'$ is certainly a valid assumption for most physical situations under the MHD approximations and hence $\mathbf{B} = \mu \mathbf{H}$ is a valid equation even though $\mu \neq \mu_0$. It should be remembered that the one basic assumption underlying the approximations $\mathbf{B} = \mathbf{B}'$ and $\mathbf{H} = \mathbf{H}'$ is that the electric field $\mathbf{E}$ is of order $\mathbf{V} \times \mathbf{B}$. In some situations where extremely high electric fields exist this assumption may not be valid and the complete Lorentz transformation must be used.

The Lorentz transformation for the electric field may be taken as $\mathbf{E}' = \mathbf{E} + \mathbf{V} \times \mathbf{B}$ and (must always be considered since $\mathbf{E}$ and $\mathbf{V} \times \mathbf{B}$ are of the same order of magnitude.) Similarly, the transformation of the $\mathbf{D}$ field must also be considered.

(3.) Phenomena involving high frequency are not considered in the MHD approximation so that the displacement current $\partial \mathbf{D}/\partial t$ is neglected compared to $\mathbf{J}$, the conduction current. This (neglect implies, of course, that we are working with conductors and not dielectrics in which case $\partial \mathbf{D}/\partial t$ would have to be retained.) Even though $\partial \mathbf{D}/\partial t$ might be small at low frequencies, it would still be larger than the conduction current $\mathbf{J}$, which would be virtually zero in a dielectric. Hence Equation (6.2-4) becomes

$$\nabla \times \mathbf{H} = \mathbf{J} \tag{6.3-2}$$

This result can be verified by assuming a relevant time scale of order L/V_0 or $1/\omega$ where L and V_0 are the characteristic length and velocity, respectively, and ω is the characteristic frequency. Then, $\mathbf{E} \approx 0(\mathbf{V} \times \mathbf{B})$, and $\mathbf{J} \approx 0(\sigma\mathbf{E})$, and $\partial\mathbf{D}/\partial t \approx 0(\omega\epsilon\mathbf{E})$. When we compare these terms, $\partial\mathbf{D}/\partial t$ is important (compared to $\mathbf{J}$) only if $\omega\epsilon$ is comparable to σ. This condition is satisfied only at very high, essentially microwave frequencies in fairly good conductors, such as ionized gases. In metals, the displacement current is a meaningless concept, as will be pointed out in Section 7 of this chapter. (In a dielectric, however, $\omega\epsilon$ can be greater than σ.) Later, we shall investigate wave propagation phenomena in which the displacement current must be retained.

4. The electric energy is negligible compared to the magnetic energy. Comparing $\epsilon_0 E^2$ to $\mu_0 H^2$ (to order $V^2/c^2 \ll 1$), remembering that $\mathbf{E} \approx 0(\mathbf{V} \times \mathbf{B})$, we get

$$\epsilon_0 E^2 \approx 0(\epsilon_0\mu_0{}^2 |\mathbf{V} \times \mathbf{H}|^2) \approx 0\left(\mu_0 \frac{V^2}{c^2} H^2\right)$$

which is negligible compared to $\mu_0 H^2$ because of the $|V|^2/c^2$ factor. Since the displacement current and electric field energy are neglected, the main interaction is between the magnetic field and the fluid—hence the name MHD.

5. In Ohm's law, ρ_e (the space charge) may be neglected in liquid conductors (but must be retained in some instances in gases). Hence $\mathbf{J}' = \sigma\mathbf{E}' = \sigma(\mathbf{E} + \mathbf{V} \times \mathbf{B})$ is assumed. In general, $\mathbf{J}' = \sigma\mathbf{E}' = \mathbf{J} - \rho_e\mathbf{V}$ and $\rho'_e = \rho_e - (\mathbf{V} \cdot \mathbf{J}/c^2)$ where the $\sqrt{1 - (|V|^2/c^2)}$ factor has been dropped. Now, in a conductor we assume that $\rho'_e = 0$ so that $\rho_e = \mathbf{V} \cdot \mathbf{J}/c^2$. Hence $\mathbf{J} = \sigma\mathbf{E}' + \rho_e\mathbf{V} = \sigma(\mathbf{E} + \mathbf{V} \times \mathbf{B}) + (\mathbf{V} \cdot \mathbf{J}/c^2)\mathbf{V}$ or $\mathbf{J}(1 - 0(|\mathbf{V}|^2/c^2) = \sigma(\mathbf{E} + \mathbf{V} \times \mathbf{B})$ and since it has already been assumed that $|V|^2/c^2 \ll 1$, it is valid to say that

$$\mathbf{J} = \mathbf{J}' = \sigma(\mathbf{E} + \mathbf{V} \times \mathbf{B}) \tag{6.3-3}$$

It is further assumed that σ is constant (with frequency) and independent of the magnetic field. This assumption implies that the period of variation of the fields must be large compared to the mean free time of the conduction electrons, and that the mean free time of the conduction electrons is small compared to the reciprocal of the electron Larmor frequency eB/m_e. In rarefied plasmas this assumption may break down, and the concept of a simple scalar conductivity is meaningless.

6. The force density is represented by

$$\mathbf{f} = \rho_e \mathbf{E} + \mathbf{J} \times \mathbf{B} \tag{6.3-4}$$

The other terms are usually very small and for fluids in which $\mu = \mu_0$ and $\epsilon = \epsilon_0$, Equation (6.3-4) is identically correct. (For plasmas or gases where $\mu = \mu_0$ and $\epsilon = \epsilon_0$ this equation is good.) Also, from the Maxwell stress tensor, the electric terms can be shown to be negligible compared to the magnetic terms (as in assumption 4 above). For this reason the term $\rho_e \mathbf{E}$ is often taken as negligible in MHD. The neglect of $\rho_e \mathbf{E}$ is valid for conductors where $\rho'_e = 0$, but in some gases which are not electrically neutral and $\rho'_e \neq 0$, the force $\rho_e \mathbf{E}$ may be very important. This is especially true in wave motion studies in plasmas where a space charge wave usually accompanies any type of transmission.

7. In using equation $\nabla \cdot \mathbf{D} = \rho_e$ great care must be exercised. If the equation $\nabla \cdot \mathbf{J} + (\partial \rho_e / \partial t) = 0$ is used in metals (even in alternating-current problems under the MHD approximation), the $\partial \rho_e / \partial t$ term may be dropped and ρ_e need never be mentioned although it is not identically zero as is ρ'_e. In a metallic conductor $\rho'_e = 0$ and $\rho_e = \mathbf{V} \cdot \mathbf{J}/c^2$. Hence

$$\nabla \cdot \mathbf{J} + \frac{\partial \rho_e}{\partial t} = \nabla \cdot \mathbf{J} + \frac{\partial}{\partial t}\left(\frac{\mathbf{V} \cdot \mathbf{J}}{c^2}\right) = 0$$

$$= \nabla \cdot \mathbf{J} + 0\left[\frac{\omega}{c^2}(\mathbf{V} \cdot \mathbf{J})\right] \tag{6.3-5}$$

Introducing a characteristic length L and velocity V_0,

$$\nabla \cdot \mathbf{J} \approx 0\left(\frac{|\mathbf{J}|}{L}\right)$$

$$\frac{\partial}{\partial t}\left(\frac{(\mathbf{V} \cdot \mathbf{J})}{c^2}\right) \approx 0\left(\frac{\omega V_0}{c^2}|\mathbf{J}|\right)$$

Comparing $1/L$ to $\omega V_0/c^2$, we see that even for high-frequency microwave phenomena where $1/L \to 0(\omega/c)$, the term $\partial \rho_e/\partial t$ is less than $\nabla \cdot \mathbf{J}$ by a factor of V_0/c, so that $\nabla \cdot \mathbf{J} = 0$ should be valid even for high-frequency phenomena as long as the fluid velocity V_0 is very small compared to c. As V_0 becomes appreciable compared to c, however, $\partial \rho_e/\partial t$ must be considered in the current continuity equation.

However, if we prefer to use the equation $\nabla \cdot \mathbf{D} = \rho_e$, the expression $\nabla' \cdot \mathbf{D}' = \rho'_e = 0$ in the rest frame is valid for a metallic conductor, but ρ_e is not necessarily zero in the laboratory frame and we must write

$$\nabla \cdot \mathbf{D} = \frac{\mathbf{V} \cdot \mathbf{J}}{c^2} = \rho_e \tag{6.3-6}$$

even for conductors in steady state operation. In fact, Equation (6.3-6) is often used to find the induced charge on a moving conductor after the currents have been established from the $\nabla \cdot \mathbf{J} = 0$ equation. The terms may be examined:

$$\nabla \cdot \mathbf{D} = 0\left(\frac{|\mathbf{D}|}{L}\right)$$

$$\rho_e = \frac{\mathbf{V} \cdot \mathbf{J}}{c^2} \approx 0\left[\frac{V_0}{c^2} |(\nabla \times \mathbf{H})|\right] \approx 0\left(\frac{|\mathbf{E}|}{c^2 L \mu_0}\right) \approx 0\left(\frac{|\mathbf{D}|}{L}\right)$$

Hence $\nabla \cdot \mathbf{D}$ and ρ_e are of the same order of magnitude (although perhaps small) even under the MHD approximation and low-frequency or steady-state conditions. This observation is often overlooked and must be remembered.

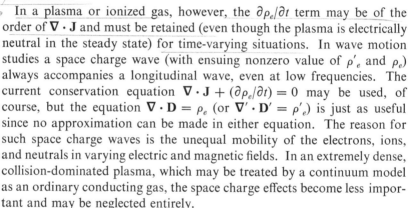

In a plasma or ionized gas, however, the $\partial \rho_e / \partial t$ term may be of the order of $\nabla \cdot \mathbf{J}$ and must be retained (even though the plasma is electrically neutral in the steady state) for time-varying situations. In wave motion studies a space charge wave (with ensuing nonzero value of ρ'_e and ρ_e) always accompanies a longitudinal wave, even at low frequencies. The current conservation equation $\nabla \cdot \mathbf{J} + (\partial \rho_e / \partial t) = 0$ may be used, of course, but the equation $\nabla \cdot \mathbf{D} = \rho_e$ (or $\nabla' \cdot \mathbf{D}' = \rho'_e$) is just as useful since no approximation can be made in either equation. The reason for such space charge waves is the unequal mobility of the electrons, ions, and neutrals in varying electric and magnetic fields. In an extremely dense, collision-dominated plasma, which may be treated by a continuum model as an ordinary conducting gas, the space charge effects become less important and may be neglected entirely.

6.4   EQUATIONS UNDER THE MHD APPROXIMATION

The basic equations under the MHD approximation may now be written. Maxwell's equations become

$$\nabla \times \mathbf{E} = -\frac{\partial \mathbf{B}}{\partial t}$$

$$\nabla \times \mathbf{H} = \mathbf{J}$$

$$\nabla \cdot \mathbf{J} = 0 \tag{6.4-1}$$

$$\nabla \cdot \mathbf{B} = 0$$

Ohm's law is

$$\mathbf{J} = \sigma(\mathbf{E} + \mathbf{V} \times \mathbf{B}) \tag{6.4-2}$$

The fluid equations are

$$\frac{\partial \rho}{\partial t} + \mathbf{V} \cdot (\rho \mathbf{V}) = 0 \tag{6.4-3}$$

for continuity; and

$$\rho \left[\frac{\partial \mathbf{V}}{\partial t} + \mathbf{V}\!\left(\frac{V^2}{2}\right) - \mathbf{V} \times (\mathbf{\nabla} \times \mathbf{V}) \right] = -\nabla P - \rho \nabla \psi + \mathbf{\nabla} \cdot \mathbf{\tau'} + \mathbf{J} \times \mathbf{B}$$
$$\tag{6.4-4}$$

for motion, where ψ is the gravitational potential. (It is sometimes assumed in the MHD approximation that the gravity forces are negligible, but this is not necessarily true. $\mathbf{\tau'}$ above is the shear part of the mechanical stress tensor $\mathbf{\tau}$.)
And for energy,

$$\rho \frac{DU}{Dt} = \Phi - P\mathbf{\nabla} \cdot \mathbf{V} + \mathbf{\nabla} \cdot (\kappa_T \mathbf{\nabla} T) + \mathbf{E'} \cdot \mathbf{J'} \tag{6.4-5}$$

(which has been discussed in detail in Chapter 5). In addition, the equation of state (which has been discussed in Chapter 4) may be used for gases. U is the specific internal energy, Φ the mechanical dissipation function, and κ_T thermal conductivity.

The term $\mathbf{J} \times \mathbf{B}$ may be written entirely in terms of the magnetic field (from Maxwell's equations) so that

$$\mathbf{J} \times \mathbf{B} = \mu(\mathbf{\nabla} \times \mathbf{H}) \times \mathbf{H} = -\mu\mathbf{H} \times (\mathbf{\nabla} \times \mathbf{H}) \tag{6.4-6}$$

and the equation of motion becomes

$$\rho \left[\frac{\partial \mathbf{V}}{\partial t} + (\mathbf{V} \cdot \mathbf{\nabla})\mathbf{V} \right] = \rho \left[\frac{\partial \mathbf{V}}{\partial t} + \mathbf{\nabla}\!\left(\frac{V^2}{2}\right) - \mathbf{V} \times (\mathbf{\nabla} \times \mathbf{V}) \right]$$
$$= -\nabla P - \rho \nabla \psi + \mathbf{\nabla} \cdot \mathbf{\tau'} - \mu\mathbf{H} \times (\mathbf{\nabla} \times \mathbf{H}) \tag{6.4-7}$$

By replacing $\mathbf{\tau'}$ by its value in terms of velocity and viscosity, we have

$$\rho \left[\frac{\partial \mathbf{V}}{\partial t} + \mathbf{\nabla}\!\left(\frac{V^2}{2}\right) - \mathbf{V} \times (\mathbf{\nabla} \times \mathbf{V}) \right] = -\nabla P - \rho \nabla \psi + \rho \nu \nabla^2 \mathbf{V}$$
$$+ (\zeta + \tfrac{1}{3}\nu\rho)\mathbf{\nabla}(\mathbf{\nabla} \cdot \mathbf{V}) + \mu(\mathbf{\nabla} \times \mathbf{H}) \times \mathbf{H} \tag{6.4-8}$$

where ν is the kinematic viscosity. For an incompressible fluid the last term involving $\mathbf{\nabla} \cdot \mathbf{V}$ goes to zero. The vector relationships may be replaced by certain pseudo-vector relationships and the motion equation may be written:

$$\rho\left[\frac{\partial \mathbf{V}}{\partial t} + (\mathbf{V} \cdot \nabla)\mathbf{V}\right] = -\nabla P - \rho\nabla\psi + \rho\nu\nabla^2\mathbf{V}$$

$$+ (\zeta + \tfrac{1}{3}\nu\rho)\nabla(\nabla \cdot \mathbf{V}) + \mu(\mathbf{H} \cdot \nabla)\mathbf{H} - \mu\nabla\left(\frac{\mathbf{H}^2}{2}\right) \quad (6.4\text{-}9)$$

We should remember that $\nabla^2\mathbf{V}$ is not the same as ∇^2 of the individual scalar components except in cartesian coordinates. In general,

$$\nabla^2\mathbf{V} = (\nabla \cdot \nabla)\mathbf{V} = \nabla(\nabla \cdot \mathbf{V}) - \nabla \times (\nabla \times \mathbf{V})$$

Several forms of Maxwell's equations can be derived under the MHD approximation. The following equation in terms $\mathbf{H}$ only can be derived. From Equation (6.2-3) and Ohm's law;

$$\nabla \times \mathbf{E} = -\frac{\partial \mathbf{B}}{\partial t} = \nabla \times (\mathbf{E}' - \mathbf{V} \times \mathbf{B})$$

$$= \nabla \times \left(\frac{\mathbf{J}'}{\sigma} - \mathbf{V} \times \mathbf{B}\right)$$

Then by combining $\nabla \times \mathbf{H} = \mathbf{J}$, we have

$$\frac{\partial \mathbf{H}}{\partial t} = \nabla \times (\mathbf{V} \times \mathbf{H}) - \nabla \times \left(\frac{\nabla \times \mathbf{H}}{\sigma\mu}\right) \quad (6.4\text{-}10)$$

By the identity $\nabla \times (\nabla \times \mathbf{H}) = \nabla(\nabla \cdot \mathbf{H}) - \nabla^2\mathbf{H}$ (assuming the magnetic permeability μ to be a constant), Equation (6.4-10) may be put into the form (remembering that $\nabla \cdot \mathbf{H} = \nabla \cdot \mathbf{B} = 0$):

$$\frac{\partial \mathbf{B}}{\partial t} = \eta\,\nabla^2\mathbf{B} + \nabla \times (\mathbf{V} \times \mathbf{B}) \quad (6.4\text{-}11)$$

where $\eta = 1/\sigma\mu$, which, for reasons to be seen, is called the magnetic diffusivity. Equation (6.4-10) as well as Equation (6.4-11), along with $\nabla \cdot \mathbf{J} = 0$, contains all the information about $\mathbf{H}$ contained in Maxwell's equations and, together with the fluid equations, completely specifies the problem.

6.5 DIMENSIONAL AND INSPECTIONAL ANALYSIS

There are two general methods of obtaining the dimensionless parameters associated with a given problem: inspectional analysis and dimensional analysis.

The inspectional analysis method is possible only when we have a complete set of descriptive differential equations. The equations are normalized (made dimensionless) and in this process certain dimensionless parameters appear as the coefficients of the various terms in the equations. These coefficients are the dimensionless parameters or so-called Π's of the system. The Π's will be different depending on how the variables appearing in the equations are normalized. However, there exists only one complete, independent set of Π's and all others may be formed by multiplying various Π's together.

We can see, then, that these parameters set the problem in terms of similitude. That is, dimensionless independent variables (or functions of them) may be plotted versus relevant dependent variables, and the results should be perfectly general for a fixed set of relevant dimensionless parameters or Π's. For this reason we speak of similitude in modeling. A plot of normalized variables should hold for either a model or prototype only if the dimensionless parameters are the same. However, it is often impossible to set all the parameters for the model and prototype equal and some approximation must be made. For instance, low-speed aerodynamics requires that the Reynolds number of the model and the prototype be the same, at the expense of differing Froude numbers. In this case the Froude number, being a measure of gravity effects, is unimportant.

It should be recognized that the differential equations do not have to be solved in order to obtain the Π's by inspectional analysis; a knowledge of what the equations are is sufficient.

In the second method, called dimensional analysis, the parameters (or Π's) are found without a knowledge of the governing differential equations. Instead, the relevant variables are collected and combined together to give the maximum number of independent dimensionless parameters. The difficulties of this system are obvious. The complete set of relevant variables must be known, and no extraneous variables can be introduced, otherwise the final set of Π's may be meaningless. Frequently in physical situations it is difficult to ascertain which variables are relevant and which are not. And the combinations chosen, while they may form a complete set, may not be the most convenient. Both of these difficulties are circumvented by the inspectional analysis method. The advantage of dimensional analysis is, of course, that the descriptive equations are not necessary and one is rewarded according to insight and cleverness. A useful rule of thumb is that the number of independent Π's is equal to the total number of independent variables in the problem minus the number of fundamental units, which may be taken as mass, length, time, and any one fundamental electrical unit, such as charge, making a total of four.

In magnetohydrodynamics, and indeed in most physical problems, the relevant physical laws can be stated in differential equation form, even though they may not be easily solvable, and inspectional analysis leads to a unique set of Π's that are reliable.

6.6 NORMALIZATION OF THE MHD EQUATIONS AND FUNDAMENTAL PARAMETERS

The variables that appear in the equations presented in the previous sections can be normalized in various ways. One consistent method that leads to an independent set of Π's is the following (dimensionless quantities are represented with an asterisk):

$$P^* = \frac{P}{\rho_0 V_0{}^2} \qquad \rho^* = \frac{\rho}{\rho_0}$$

$$T^* = \frac{T}{T_0} \qquad \mathbf{V}^* = \frac{\mathbf{V}}{V_0}$$

$$x_i{}^* = \frac{x_i}{L} \qquad t^* = \frac{t}{t_0} = \frac{tV_0}{L}$$

$$U^* = \frac{U}{c_V T_0} \qquad \Phi^* = \frac{L^2 \Phi}{V_0{}^2 \nu \rho_0}$$

$$M_0 = \frac{V_0}{a_0} \qquad a_0 = \sqrt{\gamma R T_0} \qquad (6.6\text{-}1)$$

$$\gamma = \frac{c_P}{c_V} \qquad \psi^* = \frac{\psi}{gL}$$

$$\nabla^* = L \cdot \nabla \qquad \mathbf{H}^* = \frac{\mathbf{H}}{H_0}$$

$$\mathbf{E}^* = \frac{\mathbf{E}}{E_0} \qquad \mathbf{B}^* = \frac{\mathbf{B}}{B_0} = \frac{\mathbf{H}}{H_0} = \mathbf{H}^*$$

$$\mathbf{D}^* = \frac{\mathbf{D}}{D_0}$$

In the above definitions, the subscript $(\ )_0$ refers to a characteristic value. The characteristic velocity and length are V_0 and L, respectively. a is the sonic velocity, and γ the ratio of specific heats. M_0 is the reference Mach number which is the ratio of the characteristic velocity to the characteristic sonic velocity. R is the gas constant for any particular gas and is $\bar{R}$ (the universal gas constant) divided by the molecular weight.

In terms of these dimensionless variables the basic MHD equations can be written as follows:

Continuity

$$\frac{\partial \rho^*}{\partial t^*} + \nabla^* \cdot (\rho^* V^*) = 0 \tag{6.6-2}$$

Motion

$$\rho^* \left[\frac{\partial V^*}{\partial t^*} + \nabla^* \left(\frac{V^{*2}}{2} \right) - V^* \times (\nabla^* \times V^*) \right]$$

$$= -\nabla^* P^* + \frac{1}{Re} \nabla^{*2} V^* + \left(\frac{1}{Re'} + \frac{1}{3Re} \right) \nabla^* (\nabla^* \cdot V^*)$$

$$- \rho^* \nabla^* \psi^* \cdot \frac{1}{Fr} - \frac{1}{M_m^2} H^* \times (\nabla^* \times H^*) \tag{6.6-3}$$

State

$$P^* = \frac{1}{\gamma M_0^2} \rho^* T^* \tag{6.6-4}$$

Maxwell Equations. The Maxwell equations can be combined to give two equations for the magnetic field. They are

$$\nabla^* \cdot B^* = 0 \tag{6.6-5}$$

and a magnetic diffusion equation

$$\frac{\partial H^*}{\partial t^*} = -\frac{1}{Rm} \nabla^* \times (\nabla^* \times H^*) + \nabla^* \times (V^* \times H^*) \tag{6.6-6}$$

Ohm's law and the other field equations are now redundant and unnecessary in the MHD approximation.

Energy Equation

$$\rho^* \frac{D^* U^*}{Dt^*} = \frac{\gamma(\gamma - 1) M_0^2 \Phi^*}{Re} - P^* \nabla^* \cdot V^* [\gamma(\gamma - 1) M_0^2]$$

$$+ \frac{\gamma}{PrRe} \cdot \nabla^{*2} T^* + \frac{(\nabla \times H^*)^2 \gamma(\gamma - 1) M_0^2}{M_m^2 \cdot Rm^2} \tag{6.6-7}$$

The dimensionless parameters which have appeared as coefficients in these equations can now be listed and given a physical interpretation.

Re = Reynolds number = LV_0/ν, which is a measure of the ratio of inertial to viscous force.

Re' = another Reynolds number based on second coefficient of viscosity = $\rho_0 LV_0/\zeta$

M_0 = characteristic Mach number = V_0/a_0, which is the ratio of the characteristic velocity to the characteristic sonic velocity.

Rm = magnetic Reynolds number = $V_0 L/\eta = V_0 L\sigma\mu$, which is a measure of the ratio of magnetic convection to magnetic diffusion. The magnetic Reynolds number is also a measure of the magnitude of the induced magnetic field (compared to the total magnetic field) in MFD flow problems. The induced magnetic field $\mathbf{B}_i$ is of order $\mathbf{J}\mu L$ which follows from $\nabla \times \mathbf{H} = \mathbf{J}$. Then $\mathbf{J}/\sigma = 0(V_0\mathbf{B})$ from Ohm's law, where $\mathbf{B}$ is the total magnetic field. Then $|\mathbf{B}_i|/|\mathbf{B}| \approx 0(V_0 L\sigma\mu) = 0(V_0 L/\eta)$. It is here assumed that the induced magnetic field is due to the current $\mathbf{J}$ and the total magnetic field is made up of the induced magnetic field plus an applied (usually larger) magnetic field. A small $Rm(Rm \ll 1)$ indicates that the induced magnetic field is small compared to the total or (in this case) the applied magnetic field. For most MFD flow where $\mathbf{E} = 0(\mathbf{V} \times \mathbf{B})$, Rm is usually much less than unity.

Pr = Prandtl number = ν/α, which is a measure of the ratio of kinematic viscosity (or diffusion of vorticity) to the thermal diffusivity α, which is $\kappa_T/c_P\rho_0$. Hence we can write $Pr = c_P\nu\rho_0/\kappa_T$.

Fr = Froude number = V_0^2/gL, which is a measure of the ratio of inertial force to the gravitational force.

M_m = magnetic Mach number or Alfvén number = V_0/A, which is a measure of the ratio of the characteristic fluid velocity to the Alfvén velocity. (The Alfvén velocity A is given by $A^2 = \mu H_0^2/\rho_0$ and will be explained later.)

These parameters are sufficient but are not unique. Several others may be formed by multiplying together various combinations of the preceding Π's and then given important physical interpretation. These other Π's would have arisen naturally in the equations if the variables had been normalized appropriately. Some of the other more important parameters are:

M = Hartmann number = $\sqrt{\sigma B_0^2 L^2/\mu_f} = \sqrt{\sigma B_0^2 L^2/\nu\rho_0} = \sqrt{ReRm/M_m}$, which is a measure of the ratio of ponderomotive force to the viscous force. (In this interpretation it is assumed that the ponderomotive force is of order $\sigma U_0 B_0^2$ which is certainly true for small or moderate conductivities.) Here μ_f is the fluid viscosity.

Pm = magnetic Prandtl number = $\nu/\eta = Rm/Re$, which is a measure of the ratio of vorticity diffusion to magnetic diffusion. This number is usually very small (for ordinary conductors in the laboratory), being $\approx 10^{-7}$ for mercury, so that the magnetic field diffuses much more easily than the vorticity. For cosmic problems, or in situations where the conductivity is very large, the opposite is true, as will be shown in the next section.

For small conductivity, $Rm \ll 1$, and the current is of order $\sigma V_0 B_0$. The inertial force is of order $\rho_0 V_0^2/L$, so that a parameter N_1 is defined as

$$N_1 = \frac{\sigma B_0^2 L}{\rho_0 V_0} = \frac{Rm}{M_m^2}$$

which is a measure of the ratio of ponderomotive force to inertial force. For most cases of ionized gases, the conductivity is rather small and Rm may be less than unity so that N_1 itself may be much smaller than unity or larger depending on the value of Mm. The class of problems in which N_1 is a significant parameter is important in aerodynamical problems where air, ionized by viscous heating effects, may have a relatively low conductivity. N_1 is sometimes referred to as the "interaction parameter."

In the other extreme of high conductivity, where $Rm \gg 1$, the current is of order of magnitude $\mathbf{J} \approx \nabla \times \mathbf{H} \approx 0(\mathbf{H}_0/L)$, so that

$$N_2 = \frac{(H_0/L)B_0}{\rho V_0^2/L} = \frac{1}{M_m^2}$$

which is a measure of the ratio of ponderomotive to inertial force for highly conducting fluids. This class of problems, where Rm is large, has been investigated rather extensively in plasma theory and especially in wave motion theory, where it is mathematically expedient and often a good approximation to assume σ infinite.

It should be emphasized here that only two magnetic parameters are independent and their choice is arbitrary. Depending on how the normalization of the individual variables is carried out, the inspectional analysis method yields different sets of dimensionless parameters.

Another point of interest is the concept of vectorial dimensional analysis. In an actual problem, the characteristic length L and characteristic velocity V_0 must be chosen colinear and in the direction of the variable x_i or x_i^*, V_i or V_i^*, etc. This vectorial procedure may necessitate modifying the Π's given here by dimensionless ratios of parameters, such as L_1/L_2, where L_1 and L_2 are characteristic lengths in different directions. A proper mathematical discussion of this concept may be found in the work by Birkhoff listed in the references.

6.7 OBSERVATIONS ON CONDUCTIVITY

1. *High Conductivity.* From Ohm's law in the MHD approximation $\mathbf{J} = \sigma(\mathbf{E} + \mathbf{V} \times \mathbf{B})$, it can be seen that for finite current, as $\sigma \to \infty$, $\mathbf{E}$ must be given by $\mathbf{E} = -(\mathbf{V} \times \mathbf{B})$. Then Ohm's law does not determine

the current, but rather the Maxwell equation $\nabla \times \mathbf{H} = \mathbf{J}$ determines $\mathbf{J}$. If displacement current is considered, the conclusion is the same and is determined by $\nabla \times \mathbf{H} = \mathbf{J} + (\partial \mathbf{D}/\partial t)$.

In many problems it is useful to make the assumption of infinite conductivity in order to obtain qualitative information about physical situations, since this assumption generally allows a much simpler mathematical formulation of the problem. An important application of the concept of infinite conductivity is in high temperature plasma studies such as those associated with fusion devices. Many problems become tractable, analytically, under the assumption of infinite conductivity, and the results may differ from physical reality, in some cases, only by a damping term. In other instances, however, the complete physical meaning can be lost if the assumption is not used with care.

2. *Low Conductivity.* For materials of moderate conductivity, such as metals, Ohm's law may be used in the form $\mathbf{J} = \sigma(\mathbf{E} + \mathbf{V} \times \mathbf{B})$ under the MHD approximation. In a nonneutral ionized gas, or in a dielectric, the space charge may become important. Then Ohm's law must be written in the rest frame as $\mathbf{J}' = \sigma \mathbf{E}'$ and the appropriate Lorentz transformation must be used to find $\mathbf{J}$ in the laboratory frame. Nonrelativistically, this transformation leads to $\mathbf{J} = \sigma(\mathbf{E} + \mathbf{V} \times \mathbf{B}) + \rho_e \mathbf{V}$.

If the conductivity is extremely small, as in a dielectric, the conductivity may be neglected altogether. However, in a dielectric the displacement current $\partial \mathbf{D}/\partial t$ must be taken into account, especially if high-frequency phenomena are considered.

6.8   VERY HIGH FREQUENCY PHENOMENA

The Maxwell equations

$$\nabla \cdot \mathbf{B} = 0$$
$$\nabla \times \mathbf{E} = -\frac{\partial \mathbf{B}}{\partial t} \tag{6.8-1}$$

are always valid in a metal or dielectric. The other two equations, however, must be examined carefully. In a very good dielectric the conduction current is zero and

$$\nabla \times \mathbf{H} = \frac{\partial \mathbf{D}}{\partial t}$$

In a poor conductor (for example, semiconductor) the conduction current may be retained and

$$\nabla \times \mathbf{H} = \frac{\partial \mathbf{D}}{\partial t} + \mathbf{J} \tag{6.8-2}$$

In a true metal, the displacement current is meaningless. In this case $\sigma/\omega \gg \epsilon$ over the frequency range in which σ may be considered constant, and displacement current is unimportant. In a metal, for high frequencies, the macroscopic Maxwell equations are rather meaningless since the effects of spatial nonuniformity become important sooner than the displacement current correction.*

A plasma may be thought of as a poor conductor and Equation (6.8-2) can be used along with the other Maxwell equations. However, in a dielectric, as $\omega \to \infty$, $\epsilon \to$ unity and ϵ, then, is frequency dependent.

An excellent discussion of these points may be found in the Landau and Lifshitz work listed in the references.

6.9 MAGNETIC TRANSPORT

The magnetic field vector behaves much like the vorticity vector in fluid mechanics. Both can diffuse through or be convected by the fluid. From Maxwell's equations and Ohm's law, under the MHD approximation

$$\frac{1}{\mu} \nabla \times \mathbf{B} = \nabla \times \mathbf{H} = \sigma(\mathbf{E} + \mathbf{V} \times \mathbf{B})$$
$$\nabla \cdot \mathbf{B} = 0 \qquad (6.9\text{-}1)$$
$$\nabla \times \mathbf{E} = -\frac{\partial \mathbf{B}}{\partial t}$$

and by combining and using the vector identity

$$\nabla \times (\nabla \times \mathbf{B}) = -\nabla^2 \mathbf{B} + \nabla(\nabla \cdot \mathbf{B})$$

there results

$$\frac{\partial \mathbf{B}}{\partial t} = \eta \, \nabla^2 \mathbf{B} + \nabla \times (\mathbf{V} \times \mathbf{B}) \qquad (6.9\text{-}2)$$

or in dimensionless form (from Equation (6.6-6)

$$\frac{\partial \mathbf{B}^*}{\partial t^*} = -\frac{1}{Rm} \nabla^* \times (\nabla^* \times \mathbf{B}^*) + \nabla^* \times (\mathbf{V}^* \times \mathbf{B}^*) \qquad (6.9\text{-}3)$$

where η, the magnetic diffusity, is given by $\eta = 1/\sigma\mu$ and Rm is the magnetic Reynold's number $V_0 L/\eta$. This is precisely the same equation as the vorticity transport equation and all the familiar mathematical theorems may be applied to it.

---

* However, in a metal, by considering the atomic polarization as a function of frequency, meaningful approximate results may be obtained by retaining the displacement current. See Chapter 8.

In the absence of velocity, the transport equation becomes

$$\frac{\partial \mathbf{B}}{\partial t} = \eta \, \nabla^2 \mathbf{B} \tag{6.9-4}$$

which is a pure diffusion equation, showing why η is called the magnetic diffusivity. In a solid material then, the magnetic field, once introduced, must diffuse out at some finite rate even if the external magnetic field source is removed. The characteristic time of this diffusion has a wide range in nature and depends on the value of η and the spatial dimensions which determine $\nabla^2 \mathbf{B}$. The larger the conductivity, the greater the diffusion time, and in the limit of infinite conductivity one might expect everlasting magnetic fields. The smaller the value of $\nabla^2 \mathbf{B}$, the larger the diffusion time. This condition of small $\nabla^2 \mathbf{B}$ may be satisfied if the physical dimensions are large so that the magnetic field can change slowly from place to place (and satisfy $\nabla \cdot \mathbf{B} = 0$).

In the sun and stars, where dimensions are large, long decay times would be expected. In the sun the decay time (as estimated by Cowling) is of the order of 10^{10} years and in the earth's core the decay time is estimated to be about 15,000 years (as calculated by Elsasser). We might seek the cause of the earth's magnetic field in terms of an initial field which is slowly decaying; however, the age of the éarth is estimated to be about 10^9 years, and little change in the field is evidenced by geological study. This leads to the conclusion that there must be a continual production of the terrestrial field, an essentially dynamo action. Much attention has been given to this dynamo problem, and the most plausible theories attribute the dynamo action to fluid currents in the liquid interior of the earth.

Returning to the magnetic transport equation, we see that if there is no velocity, the field lines slip or diffuse through the material and decay away. However, even if velocity is present, it is possible for the $\eta\nabla^2 \mathbf{B}$ term to dominate if the magnetic Reynold's number Rm is small ($Rm \ll 1$). Diffusion is then the dominant means of transport. The other term $\nabla \times (\mathbf{V} \times \mathbf{B})$ represents pure convection. If the $\eta\nabla^2 \mathbf{B}$ term is negligible compared to the convection term $\nabla \times (\mathbf{V} \times \mathbf{B})$ (Rm large, $\gg 1$), the magnetic field lines are transported along with the fluid and do not slip through it. As the conductivity becomes large ($\sigma \to \infty$) and $\eta \to 0$, the convection term dominates and diffusion may be neglected. The fields are then said to be "frozen in" because the field lines behave as though they were simply frozen into the fluid.

The concept of the "frozen in" field is a direct consequence of the form of the transport equation (6.9-3) in the limit of $\sigma \to \infty$:

$$\frac{\partial \mathbf{B}}{\partial t} = \nabla \times (\mathbf{V} \times \mathbf{B}) = (\mathbf{B} \cdot \nabla)\mathbf{V} - (\mathbf{V} \cdot \nabla)\mathbf{B} - \mathbf{B}(\nabla \cdot \mathbf{V}) \tag{6.9-5}$$

This equation may be put into a familiar form by combining it with the fluid continuity equation, which may be written

$$\nabla \cdot \mathbf{V} = -\frac{1}{\rho}\frac{\partial \rho}{\partial t} - \frac{\mathbf{V} \cdot \nabla \rho}{\rho} \tag{6.9-6}$$

to obtain

$$\left(\frac{\partial}{\partial t} + \mathbf{V} \cdot \nabla\right)\frac{\mathbf{B}}{\rho} = \left(\frac{\mathbf{B}}{\rho} \cdot \nabla\right)\mathbf{V} \tag{6.9-7}$$

The left-hand side is the substantial derivative and (6.9-7) may be written

$$\frac{D}{Dt}\left(\frac{\mathbf{B}}{\rho}\right) = \left(\frac{\mathbf{B}}{\rho} \cdot \nabla\right)\mathbf{V} \tag{6.9-8}$$

There is a formal analogy then between the behavior of vorticity in a frictionless, compressible fluid and the magnetic field in a compressible fluid (not necessarily frictionless) of infinite electrical conductivity.

The classical Helmholtz vortex theorems apply and we can conclude immediately that the lines of magnetic force are "frozen" into the fluid and connected with it in a manner similar to the convection of vortex lines in a nonconducting fluid. This can be visualized by saying that any closed contour composed of a "fluid line" (a line which moves with the fluid particles composing it) cuts no lines of force as the fluid moves. The quantity $|\mathbf{B}|/\rho$ (or $|\mathbf{H}|/\rho$) then varies in proportion to the extension of the fluid line. We can imagine this motion by thinking of the fluid as gripping the $\mathbf{H}/\rho$ lines at every point and holding fast as the fluid flows, but allowing the $\mathbf{H}/\rho$ lines to rotate and elongate. We can also imagine filaments of dye which move with the local velocity of the fluid, so that an $\mathbf{H}/\rho$ line always coincides with a fluid line which is always composed of the same fluid particles. A quick proof can be given as follows: Let $\delta\mathbf{l}$ be a length of a fluid line. We determine how $\delta\mathbf{l}$ varies with time. Let $\mathbf{V}$ be the velocity of the fluid at one end of $\delta\mathbf{l}$. The velocity at the other end is $\mathbf{V} + (\delta\mathbf{l} \cdot \nabla)\mathbf{V}$. During a time interval δt the vector $\delta\mathbf{l}$ changes by $\delta t(\delta\mathbf{l} \cdot \nabla)\mathbf{V}$ since $\delta\mathbf{l} = \delta\mathbf{V}\,\delta t$. Therefore, $\delta\mathbf{l}/\delta t = (\delta\mathbf{l} \cdot \nabla)\mathbf{V}$ and the rate of change of $\mathbf{H}/\rho$ and $\delta\mathbf{l}$ are identically expressed and hence must always remain parallel; thus an $\mathbf{H}/\rho$ line is always composed of the same fluid particles.

6.10   ALFVÉN WAVES

A general discussion of wave motion will be postponed until Chapter 8. However, a particularly simple mode of transverse incompressible wave propagation exists in a conducting fluid and has no analogue in a non-conducting fluid. Since this Alfvén wave velocity will play an important role when the more general wave motion is discussed, a brief description is given here.

In Chapter 3 it was mentioned that the electromagnetic stress state could be represented by a hydrostatic pressure of $\mathbf{H} \cdot \mathbf{B}/2$ and a tension of $\mathbf{H} \cdot \mathbf{B}$ along the lines of force. This tension suggests the possibility of transverse waves being propagated along the lines of force with velocity $\sqrt{\mathbf{H} \cdot \mathbf{B}/\rho}$ in much the same manner as are displacement waves along a stretched string.

Such is indeed the case, and in an infinitely conducting, inviscid fluid such waves can propagate with velocity $\sqrt{\mathbf{H} \cdot \mathbf{B}/\rho}$ along lines of force. These waves generally couple into the viscous diffusion waves in the fluid and are damped by electrical dissipation. They may also be accompanied by uncoupled longitudinal magnetoacoustic waves. A complete description of these waves will be presented later.

Assuming an infinitely conducting, inviscid fluid, we find that under the MHD approximation the basic equations may be written as follows:

$$\frac{\partial \mathbf{H}}{\partial t} = \nabla \times (\mathbf{V} \times \mathbf{H})$$

$$\rho \frac{D\mathbf{V}}{Dt} = -\nabla P + \rho \nabla \psi + \mu (\nabla \times \mathbf{H}) \times \mathbf{H} \qquad (6.10\text{-}1)$$

$$\nabla \cdot \mathbf{B} = 0$$

$$\frac{\partial \rho}{\partial t} + \nabla \cdot (\rho \mathbf{V}) = 0$$

By introducing small disturbances about a steady-state condition of no motion as $\mathbf{H} = \mathbf{H}_0 + \mathbf{h}$, $P = P_0 + p$, $\mathbf{V} = \mathbf{v}$, and $\rho = \rho_0 + \rho'$ into the equations and by linearizing (neglecting squares and products in the small quantities $\mathbf{h}$, p, $\mathbf{v}$, ρ'), we have:

$$\frac{\partial \mathbf{h}}{\partial t} = (\mathbf{H}_0 \cdot \nabla)\mathbf{v} - H_0(\nabla \cdot \mathbf{v}) \qquad (6.10\text{-}2)$$

(where the vector identity $\nabla \times (\mathbf{v} \times \mathbf{H}) = (\mathbf{H} \cdot \nabla)\mathbf{v} - \mathbf{H}(\nabla \cdot \mathbf{v}) - (\mathbf{v} \cdot \nabla)\mathbf{H} + \mathbf{v}(\nabla \cdot \mathbf{H})$ has been used along with $\nabla \cdot \mathbf{B} = 0$). Then

$$\frac{\partial \rho'}{\partial t} + \rho_0 \nabla \cdot \mathbf{v} = 0 \qquad (6.10\text{-}3)$$

$$\rho_0 \frac{\partial \mathbf{v}}{\partial t} = -\nabla p + \mu (\nabla \times \mathbf{h}) \times \mathbf{H}_0 \qquad (6.10\text{-}4)$$

If we confine ourselves to plane waves propagating in the direction of the $\mathbf{H}_0$ vector (z direction), the transverse components of the equations become uncoupled and (6.10-2) through (6.10-4) become

$$\frac{\partial \mathbf{h}_\perp}{\partial t} = (\mathbf{H}_0 \cdot \nabla)\mathbf{v}_\perp = \mathbf{H}_0 \frac{\partial \mathbf{v}_\perp}{\partial z} \qquad (6.10\text{-}5)$$

$$\rho_0 \frac{\partial \mathbf{v}_\perp}{\partial t} = \mu(\nabla \times \mathbf{h})_\perp \times \mathbf{H}_0 = \mu H_0 \frac{\partial \mathbf{h}_\perp}{\partial z} \qquad (6.10\text{-}6)$$

(There are no variations in the transverse ($\perp$) direction, since we are assuming plane waves.) The above equations give

$$\frac{\partial^2 h_\perp}{\partial t^2} = A^2 \frac{\partial^2 h_\perp}{\partial z^2}$$
$$\frac{\partial^2 v_\perp}{\partial t^2} = A^2 \frac{\partial^2 v_\perp}{\partial z^2} \qquad (6.10\text{-}7)$$

where A, the phase velocity, is given by $A^2 = \mu H_0^2 / \rho_0$. These small transverse disturbances in velocity and magnetic field propagate along the lines of force. They are not accompanied by density or pressure changes. As will be seen later, longitudinal waves involving acoustic (pressure and density) effects may be coupled into the magnetic field, but the transverse magnetohydrodynamic waves, or Alfvén waves, as they are called, are uncoupled from the longitudinal waves. Later we will generalize the Alfvén waves to take into account dissipation by viscosity and electrical resistance.

6.11 BERNOULLI'S EQUATION IN MHD

In Chapter 4 we discussed some of the properties of the equations of motion and indicated that under certain conditions the body force could be derived from a potential function. Under the action of such irrotational forces the velocity field should be irrotational (in the absence of viscosity) and the results of classical potential flow theory should be applicable. Let us examine the first integral of the equation of motion and compare it to the classical Bernoulli equation.

The equation of motion may be written (referring to Equation 6.4-9) as

$$\rho \left[\frac{\partial \mathbf{V}}{\partial t} + \nabla(\tfrac{1}{2}V^2) - \mathbf{V} \times (\nabla \times \mathbf{V}) \right] = -\nabla P - \rho \nabla \psi + \nabla \cdot \tau'$$
$$+ \frac{1}{\mu}(\mathbf{B} \cdot \nabla)\mathbf{B} - \frac{1}{\mu}\nabla\left(\frac{B^2}{2}\right) \qquad (6.11\text{-}1)$$

The irrotational part of the electromagnetic force is derived from a potential $B^2/2\mu$ which may be combined with the pressure. Equation (6.11-1) may be integrated along a streamline by taking the scalar product of $d\mathbf{s}$ (element of length along a streamline) with the equation. $d\mathbf{s}$ is colinear with $\mathbf{V}$ and hence $d\mathbf{s} \cdot [\mathbf{V} \times (\nabla \times \mathbf{V})] = 0$.

$$\rho \frac{\partial \mathbf{V}}{\partial t} \cdot d\mathbf{s} + \rho \nabla(\tfrac{1}{2}V^2 + \psi) \cdot d\mathbf{s} + \nabla\left(P + \frac{B^2}{2\mu}\right) \cdot d\mathbf{s}$$

$$(\nabla \cdot \tau') \cdot d\mathbf{s} + \frac{1}{\mu}[(\mathbf{B} \cdot \nabla)\mathbf{B}] \cdot d\mathbf{s} \quad (6.11\text{-}2)$$

Equation (6.11-2) may be integrated along a streamline. In particular, under steady-state, inviscid conditions the integral between two points 1 and 2 along a streamline becomes

$$\frac{V_2^2 - V_1^2}{2} + \psi_2 - \psi_1 + \int_1^2 \frac{d(P + B^2/2\mu)}{\rho} = \frac{1}{\mu}\int_1^2 \frac{(\mathbf{B} \cdot \nabla)\mathbf{B} \cdot d\mathbf{s}}{\rho}$$

$$(6.11\text{-}3)$$

If the right-hand side of (6.11-3) vanishes, Bernoulli's theorem for a compressible fluid (with a new pressure $P + B^2/2\mu$) holds. For an incompressible fluid we obtain (if the right-hand side vanishes):

$$\nabla\left(\frac{V^2}{2} + \psi + \frac{P}{\rho} + \frac{B^2}{2\rho\mu}\right) = 0 \quad (6.11\text{-}4)$$

which is the analogue of Bernoulli's equation, the electromagnetic body force being derived from a scalar potential $B^2/2\mu$. Under the condition of the right-hand side (6.11-3) vanishing, classical potential flow theory is valid for incompressible flow and the only modification is that the pressure of the classical flow is to be interpreted as $P + (B^2/2\mu)$.

6.12   KELVIN'S CIRCULATION THEOREM IN MHD

For an incompressible inviscid fluid the circulation Γ around a loop is defined as $\Gamma = \oint \mathbf{V} \cdot d\mathbf{r}$. The time rate of change of the circulation about a loop composed of a fluid line is obtained from the equation of motion. From (6.11-2),

$$\frac{D}{Dt}\oint_C \mathbf{V} \cdot d\mathbf{r} = \oint_C\left[-\frac{\nabla P}{\rho} \cdot d\mathbf{r} - \nabla\psi \cdot d\mathbf{r} + \nabla\left(\frac{V^2}{2}\right) \cdot d\mathbf{r}\right.$$

$$\left. - \frac{1}{\mu}\nabla\left(\frac{B^2}{2}\right) \cdot d\mathbf{r} + \frac{1}{\mu}(\mathbf{B} \cdot \nabla)\mathbf{B} \cdot d\mathbf{r}\right] \quad (6.12\text{-}1)$$

By replacing the line integral by an area integral, we have

$$\frac{D\Gamma}{Dt} = \frac{D}{Dt} \oint_C \mathbf{V} \cdot d\mathbf{r} = \frac{D}{Dt} \int_S (\nabla \times \mathbf{V}) \cdot d\mathbf{S} = \int_S \nabla \times \left[\frac{1}{\mu} (\mathbf{B} \cdot \nabla)\mathbf{B} \right] \cdot d\mathbf{S}$$

(6.12-2)

and we see that Kelvin's theorem holds if the right-hand side vanishes, that is, $\nabla \times [(\mathbf{B} \cdot \nabla)\mathbf{B}] = 0$. In general, then, Kelvin's theorem does not hold, even in an inviscid fluid. Physically, vorticity may be generated in an inviscid fluid by the rotational body forces.

6.13   THE STATIC MHD PINCH

An important static solution to the MHD equations is the so-called "pinch." If a current is passed along a column of conducting fluid, an azimuthal magnetic field is produced. This field, in turn, interacts with the current to produce a pressure which tends to pinch or confine the fluid in the column. This pinch effect was the idea behind the early concepts of plasma confinement for fusion reactors. A simple pinch of this nature is unstable in a gas column and is too short lived to be of practical use for confinement. However, the idea behind the pinch is rather important and the pinch pressure appears in quite a few MHD problems. In a liquid confined by walls the pinch is, of course, stable and gives rise to static pressure gradients.

We will analyze, as an example, the simple column pinch with a uniform current density J_z. (This column has radius a, Fig. 6.13-1.)   The magnetic field is found as

$$\oint \mathbf{H} \cdot d\mathbf{l} = \int_0^{2\pi} H_\theta r \, d\theta = \int_A J_z \, dA = \frac{Ir^2}{a^2}$$

(6.13-1)

where I is the total current.   Hence in the column

$$H_\theta = \frac{Ir}{2\pi a^2}$$

(6.13-2)

Under static equilibrium the radial momentum equation is

$$0 = -\frac{\partial P}{\partial r} + (\mathbf{J} \times \mathbf{B})_r$$

$$= -\frac{dP}{dr} - \mu \frac{I^2 r}{2\pi^2 a^4}$$

(6.13-3)

By integrating and using the condition that $P = 0$ at $r = a$, we obtain

$$P = \frac{\mu I^2}{4\pi^2 a^4}(a^2 - r^2)$$ (6.13-4)

The maximum pressure occurs at the center ($r = 0$) and is equal to $\mu I^2/4\pi^2 a^2$.

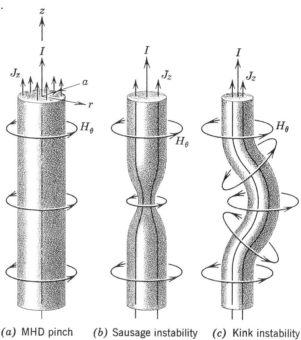

(a) MHD pinch   (b) Sausage instability   (c) Kink instability

Figure 6.13-1   The column MHD or plasma pinch. The total current is I and the current density J_z is uniform over the cross section of the column. Such a column is highly unstable unless confined by walls. Developing instabilities are shown in (b) sausage type and (c) kink type. In each case a localized increase in J_z or H_θ causes a dynamic unbalance which becomes greater as the column collapses.

Two simple types of instabilities can develop: the kink and the sausage. In each case the current density or magnetic field tends to increase in such a way that the pressure unbalance is increased as the unstable configuration develops.

6.14   A NOTE ON UNITS

As has been discussed in Chapter 2, in the electromagnetic equations the system of units determines the exact manner in which the equations are written. The constants c and 4π appear explicitly in the equations in various cgs and unrationalized systems of units, but not in the RMKS system which is used throughout this book. The fluid equations, on the other hand, have the same form (except for electromagnetic terms) regardless of the system of units used. Actually, of course, the form of the electromagnetic equations is Lorentz invariant and does not depend on units. The different constants that appear are merely a consequence of the manner in which the field quantities are defined.

In the RMKS system of units, the mechanical units of mass, length, and time are the kilogram, meter, and second. The unit of force is the Newton. Pressure then is measured in Newtons per meter^2, and temperature may be reckoned in °K. Velocity is in meters per second. Mass density ρ is in kilograms per meter^3. The units of viscosity μ_f are Newton-seconds per meter^2, or, exactly equivalent, kilogram-meters per meter second. The units of kinematic viscosity $\nu = \mu/\rho$ are then meters^2 per second.

The electromagnetic units are: $\mathbf{J}$ in amperes per meter^2, ρ_e in coulombs per meter^3, $\mathbf{E}$ in volts per meter, $\mathbf{B}$ in Teslas (webers per meter^2). One weber per meter^2 is equivalent to 10^4 Gauss. $\mathbf{H}$ and $\mathbf{M}$ are in amperes per meter. $\mathbf{D}$ and $\mathbf{P}$ are coulombs per meter^2. The conductivity σ is given in mhos per meter. The dielectric constant or specific inductive capacity ϵ is given in farads per meter or coulombs^2 seconds^2 per kilogram-meter^3 and the permeability μ is given in henrys per meter or kilogram-meter per coulomb^2. Actually, of course, all of the electromagnetic quantities can be expressed in terms of the mechanical units of MLT and one electrical unit, say, the coulomb.

PROBLEMS

1. Derive the MHD version of Crocco's theorem.
2. Show that the vorticity in a conducting fluid may be proportional to $\nabla^2\Phi$, where Φ is the electric potential. Under what conditions is this proportionality true?
3. From Ohm's law and $\nabla \cdot \mathbf{J} = 0$ it follows that $\nabla \cdot \mathbf{E} = -\nabla \cdot (\mathbf{V} \times \mathbf{B})$. Are there any conditions where $\nabla \cdot \mathbf{E} = 0$ is a valid statement? Is $\nabla \cdot \mathbf{D}' = \epsilon \nabla \cdot \mathbf{E}' = 0$ in a conductor?
4. Find the pressure distribution in a column pinch if the axial current is confined to an outer annular region of the column. Assume the current density in the annular region to be uniform. See (Martin and Young) in the references.
5. Why is the equation

$$0 = \nabla\left(P + \frac{\mathbf{B} \cdot \mathbf{H}}{2}\right)$$

incorrect for the annular pinch discussed in Section 6.13? Hint: Consider the equilibrium of a pie-shaped element. The tension along the $\mathbf{H}$ lines contributes to the force balance. In general,

$$\mathbf{J} \times \mathbf{B} = -\nabla\left(\frac{\mathbf{B} \cdot \mathbf{H}}{2}\right) + (\mathbf{B} \cdot \nabla)\mathbf{B}.$$

The second term is zero only if the field lines are uniform and have no curvature.
6. Show that the sausage-like disturbance to the pinch is unstable. Hint: Find an equation for the outer radius as a function of time assuming a small perturbation from the original radius. Linearize the radial equation of motion.

REFERENCES

Alfvén, H., *Cosmical Electrodynamics*, Oxford University Press, 1950.

Batchelor, G. K., On the Spontaneous Magnetic Field in a Conducting Liquid in Turbulent Motion, *Proc. Roy. Soc.* (London), Series A, **201**, p. 405, 1950.

Birkhoff, G., *Hydrodynamics*, Revised ed., Princeton University Press, 1960.

Cowling, T. G., *Magnetohydrodynamics*, Interscience, New York, 1957.

Ferraro, V. C. A., and C. Plumpton, *An Introduction to Magneto-Fluid Mechanics*, Oxford University Press, 1961.

Landau, L. D., and E. M. Lifshitz, *Electrodynamics of Continuous Media*, Addison-Wesley, Reading, Mass., 1960.

Martin, A. V. J., and F. J. Young, Confinement magnétique des réactions thermo-nucléaires, *J. Phys. et le Radium*, **20**, p. 1s, 1959.

Pai, S. I., *Magnetogasdynamics and Plasma Dynamics*, Prentice-Hall, Englewood Cliffs, New Jersey, 1962.

Thompson, W. B., *An Introduction to Plasma Physics*, Addison-Wesley, Reading, Mass., 1962.

7

Incompressible Viscous Magnetohydrodynamic Flow

In this chapter many one- and two-dimensional examples are considered. In each example the flow is steady and laminar. Channel flow is studied in Section 7.1–7.9 and the rest of the chapter treats some simple hydromagnetic lubrication problems. Although it might seem more reasonable to present very simple examples to illustrate the differences between ordinary hydrodynamic and hydromagnetic situations, rather detailed solutions to more complicated problems are presented. It is extremely difficult to find any really simple and meaningful two-dimensional hydromagnetic examples and most problems treated here are as elementary as possible.

The purpose of this chapter is to establish methods of solution—and to present solutions to many interesting problems that will show the student how to approach similar problems. Main results are carefully tested by limiting-case checks and are frequently illustrated by curves, many of which have not been presented in the literature before and each of which discloses interesting phenomena. The roles of the channel boundaries and the influence of the return circuit on electrical current are also investigated.

7.1 ONE-DIMENSIONAL MHD POISEUILLE FLOW

One of the simplest problems in magnetohydrodynamics, called the Hartmann problem, concerns the steady viscous laminar flow of an electrically conducting liquid between parallel planes in the presence of a magnetic field. The solution to this problem gives us insight into the MHD generator, pump, flow-meter, and bearings, and it forms the basic method for treating all viscous flow devices. The role of the external circuit and its relationship with the electric field will be investigated.

In the Hartmann problem it is assumed that electrically conducting fluid flows in a long channel of infinite width and that the flow is fully developed. Figure 7.1-1 shows two views of the channel. Figure 7.1-1*b* is

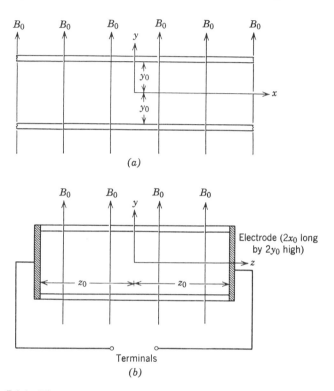

(a)

(b)

Figure 7.1-1   The geometry of the Hartmann problem in which $z_0 \gg y_0$.

not drawn in proper proportion ($z_0 \gg y_0$) but is drawn to indicate the electrodes and the external circuit. It is assumed that the electrodes are infinitely far apart and the flow is fully developed so that the problem is one-dimensional, varying only in the y direction. Physically, the half depth y_0 of the channel is much smaller than the width z_0, and the channel is very long in the x dimension so that the problem becomes one-dimensional with all quantities except pressure varying as functions of y only.

The walls and electrodes of the channel, in general, could have any value of conductivity. However, at some point in this problem the walls and electrodes are assumed to be insulators and perfect conductors, respectively. The implication here is that the walls have much lower conductivity while the electrodes have much higher conductivity than the electrically conducting fluid.*

Before fluid is made to flow in the x direction, a uniform magnetic induction B_0 is applied in the y direction. Whether or not this field is modified by currents which are induced is a matter for our investigation. Clearly, since the magnetic Reynolds number Rm is small for any laboratory experiment using viscous liquid metals, the applied magnetic field becomes only slightly distorted. We can think of the induced magnetic field H_x as resulting from a very slight stretching or deforming of the applied field in the direction of motion.

It is our goal to find the velocity profiles, pressures, and induced electric and magnetic fields and current that can flow in this configuration. At the beginning of this problem we cannot really know what components of electric and magnetic field and velocity exist. Of course, from a physical standpoint it would seem that the fluid could be forced to flow in the x direction. This motion would induce an electric field in the z direction. Current would flow in the z direction and a magnetic field in the x direction might result. We could assume, before working the problem, that these are the only quantities which exist. However, a solution based upon that assumption would not, for instance, give any indication of why there could not be any current flowing in the x or y direction, or why the velocity is zero in the y direction. Therefore, we write out the Maxwell equations and the fluid equations in full detail, assuming only that nothing is a function of x or z except pressure.

By the continuity equations of magnetic induction and fluid velocity, B_y and v (the y component of velocity) are constants. Because the applied magnetic induction is yB_0, we must set $B_y = B_0$, and B_y is not influenced by the steady motion of the conducting fluid. If the channel walls were porous, v might be taken as nonzero but in the Hartmann problem $v = 0$. As the magnetic field does not vary with time, $\nabla \times \mathbf{E} = 0$ which implies that E_z and E_x are constants. From $\nabla \times \mathbf{H} = \mathbf{J}$ we obtain

$$\frac{\partial H_z}{\partial y} = J_x \tag{7.1-1a}$$

$$-\frac{\partial H_x}{\partial y} = \mathbf{J}_z \tag{7.1-1b}$$

$$J_y = 0 \tag{7.1-1c}$$

---

* As we will see presently, the effect of finite conductivity in the top and bottom plate can be accounted for rather easily and our results applied to such cases.

From the Navier-Stokes equations,

$$0 = -\frac{\partial P}{\partial x} + \mu_f \frac{\partial^2 u}{\partial y^2} - B_0 J_z \tag{7.1-2a}$$

$$0 = -\frac{\partial P}{\partial y} + J_z B_x - J_x B_z \tag{7.1-2b}$$

$$0 = -\frac{\partial P}{\partial z} + \mu_f \frac{\partial^2 w}{\partial y^2} + B_0 J_x \tag{7.1-2c}$$

In addition to the systems of (7.1-1) and (7.1-2), Ohm's law (2.4-3) is needed. It takes the form

$$J_x = \sigma(E_x - B_0 w) \tag{7.1-3a}$$

$$J_z = \sigma(E_z + B_0 u) \tag{7.1-3b}$$

These equations can be separated into two uncoupled sets of equations. The set comprising (7.1-1a), (7.1-2c), and (7.1-3a) contains the variables J_x, H_z, w, and E_x; the set comprising (7.1-1b), (7.1-2a), and (7.1-3b) includes the variables J_z, H_x, u, and E_z. Hence we are free to orient either the x or z axis in the direction of fluid flow. Here we choose the direction of flow as the x direction and set J_x, H_z, w, and E_x to zero. It is not necessary to take E_x, J_x, and H_z as zero; if they are not zero, their only effect is to influence the pressure distribution given in (7.1-2c) provided $w = 0$. When J_x, H_z, w, and E_x are zero, $\partial P/\partial z$ also must be null. Combining (7.1-2a) and (7.1-3b) yields

$$0 = -\frac{\partial P}{\partial x} + \mu_f \frac{\partial^2 u}{\partial y^2} - \sigma(E_z + B_0 u)B_0 \tag{7.1-4}$$

By differentiating (7.1-2b) with respect to x it follows that $(\partial^2 P/\partial x\,\partial y) = 0$, and after integrating $\partial^2 P/\partial x\,\partial y$ with respect to y, it is apparent that the pressure gradient in (7.1-4) is a constant. Hence the pressure is of the form

$$P = C_1 x + f(y) \tag{7.1-5}$$

where C_1 is a constant. The $C_1 x$ term is driving the flow and $f(y)$ is the pinch pressure due to the electromagnetic body force. Because E_z and $\partial P/\partial x$ are constants, the velocity u can be obtained from (7.1-4) without recourse to the $\nabla \times \mathbf{H} = \mathbf{J}$ equation of (7.1-1b). When steady flows have a low magnetic Reynolds number, the magnetic field can be found from the current density, providing that the equations of motion and magnetic diffusion decouple. Then $\nabla \times \mathbf{H} = \mathbf{J}$ can be used to find the induced field from the current density but the current density cannot conveniently be obtained from the magnetic field. Only at high Rm (especially in cases of infinite conductivity) is it proper to think of $\mathbf{J} = \nabla \times \mathbf{H}$ as defining the current density from the magnetic field. If $v \neq 0$ in the problem we are solving, the equation of motion (7.1-2a) is coupled to the magnetic diffusion equation (7.1-1b) and the two equations must be combined. Thus, only in very simple cases can we speak of the current density defining the magnetic field or vice versa.

The solution to (7.1-4) which satisfies the no-slip boundary condition at $y = \pm y_0$ is given by

$$u = \frac{y_0^2}{M^2}\left(\frac{1}{\mu_f}\frac{\partial P}{\partial x} + \frac{M}{y_0}\sqrt{\frac{\sigma}{\mu_f}}\,E_z\right)\left(\frac{\text{ch}\,(My/y_0)}{\text{ch}\,M} - 1\right) \qquad (7.1\text{-}6)$$

where the Hartmann number is given by $M = y_0 B_0 \sqrt{\sigma/\mu_f}$ and ch and sh denote the hyperbolic cosine and sine, respectively. It is interesting to inspect (7.1-6) when $M \ll 1$, for as $M \to 0$ the velocity profile must become parabolic. Replacing the ch (My/y_0) and the ch M by the first two terms of their series expansion yields

$$\lim_{M \to 0} u = \frac{1}{\mu_f}\frac{\partial P}{\partial x}\left(\frac{y^2 - y_0^2}{2}\right) \qquad (7.1\text{-}7)$$

as it should. The velocity has been found in terms of E_z which must be related to the external circuit. Because the electric field and the total current are related, it is convenient to find the current density from Ohm's law. By (7.1-3b) and (7.1-6) the current density is given by

$$J_z = \sigma E_z \frac{\text{ch}\,My/y_0}{\text{ch}\,M} + \frac{y_0}{M}\sqrt{\frac{\sigma}{\mu_f}}\frac{\partial P}{\partial x}\left(\frac{\text{ch}\,My/y_0}{\text{ch}\,M} - 1\right) \qquad (7.1\text{-}8)$$

The total current per unit of channel length in the x direction is given by $\mathscr{I} = \int_{-y_0}^{y_0} J_z\,dy$. Then

$$\mathscr{I} = 2\sigma y_0 E_z \frac{\text{th}\,M}{M} + \frac{2y_0^2}{M}\sqrt{\frac{\sigma}{\mu_f}}\frac{\partial P}{\partial x}\left(\frac{\text{th}\,M}{M} - 1\right) \qquad (7.1\text{-}9)$$

which expresses the functional relationship between E_z and $\mathscr{I}$. When $M \to 0$, $\mathscr{I}$ is no longer dependent upon the pressure gradient and the problem reduces to purely electrical considerations. Then $\lim_{M \to 0} \mathscr{I} = 2\sigma y_0 E_z$.

The terminal voltage V_T may now be introduced. Since there are no time variations (as mentioned in Chapter 4), the terminal voltage is given simply by

$$V_{Tba} = -\int_a^b \mathbf{E} \cdot d\mathbf{l} \qquad (7.1\text{-}10)$$

In terms of our coordinate system, the voltage difference between points located at $z = +z_0$ and $z = -z_0$ is

$$V_T = -\int_{-z_0}^{z_0} E_z \, dz = -2z_0 E_z \qquad (7.1\text{-}11)$$

The value of E_z obtained from (7.1-11) is substituted into (7.1-9) and the resulting equation yields

$$V_T = -\frac{z_0 M}{\sigma y_0 \, \text{th} \, M} \mathscr{I} + \frac{2y_0 z_0}{M\sqrt{\sigma\mu_f}} \frac{\partial P}{\partial x}\left(1 - \frac{M}{\text{th} \, M}\right) \qquad (7.1\text{-}12)$$

In Fig. 7.1-2, by virtue of Thevenin's theorem, the fluid moving through the applied magnetic field may be represented as an open-circuit voltage source in series with an internal impedance. This is merely a convenient thing to do and is certainly not necessary. Actually, once the terminal voltage is found, it can be equated to the voltage drop across the external circuit. Clearly, since the drop across the external circuit may be negative in the case of an external generator or positive for an external circuit comprising resistance only, electrical energy can be fed into or extracted from the streaming fluid. Thus we have analyzed a pump or generator, depending on the magnitude and polarity of the terminal voltage.

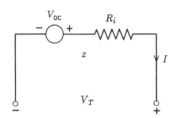

Figure 7.1-2 The equivalent circuit of the Hartmann problem.

The open-circuit voltage can be found from Equation (7.1-12) by setting $\mathscr{I} = 0$. Although the total current $\mathscr{I}$ is zero, J_z is not null. In fact, under open-circuit conditions there exist circulating currents (completing their circuit either through the electrodes or, in the case of insulating electrodes, through the fluid near the electrodes). We will discuss the circulating currents again when channels having finite cross sections are treated. The open-circuit voltage is given by

$$V_{oc} = \frac{2y_0 z_0}{M\sqrt{\sigma\mu_f}} \frac{\partial P}{\partial x}\left(1 - \frac{M}{\text{th} \, M}\right) \qquad (7.1\text{-}13)$$

When the fluid flows in the x direction, $\partial P/\partial x$ is negative and $1 - M/\text{th} \, M$ is negative. Hence V_{oc} is positive in the sense shown in Fig. 7.1-2.

The total short-circuit current is obtained when the terminal voltage is zero. It is given by Equation (7.1-12) as

$$I_{sc} = \frac{4x_0 y_0^2}{M}\sqrt{\frac{\sigma}{\mu_f}} \frac{\partial P}{\partial x}\left(\frac{\text{th} \, M}{M} - 1\right) \qquad (7.1\text{-}14)$$

which approaches zero as $M \to 0$. Here $I = \mathscr{I} \cdot 2x_0$ which is the total current and the electrodes are $2x_0$ long. This current flows in the $+z$ direction when the fluid flows in the x direction. The internal resistance at constant $\partial P/\partial x$ is given by

$$(R_i)_{\partial P/\partial x} = \frac{V_{oc}}{I_{sc}} = \frac{z_0}{2x_0 y_0 \sigma} \cdot \frac{M}{\text{th } M} \tag{7.1-15}$$

If L is the width of the device in the z direction, and A is the area of the device in the xy plane,

$$(R_i)_{\partial P/\partial x} = \frac{L}{\sigma A} \cdot \frac{M}{\text{th } M} \tag{7.1-16}$$

for $L = 2z_0$ and $A = 4x_0 y_0$. When $M \to 0$, the internal resistance reduces to $L/\sigma A$, as would be expected. For large values of M ($M > 3$), the internal resistance at constant pressure gradient increases linearly with the Hartmann number. Physically this results because at high M the flattened velocity profile decreases linearly as M is increased, causing V_{oc} to remain constant with M. However, as M increases, the current decreases with M. It is very important to remember that the internal resistance has been derived with $\partial P/\partial x$ held constant. It is also interesting to hold the flow rate constant and let $\partial P/\partial x$ vary to maintain constant flow. It is easy to show that

$$(R_i)_Q = \frac{L}{\sigma A} \tag{7.1-17}$$

where Q is the volumetric flow rate.

With V_{oc}, I_{sc}, and $(R_i)_{\partial P/\partial x}$ given by (7.1-13), (7.1-14), and (7.1-15), the equivalent circuit shown in Fig. 7.1-2 is determined. By referring to the equivalent circuit, Kirchhoff's voltage law can be applied to the loop which includes an external circuit attached to the terminals.* For the

---

* Actually the value of the conductivity of the top and bottom walls at $y = \pm y_0$ can be any value and the following analysis is still valid. However, the top and bottom walls of conductivity σ_T and σ_B, respectively, need then be considered as part of the external load resistor, since they form a return circuit for the current flowing in the generator. The load resistance R_L then must be modified by including the ohmic resistance of the two plates in parallel with it. However, the induced magnetic field may be different, depending on the geometrical configuration of the return circuits. The value of E_z must be uniform throughout the fluid around the plates. If there is no external resistor the plates act as the sole return circuit and then (where h is the thickness of the plates)

$$\mathscr{I} = -E_z(\sigma_B h_B + \sigma_T h_T)$$

and since $\mathscr{I}$ and E_z are related by Equation (7.1-9), E_z and $\mathscr{I}$ are determined. Hence for top and bottom walls of arbitrary conductivity, our analysis can be applied immediately by choosing the appropriate external load resistance.

circuit of Fig. 7.1-3

$$V_{oc} - I(R_i + R_L) - V_g = 0 \qquad (7.1\text{-}18)$$

and the total current is found by solving (7.1-18). When V_{oc} from (7.1-13) is substituted into the expression for the current and when $R_i = (R_i)_{\partial P/\partial x}$, the result is

$$I = \frac{-V_g + (2y_0z_0/M\sqrt{\sigma\mu_f})(\partial P/\partial x)[1 - (M/\text{th } M)]}{R_L + (L/\sigma A)\cdot(M/\text{th } M)} \qquad (7.1\text{-}19)$$

When $M \to 0$, the fluid can no longer generate current as it flows and

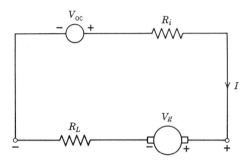

Figure 7.1-3   The complete electrical circuit of the Hartmann problem.

$\lim\limits_{M\to 0} I = -V_g/(R_L + R_i)$. It is easy to show that E_z is

$$E_z = \frac{(V_g/4\sigma x_0y_0)\cdot(M/\text{th } M) + (y_0R_L/M\sqrt{\sigma\mu_f})(\partial P/\partial x)[1 - (M/\text{th } M)]}{-[R_L + (z_0/2\sigma x_0y_0)\cdot(M/\text{th } M)]}$$

$$(7.1\text{-}20)$$

When the external generator is absent and $R_L = 0$, $E_z = 0$; and when $R_L \to \infty$

$$\lim\limits_{R_L\to\infty} E_z = \frac{-y_0}{M\sqrt{\sigma\mu_f}}\frac{\partial P}{\partial x}\left(1 - \frac{M}{\text{th } M}\right) \qquad (7.1\text{-}21)$$

which checks with (7.1-12) when $\mathscr{I}$ is set to zero. If the value of E_z from (7.1-20) is substituted into (7.1-6), the complete expression for the velocity is obtained. It is

$$u = \frac{[(z_0/2\sigma x_0y_0) + R_L](M/\text{th } M)\cdot(1/\mu_f)(\partial P/\partial x) - (M^2V_g/4x_0y_0{}^2\sqrt{\sigma\mu_f}\,\text{th } M)}{R_L + (z_0/2\sigma x_0y_0)\cdot(M/\text{th } M)}$$

$$\cdot\frac{y_0{}^2}{M^2}\left(\frac{\text{ch } My/y_0}{\text{ch } M} - 1\right) \qquad (7.1\text{-}22)$$

When V_g is zero and $\partial P/\partial x < 0$, fluid is being forced to flow in the $+x$ direction and electric power is flowing into the external circuit, provided

$R_L \neq 0$ or $R_L \neq \infty$. If V_g is positive, the external generator helps to pump the fluid in the x direction. When $V_g < 0$ and $\partial P/\partial x < 0$, the electromagnetic body force due to V_g is opposing the pressure gradient $\partial P/\partial x$. In pumping cases, R_L may be interpreted as the internal resistance of the power source. In order for pumping to take place against the pressure gradient,

$$|V_g| > \left| \frac{4}{M} [(R_i)_Q + R_L] x_0 y_0^2 \sqrt{\frac{\sigma}{\mu_f}} \frac{\partial P}{\partial x} \right| \qquad (7.1\text{-}23)$$

which summarizes the above remarks.

The solution for the velocity profile is not very complicated but is cluttered by a great many parameters. If $u^* = u/[(y_0^2/u_f)(\partial P/\partial x)]$, $y^* = y/y_0$, $R^* = R/(z_0/2\sigma x_0 y_0)$, and $V_g^* = V_g/[(2y_0 z_0/\sqrt{\sigma \mu_f})(\partial P/\partial x)]$, the velocity can be expressed as

$$u^* = f(R_L^*, V_g^*, M) \frac{\text{ch } My^* - \text{ch } M}{1 - \text{ch } M} \qquad (7.1\text{-}24a)$$

where

$$f(R_L^*, V_g^*, M) = \frac{(1 + R_L^* - MV_g^*)(1 - \text{ch } M)}{M(M \text{ ch } M + R_L^* \text{ sh } M)}$$

Hartmann's original solution was for $R_L^* = \infty$. Then

$$\lim_{R_L \to \infty} u^* = \frac{\text{ch } My^* - \text{ch } M}{M \text{ sh } M} \qquad (7.1\text{-}24b)$$

which is called the open-circuit case. For any value of $f(R_L^*, V_g^*, M)$, the velocity profile, which is parabolic when $M = 0$, becomes flatter in the center as M increases. This is illustrated in Fig. 7.1-4 where $u^*/f(R_L^*, V_g^*, M)$ is plotted as a function of y^* for various values of the Hartmann number. The "amplitude" of the profile is $f(R_L^*, V_g^*, M)$; it could be represented as a family of graphs. However, we shall confine its representation by requiring electrical matching between the external circuit and the flow device. The condition for maximum transfer of electrical power is that the internal resistance equal the external resistance. In this case $R_L^* = M/\text{th } M$ and the "amplitude" becomes

$$f(M/\text{th } M, V_g^*, M) = \tfrac{1}{2}[1 + M(\coth M - V_g^*)] \frac{1 - \text{ch } M}{M^2 \text{ ch } M} \qquad (7.1\text{-}24c)$$

A plot of the "matched amplitude" of (7.1-24c) is given in Fig. 7.1-5. It is interesting to observe that when $M \gg 1$, the "matched amplitude" varies as M^{-1} or as M^{-2} if $V_g^* = 1$. A more general plot showing the influence of terminal potential and the Hartmann number can be made by integrating the dimensionless form of (7.1-6) to obtain the normalized

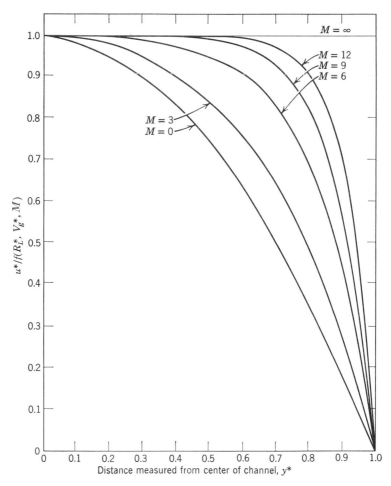

Figure 7.1-4   The normalized velocity profiles in the MHD Poiseuille flow.

flow rate. If we use the dimensionless variables defined previously, (7.1-6) becomes

$$u^* = \frac{1}{M^2}(1 - MV_T^*)\left(\frac{\text{ch } My^*}{\text{ch } M} - 1\right) \qquad (7.1\text{-}25)$$

The normalized flow rate is given by

$$Q^* = 2\int_0^1 u^* \, dy^* = \frac{2}{M^2}(1 - MV_T^*)\left(\frac{\text{th } M}{M} - 1\right) \qquad (7.1\text{-}26)$$

It is interesting to notice that the net flow can be stopped by setting

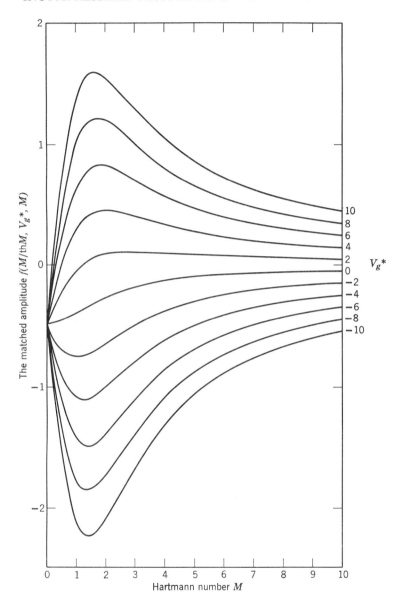

Figure 7.1-5 The matched amplitude as a function of the Hartmann number.

$V_T{}^* = M^{-1}$. The flow rate Q^* is shown in Fig. 7.1-6, where an optimum Hartmann number can be obtained to maximize the net flow rate Q^* for a given value of $V_T{}^*$. The peak is to be expected since $Q^* \rightarrow 0$ as $M \rightarrow \infty$. This curve is similar to Fig. 7.1-5 but is more general. Similarly, the current peaks at a certain value of the Hartmann number. In Fig. 7.1-11

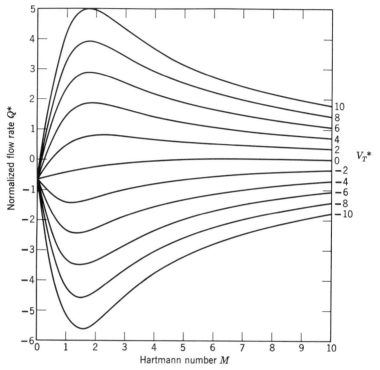

Figure 7.1-6 The normalized flow rate versus the Hartmann number for various terminal voltages.

the maximum short-circuit current occurs at $M = 1.65$. The terminal voltage is obtained from Equation (7.1-20) and becomes

$$V_T{}^* = \frac{V_g{}^* + (R_L{}^*/M)(\text{th } M/M - 1)}{1 + R_L{}^*(\text{th } M/M)} \tag{7.1-27}$$

where $V_T{}^* = V_T/[(2y_0z_0/\sqrt{\sigma\mu_f})(\partial P/\partial x)]$. This expression reduces to the normalized open-circuit voltage when $R_L{}^* \rightarrow \infty$.

It is not necessary to calculate the magnetic field; however, we shall do so to lend insight into more complicated situations where the magnetic field does not decouple from the velocity of the conducting fluid. For that purpose J_z is found in terms of the total current I. To accomplish this, let E_z from (7.1-9) be substituted into (7.1-8) to yield

$$J_z = \frac{MI}{4x_0y_0} \cdot \frac{\text{ch } My/y_0}{\text{sh } M} + \frac{y_0\sqrt{\sigma/\mu_f}(\partial P/\partial x)}{M}\left(\frac{M \text{ ch } My/y_0}{\text{sh } M} - 1\right) \quad (7.1-28)$$

which can be checked easily, since $4x_0 \int_0^{y_0} J_z \, dy \equiv I$. In dimensionless form

$$J_z^* = \frac{MI^* \text{ ch } My^*}{\text{sh } M} + \frac{1}{M}\left(\frac{M \text{ ch } My^*}{\text{sh } M} - 1\right) \quad (7.1-29)$$

where

$$J_z^* = \frac{J_z}{\left(y_0\sqrt{\dfrac{\sigma}{\mu_f}\dfrac{\partial P}{\partial x}}\right)} \quad \text{and} \quad I^* = \frac{I}{\left(4x_0y_0^2\sqrt{\dfrac{\sigma}{\mu_f}\dfrac{\partial P}{\partial x}}\right)}$$

This expression is shown in Fig. 7.1-7 for values of current ranging from the short-circuit to minus the short circuit current for $M = 2$. The cases where $0 \leq I^* \leq I_{sc}^*$ are obtained with values of load resistance ranging from zero at short- to infinity at open-circuit current. For $I^* < 0$ an external generator V_g^* must be utilized. In the open-circuit case, it is clear from Fig. 7.1-7 that the current density is zero at $y^* = 0.6$ only. The current generated by the electrically conducting fluid moving in a magnetic field flows between $y^* = -0.6$ and $y^* = +0.6$. Because the current cannot flow through the infinite load resistance, it returns in the regions $(-1 \leq y^* \leq -0.6$ and $0.6 \leq y^* \leq 1)$ where the fluid velocity is small enough for $|E_z| > |B_0u|$. It is interesting to notice that some portion of the current density always is negative for all values of $I^* < 0$. Of course, the amount of negative current density becomes negligible compared to $|I^*|$ and $|I^*| \to \infty$.

The determination of the induced magnetic field H_x requires knowledge of the geometry of the external circuit. In order to keep the problem one dimensional, we have assumed no variation of any quantity (except pressure) with x. To be consistent with this assumption, we now assume that the return path comprises two conducting plates; they are located parallel to the channel walls, in the xz plane, one above and one below the channel. It is assumed that the electrodes extend in the xy plane beyond the channel and make electrical contact with the return circuit. Such an arrangement could be obtained if $y_0 \ll z_0$ and x_0 (see Fig. 7.1-8). From Equation (7.1-1b)

$$H_x = C_1 + \frac{y_0^2\sqrt{\sigma/\mu_f}}{M}\frac{\partial P}{\partial x} \cdot \frac{y}{y_0} - \left(\frac{y_0^2\sqrt{\sigma/\mu_f}(\partial P/\partial x)}{M} + \frac{I}{4x_0}\right)\frac{\text{sh } My/y_0}{\text{sh } M}$$

$$(7.1-30)$$

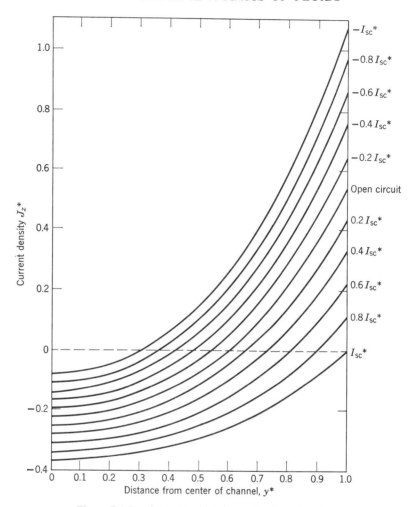

Figure 7.1-7 The current density profile for $M = 2$.

where C_1 a constant of integration, remains to be determined. Consider Ampere's circuital law applied along the path $abcdea$ of Fig. 7.1-9. The magnetic field along segment abc is $H_x(y_0)$ and is zero along segment dc, just as the field outside an infinitely long solenoid is zero. Then, from Ampere's circuital law, $2H_x(y_0)x_0 = -I_T$. By substituting $H_x(y_0)$ from (7.1-30) into the former result and solving for C_1, we obtain

$$C_1 = \frac{I - 2I_T}{4x_0} \qquad (7.1\text{-}31)$$

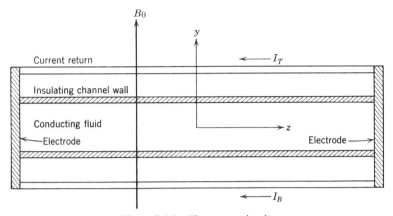

Figure 7.1-8   The return circuit.

If $I_T = I$, which means that no current is allowed to flow in the bottom plate, $C_1 = -I/4x_0$. Then $H_x(-y_0)$ should be zero because $I_B = 0$. It is easy to show that (7.1-30) satisfies this condition. When $I_T = I/2$, $H_x(0) = 0$, as it should because the magnetic field must be antisymmetrical when the return circuit is symmetrical. In dimensionless form,

$$H_x^* = I^* - 2I_T^* + \frac{y^*}{M} - \left(\frac{1}{M} + I^*\right)\frac{\text{sh } My^*}{\text{sh } M} \qquad (7.1\text{-}32)$$

where $H_x^* = H_x/[y_0^2\sqrt{\sigma/\mu_f}(\partial P/\partial x)]$. In Fig. 7.1-10, $H_x^* - I^* + 2I_T^*$ is presented as a function of y^* for various values of I^* with $M = 5$. This curve can be used for any $I_T^* \leq I^*$ appropriately shifting the y^* axis.

The more general return circuit, being a loop of wire, would require a new solution to the entire problem. In addition to calculating the induced H_x field throughout all space, a development problem would arise in the fluid because all quantities would be functions of x. Fortunately, in most

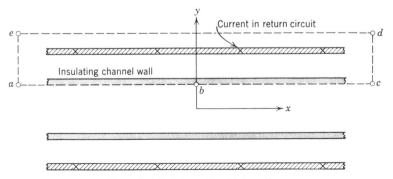

Figure 7.1-9   The path of integration.

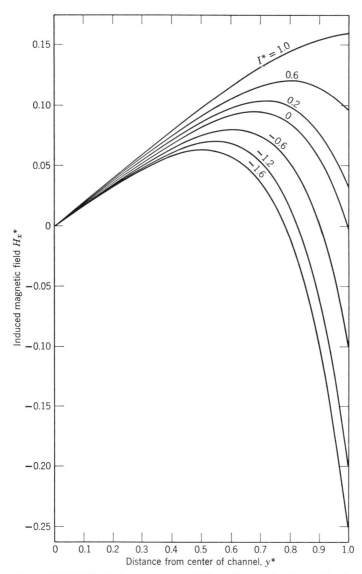

Figure 7.1-10   The induced magnetic field profile as a function of load current.

practical situations $Rm \ll 1$ and the induced field created by the return circuit is then negligible compared to the applied magnetic field so that all the solutions of this section are valid regardless of the configuration of the return circuit. It should be emphasized that in general the $\nabla \times \mathbf{H} = \mathbf{J}$ equation does not decouple as it did in this section, not even in two-dimensional steady-flow, direct current problems.

The pinch pressure gradient $\partial P/\partial y$ can be found, as a final step in this problem, from (7.1-2b). This pressure gradient tends to squeeze the fluid toward regions of the weakest induced magnetic field. Hence the pinch pressure gradient depends upon the return circuit and the amount of current it carries.

It is interesting to notice from Fig. 7.1-11 that an optimum Hartmann number exists which maximizes the short circuit current. The simple physical interpretation of the effect is left as an exercise for the reader.

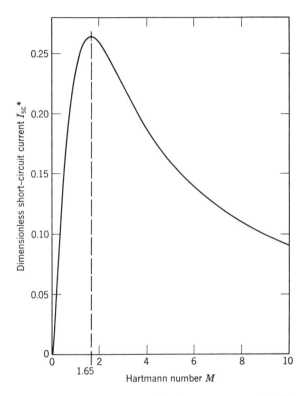

Figure 7.1-11   The dimensionless short-circuit current versus the Hartmann number.

7.2   MAGNETIC FIELD BOUNDARY CONDITIONS

In the preceding section it was not necessary to calculate the magnetic field, for in generalized Hartmann flow the velocity equation decouples from the magnetic field equation. It is usually necessary, however, to solve for the velocity and magnetic field with two coupled equations. Hence it is important to know boundary conditions for the magnetic field in the fluid at the boundaries of the channel. In this section the magnetic-field boundary conditions for the steady flow of an electrically conducting liquid are established. A derivation (Young and Hughes, 1962) is given in general cylindrical coordinates for arbitrary wall and fluid conductivity. Provisions are made for examining the influence of the electrical return circuit upon the magnetic-field boundary condition.

The General Case

When an electrically conducting fluid flows along a conductor of finite conductivity, the Maxwell equations must be solved in both the fluid and the solid conductor. Then the boundary conditions discussed in Chapter 2 can be applied. In many cases, for example, the rectangular channel, the problem is very difficult unless the channel walls are ideal insulators or conductors.

If the channel walls are either ideal insulators or ideal conductors, simple boundary conditions that eliminate the need for electrical solutions in the channel walls can be established. The current density normal to an insulator must be zero at the interface between the conducting fluid and the insulator. This boundary condition is easily expressed as

$$\mathbf{n} \cdot \mathbf{J}_f = 0$$

or

$$\mathbf{n} \cdot (\nabla \times \mathbf{H}_f) = 0 \qquad (7.2\text{-}1)$$

at the boundary regardless of the motion of the boundary. Here $\mathbf{n}$ is a unit vector normal to the boundary and the subscript f denotes variables in the fluid.

The magnetic-field boundary condition existing at the interface between an ideally conducting wall and a conducting fluid is more complicated than it was for an insulator. The fundamental principle most useful in this case is the continuity of the tangential electric field at the interface. If the ideal conducting wall is moving through the laboratory frame of coordinates with a velocity $\mathbf{V}_c$, the electric field in the conductor must be $\mathbf{E}_c = -\mathbf{V}_c \times \mathbf{B}$ so that the current density in the ideal conductor may remain finite. In the conducting fluid at the fluid-conducting wall interface, the electric field is given by

$$\mathbf{E}_f = \frac{\mathbf{J}_f}{\sigma_f} - \mathbf{V}_f \times \mathbf{B} \qquad (7.2\text{-}2)$$

Equating the tangential components of the electric field at the boundary yields

$$\mathbf{n} \times \mathbf{J}_f = \mathbf{n} \times [(\mathbf{V}_f - \mathbf{V}_c) \times \mathbf{B}]\sigma_f \qquad (7.2\text{-}3)$$

valid for $\sigma_f \neq 0$. This magnetic boundary condition is easily expressed as

$$\mathbf{n} \times (\nabla \times \mathbf{H}_f) = \mathbf{n} \times [(\mathbf{V}_f - \mathbf{V}_c) \times \mathbf{B}]\sigma_f \qquad (7.2\text{-}4)$$

In either (7.2-3) or (7.2-4) $\mathbf{H}_f$, $\mathbf{V}_f$, $\mathbf{V}_c$, and $\mathbf{B}$ must be evaluated at the interface between the ideal conductor and the conducting wall. When the fluid wets the wall, $\mathbf{V}_f - \mathbf{V}_c = 0$ and the boundary condition simplifies to $\mathbf{n} \times (\nabla \times \mathbf{H}_f) = 0$. If the fluid slips with respect to the wall, (7.2-4) applies. This condition could be used, for example, if the conducting wall is very close to the fluid but does not actually touch it.

When (7.2-1) and/or (7.2-4) apply at all boundaries in the channel, it is sufficient to solve for the velocity and magnetic field only in the conducting fluid. In the remainder of this section a special class of configurations is considered in which it is possible to account for the wall conductivity regardless of its magnitude.

Magnetic Boundary Conditions in a Special Class

In Fig. 7.2-1, fluid flows adjacent to the channel wall which is parallel to the x_1 axis and extends from $x_2 = a$ to $x_2 = b$. The surface of the wall is in

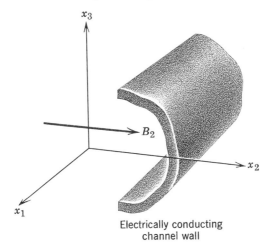

Electrically conducting
channel wall

Figure 7.2-1   A channel wall in curvilinear coordinates.

the $x_1 x_3$ plane. Fluid flows in the region $0 < x_2 < a$, and the region $x_2 > b$ is considered a vacuum. The coordinate system x_1, x_2, x_3 is a general orthogonal curvilinear system in which x_1, as the center line of the channel, is assumed essentially straight. The applied magnetic field is assumed in the x_2 direction perpendicular to the channel wall. The fluid flows in the x_1 direction inducing a magnetic field in that direction. The electric field components (assuming no Hall effect) E_1 and E_2 can be shown to be zero. The electrodes, if present, are located at some distance out along the x_3 axis so that an E_3 can exist. From Ohm's law

$$\mathbf{J} = \sigma(\mathbf{E} + \mathbf{V} \times \mathbf{B}) \tag{7.2-5}$$

and the Maxwell equation

$$\nabla \times \mathbf{H} = \mathbf{J} \tag{7.2-6}$$

it follows that in the fluid

$$-\frac{\partial H_{1f}}{\partial x_2} = e_2 \sigma_f (E_{3f} + V_f B_{2f}) \tag{7.2-7}$$

where the subscripts f denote variables in the fluid and e_i are the coefficients which define the metric in the curvilinear coordinate system (e_1 is taken as unity for a straight channel). In the conducting wall

$$-\frac{\partial H_{1c}}{\partial x_2} = e_2 \sigma_c (E_{3c} + V_c B_{2c}) \tag{7.2-8}$$

and in the vacuum

$$-\frac{\partial H_{1v}}{\partial x_2} = 0 \tag{7.2-9}$$

where the subscripts c and v refer to the conducting wall in the $x_1 x_3$ plane and the vacuum, respectively. From the Maxwell equation $\nabla \times \mathbf{E} = 0$, it follows that

$$\frac{1}{e_2 e_3} \frac{\partial}{\partial x_2} (e_3 E_3) = 0 \tag{7.2-10}$$

so that

$$E_{3f} = \frac{C_{1f}}{e_3}$$

$$E_{3c} = \frac{C_{1c}}{e_3} \tag{7.2-11}$$

From $\nabla \cdot \mathbf{B} = 0$,

$$\frac{1}{e_2 e_3} \frac{\partial}{\partial x_2} (e_3 B_2) = 0 \tag{7.2-12}$$

we obtain

$$B_{2f} = \frac{C_{2f}}{e_3}$$

$$B_{2c} = \frac{C_{2c}}{e_3} \tag{7.2-13}$$

The integration of (7.2-8) and (7.2-9) yields

$$H_{1c} = C_3 - \sigma_c f(x_2)(C_{1c} + V_c C_{2c})$$
$$H_{1v} = C_{1v} \tag{7.2-14}$$

where $f(x_2) = \int (e_2/e_3) \, dx_2$. But since $H_{1c}(x_2 = b) = H_{1v}$ it follows that

$$C_{1v} = C_3 - \sigma_c f(b)(C_{1c} + V_c C_{2c}) \tag{7.2-15}$$

Now from (7.2-2), $\oint \mathbf{H} \cdot d\mathbf{l} = I$ in which the path of integration is taken in the $x_1 x_2$ plane about a rectangular circuit coincident with the x_1 axis on one side, with $x_2 = b$ as the opposite side (enclosing the conducting wall), and of unit length in the x_1 direction. From the integration,

$$H_{1f}(0) - H_{1v}(b) = \mathscr{I}_3 \tag{7.2-16}$$

where $\mathscr{I}_3$ is the total current (including current flowing in the conducting wall) flowing between $x_2 = 0$ and $x_2 = b$ in the x_3 direction, per unit length of the x_1 axis. $H_{1f}(0)$ is a constant which depends on the return external circuit and is zero only if the channel and return circuit are symmetrical about the line $x_2 = 0$. From (7.2-15) and (7.2-14) we obtain

$$C_3 - \sigma_c f(b)(C_{1c} + V_c C_{2c}) = H_{1f}(0) - \mathscr{I}_3 \tag{7.2-17}$$

Because $E_{3f}(a) = E_{3c}(a)$ and $B_{2f}(a) = B_{2c}(a)$ it is easy to show that

$$C_{1c} = C_{1f} \quad \text{and} \quad C_{2c} = C_{2f} \tag{7.2-18}$$

and from (7.2-7)

$$C_{1f} = C_{1c} = -\left(\frac{e_3}{e_2 \sigma_f} \frac{\partial H_{1f}}{\partial x_2} + V_f C_{2f} \right)_{x_2 = a} \tag{7.2-19}$$

From (7.2-14) we obtain H_{1c}, which simplifies by (7.2-17) to yield

$$H_{1c} = H_{1f}(0) - \mathscr{I}_3 + \sigma_c [f(b) - f(x_2)](C_{1f} + V_c C_{2f}) \tag{7.2-20}$$

Equations (7.2-19) and (7.2-20) now combine to give the final form (when 7.2-20 is evaluated at $x_2 = a$, $H_{1c} = H_{1f}$)

$$[f(b) - f(a)] \frac{\sigma_c e_3(a)}{\sigma_f e_2(a)} \cdot \frac{\partial H_{1f}}{\partial x_z} \bigg|_{x_2 = a} + H_{1f}(x_2 = a) = H_{1f}(x_2 = 0) - \mathscr{I}_3$$
$$- \sigma_c [f(b) - f(a)][V_f(a) - V_c(a)] e_3(a) B_2(x_2 = a) \tag{7.2-21}$$

Ordinarily the quantity $V_f(a) - V_c(a)$ is zero and the right-hand member of (7.2-21) vanishes. When $\sigma_c \to \infty$, (7.2-21) reduces to the condition previously established at an ideal conducting wall and given by (7.2-4). If $\sigma_c/\sigma_f \to 0$, as it would for an insulating wall, (7.2-21) becomes

$$H_{1f}(x_2 = a) = H_{1f}(x_2 = 0) - \mathscr{I}_3 \tag{7.2-22}$$

$H_{1f}(x_2 = 0)$ is zero only if the external-current return path is symmetrical.

Therefore, $H_{1f}(x_2 = a) = 0$ only when no current flows in the external circuit. This condition can be shown to be consistent with (7.2-1).

In cartesian coordinates, $x_1 = x$, $x_2 = y$, $x_3 = z$, and $e_1 = e_2 = e_3 = 1$. The boundary condition of (7.2-21) becomes

$$(b - a)\frac{\sigma_c}{\sigma_f}\frac{\partial H_{xf}}{\partial y}\bigg|_{y=a} + H_{xf}(y = a) = H_{xf}(y = 0) - \mathcal{I}_z$$
$$- \sigma_c(b - a)[V_f(a) - V_c(a)]B_y(y = a) \quad (7.2\text{-}23)$$

In polar coordinates, $x_1 = z$, $x_2 = r$, $x_3 = \varphi$, $e_1 = 1$, $e_2 = 1$, and $e_3 = r$. Then $f(r) = \ln r$ and the magnetic boundary condition of (7.2-21) becomes

$$\left(a \ln \frac{b}{a}\right)\frac{\sigma_c}{\sigma_f}\frac{\partial H_{zf}}{\partial r}\bigg|_{r=a} + H_{zf}(r = a) = H_{zf}(r = 0) - \mathcal{I}_\varphi$$
$$- \sigma_c[V_f(a) - V_c(a)]B_r(r = a)a \ln \frac{b}{a} \quad (7.2\text{-}24)$$

It is easy to write (7.2-21) also in elliptic and parabolic cylinder coordinates.

The magnetic boundary condition at the interface between a wall of any conductivity and a fluid has been derived for the case where the flow is along x_1, the applied magnetic field is along x_2, and the channel wall is in the x_1x_3 plane.

7.3   ONE-DIMENSIONAL MHD COUETTE FLOW

Introduction

In this section we will consider the steady flow of an incompressible, viscous, electrically conducting liquid between parallel insulating planes. As indicated in Fig. 7.3-1, there is relative motion between the planes, and a uniform steady magnetic field is applied in the y direction. This infinite model is chosen to approximate the two-dimensional model of Fig. 7.3-2 in cases where $z_0 \gg y_0$. The problem is to find the velocity, current density, and magnetic field profiles in this device and their dependence upon applied magnetic field, fluid conductivity, channel material, and

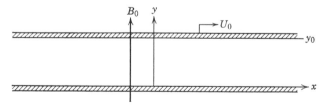

Figure 7.3-1   One-dimensional MHD Couette flow.

external circuit. The equations describing Couette flow are the same as those of one-dimensional MHD Poiseuille flow and they decouple in the same way. The difference between the two problems arises by virtue of different boundary conditions, for in Couette flow the fluid velocity at the top plate is U_0. The top and bottom plate here are assumed to be insulators. The effect of finite conductivity may easily be accounted for as it was in the Hartmann problem of Section 7.1, but the $\mathbf{V} \times \mathbf{B}$ term in the moving plate must now be considered. See Problem 37 at the end of the chapter for a detailed discussion of this point.

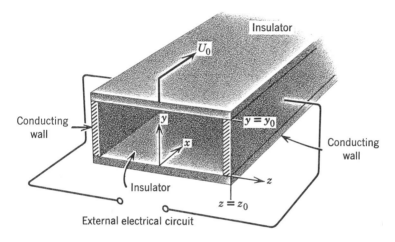

Figure 7.3-2   The physical device approximated by Fig. 7.3-1.

Solution

As was discussed in Section 7.1, B_y, v (the y component of velocity), E_z and E_x are constants. The Maxwell equations decouple such that $E_x = 0$ and, since the channel walls are solid, $v = 0$. The equations describing the flow are (7.1-4) and (7.1-1b). Because E_z is a constant, the equations for the velocity and the magnetic field decouple. Then (7.1-4) must be solved subject to the boundary conditions $u(y = 0) = 0$ and $u(y = y_0) = U_0$. The solution to (7.1-4) which satisfies these conditions is

$$u = U_0 \frac{\text{sh } My/y_0}{\text{sh } M} - \frac{y_0^2}{M^2 \text{ sh } M}\left(\frac{1}{\mu_f}\frac{\partial P}{\partial x} + \frac{M}{y_0}\sqrt{\frac{\sigma}{\mu_f}}E_z\right)$$

$$\times \left[\text{sh } M - \text{sh } \frac{My}{y_0} - \text{sh } M\left(\frac{(1 - y)}{y_0}\right)\right] \quad (7.3\text{-}1)$$

where $M = y_0 B_0 \sqrt{\sigma/\mu_f}$. This result is more complicated than the solution to one-dimensional MHD Poiseuille flow because an additional parameter U_0 is included. It can be shown that

$$\lim_{M \to 0} u = U_0 \frac{y}{y_0} - \frac{y_0^2}{2} \frac{\partial P}{\partial x} \left(-\frac{y^2}{y_0^2} + \frac{y}{y_0} \right) \tag{7.3-2}$$

which is the solution to ordinary Couette flow. Before relating E_z to the external electrical circuit it is convenient to put the velocity solution into dimensionless form. The normalization of Section 7.1 could be used, but is not preferred because $\partial P/\partial x$ may be zero in a special case of interest. Therefore, let $u^* = u/U_0$, $G^* = (y_0^2/\mu_f U_0)(\partial P/\partial x)$, $y^* = y/y_0$, and $E_z^* = (y_0/U_0)\sqrt{\sigma/\mu_f}(E_z)$. This reduces (7.3-1) to

$$u^* = \frac{\text{sh } My^*}{\text{sh } M} - \frac{G^* + ME_z^*}{M^2 \text{ sh } M} [\text{sh } M - \text{sh } My^* - \text{sh } M(1 - y^*)] \tag{7.3-3a}$$

The electric field can be related to the terminal voltage by (7.1-11), which applies here also. Then $V_T^* = -E_z^*$, where $V_T^* = (y_0/2z_0 U_0)\sqrt{\sigma/\mu_f}(V_T)$, so the normalized velocity is given by

$$u^* = \frac{\text{sh } My^*}{\text{sh } M} - \frac{G^* - MV_T^*}{M^2 \text{ sh } M} [\text{sh } M - \text{sh } My^* - \text{sh } M(1 - y^*)] \tag{7.3-3b}$$

The normalized flow rate, Q^* is given by $Q^* = \int_0^1 u^* \, dy^*$ and becomes

$$Q^* = \frac{\text{ch } M - 1}{M \text{ sh } M} - \frac{G^* - MV_T^*}{M^3 \text{ sh } M} (2 - 2 \text{ ch } M + M \text{ sh } M) \tag{7.3-4}$$

where $Q^* = Q/2y_0 z_0 U_0$ and $Q = \int_{-z_0}^{z_0} \int_0^{y_0} u \, dy \, dz$.

It is interesting to observe that the flow rate can be reduced to zero for any Hartmann number and terminal voltage by adjusting G^*. For example, if the channel were closed by boundaries located in the yz plane at $x = \pm x_0 (x_0 \gg y_0)$, the flow rate would be zero and the pressure would adjust accordingly. It is important to inspect limiting values of flow rate. When $M \to 0$, the flow rate can be obtained by using the first three terms of the series expansions of the hyperbolic functions. The result, which agrees with ordinary Couette flow, is

$$\lim_{M \to 0} Q^* = \frac{1}{2} - \frac{G^*}{12} \tag{7.3-5a}$$

in which case $Q^* = 0$ when $G^* = 6$. At very high Hartmann numbers the flow rate should approach zero. It is easy to show that for large M

$$Q^* = \frac{1}{M} - \frac{G^* - MV_T^*}{M^2} \tag{7.3-5b}$$

for which $Q^* = 0$ when $G^* = M(1 + V_T^*)$. If a more practical configuration could be constructed, it could be used as an MHD viscometer to detect the influence of electric and magnetic fields upon the viscosity of liquid metals.

The current density is given by (7.1-3b). When the velocity from (7.3-1) is substituted into (7.1-3b), the result is

$$J_z = \sigma E_z + \frac{M\sqrt{\sigma\mu_f}}{y_0 \operatorname{sh} M}\left\{ U_0 \operatorname{sh} \frac{My}{y_0} - \frac{y_0^2}{M^2}\left(\frac{1}{\mu_f}\frac{\partial P}{\partial x} + \frac{M}{y_0}\sqrt{\frac{\sigma}{\mu_f}}E_z\right)\right.$$
$$\left. \times \left[\operatorname{sh} M - \operatorname{sh}\frac{My}{y_0} - \operatorname{sh} M\left(1 - \frac{y}{y_0}\right)\right]\right\} \tag{7.3-6}$$

The total current per unit channel length is $\mathscr{I} = \int_0^{y_0} J_z\, dy$. In terms of the flow rate, the current per unit channel width is (from 7.1-3b)

$$\mathscr{I} = \sigma y_0 E_z + \frac{M}{2y_0 z_0}\sqrt{\sigma\mu_f}Q \tag{7.3-7a}$$

or in dimensionless form

$$\mathscr{I}^* = E_z^* + MQ^* \tag{7.3-7b}$$

where $\mathscr{I}^* = \mathscr{I}/U_0\sqrt{\sigma\mu_f}$ and $E_z^* = [y_0\sqrt{\sigma/\mu_f}(E_z)]/U_0$. When the external circuit is open, $\mathscr{I}^* = 0$ so that $E_z^* + MQ^* = 0$. This relationship can be solved for the open-circuit voltage. The result is

$$V_{oc}^* = \frac{M}{2} + \frac{G^*}{M}\left[1 + \frac{M \operatorname{sh} M}{2(1 - \operatorname{ch} M)}\right] \tag{7.3-8}$$

which increases linearly with the Hartmann number when M is large. As M increases to very high values, fluid flows only in a boundary layer along the moving channel wall. Since the total current must be zero in the open-circuit case, the electric field must be proportional to M from (7.3-7b). Hence, for large M, V_{oc}^* increases linearly with M.

From (7.3-7a) the short-circuit current is given by ($I = 2x_0\mathscr{I}$)

$$I_{sc} = \frac{x_0\sqrt{\sigma\mu_f}}{y_0 z_0}MQ \tag{7.3-9a}$$

or in dimensionless form

$$I_{sc}^* = MQ^* \tag{7.3-9b}$$

where $I_{sc}^* = I/(2x_0\sqrt{\sigma\mu_f}U_0)$. For large Hartmann numbers, I_{sc}^* approaches unity. This is easily explained physically; the short-circuited current density (from Ohm's law) is directly proportional to the Hartmann number and flow rate, and as the flow rate is inversely proportional to the Hartmann number, the short-circuit current must not be a function of the Hartmann number.

The induced magnetic field in this configuration, as in Poiseuille flow, decouples from the equation of fluid motion. It can be obtained from the integration of (7.1-1b) and the application of the boundary condition given by (7.2-23).

Discussion

In MHD Couette flow, as in MHD Poiseiulle flow, the external circuit greatly influences the velocity profile. The role of the external circuit is well illustrated by the comparison of the short- and open-circuited velocity profiles shown in Figs. 7.3-3 and 7.3-4. In the short-circuited

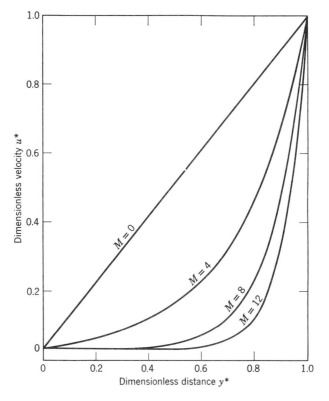

Figure 7.3-3 The velocity profile in short-circuited MHD Couette flow for various Hartmann numbers when $G^* = 0$.

case, the induced current density is unidirectional and the resulting electromagnetic body force is a retarding force. In the open-circuited case, the induced current density is not unidirectional because the total current is zero. In the top half ($y^* > 0.5$) the current density is in the positive z direction and leads to a $\mathbf{J} \times \mathbf{B}$ force which retards the fluid flow. For $y < 0.5$ the current density is in the negative z direction and causes an

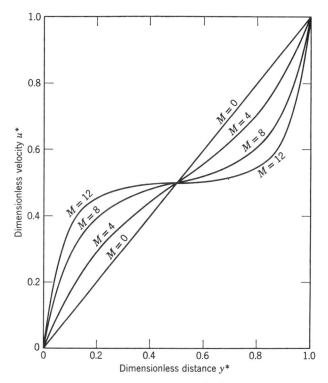

Figure 7.3-4 The velocity profile in open-circuited MHD Couette flow for various Hartmann numbers when $G^* = 0$.

electromagnetic body force which increases the fluid velocity near the stationary wall. This effect becomes more pronounced as the Hartmann number is increased. In addition, a wide variety of open- and short-circuited velocity profiles can be obtained for positive and negative values of the dimensionless pressure gradient G^*.

The influence of the dimensionless pressure gradient is illustrated in Fig. 7.3-5. For $G^* > 0$ the pressure gradient is opposed to the flow caused by the moving boundary. Hence, as G^* increases, the open-circuit voltage decreases and changes sign when $G^* > 6$. For $G^* > 6$ the open-circuit voltage is negative for low Hartmann numbers. However, at Hartmann numbers larger than G^*, the open-circuit voltage becomes positive. At these Hartmann numbers the viscous drag of the plate overpowers the adverse pressure gradient.

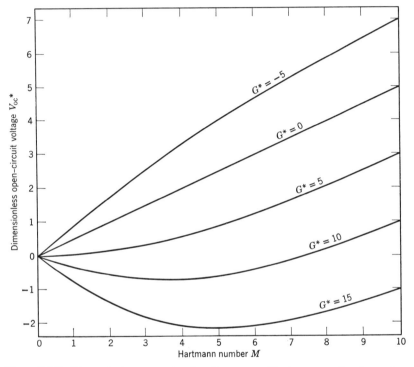

Figure 7.3-5   Dimensionless open-circuit voltage versus Hartmann number for various pressure gradients.

The interaction of the Hartmann number and the dimensionless pressure gradient is shown in Fig. 7.3-6. The flow can be stopped by choosing a dimensionless pressure gradient greater than $G^* = 6$. However, as the Hartmann number increases, a larger value of G^* is required to stop the flow.

If the configuration treated here (see Fig. 7.3-2) is used as an MHD viscometer, walls must be erected in the yz plane at $x = \pm x_0$. Then the dimensionless flow rate Q^* must be zero. Under this condition the dimensionless pressure gradient adjusts itself in accordance with the Hartmann number so that $Q^* = 0$.

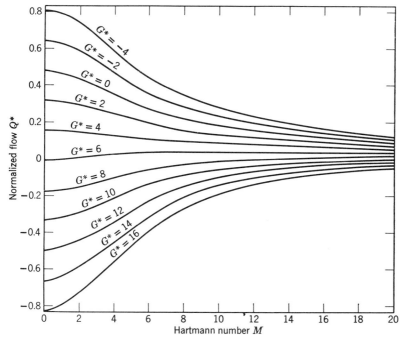

Figure 7.3-6 Flow versus Hartmann number for various pressure gradients in short-circuited Couette flow.

7.4 TWO-DIMENSIONAL MHD CHANNEL FLOW

Introduction

In the few cases of two-dimensional MHD channel flow found in the literature, the cross sections considered are rectangular or circular. Although other cross sections, that is, elliptical, parabolic, etc., might be solved in special cases, the rectangular and circular geometries have not been exhaustively studied. It is the purpose of this section to define the problems of MHD channel flow in rectangular and polar coordinates and to discuss their solutions qualitatively.

In ordinary hydrodynamics only one velocity profile exists for each kind of channel, providing that the flow is laminar and steady. When the fluid is an electrical conductor passing through a magnetic field, however, an infinity of velocity profiles is possible, each one resulting from a different return circuit for the electric current. We shall refer to about a dozen of the simplest profiles and in later sections of this chapter a few of these will be worked in detail.

The Rectangular Channel

The general problem of MHD flow in a rectangular channel having walls of finite, nonzero conductivity is a very difficult one, involving the magnetic field solutions not only in the conducting fluid but in the space outside the channel as well. For any given problem a finite difference equation computer solution can be obtained but it seems unlikely that an analytical solution is practical. Several configurations comprising insulating and high-conductivity walls may be tractable. Throughout this section a high-conductivity wall is assumed to have infinite conductivity when compared to the conducting liquid. The configurations that are possible using four insulating or ideally conducting walls are illustrated in Fig. 7.4-1a through i. In Fig. 7.4-1 the cross-hatched walls are insulators, the applied magnetic field is uniform and directed vertically across the channel, and the fluid flow is into the plane of the figure. The lines in Fig. 7.4-1 indicate (approximately) how the electric current flows in each case. Because the current-flow patterns are different in each case, the forces exerted on the fluid by electromagnetic effects are different in each case. For each of the configurations in Fig. 7.4-1 a different velocity profile results. The current patterns are easily sketched by observing three rules: (1) the current is either normal to or zero at ideal conducting boundaries, (2) at insulating boundaries the normal component of current is zero, and (3) the current curls about the induced magnetic field. These rules result from the boundary conditions existing at insulators and conductors and from Maxwell's equations.

In 7.4-1a the current generated in the center of the channel flows to the right vertical ideal conducting wall and is returned to the left vertical wall via the top and bottom walls. In this case, the induced magnetic field is zero in the center of the channel and increases or decreases to its extrema at the top and bottom of the channel. The effect is similar to two opposite excited rectangular solenoids stacked one on the other, the magnetic field in the top solenoid being directed out of the paper in Fig. 7.4-1a. Figure 7.4-1b is similar to Fig. 7.4-1a except that in the former case the return current does not return in the channel walls and in the latter case it does. This fact causes the current distribution to be very different in the two cases. In the insulating-channel case the induced magnetic field is zero along the boundaries. The current and field distributions of the rest of Fig. 7.4-1 are easily explained physically.

The configuration of Fig. 7.4-1c is a simple MHD generator. Here current is generated in the center of the channel; some of it flows back through the fluid, and the remainder returns through the load resistance. In the short-circuit case, nearly all of the current flows in the external

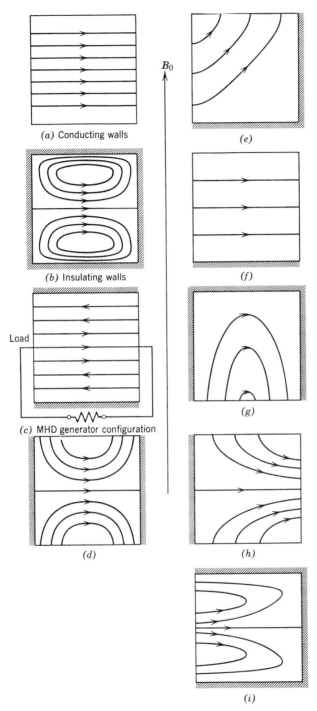

(a) Conducting walls

(b) Insulating walls

Load

(c) MHD generator configuration

(d)

B_0

(e)

(f)

(g)

(h)

(i)

Figure 7.4-1 Various simple channel configurations and sketches of electric current lines. Cross-hatched channel walls are insulators and other channel walls are ideal conductors. The applied magnetic field is directed vertically.

circuit and very little, if any, returns in the fluid. Figure 7.4-1c represents a case where about one-half of the current generated returns inside the generator. If one of the channel walls is removed and the fluid is held in by a gravitational field, over a dozen more cases result. Because there are so many cases that can be studied, it is useful to inspect the equations of MHD steady incompressible two-dimensional channel flow in cartesian coordinates with a view to finding simple solutions.

The MHD Channel Flow Equations in Cartesian Coordinates

Consider the case, illustrated in Fig. 7.4-2, where the fluid flows in the x direction and the applied magnetic field is uniform and directed along

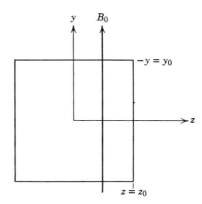

Figure 7.4-2   Coordinate system used in channel flow.

the y axis. Because $\mathbf{V} \times \mathbf{B}$ has a component in the z direction, it is expected that currents will flow in the z direction giving support to a magnetic field in the x direction. Since the current needs a return path, there generally must be y components of current as well. Because the flow is fully developed, no x variation of any quantities (except pressure) is possible. Our task involves finding $\mathbf{J}$, $\mathbf{E}$, $\mathbf{H}$, $\mathbf{B}$, and $\mathbf{V}$ as functions of x, y, B_0, σ, μ_f, μ_0, y_0, z_0, and the boundary conditions. Thus the solution involves two of Maxwell's curl equations, the Navier-Stokes equation and two constitutive equations. Since there is no time variation, the electric field is irrotational and $\nabla \times \mathbf{E} = 0$ becomes

$$\frac{\partial E_z}{\partial y} = \frac{\partial E_y}{\partial z} \tag{7.4-1}$$

Displacement current and space charge are neglected and (2.4-3) is used in the $\nabla \times \mathbf{H} = \mathbf{J}$ equation. Then, since $\partial H_y/\partial z = J_x = 0$, we conclude that H_y is a constant, $H_y = B_0/\mu_0$. The remaining parts of $\nabla \times \mathbf{H} = \mathbf{J}$ yield

$$\frac{\partial H_x}{\partial z} = J_y = \sigma E_y \tag{7.4-2}$$

$$-\frac{\partial H_x}{\partial y} = \sigma E_z + \sigma B_0 u \tag{7.4-3}$$

It is easy to combine (7.4-1), (7.4-2), and (7.4-3) to obtain

$$\frac{\partial^2 H_x}{\partial y^2} + \frac{\partial^2 H_x}{\partial z^2} + \sigma B_0 \frac{\partial u}{\partial y} = 0 \tag{7.4-4}$$

The Navier-Stokes equation is

$$0 = -\frac{\partial P}{\partial x} + \mu_f \frac{\partial^2 u}{\partial y^2} + \mu_f \frac{\partial^2 u}{\partial z^2} - J_z B_0 \tag{7.4-5}$$

$$0 = -\frac{\partial P}{\partial y} + J_z B_x \tag{7.4-6}$$

and

$$0 = -\frac{\partial P}{\partial z} - J_y B_x \tag{7.4-7}$$

From (7.4-6) $\partial^2 P/\partial x\,\partial y = 0$ and from (7.4-7) $\partial^2 P/\partial x\,\partial z = 0$, which is satisfied only when $\partial P/\partial x$ is a constant. In our problem, if fluid is being pumped in the x direction down the channel $\partial P/\partial x$ is taken to be a negative constant. Equations (7.4-6) and (7.4-7) are good for finding $\partial P/\partial y$ and $\partial P/\partial z$ after the currents and magnetic fields have been found. Since $J_z = -\partial H_x/\partial y$, (7.4-5) becomes

$$\frac{\partial^2 u}{\partial y^2} + \frac{\partial^2 u}{\partial z^2} + \frac{B_0}{\mu_f}\frac{\partial H_x}{\partial y} = \frac{1}{\mu_f}\frac{\partial P}{\partial x} \tag{7.4-8}$$

Equations (7.4-4) and (7.4-8) must be solved simultaneously and subjected to the appropriate boundary conditions.

Boundary Conditions

Because there are four walls (assumed here to be either insulators, very good conductors, or free surfaces), there are many different arrangements which yield different boundary conditions. At conducting or insulating walls the fluid velocity is zero and at free surfaces the shear is zero. For material boundaries

$$u \big|_{\text{Boundary}} = 0 \qquad (7.4\text{-}9a)$$

and for free surfaces

$$\frac{\partial u}{\partial n}\bigg|_{\text{Boundary}} = 0 \qquad (7.4\text{-}9b)$$

where $\partial/\partial n$ denotes the normal derivative. When the walls are ideal conductors, the electric field tangential to the walls must be zero or infinite current will flow in the conductor. Hence at ideal conducting walls (at rest in the laboratory frame)

$$\frac{\partial H_x}{\partial n}\bigg|_{\text{Boundary}} = 0 \qquad (7.4\text{-}10a)$$

At insulating walls the normal component of the current density must be zero and therefore

$$\frac{\partial H_x}{\partial T}\bigg|_{\text{Boundary}} = 0 \qquad (7.4\text{-}10b)$$

where $\partial/\partial T$ is the tangential derivative. (See Section 7.2.)

Possible Solutions

1. If (7.4-4) and (7.4-8) are combined, a fourth-order partial differential equation in either u or H_x can be obtained. The common method of assuming a product solution, however, is not fruitful. Instead, following Shercliff (1953), we assume that $u = f(y, z) + g(y, z) + u_p$ and that $H_x = \sqrt{\sigma \mu_f}[f(y, z) - g(y, z)]$, where u_p is the particular integral solution. These assumptions are substituted into (7.4-4) and (7.4-8) and the sums and differences of the resulting homogeneous system yield

$$\frac{\partial^2 f}{\partial y^2} + \frac{\partial^2 f}{\partial z^2} + B_0\sqrt{\frac{\sigma}{\mu_f}}\frac{\partial f}{\partial y} = 0 \qquad (7.4\text{-}11a)$$

and

$$\frac{\partial^2 g}{\partial y^2} + \frac{\partial^2 g}{\partial z^2} - B_0\sqrt{\frac{\sigma}{\mu_f}}\frac{\partial g}{\partial y} = 0 \qquad (7.4\text{-}11b)$$

which are separable. This form of solution is applied easily only when both u and H_x go to zero on the boundaries. Hence this form of solution is most useful in channels having insulating walls because $f(y, z)$ and $g(y, z)$ are then zero on the boundaries. In all other cases it would be difficult to satisfy the boundary conditions by a Fourier series solution to (7.4-11a) and (7.4-11b).

2. By assuming the coordinate system of Fig. 7.4-2 for the configurations of Fig. 7.4-1, we can inspect Fig. 7.4-1 for symmetry. In configurations (a), (b), (c), (d), (h), and (i), the body force exerted on the fluid is an even function of y. The velocity should also be an even function of y. And the induced magnetic field is antisymmetric in y. Therefore, it seems reasonable to assume

$$u(y, z) = u_p + \sum_{n=0}^{\infty} f_n(z) \cos \lambda_n y \qquad (7.4\text{-}12a)$$

where u_p is a particular solution to (7.4-4) and (7.4-8) and $\lambda_n = (2n + 1)\pi/(2y_0)$. By integrating (7.4-8) with respect to y, we can see that the correct form for $H_x(y, z)$ is

$$H_x(y, z) = H_p + \sum_{n=0}^{\infty} g_n(z) \sin \lambda_n y \qquad (7.4\text{-}12b)$$

The assumed solutions must be adjusted to satisfy the appropriate boundary conditions. Since $u_0(y, \pm z_0) = 0$, the coefficients of the series must be adjusted so that $u_p(y, \pm z_0) = -\sum_{n=0}^{\infty} f_n(\pm z_0) \cos \lambda_n y$. The other boundary condition, $u(\pm y_0, z) = 0$, is automatically satisfied if $u_p(\pm y_0, z) = 0$. The one-dimensional Poiseuille flow of Section 7.1 exhibits solutions of that form. The solution for velocity given in (7.4-12a) can be adjusted to satisfy configurations (a), (b), (c), (d), (h), and (i) of Fig. 7.4-1. However, the solution to the induced magnetic field, assumed in (7.4-12b), may not fit the boundary conditions in these configurations. By inspecting expressions for current density along the boundaries, we can decide which problems can be solved with the assumption of (7.4-12b). By (7.4-2) and (7.4-3) the current densities are

$$J_y(y, z) = \frac{\partial H_p}{\partial z} + \sum_{n=0}^{\infty} \frac{dg_n(z)}{dz} \sin \lambda_n y \qquad (7.4\text{-}13a)$$

and

$$J_z(y, z) = -\frac{\partial H_p}{\partial y} - \sum_{n=0}^{\infty} \lambda_n g_n(z) \cos \lambda_n y \qquad (7.4\text{-}13b)$$

At the top and bottom boundaries $J_z(\pm y_0, z) = -\dfrac{\partial H_p}{\partial y}\bigg|_{\pm y_0}$ which indicates that the top and bottom channel walls could be conductors if $\dfrac{\partial H_p}{\partial y}\bigg|_{\pm y_0} = 0$. If the top and bottom walls are conductors, $J_y(\pm y_0, z)$ takes on a value and does not concern us. Assuming this is so, let us consider the right and left sides of the channel. If they are insulators,

$J_z(y, \pm z_0) = 0$, which can be satisfied by requiring that

$$\left.\frac{\partial H_p}{\partial y}\right|_{\pm z_0} = -\sum_{n=0}^{\infty} \lambda_n g_n(\pm z_0) \cos \lambda_n y.$$

If the right and left walls are ideal conductors, the boundary condition that applies is $J_y(y, \pm z_0) = 0$, which is easily satisfied. Similarly, one side wall can be an insulator and the other a conductor and no serious difficulties will occur. Therefore (7.4-12a) and (7.4-12b) are the solutions to channels (a), (d), and (h) of Fig. 7.4-1. To complete our discussion of (7.4-12a) and (7.4-12b), the possibility of the top and bottom being insulators must be considered. In that case $J_y(\pm y_0, z) = 0$ for all values of z; but from (7.4-13a) it would seem that such a solution, if it exists at all, would be difficult to obtain and so we conclude that the assumed solutions (7.4-13a) and (7.4-13b) can be easily applied to channels whose top and bottom walls are conductors (the applied magnetic field being normal to the conducting walls) but that if the top and bottom walls are insulators, it would be wise to seek another form of solution.

3. It is possible to assume another solution for the velocity in which the Fourier series is in terms of $\cos \lambda_n z$ rather than $\cos \lambda_n y$. This solution is given by

$$u(y, z) = u_p + \sum_{n=0}^{\infty} f_n(y) \cos \lambda_n z \qquad (7.4\text{-}14a)$$

where u_p is a particular solution and $\lambda_n = (2n + 1)\pi/2z_0$. The assumed solution for the induced magnetic field is

$$H_x(y, z) = H_p + \sum_{n=0}^{\infty} g_n(y) \cos \lambda_n z \qquad (7.4\text{-}14b)$$

The no-slip boundary condition is immediately met by (7.4-14a) along $\pm z_0$ and if $u_p\big|_{\pm y_0} = -\sum_{n=0}^{\infty} f_n(\pm y_0) \cos \lambda_n z$, the remaining boundary conditions on velocity are satisfied at the channel walls. From the assumed solution (7.4-14b) the current densities are obtained. From (7.4-2)

$$J_y = \frac{\partial H_p}{\partial z} - \sum_{n=0}^{\infty} \lambda_n g_n(y) \sin \lambda_n z \qquad (7.4\text{-}15a)$$

and from (7.4-3)

$$J_z = -\frac{\partial H_p}{\partial y} - \sum_{n=0}^{\infty} \frac{dg_n(y)}{dy} \cos \lambda_n z \qquad (7.4\text{-}15b)$$

which are to be inspected along the boundaries. If $\partial H_p/\partial y\big|_{\pm z_0} = 0$, $J_z(y, \pm z_0) = 0$ and the right and left walls are insulators. Now as far as (7.4-15b) is concerned, these walls could be conductors, for $\partial H_p/\partial y\big|_{\pm z_0}$ need not be zero. However, if the walls are ideal conductors, $J_y\big|_{\pm z_0} = 0$, a condition not easily satisfied by (7.4-15a). Hence the assumed solutions of (7.4-14a) and (7.4-14b) are most easily used when the right and left walls are insulators, as in Fig. 7.4-1 (b), (d), and (g). If the top and bottom walls are insulators, $J_y(\pm y_0, z) = 0$ and this condition can be satisfied if $(\partial H_p/\partial z)\big|_{\pm y_0} = \sum\limits_{n=0}^{\infty} \lambda_n g_n(\pm y_0) \sin \lambda_n z$. When the top and bottom walls are conductors, the boundary condition is $J_z(\pm y_0, z) = 0$. This condition is satisfied if $\partial H_p/\partial y\big|_{\pm y_0} = -\sum\limits_{n=0}^{\infty} \dfrac{dg_n}{dy}\bigg|_{\pm y_0} \cos \lambda_n z$. It is also possible to use (7.4-14a) and (7.4-14b) if the top wall is an insulator and the bottom wall a conductor and vice versa. In summary, (7.4-14a) and (7.4-14b) can be used to solve channels (b), (d), and (g) of Fig. 7.4-1.

Summary

By assuming simple Fourier series solutions, channels (a), (b), (d), (g), and (h) of Fig. 7.4-1 can be solved. These channels all have a velocity profile that is symmetrical about either the y or the z axis, or both. Symmetry exists in the velocity profile of configurations (c), (f), and (i) but these cannot be solved easily with sinusoidal solutions because the magnetic-field boundary conditions dictate that the normal derivative of velocity be zero along one or more boundaries. The vanishing of the normal derivative of velocity implies zero shear along the boundary and this is clearly not possible. Hence sinusoidal solutions are not suitable for (c), (f), and (i). In problems of this kind it is better to abandon exact methods in favor of an approximate method, such as the Galerkin method (Kantorovich and Krylov, 1958).

It is unfortunate that (c) cannot be easily solved, for it is the common magnetohydrodynamic generator configuration. However, solutions to some of the free surface channel flow problems can be obtained by using the assumed solutions of this section. For example, when channels (a), (b), (c) (if originally symmetrically loaded), (d), (h), and (i) are cut in half along the xz plane, the solutions presented here still hold.

7.5 RECTANGULAR CHANNEL WITH INSULATING WALLS

Introduction

The problem of the steady flow of an incompressible, viscous, electrically conducting fluid through a rectangular pipe in the presence of a transverse applied magnetic field was solved by Shercliff (1953). It is a problem of considerable practical interest because of the utility of induction flow meters. The results of Shercliff's solution were used to check the well-known experimental results of Hartmann and Lazarus (1937). Our solution appears to be different from Shercliff's because we do not separate the variables as he does. However, both solutions are equivalent and it is important to realize there are usually many ways to solve a given boundary value problem.

Solution to the Boundary Value Problem

When the walls are perfect insulators, no current flows from the fluid into the walls. Thus the component of current normal to each wall must be zero, as was discussed in Section 7.4. Using the choice of coordinates illustrated in Fig. 7.5-1, the boundary conditions become

$$u(\pm y_0, z) = u(y, \pm z_0) = 0 \qquad (7.5\text{-}1a)$$

and

$$\frac{\partial H_x}{\partial z}(\pm y_0, z) = \frac{\partial H_x}{\partial y}(y, \pm z_0) = 0 \qquad (7.5\text{-}1b)$$

According to the conclusion of Section 7.4, the form of the assumed

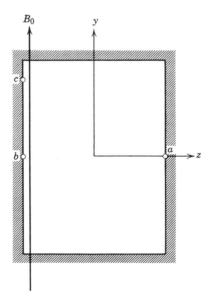

Figure 7.5-1   The rectangular channel with insulating walls.

solution should be

$$u(y, z) = u_{y_0 \to \infty} + \sum_{n=0}^{\infty} u_n(y) \cos \lambda_n z \qquad (7.5\text{-}2a)$$

and

$$H_x(y, z) = \sum_{n=0}^{\infty} H_n(y) \cos \lambda_n z \qquad (7.5\text{-}2b)$$

where $\lambda_n = (2n + 1)\pi/(2z_0)$ and $u_{y_0 \to \infty} = (z_0^2/2\mu_f)(\partial P/\partial x) \cdot [(z^2/z_0^2) - 1]$ which is the velocity profile in a channel having $y_0 \gg z_0$ and no applied magnetic field. This assumption of $u_p = u_{y_0 \to \infty}$ and $H_p = 0$ is sufficient to make homogeneous the two governing equations (7.4-4) and (7.4-8).

When (7.5-2a) and (7.5-2b) are substituted into (7.4-4) and (7.4-8), we have

$$\frac{d^2 u_n(y)}{dy^2} - \lambda_n^2 u_n(y) + \frac{B_0}{\mu_f} \frac{\partial H_n(y)}{dy} = 0 \qquad (7.5\text{-}3a)$$

and

$$\frac{d^2 H_n(y)}{dy^2} - \lambda_n^2 H_n(y) + \sigma B_0 \frac{d u_n(y)}{dy} = 0 \qquad (7.5\text{-}3b)$$

These equations must be combined to yield an equation in $u_n(y)$ which is

$$\frac{d^4 u_n(y)}{dy^4} - \left(2\lambda_n^2 + \frac{M^2}{k^2 z_0^2}\right)\frac{d^2 u_n(y)}{dy^2} + \lambda_n^4 u_n(y) = 0 \qquad (7.5\text{-}4)$$

where $M = B_0 y_0 \sqrt{\sigma/\mu_f}$ and $k = y_0/z_0$. As the velocity profile should be the same for the positive and negative values of y, the solution to (7.5-4) is

$$u_n(y) = A_n \operatorname{ch} p_1 y + B_n \operatorname{ch} p_2 y \qquad (7.5\text{-}5)$$

where

$$p_{1,2}^2 = \lambda_n^2 + \frac{M^2}{2z_0^2 k^2} \pm \frac{M}{z_0 k}\sqrt{\lambda_n^2 + \frac{M^2}{4z_0^2 k^2}} \qquad (7.5\text{-}6)$$

The quantity $H_n(y)$ is easily found from (7.5-3a), and assuming $H_n(y = 0)$ is zero, the result is

$$H_n(y) = \frac{kz_0\sqrt{\sigma\mu_f}}{M}\left[\frac{A_n(\lambda_n^2 - p_1^2)}{p_1} \operatorname{sh} p_1 y + \frac{B_n(\lambda_n^2 - p_2^2)}{p_2} \operatorname{sh} p_2 y\right] \qquad (7.5\text{-}7)$$

The assumption $H_n(y = 0) = 0$ can be interpreted to mean that no external axial field has been applied to the channel. From the magnetic-field boundary condition $(\partial H_x/\partial z)(y, z)|_{\pm y_0} = 0$, it is apparent that $H_n(\pm y_0) = 0$. Accordingly,

$$A_n p_2(\lambda_n^2 - p_1^2) \operatorname{sh} p_1 y_0 + B_n p_1(\lambda_n^2 - p_2^2) \operatorname{sh} p_2 y_0 = 0 \qquad (7.5\text{-}8)$$

The only unsatisfied boundary condition is $u(\pm y_0, z) = 0$. Expanding in a Fourier series, as indicated in Section 7.4, yields

$$u_n(y_0) = \frac{2(-1)^n}{\lambda_n^3 \mu_f z_0} \frac{\partial P}{\partial x} \qquad (7.5\text{-}9)$$

Applying the boundary condition $u(\pm y_0, z) = 0$ yields

$$A_n \operatorname{ch} p_1 y_0 + B_n \operatorname{ch} p_2 y_0 = u_n(y_0) \qquad (7.5\text{-}10)$$

which can be solved simultaneously to yield A_n and B_n. These quantities are given by

$$A_n = \frac{-p_1(\lambda_n^2 - p_2^2)}{\Delta_n} u_n(y_0) \operatorname{sh} p_2 y_0 \qquad (7.5\text{-}11a)$$

and

$$B_n = \frac{p_2(\lambda_n^2 - p_1^2)}{\Delta_n} u_n(y_0) \operatorname{sh} p_1 y_0 \qquad (7.5\text{-}11b)$$

where

$$\Delta_n = p_2(\lambda_n^2 - p_1^2) \operatorname{sh} p_1 y_0 \operatorname{ch} p_2 y_0 - p_1(\lambda_n^2 - p_2^2) \operatorname{sh} p_2 y_0 \operatorname{ch} p_1 y_0 \qquad (7.5\text{-}11c)$$

The solution for the velocity is

$$u(y, z) = \frac{z_0^2}{2\mu_f} \frac{\partial P}{\partial x} \left[\frac{z^2}{z_0^2} - 1 + \frac{4}{z_0^3} \sum_{n=0}^{\infty} \frac{(-1)^n \alpha_n(y) \cos \lambda_n z}{\lambda_n^3 \Delta_n} \right] \qquad (7.5\text{-}12a)$$

where

$$\alpha_n(y) = -p_1(\lambda_n^2 - p_2^2) \operatorname{sh} p_2 y_0 \operatorname{ch} p_1 y + p_2(\lambda_n^2 - p_1^2) \operatorname{sh} p_1 y_0 \operatorname{ch} p_2 y \qquad (7.5\text{-}12b)$$

It is easy to show that as $M \to 0$ Equation (7.5-12a) reduces to the solution for viscous, incompressible channel flow. If we take into account (7.5-2b) and use all the necessary constants, the solution for the magnetic field becomes

$$H_x(y, z) = \frac{2M}{kz_0^2} \sqrt{\frac{\sigma}{\mu_f}} \frac{\partial P}{\partial x} \sum_{n=0}^{\infty} \frac{(-1)^n \beta_n(y) \cos \lambda_n z}{\lambda_n \Delta_n} \qquad (7.5\text{-}13a)$$

where

$$\beta_n = \operatorname{sh} p_2 y_0 \operatorname{sh} p_1 y - \operatorname{sh} p_1 y_0 \operatorname{sh} p_2 y \qquad (7.5\text{-}13b)$$

For the purpose of calculating curves it is convenient to place the solutions in dimensionless form. Here we let $k = y_0/z_0$, $z^* = z/z_0$, $y^* = y/z_0$, $\lambda_n^* = \lambda_n z_0$, $p_i^* = p_i z_0$, $u^*(y, z) = \mu_f u(y, z) \left[z_0^2 \left(\frac{\partial P}{\partial x} \right) \right]^{-1}$ and $H_x^*(y, z) = H_x(y, z) \left[z_0^2 \sqrt{\sigma/\mu_f} \left(\frac{\partial P}{\partial x} \right) \right]^{-1}$. Then (7.5-12a) and (7.5-12b) become

$$u^*(y^*, z^*) = \frac{z^{*2} - 1}{2} + 2 \sum_{n=0}^{\infty} \frac{(-1)^n \alpha_n^*(y^*) \cos \lambda_n^* z^*}{\lambda_n^{*3} \alpha_n^*(k)} \qquad (7.5\text{-}14a)$$

and

$$H_x^*(y^*, z^*) = \frac{2M}{k} \sum_{n=0}^{\infty} \frac{(-1)^n \beta^*(y^*) \cos \lambda_n^* z^*}{\lambda_n^* \alpha_n^*(k)} \qquad (7.5\text{-}14\text{b})$$

where

$$\alpha_n^*(y^*) = -p_1^*(\lambda_n^{*2} - p_2^{*2}) \operatorname{sh} p_2^* k \operatorname{ch} p_1^* y^*$$

$$+ p_2^*(\lambda_n^{*2} - p_1^{*2}) \operatorname{sh} p_1^* k \operatorname{ch} p_2^* y^*$$

$$\beta_n^*(y^*) = \operatorname{sh} p_2^* k \operatorname{sh} p_1^* y^* - \operatorname{sh} p_1^* k \operatorname{sh} p_2^* y^*$$

$$p_{1,2}^* = \sqrt{\lambda_n^{*2} + \frac{M^2}{2k^2} \pm \frac{M}{k} \sqrt{\lambda_n^{*2} + \frac{M^2}{4k^2}}} \qquad (7.5\text{-}15)$$

$$\lambda^* = \frac{2n + 1}{2} \pi$$

The dimensionless flow rate Q is defined as

$$Q^* = 4 \int_0^k \int_0^1 u^*(y^*, z^*) \, dz^* \, dy^*$$

When we evaluate this for $u^*(y^*, z^*)$ given by (7.5-14a), we have

$$Q^* = -4 \left[\frac{k}{3} + \frac{4M}{k} \sum_{n=0}^{\infty} \frac{\sqrt{\lambda_n^{*2} + (M^2/4k^2)} \operatorname{sh} p_1^* k \operatorname{sh} p_2^* k}{\lambda_n^{*4} \alpha_n^*(k)} \right] \qquad (7.5\text{-}16)$$

Because this configuration might be used as a flow meter, we must calculate electrical potential differences When the $\nabla \times \mathbf{H} = \mathbf{J}$ equation is written in dimensionless form,

$$-\frac{\partial H_x^*}{\partial y^*} = E_z^* + \frac{M}{k} u^* \qquad (7.5\text{-}17\text{a})$$

and

$$\frac{\partial H_x^*}{\partial z^*} = E_y^* \qquad (7.5\text{-}17\text{b})$$

where $E^* = E\sqrt{\sigma \mu_f}/[z_0(\partial P/\partial x)]$. If the dimensionless voltage is defined as $V^* = V\sqrt{\sigma \mu_f}/[z_0^2(\partial P/\partial x)]$, it can be calculated from $V_{ab}^* = -\int_a^b \mathbf{E} \cdot d\mathbf{l}^*$. By referring to Fig. 7.5-1, we shall calculate V_{ac}^*. This calculation is done by observing that $V_{ac}^* = V_{ab}^* + V_{bc}^*$. Knowing V_{ab}^* and V_{bc}^*, we can calculate the potential difference between any two points on the surface of the channel walls. First,

$$V_{ab}* = -\int_{-1}^{1} \left(\frac{\partial H_x*}{\partial y*} + \frac{M}{k} u*\right) dz* \qquad (7.5\text{-}18a)$$

When the details of this integration are completed, the result is

$$V_{ab}* = -2\left[\frac{1}{3} + 2\sum_{n=0}^{\infty} \frac{\alpha_n*(0) + (M/k)\lambda_n*^2(\partial\beta*/\partial y*)|_{y*=0}}{\lambda_n*^4\alpha_n*(k)}\right] \qquad (7.5\text{-}18b)$$

and

$$V_{cb}* = -\frac{2M}{k}\sum_{n=0}^{\infty} \frac{\gamma*(y*) - \gamma*(0)}{\alpha_n*(k)} \qquad (7.5\text{-}18c)$$

where

$$\gamma*(y*) = \frac{1}{p_1*} \text{sh } p_2*k \text{ ch } p_1*y* - \frac{1}{p_2*} \text{sh } p_1*k \text{ ch } p_2*y*$$

Discussion

For various values of k, it is interesting to see plots of constant-velocity contours and constant induced magnetic-field contours. The magnetic-field contours are easily shown to be current lines. The constant velocity contours are given in Figs. 7.5-2 through 7.5-7. The current lines are shown in Figs. 7.5-8 through 7.5-13. In Figs. 7.5-8 through 7.5-10 $M = 0.001$ so that MHD distortion of the velocity profile is negligible, and the resulting current lines represent a limiting case. As $M \to 0$, the current becomes very small and its path is influenced only by the velocity profile and not by the combination of the velocity profile and the electro-magnetic body force. For $M = 5$, the current lines are given in Figs. 7.5-11 through 7.5-13. Comparing these to cases where $M = 0.001$ shows us that increasing M tends to increase the length of the current line, a result of the flattened velocity profile caused by the electromagnetic body force. Increasing M, as should be expected, increases the current density near the channel walls. The greatest induced magnetic field results when $k = 2$, because the most current is generated when the height to width ratio is 2. Conversely, when $k = 0.5$, the least magnetic field results.

Figure 7.5-13 shows a plot of flow rate versus Hartmann number for various values of height to width ratio. (Figure 7.5-14 is included for reference in using Fig. 7.5-13.) As $k \to \infty$, this ratio should become unity because the component of electromagnetic body force, which distorts the velocity profile, is zero as the current flows only in the y direction. When $k \to 0$, the classical result for open-circuited MHD Poiseuille flow occurs.

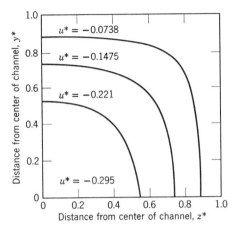

Figure 7.5-2 Constant velocity contours in a channel of square cross section for $M = 0$ (only one quadrant is shown).

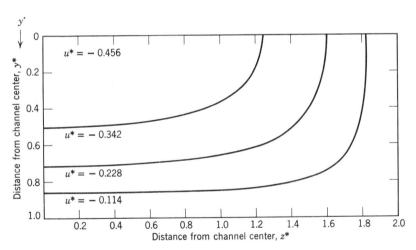

Figure 7.5-3 Constant velocity contours in a channel ($k = 0.5$) of rectangular cross section for $M = 0$ (only one quadrant is shown).

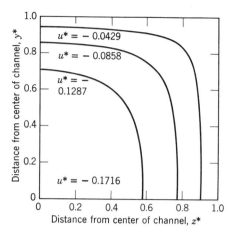

Figure 7.5-4 Constant velocity contours in a channel of square cross section for $M = 5$ (only one quadrant is shown).

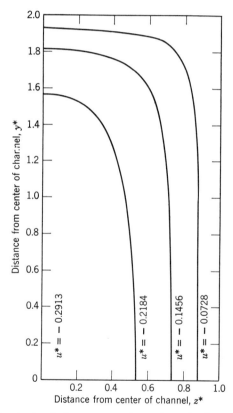

Figure 7.5-5 Constant velocity contours in a channel where $k = 2$ and $M = 10$ (only one quadrant is shown).

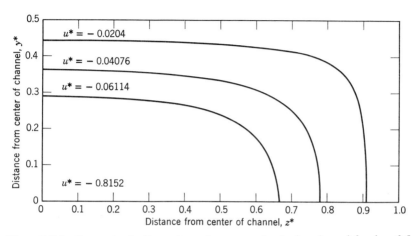

Figure 7.5-6 Constant velocity contours in one quadrant of a channel for $k = 0.5$ and $M = 2.5$.

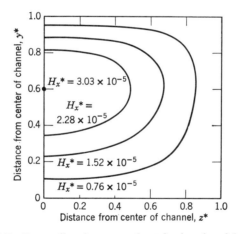

Figure 7.5-7 Current lines in one quadrant for $k = 1$ and $M = 0.001$.

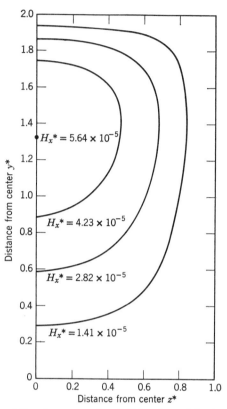

Figure 7.5-8   Current lines in one quadrant of the channel for $k = 2$ and $M = 0.001$.

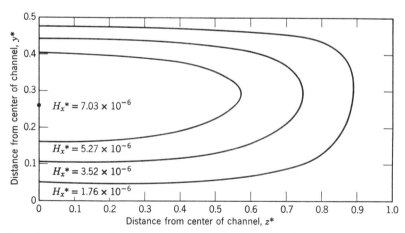

Figure 7.5-9   Current lines in one quadrant of the channel for $k = 0.5$ and $M = 0.001$.

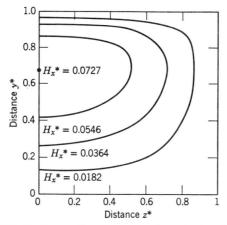

Figure 7.5-10   Current lines in one quadrant for $k = 1$ and $M = 5$.

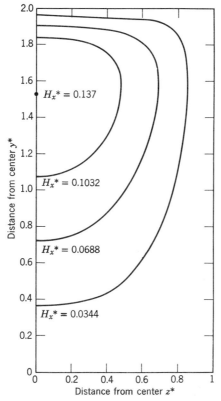

Figure 7.5-11   Current lines in one quadrant of the channel for $k = 2$ and $M = 10$.

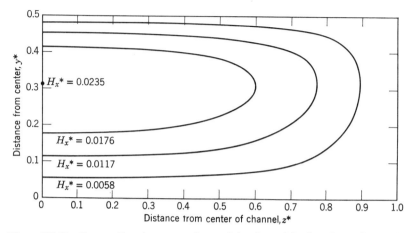

Figure 7.5-12   Current lines in one quadrant of the channel for $k = 0.5$ and $M = 2.5$.

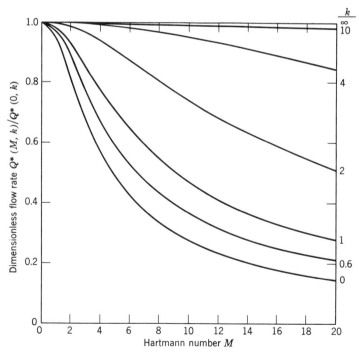

Figure 7.5-13   The normalized dimensionless flow rate as a function of Hartmann number for various values of channel height-to-width ratio.

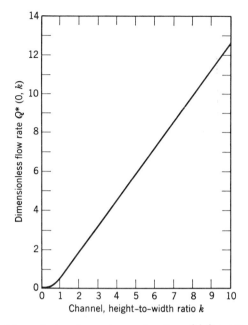

Figure 7.5-14   Dimensionless flow rate as a function of k for zero Hartmann number.

7.6   RECTANGULAR CHANNEL WITH IDEALLY CONDUCTING WALLS

Introduction

The problem of the steady flow of an incompressible, viscous, conducting liquid through a channel with ideally conducting walls in the presence of a uniform transverse magnetic field was considered by Uflyand (1960) and later by Chang and Lundgren (1961). A treatment of this problem similar to Uflyand's solution is given in this section, and curves not given in the literature are presented.

The appropriate form of solution for the boundary value problem is given by (7.4-12a) and (7.4-12b).

Solution to the Boundary Value Problem

When the walls are ideal conductors, the electric field parallel to each wall must be zero at the wall; otherwise, infinite current will flow in the wall. In addition, if the channel is fixed in the laboratory frame, the fluid velocity at each wall must be zero. Then the boundary conditions become

$$u(y, \pm z_0) = u(\pm y_0, z) = 0 \tag{7.6-1}$$

and

$$\frac{\partial H_x}{\partial z}(y, \pm z_0) = \frac{\partial H_x}{\partial y}(\pm y_0, z) = 0 \tag{7.6-2}$$

To solve (7.4-4) and (7.4-8), we assume solutions of the form

$$u(y, z) = \underset{z \to \infty}{u} + \sum_{n=0}^{\infty} u_n(z) \cos \lambda_n y \tag{7.6-3a}$$

$$H_x(y, z) = \underset{z \to \infty}{H_x} + \sum_{n=0}^{\infty} H_n(z) \sin \lambda_n y \tag{7.6-3b}$$

where $\underset{z \to \infty}{u}$ and $\underset{z \to \infty}{H_x}$ are the solution to the problem of flow between two ideally conducting plates of infinite extent. These solutions are obtained from the Hartmann problem by letting $E_z \to 0$. Then, by defining the Hartmann number as $M = y_0 B_0 \sqrt{\sigma/\mu_f}$ and making use of (7.1-6) and (7.1-30), we obtain

$$\underset{z \to \infty}{u} = \frac{y_0^2}{\mu_f M^2} \frac{\partial P}{\partial x} \left(\frac{\operatorname{ch} My/y_0}{\operatorname{ch} M} - 1 \right) \tag{7.6-4a}$$

and

$$\underset{z \to \infty}{H_x} = \frac{1}{B_0} \frac{\partial P}{\partial x} \left(y - \frac{y_0}{M} \frac{\operatorname{sh} My/y_0}{\operatorname{ch} M} \right) \tag{7.6-4b}$$

The solutions of (7.6-3a) and (7.6-3b) are chosen so that u is an even function of y and so that H_x is an odd function of y, as the magnetic field must be, because equal and opposite currents flow in the walls to complete the electrical circuit of the current. Each half of the channel (see Fig. 7.6-1) is like a fat solenoid wound on either the line $y = y_0/2$ or the line $y = -y_0/2$. Each half would have an opposite flow of current, counterclockwise for $y > 0$ and clockwise for $y < 0$. Hence the H_z field is an odd function and should reach extrema at the points $(x, \pm y_0, 0)$. Now we substitute (7.6-3a) and (7.6-3b) into (7.4-8) and (7.4-4) to obtain

$$\frac{d^2 u_n}{dz^2} - \lambda_n^2 u_n + \lambda_n \frac{B_0}{\mu_f} H_n = 0 \tag{7.6-5a}$$

and

$$\frac{d^2 H_n}{dz^2} - \lambda_n^2 H_n - \lambda_n \sigma B_0 u_n = 0 \tag{7.6-5b}$$

To solve this system we find H_n from (7.6-5a) and substitute it into (7.6-5b) to obtain

$$\frac{d^4 u_n}{dz^4} - 2\lambda_n{}^2 \frac{d^2 u_n}{dz^2} + \lambda_n{}^2 \left(\lambda_n{}^2 + \frac{M^2}{y_0{}^2} \right) u_n = 0 \qquad (7.6\text{-}6)$$

Because u must be symmetrical about the y axis, we assume

$$u_n = C_1 \operatorname{ch} p_1 z + C_2 \operatorname{ch} p_2 z \qquad (7.6\text{-}7)$$

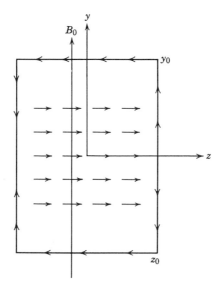

Figure 7.6-1 The channel with ideally conducting walls. The arrows represent current lines in the fluid and channel walls.

for clearly there will be four values of p. Accordingly p is given by

$$p^4 - 2\lambda_n{}^2 p^2 + \lambda_n{}^2 \left(\lambda_n{}^2 + \frac{M^2}{y_0{}^2} \right) = 0 \qquad (7.6\text{-}8a)$$

or

$$p_{1,2} = \sqrt{\lambda_n{}^2 \pm j\lambda_n M / y_0} \qquad (7.6\text{-}8b)$$

or, separating $p_{1,2}$ into its real (r_n) and imaginary (s_n) parts, we obtain

$$p_{1,2} = \sqrt{\frac{\lambda_n}{2}} \left(\sqrt{\sqrt{\frac{M^2}{y_0{}^2} + \lambda_n{}^2} + \lambda_n} \pm j \sqrt{\sqrt{\frac{M^2}{y_0{}^2} + \lambda_n{}^2} - \lambda_n} \right)$$

$$= r_n \pm j s_n \qquad (7.6\text{-}8c)$$

The solution for u_n can be expressed as

$$u_n = C_1 \, \text{ch} \, (r_n + js_n)z + C_2 \, \text{ch} \, (r_n - js_n)z \qquad (7.6\text{-}9a)$$

or more simply as

$$u_n = A_n \, \text{sh} \, r_n z \sin s_n z + B_n \, \text{ch} \, r_n z \cos s_n z \qquad (7.6\text{-}9b)$$

where $A_n = j(C_1 - C_2)$ and $B_n = C_1 + C_2$. Before evaluating the various constants by means of the boundary conditions, we must calculate H_n. From (7.6-5a) we obtain

$$H_n = \frac{-\mu_f}{\lambda_n B_0} \left(\frac{d^2 u_n}{dz^2} - \lambda_n{}^2 u_n \right) \qquad (7.6\text{-}10)$$

To find H_n, it is convenient to use (7.6-7) rather than (7.6-9b). Accordingly, (7.6-10) becomes

$$H_n = \frac{-\mu_f}{\lambda_n B_0} [(p_1{}^2 - \lambda_n{}^2)C_1 \, \text{ch} \, p_1 z + (p_2{}^2 - \lambda_n{}^2)C_2 \, \text{ch} \, p_2 z] \qquad (7.6\text{-}11)$$

which simplifies because

$$p_1{}^2 - \lambda_n{}^2 = j(M/y_0)\lambda_n \qquad \text{and} \qquad p_2{}^2 - \lambda_n{}^2 = -j(M/y_0)\lambda_n$$

Hence H_n is given by

$$H_n = -\frac{\mu_f M}{B_0 y_0} (jC_1 \, \text{ch} \, p_1 z - jC_2 \, \text{ch} \, p_2 z) \qquad (7.6\text{-}12)$$

or, in a fashion similar to (7.6-9b), (7.6-12) becomes

$$H_n = \frac{\mu_f M}{B_0 y_0} (B_n \, \text{sh} \, r_n z \sin s_n z - A_n \, \text{ch} \, r_n z \cos s_n z) \qquad (7.6\text{-}13)$$

Next let us apply the boundary conditions that exist along the line $z = \pm z_0$. To do this, we need dH_n/dz which is given by

$$\frac{dH_n}{dz} = \frac{\mu_f M}{B_0 y_0} [B_n(r_n \, \text{ch} \, r_n z \sin s_n z + s_n \, \text{sh} \, r_n z \cos s_n z)$$
$$- A_n(r_n \, \text{sh} \, r_n z \cos s_n z - s_n \, \text{ch} \, r_n z \sin s_n z)] \qquad (7.6\text{-}14)$$

From (7.6-3b), $(\partial H_x/\partial z) = \sum (dH_n/dz) \sin \lambda_n y$ and when $z = \pm z_0$, $\partial H_x/\partial z$ must be zero for all values of y. Therefore,

$$B_n(r_n \, \text{ch} \, r_n z_0 \sin s_n z_0 + s_n \, \text{sh} \, r_n z_0 \cos s_n z_0)$$
$$- A_n(r_n \, \text{sh} \, r_n z_0 \cos s_n z_0 - s_n \, \text{ch} \, r_n z_0 \sin s_n z_0) = 0 \qquad (7.6\text{-}15)$$

We must satisfy the condition $u(\pm y_0, z) = 0$. At $\pm y_0$, $u_{z \to \infty} = 0$ by (7.6-4a) so this condition, which must be valid for all values of $z \le z_0$, dictates that

$\lambda_n = (2n + 1)\pi/2y_0$. From the condition $u(y, \pm z_0)$, we obtain

$$-u \underset{z \to \infty}{=} \sum_{n=0}^{\infty} u_n(z_0) \cos \lambda_n y \tag{7.6-16}$$

When we multiply both sides of (7.6-16) by $\cos \lambda_m y$ and integrate over dy from 0 to y_0, all terms of the summation vanish except for $n = m$. The result is

$$u_n(z_0) = \frac{2(-1)^n(\partial P/\partial x)}{\mu_f y_0 \lambda_n[(M^2/y_0^2) + \lambda_n^2]} \tag{7.6-17}$$

Then

$$A_n \operatorname{sh} r_n z_0 \sin s_n z_0 + B_n \operatorname{ch} r_n z_0 \cos s_n z_0 = u_n(z_0) \tag{7.6-18}$$

The coefficients A_n and B_n are evaluated by solving (7.6-15) and (7.6-18) simultaneously. The solutions are $A_n = \gamma_n u_n(z_0)/\Delta_n$ and $B_n = \delta_n u_n(z_0)/\Delta_n$, where

$$\Delta_n = \tfrac{1}{2}(-s_n \sin 2s_n z_0 + r_n \operatorname{sh} 2r_n z_0)$$

$$\gamma_n = r_n \operatorname{ch} r_n z_0 \sin s_n z_0 + s_n \operatorname{sh} r_n z_0 \cos s_n z_0 \tag{7.6-19}$$

$$\delta_n = r_n \operatorname{sh} r_n z_0 \cos s_n z_0 - s_n \operatorname{ch} r_n z_0 \sin s_n z_0$$

Therefore, the solution for the velocity is

$$u(y, z) = \frac{y_0^2}{\mu_f} \frac{\partial P}{\partial x} \left\{ \frac{\operatorname{ch} My/y_0 - \operatorname{ch} M}{M^2 \operatorname{ch} M} + \frac{2}{y_0^3} \sum_{n=0}^{\infty} \frac{(-1)^n \alpha_n(z) \cos \lambda_n y}{\lambda_n[\lambda_n^2 + (M^2/y_0^2)] \Delta_n} \right\} \tag{7.6-20}$$

where

$$\alpha_n(z) = \gamma_n \operatorname{sh} r_n z \sin s_n z + \delta_n \operatorname{ch} r_n z \cos s_n z \tag{7.6-21}$$

When the magnetic field or the conductivity approaches zero, the velocity given by (7.6-20) should approach the well-known solution to viscous flow in a channel of rectangular cross section. Before taking the limit of $u(y, z)$ as $M \to 0$, we note that

$$\lim_{M \to 0} r_n = \lambda_n$$

$$\lim_{M \to 0} s_n = \lim_{M \to 0} \gamma_n = 0$$

$$\lim_{M \to 0} \Delta_n = \tfrac{1}{2}\lambda_n \operatorname{sh} 2\lambda_n z_0 = \lambda_n \operatorname{sh} \lambda_n z_0 \operatorname{ch} \lambda_n z_0 \tag{7.6-22}$$

$$\lim_{M \to 0} \delta_n = \lambda_n \operatorname{sh} \lambda_n z_0$$

The limit as $M \to 0$ of the quantity being summed in (7.6-20) is not indeterminate and is easily formed by using products and quotients of the quantities given in (7.6-22). However, the limit of $u_{z\to\infty}$ (the first term of 7.6-20) is indeterminate. By applying L'Hospital's rule twice or by expanding ch My/y_0 — ch M into a series before letting $M \to 0$, we obtain

$$\lim_{M\to 0} \frac{\text{ch } My/y_0 - \text{ch } M}{M^2 \text{ch } M} = \frac{1}{2}\left(\frac{y^2}{y_0^2} - 1\right) \qquad (7.6\text{-}23)$$

Hence

$$\lim_{M\to 0} u(y, z) = \frac{y_0^2}{2\mu_f} \frac{\partial P}{\partial x}\left[\frac{y^2}{y_0^2} - 1 + \frac{4}{y_0^3} \sum_{n=0}^{\infty} \frac{(-1)^n \text{ ch } \lambda_n z \cos \lambda_n y}{\lambda_n^3 \text{ ch } \lambda_n z_0}\right] \qquad (7.6\text{-}24)$$

which is indeed the solution to the ordinary viscous flow problem.

Using the relationships given in (7.6-13), (7.6-17), (7.6-19), (7.6-3a), and (7.6-4b), we find that the x component of the magnetic field becomes

$$H_x = y_0^2 \sqrt{\frac{\sigma}{\mu_f}} \frac{\partial P}{\partial x}\left[\frac{(My/y_0) \text{ ch } M - \text{ch } My/y_0}{M^2 \text{ch } M}\right.$$
$$\left. + \frac{2}{y_0^3} \sum_{n=0}^{\infty} \frac{(-1)^n \beta_n(z) \sin \lambda_n y}{\lambda_n(\lambda_n^2 + M^2/y_0^2) \Delta_n}\right] \qquad (7.6\text{-}25)$$

where $\beta_n(z) = \delta_n \text{ sh } r_n z \sin s_n z - \gamma_n \text{ ch } r_n z \cos s_n z$.

Now it is convenient to place the solutions in dimensionless form. The dimensionless variables corresponding to the various dimensional variables are denoted with asterisks. In addition let $k = z_0/y_0$, $y^* = y/y_0$, $z^* = z/y_0$, $u^*(y, z) = u(y, z)\mu_f/(y_0^2 \partial P/\partial x)$, and $H_x^* = H_x/[y_0^2(\partial P/\partial x)\sqrt{\sigma/\mu_f}]$. Then

$$u^*(y^*, z^*) = \frac{\text{ch } My^* - \text{ch } M}{M^2 \text{ch } M} + 2\sum_{n=0}^{\infty} \frac{(-1)^n \alpha_n^*(z^*) \cos \lambda_n^* y^*}{\lambda_n^*(\lambda_n^{*2} + M^2) \Delta_n^*} \qquad (7.6\text{-}26)$$

and

$$H_x^*(y^*, z^*) = \frac{My^* \text{ ch } M - 2 \text{ sh } My^*}{M^2 \text{ch } M} + 2\sum_{n=0}^{\infty} \frac{(-1)^n \beta_n^*(z^*) \sin \lambda_n^* y^*}{\lambda_n^*(\lambda_n^{*2} + M^2) \Delta_n^*}$$
$$(7.6\text{-}27)$$

where

$$\lambda_n^* = \frac{2n + 1}{2}\pi$$

$$\alpha_n^*(z^*) = \gamma_n^* \text{ sh } r_n^* z^* \sin s_n^* z^* + \delta_n^* \text{ ch } r_n^* z^* \cos s_n^* z^*$$

$$\beta_n^*(z^*) = \delta_n^* \text{ sh } r_n^* z^* \sin s_n^* z^* - \gamma_n^* \text{ ch } r_n^* z^* \cos s_n^* z^*$$

$$\gamma_n^* = \text{ch } r_n^* k \sin s_n^* k + s_n^* \text{ sh } r_n^* k \cos s_n^* k$$

$$\delta_n^* = r_n^* \text{ sh } r_n^* k \cos s_n^* k - s_n^* \text{ ch } r_n^* k \sin s_n^* k$$

$$r_n^* = \sqrt{\frac{\lambda_n^*}{2}}\sqrt{\sqrt{M^2 + \lambda_n^{*2}} + \lambda_n^*}$$

and

$$s_n{}^* = \sqrt{\frac{\lambda_n{}^*}{2}} \sqrt{\sqrt{M^2 + \lambda_n{}^{*2}} - \lambda_n{}^*} \tag{7.6-28}$$

$$k = z_0/y_0$$

$$\Delta_n{}^* = \tfrac{1}{2}(-s_n{}^* \sin 2s_n{}^* k + r_n{}^* \text{ sh } 2r_n{}^* k)$$

This solution is very similar to the solution by Uflyand. In his solution, however, (in our notation)

$$\Delta_n{}^* = \tfrac{1}{2}(-s_n{}^* \sin 2s_n{}^* k + r_n{}^* \text{ ch } 2r_n{}^* k) \tag{7.6-29}$$

which prevents his solution from reducing to the solution of (7.6-24) for ordinary viscous flow in a rectangular channel when $M \to 0$.

The dimensionless rate of flow is given by $Q^* = 4 \displaystyle\int_0^k \int_0^1 u_x{}^* \, dy^* \, dz^*$. After a modest amount of manipulation, Q^* can be given by

$$
\begin{aligned}
Q^* = 4 \Bigg[&\frac{\text{th } M - M}{M^3} k \\
&+ 2 \sum_{n=0}^{\infty} \frac{(r_n{}^{*2}/s_n{}^{*2})(\text{ch}^2 r_n{}^* k \sin^2 s_n{}^* k + \text{sh}^2 r_n{}^* k \cos^2 s_n{}^* k)}{\lambda_n{}^{*2}(\lambda_n{}^{*2} + M^2)(1 + r_n{}^{*2}/s_n{}^{*2}) \Delta_n{}^*} \\
&\qquad\qquad\qquad \frac{- (r_n{}^*/2s_n{}^*) \sin 2s_n{}^* k - \tfrac{1}{2} \text{ sh } 2r_n{}^* k}{} \Bigg]
\end{aligned}
\tag{7.6-30}
$$

The reader should note that k and the other dimensionless variables are defined differently in different sections.

Discussion

Velocity contours for $M = 5$ and $k = 1, 2$, and 0.5 are given in Figs. 7.6-2, -3, and -4. The velocity is smaller in the conducting-wall channel than in the insulating-wall channel because the induced currents in the former exceed those in the latter. Comparing the contours given by Fig. 7.6-2 and Fig. 7.5-4 indicates that no great difference in velocity contour is caused by the wall conductivity. In the conducting-wall case the constant velocity contours have a tendency to crowd into the corners. In Figs. 7.6-5, -6, and -7 we can observe a decrease of current density with the increase of the y^* coordinate. Hence, as would be dictated by the boundary conditions at $y^* = \pm 1$, the z^* component of the current density vanishes. Consequently, the electromagnetic body force diminishes as y^* increases.

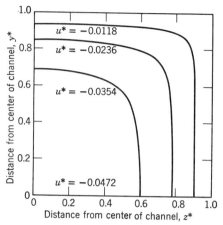

Figure 7.6-2   Constant velocity contours in one quadrant of a square cross section channel ($k = 1$) for a Hartmann number of 5 ($M = 5$).

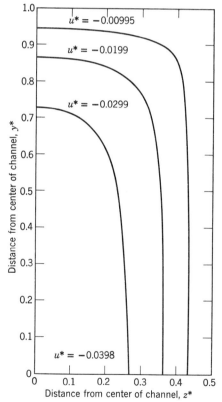

Figure 7.6-3   Constant velocity contours in one quadrant of a channel for $k = 0.5$ and $M = 5$.

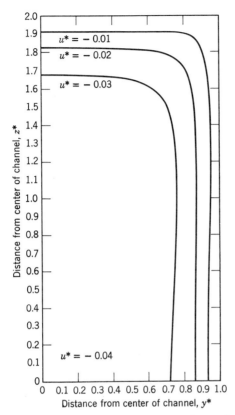

Figure 7.6-4 Constant velocity contours in one quadrant of a channel for $k = 2$ and $M = 5$.

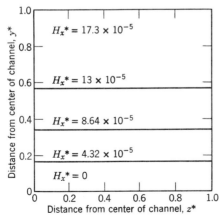

Figure 7.6-5 Current lines in one quadrant of a square cross section channel ($k = 1$) for a Hartmann number of 0.001 ($M = 0.001$).

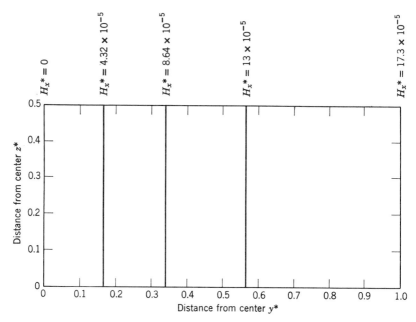

Figure 7.6-6 Current lines in one quadrant of the channel for $k = 0.5$ and $M = 0.001$.

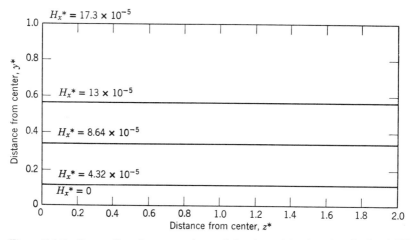

Figure 7.6-7 Current lines in one quadrant of the channel for $k = 2$ and $M = 0.001$.

Figures 7.6-5, -6, and -7 show the current lines produced for $M = 0.001$. The current does not appreciably influence the velocity contours when $M = 5$. Thus, when $M = 5$, the current lines are also modified. This effect is readily seen by comparing Figs. 7.6-8, -9, and -10 to Figs. 7.6-5, -6, and -7. Increasing the Hartmann number tends to make the current lines more equally spaced.

The normalized dimensionless flow rate $Q^*(M, k)/Q^*(0, k)$ is given in Fig. 7.6-11 as a function of the Hartmann number for various values of k.

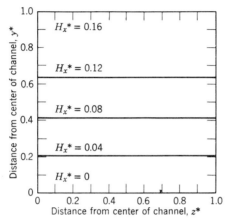

Figure 7.6-8 Current lines in one quadrant of a square cross section channel ($k = 1$) for a Hartmann number of 5 ($M = 5$).

For values of $k < 1$ the normalized dimensionless flow rate exceeds unity at a certain Hartmann number. When $k < 1$, the channel is long in the direction of the applied magnetic field and short in the z^* direction. As k is decreased toward zero, the channel becomes infinitely long in the y^* direction and a very large amount of current must return in the channel walls. When $k = 0$, it should not matter if the conducting walls at $y^* = \pm\infty$ are removed. Hence, as k is decreased toward zero, more and more of the return current passes back through the fluid near the conducting plates located at $y^* = \pm\infty$. These currents propel rather than retard the conducting liquid. The effect is most prominent at certain Hartmann numbers because at those numbers the maximum amount of current is generated. If we imagine that the liquid is flowing because of the force of gravity, it is clear that the electromagnetic forces do no work on the fluid but, instead, produce Joule heating. In addition, the electromagnetic forces modify the velocity profile in a way that reduces the viscous shear. This reduction allows the flow rate to exceed that of the non-MHD case when the optimum Hartmann number is used.

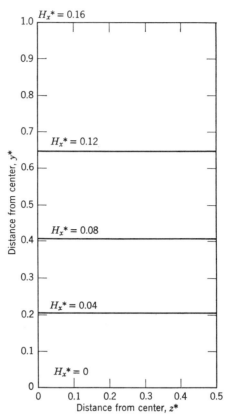

Figure 7.6-9 Current lines in one quadrant of the channel for $k = 0.5$ and $M = 5$.

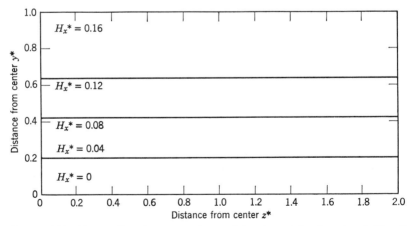

Figure 7.6-10 Current lines in one quadrant of the channel for $k = 2$ and $M = 5$.

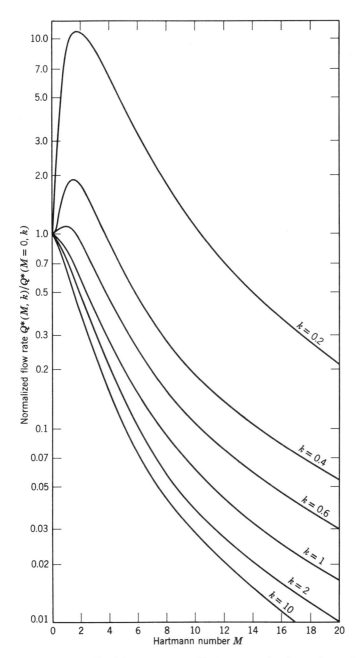

Figure 7.6-11   Normalized flow rate versus Hartmann number for various values of k.

When $k \geq 1$, no unusual phenomena result. As k is increased, the normalized dimensionless flow rate approaches that of short-circuited one-dimensional MHD Poiseuille flow.

The series given in this section were summed on a digital computer to better than three significant figures—an accuracy sufficient for most purposes. In most of the calculations, two, three, or four terms of the series were sufficient. In a few instances, particularly on or near the boundaries, more terms had to be included.

7.7   RECTANGULAR CHANNEL WITH CONDUCTING WALL PERPENDICULAR TO THE APPLIED MAGNETIC FIELD

Introduction

The configuration illustrated in Fig. 7.7-1 is one of the easier rectangular channel problems because its solution can be obtained without difficulty in at least three different ways. As we saw in Section 7.4, this problem can be solved by either of two pairs of solutions: Equations (7.4-12a) and (7.4-12b) as well as (7.4-14a) and (7.4-14b) can be made to satisfy the boundary conditions and the partial differential equations describing the problem. The execution of either or both of those solutions is left as an exercise for the reader, and we will solve this problem in this section by a double Fourier series which lends great simplicity to the solution and allows rather simple calculations.

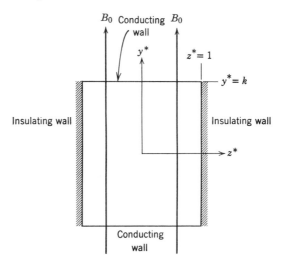

Figure 7.7-1   The configuration of Section 7.7.

An Alternate Method

The equations of channel flow (written in dimensionless form) are

$$\frac{\partial^2 H_x{}^*}{\partial y^{*2}} + \frac{\partial^2 H_x{}^*}{\partial z^{*2}} + \frac{M}{k}\frac{\partial u^*}{\partial y^*} = 0 \tag{7.7-1a}$$

$$\frac{\partial^2 u^*}{\partial y^{*2}} + \frac{\partial^2 u^*}{\partial z^{*2}} + \frac{M}{k}\frac{\partial H_x{}^*}{\partial y^*} = 1 \tag{7.7-1b}$$

where $H_x{}^*$, u^*, y^*, z^*, k, and M are those variables used in Section 7.5. Here the dimensionless forms have been chosen to simplify the fundamental equations. However, in general, dimensionless forms should not be chosen until the problem is rather well understood.

We shall assume a solution for u^* which satisfies the no-slip condition at the channel boundaries. The most straightforward choice is

$$u^*(^*y, z^*) = \sum_{n=1,3,5\cdots}^{\infty} \sum_{m=1,3,5\cdots}^{\infty} A_{nm} \cos\frac{n\pi y^*}{2k} \cos\frac{m\pi z^*}{2} \tag{7.7-2}$$

where $k = y_0/z_0$. Clearly, at the boundaries $u^* = 0$. Now we compute $\partial u^*/\partial y^*$ and substitute it into (7.7-1a) to obtain

$$\frac{\partial^2 H_x{}^*}{\partial y^{*2}} + \frac{\partial^2 H_x{}^*}{\partial z^{*2}} = \frac{M\pi}{2k^2}\sum_{n=1,3,5\cdots}^{\infty}\sum_{m=1,3,5\cdots}^{\infty} nA_{nm}\sin\frac{n\pi y^*}{2k}\cos\frac{m\pi z^*}{2} \tag{7.7-3}$$

which is easy to solve. The particular solution is given by

$$H_{xp}{}^*(y^*, z^*) = \frac{-2M}{k^2\pi}\sum_{n=1,3,5\cdots}^{\infty}\sum_{m=1,3,5\cdots}^{\infty}\frac{nA_{nm}}{m^2 + n^2/k^2}\sin\frac{n\pi y^*}{2k}\cos\frac{m\pi z^*}{2}$$

$$\tag{7.7-4}$$

and the complimentary solution is any solution $H_{xc}{}^*(y^*, z^*)$ satisfying Laplace's equation. Therefore,

$$H_x{}^*(y^*, z^*) = H_{xc}{}^*(y^*, z^*)$$

$$- \frac{2M}{k^2\pi}\sum_{n=1,3,5\cdots}^{\infty}\sum_{m=1,3,5\cdots}^{\infty}\frac{nA_{nm}}{m^2 + n^2/k^2}\sin\frac{n\pi y^*}{2k}\cos\frac{m\pi z^*}{2}$$

$$\tag{7.7-5}$$

is the solution for the magnetic field. In dimensionless form the current densities are

$$J_y{}^* = \frac{\partial H_x{}^*}{\partial z^*} \tag{7.7-6a}$$

and

$$J_z^* = -\frac{\partial H_x^*}{\partial y^*} \tag{7.7-6b}$$

where $J^* = J/[z_0\sqrt{\sigma/\mu_f}(\partial P/\partial x)]$. Then, from (7.7-6a), (7.7-6b), and (7.7-5), the dimensionless current densities are

$$J_y^* = \frac{\partial H_{xc}^*}{\partial z^*} + \frac{M}{k^2} \sum_{n=1,3,5\cdots}^{\infty} \sum_{m=1,3,5\cdots}^{\infty} \frac{mnA_{nm}}{m^2 + n^2/k^2} \sin\frac{n\pi y^*}{2k} \sin\frac{m\pi z^*}{2} \tag{7.7-7a}$$

and

$$J_z^* = -\frac{\partial H_{xc}^*}{\partial y^*} + \frac{M}{k^3} \sum_{n=1,3,5\cdots}^{\infty} \sum_{m=1,3,5\cdots}^{\infty} \frac{n^2 A_{nm}}{m^2 + n^2/k^2} \cos\frac{n\pi y^*}{2k} \cos\frac{m\pi z^*}{2} \tag{7.7-7b}$$

Inspection of the current density solution indicates that the particular solution for H_x^* satisfies the boundary conditions which exist when the top and bottom walls are ideal conductors and the side walls are insulators. Now let $H_{xc}^* = 0$. To complete the solution to the problem of Fig. 7.7-1, A_{nm} remains to be found. So far (7.7-1a) has been satisfied but (7.7-1b) has not. To find A_{nm}, $\partial H_x^*/\partial y^*$ (from (7.7-7b)) and u^* (from (7.7-2)) are substituted into (7.7-1b). The usual method for finding the Fourier coefficients yields

$$A_{nm} = \frac{-16(n^2/k^2 + m^2)\sin(n\pi/2)\sin(m\pi/2)}{nm\pi^2[(\pi^2/4)(n^2/k^2 + m^2)^2 + M^2 n^2/k^4]} \tag{7.7-8}$$

The result is rather complicated and should be checked carefully. When $M \to 0$, the solution should be that obtained for flow in a rectangular channel with no electromagnetic effects present. In that case

$$\lim_{M\to 0} A_{nm} = \frac{-64\sin(n\pi/2)\sin(m\pi/2)}{\pi^4 nm(n^2/k^2 + m^2)} \tag{7.7-9}$$

which is the usual result when the non-MHD solution is expanded in a double series. When $z_0 \to \infty$, $k \to 0$ and the result should be equivalent to (7.6-4a) obtained for the short-circuited Hartmann problem. As $z_0 \to \infty$ or $k \to 0$ the expression for the velocity becomes

$$\lim_{k\to 0} u(y) = -\left[\frac{16}{\pi^2} \sum_{n=1,3,5\cdots}^{\infty} \frac{\sin(\pi n/2)\cos(n\pi y/y_0)}{n(\pi^2 n^2/4 + M^2)} \sum_{m=1,3,5\cdots}^{\infty} \frac{\sin(m\pi/2)}{m}\right]$$

$$\times \frac{y_0^2\, \partial P/\partial x}{\mu_f}$$

$$= -\frac{4}{\pi}\left[\sum_{n=1,3,5\cdots}^{\infty} \frac{\sin(n\pi/2)\cos(n\pi y/y_0)}{n(\pi^2 n^2/4 + M^2)}\right]\frac{y_0^2\, \partial P/\partial x}{\mu_f} \tag{7.7-10}$$

The result of (7.7-10) is easily shown to be equivalent to

$$\lim_{k \to 0} u(y) = \left(\frac{\text{ch } My/y_0 - \text{ch } M}{M^2 \text{ ch } M} \right) \frac{y_0^2 \, \partial P/\partial x}{\mu_f} \tag{7.7-11}$$

which is the short-circuit solution given by (7.1-25) when $V_T = 0$. In this problem the ideal conductors short the channel when $z_0 \to \infty$. It is also easy to check the magnetic field solution. In checking the magnetic field solution for $z_0 \to \infty$ the dimensionless forms should not be used.

Hence the solutions for the velocity and magnetic field are

$$u^*(y^*, z^*) = \sum_{n=1,3,5\cdots}^{\infty} \sum_{m=1,3,5\cdots}^{\infty} A_{nm} \cos \frac{n\pi y^*}{2k} \cos \frac{m\pi}{2} z^* \tag{7.7-12}$$

and

$$H_x^*(y^*, z^*) = \frac{-2M}{\pi k^2} \sum_{n=1,3,5\cdots}^{\infty} \sum_{m=1,3,5\cdots}^{\infty} B_{nm} \sin \frac{n\pi y^*}{2k} \cos \frac{m\pi z^*}{2} \tag{7.7-13}$$

where A_{nm} is given in (7.7-8) and

$$B_{nm} = \frac{-16 \sin (n\pi/2) \sin (m\pi/2)}{\pi^2 m[(\pi^2/4)(n^2/k^2 + m^2)^2 + M^2 n^2/k^4]} \tag{7.7-14}$$

The dimensionless flow rate Q^* is given by

$$Q^* = -\frac{256}{\pi^4 k} \sum_{n=1,3,5\cdots}^{\infty} \sum_{m=1,3,5\cdots}^{\infty} \frac{(n^2/k^2) + m^2}{m^2 n^2[(\pi^2/4)(n^2/k^2 + m^2)^2 + M^2 n^2/k^4]} \tag{7.7-15}$$

Summary

The double series solution used in this problem is very convenient because it eliminates the hyperbolic functions and attendant problems that are manifested when $M \to 0$. The numerical computation is simpler for the double series solution than it would be for a single series solution. Constant velocity contours are presented for $k = 1.0$, 2.0, and 0.5 for a Hartmann number $M = 5$. It is interesting to compare these curves with the corresponding curves for zero Hartmann number. In Fig. 7.5-2 symmetry exists about the diagonal passing through the center of the channel for $M = 0$. By comparing Fig. 7.7-2 with Fig. 7.5-2 we see that the symmetry is destroyed by the electromagnetic body force. The velocity profile is flattened when $M = 5$. When $k = 2$, the difference between the velocity contours for $M = 0$ and $M = 5$ is very slight. This is easily seen by comparing Figs. 7.7-3 and 7.5-3. The electromagnetic body force is rather weak when $k = 2$ because so much of the current flows in the

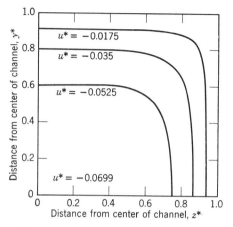

Figure 7.7-2 Constant velocity contours for $k = 1$ and $M = 5$.

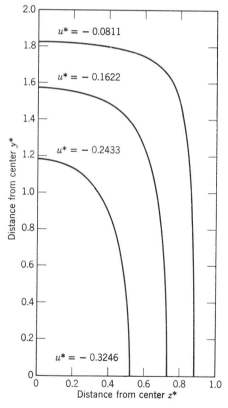

Figure 7.7-3 Constant velocity contours for $k = 2$ and $M = 5$.

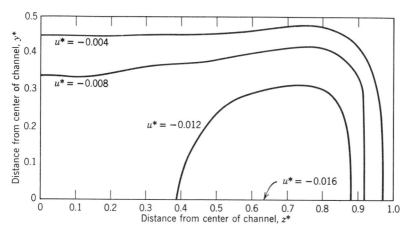

Figure 7.7-4   Constant velocity contours for $k = 0.5$ and $M = 5$.

same direction as the applied magnetic field. Fig. 7.7-9 clearly illustrates this point and, of course, Fig. 7.7-9 ($M = 5$) differs only slightly from Fig. 7.7-6 ($M = 0$) because the velocity profiles are not strongly influenced by the Hartmann number. If the z^* and y^* axes are interchanged in Fig. 7.5-3, it becomes the plot of constant velocity contours for $k = 0.5$ and $M = 0$. The resulting curve is compared to Fig. 7.7-4. In this case the magnetic field has greatly altered the velocity profile because the electromagnetic body force is large in the central region of the channel. This is apparent from Fig. 7.7-10. There, although the width-to-height ratio is

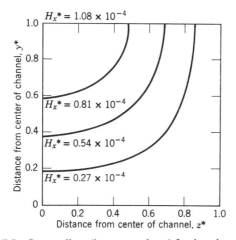

Figure 7.7-5   Current lines (in one quadrant) for $k = 1$ and $M = 0.001$.

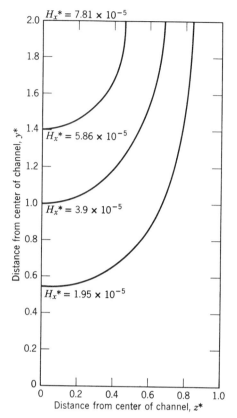

Figure 7.7-6   Current lines (in one quadrant) for $k = 2$ and $M = 0.001$.

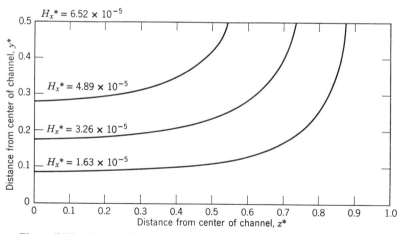

Figure 7.7-7   Current lines (in one quadrant) for $k = 0.5$ and $M = 0.001$.

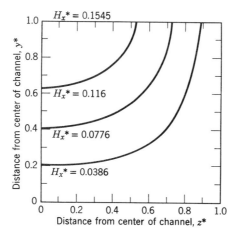

Figure 7.7-8   Current lines (in one quadrant) for $k = 1$ and $M = 5$.

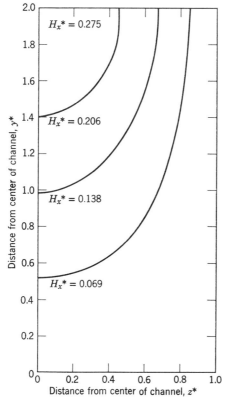

Figure 7.7-9   Current lines (in one quadrant) for $k = 2$ and $M = 5$.

only 2, the distribution of current density in the central region of the channel is close to the distribution found in short-circuited Hartmann flow in Section 7.1. By comparing Fig. 7.7-10 and Fig. 7.7-7, we see that for $k = 0.5$ the current lines are strongly influenced by the Hartmann number.

In Fig. 7.7-11 the ratio of $Q^*(M, k)/Q^*(0, k)$ is displayed as a function of the Hartmann number. From the preceding discussion it is apparent that as $k \to \infty$, the normalized dimensionless flow rate should become unity, independent of the Hartmann number. As $k \to 0$, the ratio is

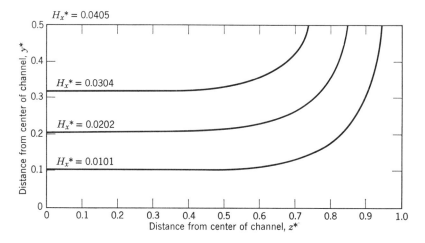

Figure 7.7-10 Current lines (in one quadrant) for $k = 0.5$ and $M = 5$.

strongly influenced by the Hartmann number and assumes the curve for short-circuited Hartmann flow. When $k = 1/9$, the channel is closely approximating short-circuited Hartmann flow. On the other hand, when $k = 9$, the channel is not influenced much by the magnetic field, and the resulting electromagnetic body force is weak.

The maximum fluid velocity does not always occur in the center of the channel. For example, in Fig. 7.7-2, where $k = 1$ and $M = 5$, the maximum velocity occurs at the point $(x, 0, \pm0.3)$. The maximum velocity is less than 1 per cent greater than the center-line velocity. For $k = 2$ and $M = 5$, the maximum velocity is very close to $(x, 0, 0)$, the center line. In Fig. 7.7-4, where $k = 0.5$ and $M = 5$, it is clear that the maximum velocity is not on the center line but instead at $(x, 0, \pm0.73)$. The explanation of this is found by considering the forces acting upon the fluid. In Fig. 7.7-10 the electric current flows in the z^* direction in the central portion of the channel. This current interacts with the applied magnetic field to produce a retarding force which is exerted on the fluid. As the current travels in the z^* direction, its z^* component weakens, its y^* component grows, and the retarding force in the x^* direction diminishes. The viscous forces are small near the center of the channel and they grow near the wall. At the points $(x, 0, \pm 0.73)$ the sum of the viscous and

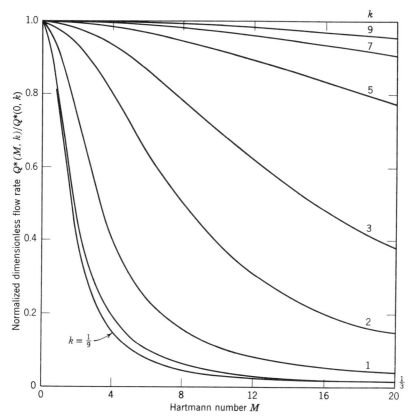

Figure 7.7-11 The normalized dimensionless flow rate as a function of Hartmann number for various height-to-width ratios.

electromagnetic retarding forces is a minimum and the maximum velocity results. This phenomenon is amplified by increasing the Hartmann number. The velocity contours of Figs. 7.7-12, -13, and -14 are given for $M = 50$ and $k = 1$, 2, and 0.5. Fig. 7.7-14 is a striking example of a true magnetohydrodynamic effect. Its corresponding current lines are given in Fig. 7.7-17 and they explain why the peak velocity occurs so near the insulating wall. Fig. 7.7-18 gives the location along the z^* axis of the

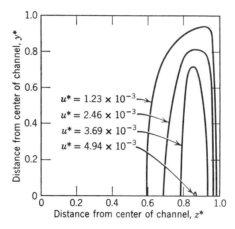

Figure 7.7-12   Constant velocity contours for $k = 1$ and $M = 50$.

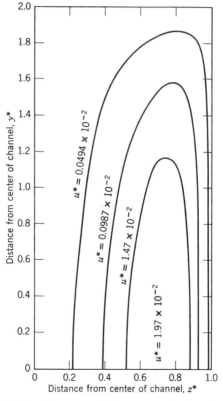

Figure 7.7-13   Constant velocity contours for $k = 2$ and $M = 50$.

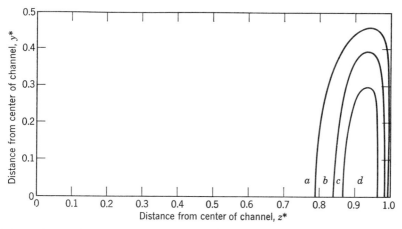

Figure 7.7-14 Constant velocity contours for $k = 0.5$ and $M = 50$. For curves a, b, c, and point d, u^* is 0.0295×10^{-3}, 0.059×10^{-3}, 0.0885×10^{-3}, and 1.18×10^{-3}, respectively.

peak fluid velocity as a function of the Hartmann number for various values of k. As the channel becomes longer in the direction of the applied magnetic field, the effect occurs only at higher Hartmann numbers. Here we see that at high Hartmann numbers, although the fluid in the channel may flow in a constant velocity core over most of the cross section of the channel (as in Fig. 7.7-14), the maximum fluid velocity is not the velocity of the core. Instead, the maximum velocity occurs near the insulating wall and is an order of magnitude greater than the core velocity. This

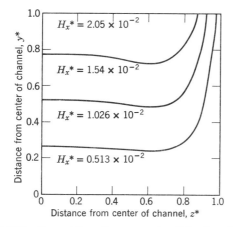

Figure 7.7-15 Current lines (in one quadrant) for $k = 1$ and $M = 50$.

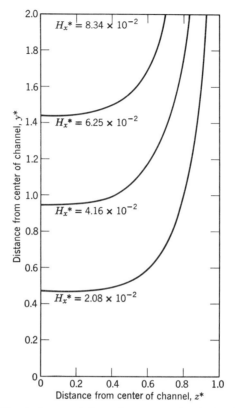

Figure 7.7-16 Constant current lines (in one quadrant) for $k = 2$ and $M = 50$.

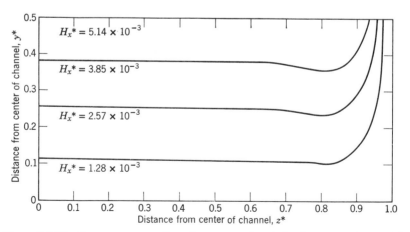

Figure 7.7-17 Constant current lines (in one quadrant) for $k = 0.5$ and $M = 50$.

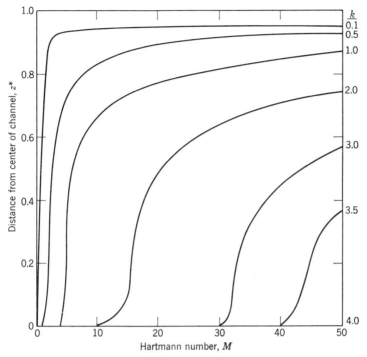

Figure 7.7-18   The location along the z^* axis of the peak fluid velocity versus Hartmann number for various values of k.

effect does not occur in the all-insulating or all-conducting wall channels but undoubtedly occurs in channels (e), (g), (h), and (i) of Fig. 7.4-1. Hence great care must be exercised in any approximate method of solution that assumes a constant velocity core separated from the walls by a boundary layer.

7.8   MHD FLOW IN CIRCULAR CROSS SECTION PIPES

Introduction

In our study of MHD flow in tubes of rectangular cross section, the applied magnetic field was normal to two of the walls and parallel to the other walls. The analogous problem for the circular pipe, where the applied field is in the radial direction, has been treated by Pai (1954). Although it is possible to obtain a radial magnetic field between two concentric iron pipes, it is more interesting to discuss the problem of MHD flow through a circular pipe in a uniform magnetic field. This latter problem is two-dimensional, whereas the former is one-dimensional and very similar to MHD Poiseuille flow. The latter problem is of practical interest because of the occurrence of pipe flow through transverse magnetic fields in MHD pumps, generators, and flow-meters. Exact analyses have been made only in the case of an insulating pipe. An approximate analysis, valid at high values of the Hartmann number for *any* cross section, is given by Shercliff (1962). Let us now turn to the general

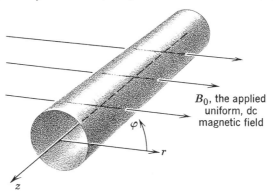

B_0, the applied uniform, dc magnetic field

Figure 7.8-1   The circular channel.

problem of the flow of an incompressible, electrically conducting, viscous fluid through a circular pipe. The flow is along the z axis, which is the axis of the cylinder, and the applied magnetic field is uniform and directed along the x axis. (See Fig. 7.8-1.)

The MHD Equations

The applied magnetic field is given by

$$B_r = B_0 \cos \varphi \quad \text{and} \quad B_\varphi = -B_0 \sin \varphi \tag{7.8-1}$$

As the flow is fully developed, ∂/∂_z of all quantities, except pressure, is zero and $\nabla \cdot \mathbf{B} = 0$ is satisfied by

$$\mathbf{B} = \hat{r} B_0 \cos \varphi - \hat{\varphi} B_0 \sin \varphi + \hat{z} B_z(r, \varphi) \tag{7.8-2}$$

indicating that the applied magnetic field is distorted only in the direction of fluid flow. In accord with the continuity equation, it is assumed that $v_r = v_\varphi = 0$ and that v_z is a function of r and φ. In polar coordinates, the z component of the Navier-Stokes equation is given by

$$\frac{\partial^2 w}{\partial r^2} + \frac{1}{r}\frac{\partial w}{\partial r} + \frac{1}{r^2}\frac{\partial^2 w}{\partial \varphi^2} - \frac{B_0}{\mu_f r}\sin \varphi \frac{\partial H_z}{\partial \varphi} + \frac{B_0}{\mu_f}\cos \varphi \frac{\partial H_z}{\partial r} = \frac{1}{\mu_f}\frac{\partial P}{\partial z} \tag{7.8-3a}$$

where w is the z component of velocity. The other components of the Navier-Stokes equations are useful for determining the pressure. The magnetic induction equation becomes

$$\frac{1}{r}\frac{\partial}{\partial r}\left(r\frac{\partial H_z}{\partial r}\right) + \frac{1}{r^2}\frac{\partial^2 H_z}{\partial \varphi^2} + \frac{\sigma B_0}{r}\left[\cos\varphi\frac{\partial}{\partial r}(rw) - \frac{\partial}{\partial\varphi}(w\sin\varphi)\right] = 0 \quad (7.8\text{-}3b)$$

On the basis of our discussion in previous sections, we can define the following dimensionless variables: $r^* = r/r_0$, $w^* = w/[(r_0^2/\mu_f)(\partial P/\partial z)]$,

$$H^* = \frac{H_z}{(r_0^2\sqrt{\sigma/\mu_f}(\partial P/\partial z))}, \quad J^* = \frac{J}{(r_0\sqrt{\sigma/\mu_f}(\partial P/\partial z))}, \quad \text{and} \quad M = r_0 B_0\sqrt{\frac{\sigma}{\mu_f}}$$

where r_0 is the radius of the pipe. Under these transformations (7.8-3a) and (7.8-3b) become

$$\frac{\partial^2 w^*}{\partial r^{*2}} + \frac{1}{r^*}\frac{\partial w^*}{\partial r^*} + \frac{1}{r^{*2}}\frac{\partial^2 w^*}{\partial\varphi^2} - \frac{M}{r^*}\sin\varphi\frac{\partial H^*}{\partial\varphi} + M\cos\varphi\frac{\partial H^*}{\partial r^*} = 1 \quad (7.8\text{-}4a)$$

$$\frac{\partial^2 H^*}{\partial r^{*2}} + \frac{1}{r^*}\frac{\partial H^*}{\partial r^*} + \frac{1}{r^{*2}}\frac{\partial^2 H^*}{\partial\varphi^2} - M\frac{\sin\varphi}{r^*}\frac{\partial w^*}{\partial\varphi} + M\cos\varphi\frac{\partial w^*}{\partial r^*} = 0 \quad (7.8\text{-}4b)$$

The dimensionless current density is given by

$$J_r^* = \frac{1}{r^*}\frac{\partial H^*}{\partial\varphi} \quad (7.8\text{-}5a)$$

$$J_\varphi^* = -\frac{\partial H^*}{\partial r^*} \quad (7.8\text{-}5b)$$

By Section 7.2 the magnetic boundary conditions are

$$H^*(r^* = 1, \varphi) = 0 \quad (7.8\text{-}6a)$$

and

$$\left.\frac{\partial H^*}{\partial r^*}\right|_{r^*=1} = 0 \quad (7.8\text{-}6b)$$

for insulating and perfectly conducting channel walls, respectively. For $\sigma_w \to \infty$ this condition becomes $\left.\dfrac{\partial H^*}{\partial r^*}\right|_{r^*=1} = 0$, which is in agreement with (7.8-5b) because for $\sigma_w \to \infty$, $E_\varphi^*(r^* = 1, \varphi)$ must be zero. At the other extreme, when $\sigma_w = 0$, (7.8-6) yields $H^*(r^* = 1, \varphi) = 0$. The remaining boundary condition is $w^*(r^* = 1, \varphi) = 0$. It is interesting to note that the governing equations can be written (see Hasimoto, 1960) as

$$\nabla_T^2 w^* + M\frac{\partial H^*}{\partial\xi} = 1 \quad (7.8\text{-}7a)$$

and

$$\nabla_T^2 H^* + M \frac{\partial W^*}{\partial \xi} = 0 \qquad (7.8\text{-}7b)$$

where $\nabla_T^2 = (\partial^2/\partial r^{*2}) + (1/r^*)(\partial/\partial r^*) + (1/r^{*2})(\partial^2/\partial \varphi^2)$ and $\xi = r^* \cos \varphi$. In this form the governing equations are very similar to those derived in Section 7.4 for rectangular coordinates. These equations are valid regardless of boundary conditions. When the pipe wall is an insulator both $w(r^* = 1, \varphi) = 0$ and $H(r^* = 1, \varphi) = 0$ at the boundary $r^* = 1$. Then the first solution of Section 7.4 is applicable. For an insulating pipe it is useful to assume

$$w^* = f(r, \varphi)e^{-M\xi} + g(r, \varphi)e^{M\xi} \qquad (7.8\text{-}8a)$$

and

$$H^* = f(r, \varphi)e^{-M\xi} - g(r, \varphi)e^{M\xi} + \frac{\xi}{M} \qquad (7.8\text{-}8b)$$

because they uncouple (7.8-7a) and (7.8-7b). The resulting equations are

$$\nabla_T^2 f - M^2 f = 0 \qquad (7.8\text{-}9a)$$

and

$$\nabla_T^2 g - M^2 g = 0 \qquad (7.8\text{-}9b)$$

which apply in general to MHD pipe flow. These equations are most easily solved, however, for the insulating pipe. Then the boundary conditions of f and g are

$$f(1, \varphi) = - \frac{\cos \varphi}{2M} e^{M \cos \varphi} \qquad (7.8\text{-}10a)$$

$$g(1, \varphi) = \frac{\cos \varphi}{2M} e^{-M \cos \varphi} \qquad (7.8\text{-}10b)$$

The solutions to (7.8-9a) and (7.8-9b) obtained by the method of separation of variables are

$$f = \sum_{n=0}^{\infty} A_n I_n(Mr^*) \cos n\varphi \qquad (7.8\text{-}11a)$$

and

$$g = \sum_{n=0}^{\infty} B_n I_n(Mr^*) \cos n\varphi \qquad (7.8\text{-}11b)$$

By the boundary condition (7.8-10a), A_n becomes

$$A_n = - \frac{1}{2\pi M I_n(M)} \int_0^{2\pi} e^{M \cos \varphi} \cos \varphi \cos n\, \varphi\, d\varphi \qquad (7.8\text{-}12a)$$

or

$$A_n = -\frac{1}{4\pi M I_n(M)} \int_0^{2\pi} e^{M \cos \varphi}[\cos(n+1)\varphi + \cos(n-1)\varphi]\, d\varphi$$

(7.8-12b)

From the relationships for Bessel functions

$$J_q(z) = \frac{1}{2\pi j^q} \int_0^{2\pi} e^{jz \cos u} \cos qu\, du$$

(7.8-13a)

and

$$I_q(z) = j^{-q} J_q(jz) = j^q J_q(-jz)$$

(7.8-13b)

it is easy to show that

$$A_n = -\frac{1}{2MI_n(M)}[I_{n+1}(M) + I_{n-1}(M)] = -\frac{1}{M} \cdot \frac{I'_n(M)}{I_n(M)}$$

(7.8-14a)

Similarly,

$$B_n = \frac{-(-1)^n}{2MI_n(M)}[I_{n+1}(M) + I_{n-1}(M)] = -\frac{(-1)^n}{M} \cdot \frac{I'_n(M)}{I_n(M)}$$

(7.8-14b)

Hence the solutions for velocity and magnetic field become

$$w^* = -\frac{1}{M}\sum_{n=0}^{\infty}[e^{-Mr^* \cos \varphi} + (-1)^n e^{Mr^* \cos \varphi}]$$
$$\times \frac{I'_n(M)}{I_n(M)} I_n(Mr^*) \cos n\varphi$$

(7.8-15a)

$$H^* = \frac{r^*}{M}\cos \varphi - \frac{1}{M}\sum_{n=0}^{\infty}[e^{-Mr^* \cos \varphi} - (-1)^n e^{Mr^* \cos \varphi}]$$
$$\times \frac{I'_n(M)}{I_n(M)} I_n(Mr^*) \cos n\varphi$$

(7.8-15b)

These results appear in various forms in the literature; (7.8-15a) and (7.8-15b) are in the form given by Uhlenbusch and Fischer (1961). It is easy to show that for small values of M, $\lim\limits_{M \to 0} w^* = \frac{1}{4}(r^{*2} - 1)$ and the magnetic field approaches zero. Here the prime on I_n denotes the derivative.

Discussion

The constant velocity contours are plotted in Fig. 7.8-2 for a Hartmann number of 10. We can see that the velocity profile is almost parabolic, as in Hartmann flow along the line $\varphi = \pi/2$. As φ decreases toward zero, the flattening weakens because the electromagnetic body force decreases. The current lines are given in Fig. 7.8-3 for $M = 10$. The current flows in

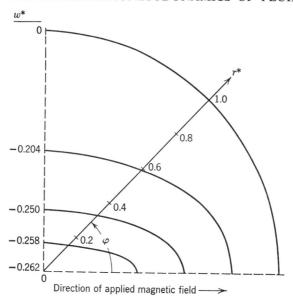

Figure 7.8-2 The constant velocity contours of one quadrant of the circular channel for $M = 10$.

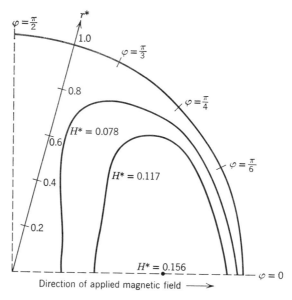

Figure 7.8-3 Current lines in one quadrant of the circular channel for $M = 10$.

the same way as it did in the rectangular channel with insulating walls. For additional curves and computational details, the works of Gold, Fucks, and Singh should be consulted.

7.9   TWO-DIMENSIONAL MHD COUETTE FLOW IN AN INSULATING CHANNEL

Introduction

This problem is a natural outgrowth of one-dimensional Couette flow. The two-dimensional geometry of this problem is shown in Fig. 7.3-2. Although this configuration is not as widely used as the stationary insulating-wall channel of Section 7.5, it can be used as an MHD viscometer. In a viscometer a finite-length (in the x direction) channel, closed at both ends, is used. The top channel wall, which has a uniform direct-current magnetic field applied normal to it, is moved with a constant velocity U_0. The difference in pressure between the channel ends (located at $x = x_0$ and $x = -x_0$) is measured. From these simple data the viscosity can be calculated if the flow problem has been solved. In this application the velocity profile must be found for any applied magnetic field and flow rate calculated therefrom and set to zero. This resulting expression can be solved for viscosity, the solution being a function of the applied magnetic field. For example, this device might be used to measure the viscosity as a function of applied magnetic field in a colloidal suspension of iron particles in mercury, and in this case a solution to the two-dimensional MHD Couette problem would be useful.

Although the channel walls are all insulators, the movement of the top wall precludes the use of (7.4-11a) and (7.4-11b). To solve the boundary value problem, we must make use of (7.4-14a) and (7.4-14b). The procedure for solving this problem is very similar to the analysis, in Section 7.5, of the channel with insulating walls. However, just as MHD one-dimensional Couette flow is more complicated than MHD one-dimensional Poiseuille flow, the solution here should be more difficult than that of Section 7.5. Additional terms should result because no symmetry about any z axis exists in Couette flow. Nevertheless, the concepts and techniques used here parallel those of Section 7.5.

Solution to the Boundary Value Problem

The solution to this problem is facilitated by putting the fundamental equations of steady, incompressible, viscous MHD channel flow into dimensionless form. It is convenient to let $z^* = z/y_0$, $y^* = y/y_0$, $u^* = u/U_0$, $M = y_0 B_0 \sqrt{\sigma/\mu_f}$, $H_x^* = H_x/U_0\sqrt{\sigma\mu_f}$, and $G^* = (y_0^2/\mu_f U_0)(\partial P/\partial x)$. These dimensionless quantities are similar to those encountered in Section 7.3 with regard to one-dimensional Couette flow. Under these substitutions (7.4-4) and (7.4-8) become

$$\frac{\partial^2 H_x^*}{\partial y^{*2}} + \frac{\partial^2 H_x^*}{\partial z^{*2}} + M\frac{\partial u^*}{\partial y^*} = 0 \tag{7.9-1a}$$

$$\frac{\partial^2 u^*}{\partial y^{*2}} + \frac{\partial^2 u^*}{\partial z^{*2}} + M\frac{\partial H_x^*}{\partial y^*} = G^* \tag{7.9-1b}$$

A solution similar to the one valid for MHD flow in an insulating channel with no moving walls is assumed. The assumed solutions are similar to those given by (7.5-2a) and (7.5-2b). However, $u^*|_{y^* \to \infty}$ must now be multiplied by G^*. The assumed solutions are thus

$$u^* = \frac{z^{*2} - k^2}{2}G^* + \sum_{n=0}^{\infty} u_n(y^*)\cos\lambda_n^* z^* \tag{7.9-2a}$$

$$H_x^* = \sum_{n=0}^{\infty} H_n(y^*)\cos\lambda_n^* z^* \tag{7.9-2b}$$

where $\lambda_n^* = (2n + 1)\pi/2k$, and $k = z_0/y_0$.

When (7.9-2a) and (7.9-2b) are substituted into (7.9-1a) and (7.9-1b), the resulting equations become ordinary homogeneous differential equations. They are

$$\frac{d^2 u_n}{dy^{*2}} - \lambda_n^{*2} u_n + M\frac{dH_n}{dy^*} = 0 \tag{7.9-3a}$$

$$\frac{d^2 H_n}{dy^{*2}} - \lambda_n^{*2} H_n + M\frac{du_n}{dy^*} = 0 \tag{7.9-3b}$$

The solutions to this system are

$$u_n = A_n \operatorname{sh} p_1^* y^* + B_n \operatorname{sh} p_2^* y^* + C_n \operatorname{ch} p_1^* y^* + D_n \operatorname{ch} p_2^* y^* \tag{7.9-4a}$$

$$H_n = (a_1 A_n \operatorname{ch} p_1^* y^* + a_2 B_n \operatorname{ch} p_2^* y^* + a_1 C_n \operatorname{sh} p_1^* y^* + a_2 D_n \operatorname{sh} p_2^* y^*)/M \tag{7.9-4b}$$

where

$$p_{1,2}^{*2} = \lambda_n^{*2} + \frac{M^2}{2} \pm M\sqrt{\lambda_n^{*2} + \frac{M^2}{4}} \tag{7.9-5a}$$

$$a_1 = (p_1^{*2} - \lambda_n^{*2})/p_1^* \tag{7.9-5b}$$

$$a_2 = (p_2^{*2} - \lambda_n^{*2})/p_2^* \tag{7.9-5c}$$

In this problem no symmetry or antisymmetry exists in either the velocity or magnetic field profile; hence all four solutions are necessary.

Because of the form of the assumed solution, the no-slip condition on the velocity has been satisfied at $z^* = \pm k$. Four boundary conditions remain, for the assumed solution makes $J_z^*(y^*, \pm k) = 0$. These conditions are that $u^*(1, z^*) = 1$, $u^*(0, z^*) = 0$, $J_y^*(1, z^*) = 0$, and $J_y^*(0, z^*) = 0$. From the last conditions $H_n(1) = H_n(0) = 0$. The first two conditions must be obtained by a Fourier expansion which yields values for $u_n(1)$ and $u_n(0)$. The boundary conditions result in the following system of equations:

$$A_n \operatorname{sh} p_1^* + B_n \operatorname{sh} p_2^* + C_n \operatorname{ch} p_1^* + D_n \operatorname{ch} p_2^* = u_n(1) \quad (7.9\text{-}6)$$

$$C_n + D_n = u_n(0) \quad (7.9\text{-}7)$$

$$A_n a_1 \operatorname{ch} p_1^* + B_n a_2 \operatorname{ch} p_2^* + C_n a_1 \operatorname{sh} p_1^* + D_n a_2 \operatorname{sh} p_2^* = 0 \quad (7.9\text{-}8)$$

$$A_n a_1 + B_n a_2 = 0 \quad (7.9\text{-}9)$$

The solutions to this system are

$$A_n = \frac{a_2}{\Delta_n} [u_n(1)(a_1 \operatorname{sh} p_1^* - a_2 \operatorname{sh} p_2^*) - u_n(0)(a_1 \operatorname{sh} p_1^* \operatorname{ch} p_2^*$$
$$- a_2 \operatorname{ch} p_1^* \operatorname{sh} p_2^*)] \quad (7.9\text{-}10a)$$

$$B_n = -\frac{a_1}{\Delta_n} [u_n(1)(a_1 \operatorname{sh} p_1^* - a_2 \operatorname{sh} p_2^*) - u_n(0)(a_1 \operatorname{sh} p_1^* \operatorname{ch} p_2^*$$
$$- a_2 \operatorname{ch} p_1^* \operatorname{sh} p_2^*)] \quad (7.9\text{-}10b)$$

$$C_n = \frac{1}{\Delta_n} [u_n(0)(-a_1 a_2 - a_2^2 \operatorname{sh} p_1^* \operatorname{sh} p_2^* + a_1 a_2 \operatorname{ch} p_1^* \operatorname{ch} p_2^*$$
$$- a_1 a_2 u_n(1) \cdot (\operatorname{ch} p_1^* - \operatorname{ch} p_2^*)] \quad (7.9\text{-}10c)$$

$$D_n = \frac{1}{\Delta_n} [u_n(0)(-a_1 a_2 - a_1^2 \operatorname{sh} p_1^* \operatorname{sh} p_2^* + a_1 a_2 \operatorname{ch} p_1^* \operatorname{ch} p_2^*$$
$$+ a_1 a_2 u_n(1) \cdot (\operatorname{ch} p_1^* - \operatorname{ch} p_2^*)] \quad (7.9\text{-}10d)$$

$$\Delta_n = -2a_1 a_2 - (a_1^2 + a_2^2) \operatorname{sh} p_1^* \operatorname{ch} p_2^*$$
$$+ 2a_1 a_2 \operatorname{ch} p_1^* \operatorname{ch} p_2^* \quad (7.9\text{-}10e)$$

To complete the solution $u_n(1)$ and $u_n(0)$ must be found. They are obtained from

$$\sum_{n=0}^{\infty} u_n(1) \cos \lambda_n^* z^* + \frac{z^{*2} - k^2}{2} G^* = 1 \quad (7.9\text{-}11a)$$

and

$$\sum_{n=0}^{\infty} u_n(0) \cos \lambda_n^* z^* + \frac{z^{*2} - k^2}{2} G^* = 0 \quad (7.9\text{-}11b)$$

By Fourier analysis it is easy to show that

$$u_n(1) = \frac{2(-1)^n}{k\lambda_n{}^*}\left(1 + \frac{G^*}{\lambda_n{}^{*2}}\right)$$

$$u_n(0) = \frac{2(-1)^n G^*}{k\lambda_n{}^{*3}}$$

$$(7.9\text{-}12)$$

The dimensionless flow rate $Q^* = \int_0^k \int_0^1 u^* \, dy^* \, dz^*$ is easily evaluated from Equations (7.9-2a) through (7.9-4a). The result is

$$Q^* = \frac{2}{k}\sum_{n=0}^{\infty}\frac{\zeta_n}{\lambda_n{}^{*2}\Delta_n} - G^*\left(\frac{k^3}{3} - 2\sum_{n=0}^{\infty}\frac{\xi_n}{\lambda_n{}^{*3}\Delta_n}\right) \qquad (7.9\text{-}13a)$$

where

$$\zeta_n = (a_1 \text{ sh } p_1{}^* - a_2 \text{ sh } p_2{}^*)\left[\frac{a_2}{p_1{}^*}(-1 + \text{ch } p_1{}^*) - \frac{a_1}{p_2{}^*}(-1 + \text{ch } p_2{}^*)\right]$$

$$+ a_1 a_2(\text{ch } p_1{}^* - \text{ch } p_2{}^*)\left(-\frac{\text{sh } p_1{}^*}{p_1{}^*} + \frac{\text{sh } p_2{}^*}{p_2{}^*}\right) \qquad (7.9\text{-}13b)$$

and

$$\xi_n = \left(\frac{-1 + \text{ch } p_1{}^*}{p_1{}^*}a_2 - \frac{-1 + \text{ch } p_2{}^*}{p_2{}^*}a_1\right)\left[(a_1 \text{ sh } p_1{}^*)(1 - \text{ch } p_2{}^*)\right.$$

$$- (a_2 \text{ sh } p_2{}^*)(1 - \text{ch } p_1{}^*)] + [a_1 a_2(\text{ch } p_1{}^* \text{ ch } p_2{}^* - 1)$$

$$- a_2{}^2 \text{ sh } p_1{}^* \text{ sh } p_2{}^* - a_1 a_2(\text{ch } p_1{}^* - \text{ch } p_2{}^*)]\frac{\text{sh } p_1{}^*}{p_1{}^*}$$

$$+ [a_1 a_2(\text{ch } p_1{}^* \text{ ch } p_2{}^* - 1) - a_1{}^2 \text{ sh } p_1{}^* \text{ sh } p_2{}^*$$

$$+ a_1 a_2(\text{ch } p_1{}^* - \text{ch } p_2{}^*)]\frac{\text{sh } p_2{}^*}{p_2{}^*} \qquad (7.9\text{-}13c)$$

If the channel has walls located at $x = \pm x_0$ where $x_0 \gg ky_0$, there is no net flow and $Q^* = 0$. Then a pressure gradient exists which causes as much fluid to flow in the positive as in the negative x direction. When the flow rate is zero, the resulting dimensionless pressure gradient is given by

$$G^* = \frac{\dfrac{2}{k}\displaystyle\sum_{n=0}^{\infty}\dfrac{\zeta_n}{\lambda_n{}^{*2}\Delta_n}}{\dfrac{k^3}{3} - \dfrac{2}{k}\displaystyle\sum_{n=0}^{\infty}\dfrac{\xi_n}{\lambda_n{}^{*4}\Delta_n}} \qquad (7.9\text{-}14)$$

If $M \to 0$, it can be shown that

$$\lim_{M \to 0} u^* = \frac{G^*}{2}(z^{*2} - k^{*2}) + 2\sum_{n=0}^{\infty} \frac{(-1)^n}{k\lambda_n^* \operatorname{sh} \lambda^*}\left\{\left(1 + \frac{G^*}{\lambda_n^{*2}}\right) \operatorname{sh} \lambda_n^* y^*\right.$$

$$\left. + \frac{G^*}{\lambda_n^{*2}} \operatorname{sh}[\lambda_n^*(1 - y^*)]\right\} \cos \lambda_n^* z^* \quad (7.9\text{-}15)$$

When the flow rate is zero and the Hartmann number is zero, (7.9-14) reduces to

$$\lim_{M \to 0} G^* = \frac{2\displaystyle\sum_{n=0}^{\infty} \frac{\operatorname{ch} \lambda_n^* - 1}{k^3 \lambda_n^{*3} \operatorname{sh} \lambda_n^*}}{\dfrac{k}{3} - 4\displaystyle\sum_{n=0}^{\infty} \frac{\operatorname{ch} \lambda_n^* - 1}{k^3 \lambda_n^{*5} \operatorname{sh} \lambda_n^*}} \quad (7.9\text{-}16)$$

Discussion

In Fig. 7.9-1 we show constant velocity contours for $k = 1$, $G^* = 0$, and $M = 0$. In this case the flow is unidirectional because $G^* = 0$ but when G^* is adjusted (by using 7.9-16) so that the flow rate Q^* is zero, the more complicated velocity contours of Fig. 7.9-2 result. Hence it is clear that the pressure gradient exerts a great influence upon the velocity profile. When the Hartmann number is not zero, the velocity contours are modified by the action of the electromagnetic body force. We see from Fig. 7.9-3 that the fluid near the bottom wall (in the region $0 \le y^* \le 0.5$) of the channel flows faster in the magnetohydrodynamic case than in

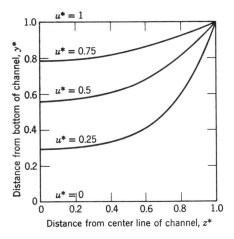

Figure 7.9-1   Velocity contours for $M = 0$, $G^* = 0$, and $k = 1$.

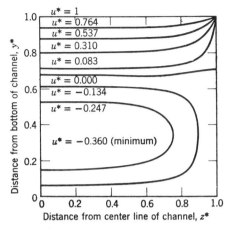

Figure 7.9-2 Velocity contours for $M = 0$, $G^* = 6.38057$, and $k = 1.0$.

the case of $M = 0$. The current lines for $M = 5$ and $G^* = 0$ are given in Fig. 7.9-4. Below the plane (x^*, 0.54, z^*) the **J** x **B** force accelerates the fluid whereas above that plane the **J** x **B** force is a retarding force. This accounts for the difference between the velocity contours of Fig. 7.9-1 and Fig. 7.9-3.

The problem solved in this section is a member of a set of problems comprising rectangular channels with some combination of moving walls and stationary walls, conducting and/or nonconducting. Solutions to other members of this set are left as exercises for the mature student.

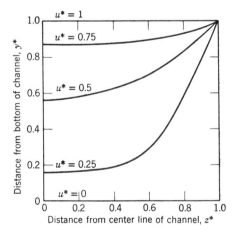

Figure 7.9-3 Velocity contours for $M = 5$, $G^* = 0$, and $k = 1$.

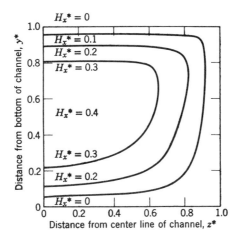

Figure 7.9-4   Current lines for $M = 5$, $G^* = 0$, and $k = 1$.

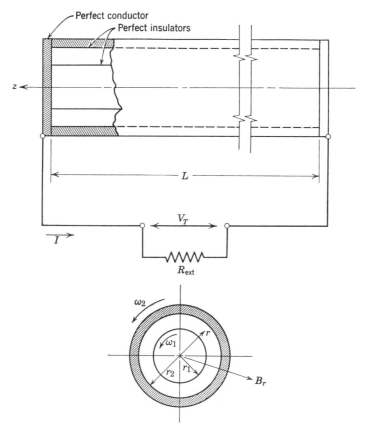

Figure 7.10-1   Flow between two rotating coaxial cylinders.

7.10 FLOW BETWEEN TWO COAXIAL ROTATING CYLINDERS WITH A RADIAL MAGNETIC FIELD

We now consider the steady flow of an incompressible conducting fluid between two concentric rotating cylinders composed of an insulating material. A uniform radial magnetic field of the form $B_r = A/r$ is applied throughout the flow region. The cylinders terminate at perfect electrodes which are connected through a load, as shown in Fig. 7.10-1. The cylinders are long enough that axial variations are negligible, and since there is no preferred orientation for stable laminar flow, there can be no angular variations. Here A is a constant (not the Alfvén speed).

Keeping in mind that the only variations are in the radial direction, Equations (6.4-1) through (6.4-4) yield

$$\frac{dE_z}{dr} = 0 \tag{7.10-1}$$

$$\frac{d}{dr}(rE_\theta) = 0 \tag{7.10-2}$$

$$J_r = 0 \tag{7.10-3}$$

$$\mu_0 J_\theta = -\frac{dB_\theta}{dr} \tag{7.10-4}$$

$$\mu_0 J_z = \frac{1}{r}\frac{d}{dr}(rB_\theta) \tag{7.10-5}$$

$$\frac{d}{dr}(rB_r) = 0 \tag{7.10-6}$$

$$J_r = \sigma(E_r + v_\theta B_z - v_z B_\theta) \tag{7.10-7}$$

$$J_\theta = \sigma(E_\theta + v_z B_r - v_r B_z) \tag{7.10-8}$$

$$J_z = \sigma(E_z + v_r B_\theta - v_\theta B_r) \tag{7.10-9}$$

$$\frac{d}{dr}(rv_r) = 0 \tag{7.10-10}$$

$$\rho\left(v_r\frac{dv_r}{dr} - \frac{v_\theta^2}{r}\right) = -\frac{dP}{dr} + \mu_f\left(\frac{d^2v_r}{\partial r^2} + \frac{1}{r}\frac{\partial v_r}{\partial r} - \frac{v_r}{r^2}\right) - J_\theta B_z - J_z B_\theta \tag{7.10-11}$$

$$\rho v_r\left(\frac{dv_\theta}{dr} + \frac{v_\theta}{r}\right) = \mu_f\left(\frac{d^2v_\theta}{dr^2} + \frac{1}{r}\frac{dv_\theta}{dr} - \frac{v_\theta}{r^2}\right) + J_z B_r - J_r B_z \tag{7.10-12}$$

$$\rho v_r\frac{dv_z}{dr} = \mu_f\left(\frac{d^2v_z}{dr^2} + \frac{1}{r}\frac{dv_z}{dr}\right) + J_r B_\theta - J_\theta B_r \tag{7.10-13}$$

From Equation (7.10-2), $E_\theta = C/r$. But there can be no E field tangent to a perfect conductor, so that E_θ is zero for all r at the ends of the cylinders. Hence $E_\theta = 0$. From Equation (7.10-10), $r v_r = $ constant. But v_r must be zero at $r = r_1$ and r_2, the surfaces of the cylinders. Hence $v_r = 0$. From Equation (7.10-6), B_r is proportional to $(1/r)$, and since at $r = r_1$, $B_r = A/r_1$, it follows that

$$B_r = \frac{A}{r}$$

Combining Equations (7.10-8) and (7.10-13), together with the above results, gives us

$$\frac{d^2 v_z}{dr^2} + \frac{1}{r}\frac{dv_z}{dr} - \frac{\alpha}{r^2} v_z = 0 \qquad (7.10\text{-}14)$$

where $\alpha = A^2\sigma/\mu_f$. The solution to this equation is

$$v_z = C_1 r^\alpha + C_2 r^{-\alpha}$$

subject to the condition that v_z is zero at $r = r_1$ and r_2. Hence

$$v_z = 0 \qquad (7.10\text{-}15)$$

and from Equation (7.10-8),

$$J_\theta = 0$$

From Equation (7.10-4), B_z is constant. But B_z must be zero as $r \to \infty$ so that

$$B_z = 0$$

Then, from Equation (7.10-7),

$$E_r = 0$$

From Equation (7.10-1), E_z is constant, and we can combine Equations (7.10-9) and (7.10-12) to obtain

$$\frac{d^2 v_\theta}{dr^2} + \frac{1}{r}\frac{dv_\theta}{dr} - \left(1 + \frac{\sigma A^2}{\mu_f}\right)\frac{1}{r^2} v_\theta = -\frac{\sigma A E_z}{\mu_f}\cdot\frac{1}{r} \qquad (7.10\text{-}16)$$

whose solution is

$$v_\theta = D_1 r^N + D_2 r^{-N} + \frac{E_z}{A}\cdot r \qquad (7.10\text{-}17)$$

where $N = \sqrt{1 + \sigma A^2/\mu_f}$. The constants D_1 and D_2 may be evaluated by applying the conditions

$$v_\theta(r_1) = r_1\omega_1$$

$$v_\theta(r_2) = r_2\omega_2$$

yielding finally

$$
\begin{aligned}
v_\theta =\ & \frac{(\omega_2 r_2^{N+1} - \omega_2 r_1^{N+1})r^N + (r_1 r_2)^{N+1}(\omega_1 r_2^{N-1} - \omega_2 r_1^{N-1})r^{-N}}{r_2^{2N} - r_1^{2N}} \\
& - \frac{E_z}{A}\left[\frac{(r_2^{N+1} - r_1^{N+1})r^N + (r_1 r_2)^{N+1}(r_2^{N-1} - r_1^{N-1})r^{-N}}{r_2^{2N} - r_1^{2N}} - r\right]
\end{aligned}
\tag{7.10-18}
$$

Now, from Equations (7.10-9) and (7.10-15),

$$
J_z = -\frac{\sigma A}{r}\cdot v_\theta
\tag{7.10-19}
$$

Equations (7.10-5) and (7.10-19) yield

$$
B_\theta = \frac{\begin{array}{l}-\sigma\mu_0 A(N-1)(\omega_2 r_2^{N+1} - \omega_1 r_1^{N+1})(r^{N+1} - r_1^{N+1}) \\ \quad - (N+1)(r_1 r_2)^{N+1}(\omega_1 r_2^{N-1} - \omega_2 r_1^{N-1})(r^{1-N} - r_1^{1-N})\end{array}}{(N^2 - 1)(r_2^{2N} - r_1^{2N})r}
$$

$$
+ \frac{\begin{array}{l}\sigma\mu_0 E_z(N-1)(r_2^{N+1} - r_1^{N+1})(r^{N+1} - r_1^{N+1}) \\ \quad - (N+1)(r_1 r_2)^{N+1}(r_2^{N-1} - r_1^{N-1})(r^{1-N} - r_1^{1-N})\end{array}}{(N^2 - 1)(r_2^{2N} - r_1^{2N})r}
\tag{7.10-20}
$$

Equation (7.10-11) now becomes

$$
\frac{dP}{dr} = \rho\frac{v_\theta^2}{r} - J_z B_\theta
\tag{7.10-21}
$$

from which the radial pressure variation may be found to within a constant. The total current I is given by

$$
I = 2\pi\int_{r_1}^{r_2} J_z r\, dr
\tag{7.10-22}
$$

which yields

$$
\begin{aligned}
I =\ & 2\pi\sigma\left[E_z\frac{(N-1)(r_2^{N+1} - r_1^{N+1})^2 + (N+1)(r_2^{N-1} - r_1^{N-1})^2 r_1^2 r_2^2}{(N^2 - 1)(r_2^{2N} - r_1^{2N})}\right. \\
& \left. - A\frac{\begin{array}{l}(N-1)(\omega_2 r_2^{N+1} - \omega_1 r_1^{N+1})(r_2^{N+1} - r_1^{N+1}) \\ + (N+1)(\omega_1 r_2^{N-1} - \omega_2 r_1^{N-1})(r_2^{N-1} - r_1^{N-1})r_1^2 r_2^2\end{array}}{(N^2 - 1)(r_2^{2N} - r_1^{2N})}\right]
\end{aligned}
\tag{7.10-23}
$$

This may be solved for E_z, giving

$$E_z = \frac{\begin{aligned}&A(N-1)(\omega_2 r_2^{N+1} - \omega_1 r_1^{N+1})(r_2^{N+1} - r_1^{N+1}) \\ &+ A(N+1)(\omega_1 r_2^{N-1} - \omega_2 r_1^{N-1})(r_2^{N-1} - r_1^{N-1})r_1^2 r_2^2 \\ &+ (I/2\pi\sigma)(N^2 - 1)(r_2^{2N} - r_1^{2N})\end{aligned}}{(N-1)(r_2^{N+1} - r_1^{N+1})^2 + (N+1)(r_2^{N-1} - r_1^{N-1})^2 r_1^2 r_2^2}$$

(7.10-24)

The terminal voltage V_T is found from

$$V_T = -\int_A^B \mathbf{E} \cdot d\mathbf{l} = -LE_z \qquad (7.10\text{-}25)$$

Then the open-circuit voltage V_{oc} is

$$V_{oc} = -LA \frac{\begin{aligned}&(N-1)(\omega_2 r_2^{N+1} - \omega_1 r_1^{N+1})(r_2^{N+1} - r_1^{N+1}) \\ &+ (N+1)(\omega_1 r_2^{N-1} - \omega_2 r_1^{N-1})(r_2^{N-1} - r_1^{N-1})r_1^2 r_2^2\end{aligned}}{(N-1)(r_2^{N+1} - r_1^{N+1}) + (N+1)(r_2^{N-1} - r_1^{N-1})r_1^2 r_2^2}$$

(7.10-26)

and the short-circuit current I_{sc} is

$$I_{sc} = -2\pi\sigma A \frac{\begin{aligned}&(N-1)(\omega_2 r_2^{N+1} - \omega_1 r_1^{N+1})(r_2^{N+1} - r_1^{N+1}) \\ &+ (N+1)(\omega_1 r_2^{N-1} - \omega_2 r_1^{N-1})(r_2^{N-1} - r_1^{N-1})r_1^2 r_2^2\end{aligned}}{(N^2 - 1)(r_2^{2N} - r_1^{2N})}$$

(7.10-27)

From these equations the internal resistance R_i may be found:

$$R_i = \frac{V_{oc}}{I_{sc}} = \left(\frac{L}{2\pi\sigma}\right) \frac{(N^2 - 1)(r_2^{2N} - r_1^{2N})}{(N-1)(r_2^{N+1} - r_1^{N+1}) + (N+1)(r_2^{N-1} - r_1^{N-1})^2 r_1^2 r_2^2}$$

(7.10-28)

In order to write the results of our calculations simply, we now introduce the following dimensionless parameters:

$$\eta = \frac{r}{r_2}$$

$$\eta_1 = \frac{r_1}{r_2}$$

$$\Omega = \frac{\omega_1}{\omega_2}$$

$$V_\theta = \frac{v_\theta}{r_2 \omega_2}$$

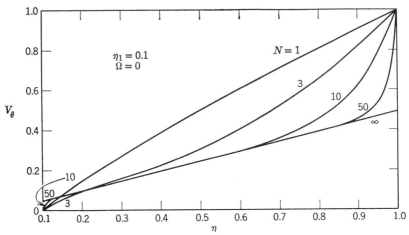

Figure 7.10-2 Normalized velocity versus normalized radial distance for flow between coaxial rotating cylinders.

If ω_z is zero, v_θ may be normalized with respect to $r_1\omega_1$ instead of $r_2\omega_2$. We present only two sample calculations here. Figure 7.10-2 is a plot of V_θ versus η for $\eta_1 = 0.1$ and $\Omega = 0$ for matched loading conditions. The angular velocity ω_1 of the inner cylinder is taken as zero so that Ω is zero. For matched load the external load resistor R_{ext} is set equal to R_i at each value of N (since R_i is a function of N). Figure 7.10-3 is a similar plot except that $\Omega = 10$.

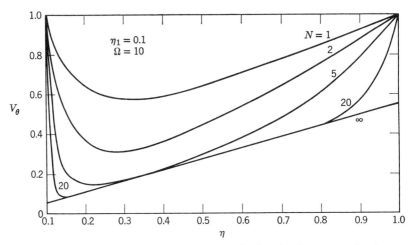

Figure 7.10-3 Normalized velocity versus normalized radial distance for flow between coaxial rotating cylinders.

Throughout this chapter we have confined ourselves to stable laminar flow, and it should be remembered that at sufficiently high Reynolds numbers the flow might become unstable and develop into another, more complex laminar configuration, or go turbulent. Taylor instabilities may occur in the flow between rotating cylinders, but we will not discuss this problem here. The reader is referred to the text by S. Chandrasekhar (1961).

7.11 VERY VISCOUS FLOW AND APPLICATIONS

In the following few sections we will look at some problems of viscous flow in channels where the inertia forces are negligible compared to the viscous, pressure, and electromagnetic forces. Application will be made to some theoretically proposed devices of possible engineering use and, more important, methods of approximation and analysis will be developed. We will be concerned particularly with lubrication-type flow, viscous clutch and control devices, and an analysis of the MHD "pinch" problem.

We will not treat hydrostatic problems as a separate subject here, as we have adopted the attitude that static devices are merely special cases of dynamic situations. The "pinch" problem is discussed under the condition of no flow.

Liquid metals are used as lubricants under certain high temperature conditions, but their lubricating quality is poor because of their relatively low viscosity (an order of about 10^2 less than that of ordinary lubricating oil). Consequently, the load capacity of a liquid metal bearing is decreased because of this low viscosity.

If the liquid metal could be made more viscous or pumped between the hydrodynamical surfaces, more load could be supported (for a given film thickness). The MHD effect can do just this. If we apply a large external magnetic field, the motion of the conducting fluid through the magnetic field may induce circulating currents which, in turn, interact with the magnetic field to create a body force. This body force can then actually pump the fluid between the bearing surfaces, enhancing the hydrodynamical lubrication effect and increasing the pressure. Admittedly, the frictional drag may be increased by the application of the magnetic field. We shall now examine the orders of magnitude of these effects and their feasibility.

Let us examine the magnitude of a typical body force density so that we can get an idea of the magnitude of the pressurization that can be achieved in a MHD bearing. The body force can be written $\mathbf{J} \times \mathbf{B}$, where $\mathbf{J}$ is the current density vector and $\mathbf{B}$ is the induction field. In RMKS units, $\mathbf{J}$ is measured in amperes per meters^2 and $\mathbf{B}$ in Webers per meters^2. One Weber per meters^2 is a flux density of 10^4 gauss. From Ohm's law,

$J = \sigma E'$ and from the Lorentz transformation on the electric field, $E' = E + (V \times B)$, and $J \times B$ is of order $\sigma V B^2$. This fluid body force can of course contribute to the pressure gradient. For a typical value of $B = 1(10^4 \text{ gauss})$ and $V = 10$ meters/sec, $\sigma V B^2$ is about 10^8 Newtons/meters^3 for sodium and 10^7 Newtons/meters^3 for mercury. These figures correspond to a pressure gradient of about 100 psi/in. and 10 psi/in. for sodium and mercury, respectively. These are not very large figures, but they depend on the square of the magnetic induction and can become appreciable for larger magnetic fields which may be obtainable in practice. It would appear, then, that MHD lubrication is feasible and should be investigated further.

Two distinct geometries are possible. A magnetic field may be applied transversely across the fluid film, or tangentially along it perpendicular to the direction of motion. It can easily be shown that the transverse type of geometry is more practical.

Since the $J \times B$ force per unit volume is the important factor, the current density J should be the same order of magnitude in both geometries if the same pressurization and magnetic field are used. The necessary current for the transverse field bearing can be achieved under open-circuit conditions, but in the tangential field geometry extremely high currents from an outside source must be supplied. In the tangential field bearing the total current is of the order JLW, where W and L are the width and length of the bearing, respectively. The total current necessary for the transverse field bearing is of the order JLh, where h is the film thickness. Hence the ratio of the necessary current for the two bearings is W/h or a factor of about 10^3 to 10^5 times as much current for the tangential field bearing compared to the transverse field bearing. The necessary current for effective operation of the tangential field bearing may become impracticably large, while the transverse field bearing can operate effectively under open-circuit conditions with self-generated currents.

In the following sections we will consider some proposed arrangements for MHD bearings and their predicted performance.

7.12 MAGNETOHYDRODYNAMIC LUBRICATION FLOW BETWEEN PARALLEL ROTATING DISCS

Perhaps the simplest arrangement is the hydrostatic thrust bearing shown in Fig. 7.12-1. This bearing may be entirely open-circuited, or it may have ring or screen electrodes as shown. The lubricant is supplied under pressure P_0 and flows radially outward from the plenum recess to the exhaust atmospheric pressure P_e. The axial magnetic field interacts with the flowing fluid and generates a circulating azimuthal current which interacts with the axial field and retards the radial flow of fluid. The bearing geometry considered here consists of two plane parallel discs, one of which, the rotor, rotates at an angular speed with respect to the second disc, or stator. As is usual in a pressurized thrust bearing, the stator has a

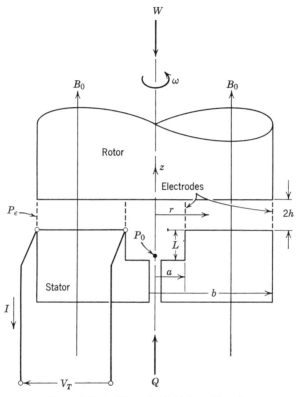

Figure 7.12-1   The axial field thrust bearing.

recessed region. However, for simplicity of analysis, the electrode geometries considered here are such that the flow in the recess is not affected by the applied fields. The results obtained, however, could easily be extended to include such effects.

For an axially applied magnetic field, the electrodes are concentric cylinders, as shown in Fig. 7.12-1. It is assumed that they are ideal conductors and porous to the fluid flow. Physically, these electrodes represent equipotential surfaces at the step of the recess and exit radius of the bearing. This idealization is permissible because the separation between the rotor and stator is much less than the recess depth. The actual electrodes in a real bearing would probably be located in the recess and at the outer radius of the stator. The stator and rotor are assumed to be nonmagnetic insulators—the magnetic field extending only over the region between the electrodes.

The flow is considered to be steady state, incompressible, and viscous, with constant conductivity σ and viscosity μ_f. The inertia of the fluid is assumed to be small compared to the viscous forces—a valid approximation for the flow considered here.

Under the present assumptions, then, the components of the equation of motion, assuming cylindrical symmetry and lubrication flow ($h \ll b$), are

$$\frac{\partial P}{\partial r} = \mu_f \frac{\partial^2 u}{\partial z^2} + (J_\theta B_z - J_z B_\theta)$$

$$0 = \mu_f \frac{\partial^2 v}{\partial z^2} + (J_z B_r - J_r B_z) \qquad (7.12\text{-}1)$$

$$\frac{\partial P}{\partial z} = (J_r B_\theta - J_\theta B_r)$$

where u and v are the radial and tangential velocities, respectively. The continuity equation can be written as

$$Q = \int_{-h}^{h} 2\pi r u \, dz \qquad (7.12\text{-}2)$$

where Q is the flow rate and h is the half-height of the fluid film between the stator and rotor (for $a < r < b$).

In Fig. 7.12-1 the external magnetic field B_0 is applied axially in the z direction, and the electrodes are located at $r = b$ and $r = a$. The induced magnetic fields B_r and B_θ and the induced variations in B_z are assumed to be very small compared to B_0. From $\nabla \times \mathbf{B} = \mu_0 \mathbf{J}$, an order-of-magnitude study shows that B_θ is of order $\mu_0 h b \omega B_0$ and B_r of order $\mu_0 h u B_0$. Only for physically unrealizable velocities of the order 10^9 m/sec would the induced fields become comparable to B_0. Because the induced magnetic fields are small, only the terms in the equation of motion containing B_z need be considered and the equations become

$$\frac{\partial P}{\partial r} = \mu_f \frac{\partial^2 u}{\partial z^2} + J_\theta B_0$$

$$0 = \mu_f \frac{\partial^2 v}{\partial z^2} - J_r B_0 \qquad (7.12\text{-}3)$$

$$\frac{\partial P}{\partial z} = 0$$

where the z variation in pressure is negligible.

From $\nabla \times \mathbf{E} = 0$ and the assumption of cylindrical symmetry it follows that

$$\frac{\partial E_\theta}{\partial z} = 0 \qquad \frac{1}{r} \frac{\partial}{\partial r} (r E_\theta) = 0 \tag{7.12-4}$$

Hence E_θ must be of the form $1/r$; but, since E_θ is zero at the inner and outer electrodes, E_θ must be zero everywhere. Substituting for J_θ from Ohm's law into the r part of Equation (7.12-3) results in the following differential equation for the radial velocity u:

$$\frac{\partial^2 u}{\partial z^2} - \frac{\sigma B_0^2}{\mu_f} u = \frac{1}{\mu_f} \frac{\partial P}{\partial r} \tag{7.12-5}$$

where $\partial P/\partial r$ is a function of r only. Using the boundary conditions that $u = 0$ at $z = \pm h$, we have as the solution to Equation (7.12-5)

$$u = \frac{h^2}{M^2 \mu_f} \frac{\partial P}{\partial r} \left(\frac{\text{ch}\,(Mz/h)}{\text{ch}\,M} - 1 \right) \tag{7.12-6}$$

where M is the Hartmann number $(\sigma h^2 B_0^2/\mu_f)^{1/2}$. ($\mu_f$ here is fluid viscosity.)

From the continuity equation (7.12-2), the flow rate is

$$Q = \frac{4\pi r h^3}{\mu_f M^3} \frac{\partial P}{\partial r} (\text{th}\,M - M) \tag{7.12-7}$$

Then, by the condition that $P = P_e$ at $r = b$ and $P = P_0$ at $r = a$, integration of equation (7.12-7) over r gives the flow rate

$$Q = \frac{4\pi h^3 (P_0 - P_e)}{\mu_f \ln (b/a)} \left(\frac{M - \text{th}\,M}{M^3} \right) = 3 Q_0 \left(\frac{M - \text{th}\,M}{M^3} \right) \tag{7.12-8}$$

where Q_0 is the flow rate for zero Hartmann number (no applied field) and the pressure distribution is

$$P_0 - P = \frac{(P_0 - P_e) \ln (r/a)}{\ln (b/a)} \tag{7.12-9}$$

The radial velocity u is then determined from (7.12-6) and (7.12-9) as

$$u = \frac{h^2 (P_0 - P_e)}{\mu_f M^2 \ln (b/a)} \frac{1}{r} \left[1 - \frac{\text{ch}\,(Mz/h)}{\text{ch}\,M} \right] \tag{7.12-10}$$

For a fixed $(P_0 - P_e)$, the pressure distribution given by (7.12-9) is the same as that obtained when no fields are present, and it is evident that only the flow rate and radial velocity profile are affected by the application of an axial magnetic field. In the recess region, u can be neglected and the recess is essentially at a constant pressure P_0 which is the pump supply pressure. The fluid flow rate is decreased by the application of the magnetic field, implying that in order to maintain a given pressure P_0 or a given

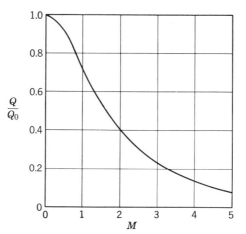

Figure 7.12-2 Plot of the normalized flow rate versus Hartmann number M for the axial field bearing, the load W (and pressure difference $P_0 - P_e$) being held constant.

pressure load on the rotor, less pump work is necessary. The normalized flow rate as a function of the Hartmann number M, for a fixed pressure difference $(P_0 - P_e)$, is shown in Fig. 7.12-2. Conversely, if the flow rate is held constant, the recess pressure and the load increase with increasing M, as shown in Fig. 7.12-3. The relations for u, P, and Q are independent of the external electrical characteristics.

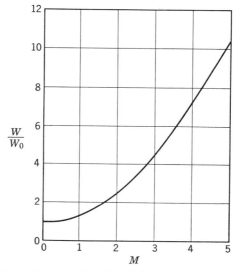

Figure 7.12-3 Plot of the normalized load W/W_0 as a function of the Hartmann number M for the axial field bearing, the flow rate Q being held constant.

The total pressure load W of the bearing can be expressed as

$$W = \int_a^b 2(P - P_e)\pi r\, dr + \pi a^2(P_0 - P_e) \qquad (7.12\text{-}11)$$

Substituting for P and integrating gives

$$W = \frac{\pi(b^2 - a^2)(P_0 - P_e)}{2 \ln (b/a)} = \frac{Q(b^2 - a^2)\mu M^3}{8h^3(M - \text{th } M)} = \frac{W_0}{3}\frac{M^3}{(M - \text{th } M)}$$
$$(7.12\text{-}12)$$

where W_0 is defined by the above equation.

The tangential velocity v can now be found. From the equation $\nabla \times \mathbf{E} = 0$ the potential between the electrodes may be defined as

$$V_T = -\int_a^b E_r\, dr \qquad (7.12\text{-}13)$$

where V_T is the terminal voltage, a constant. Then, because J_z is of order $\sigma v B_r$ or $\sigma u B_\theta$, it is negligible compared to J_r which is of order $\sigma v B_0$. From the equations $\nabla \times \mathbf{E} = 0$ and $\nabla \cdot \mathbf{J} = 0$, we find that

$$\frac{1}{r}\frac{\partial}{\partial r}(rJ_r) + \frac{\partial J_z}{\partial z} = 0 \qquad \frac{\partial E_r}{\partial z} - \frac{\partial E_z}{\partial r} = 0 \qquad (7.12\text{-}14)$$

Since $h \ll b$, the first equation is not useful even though $J_z \ll J_r$. However, E_r is of order J_r/σ and E_z is of order J_z/σ, so that $E_r \gg E_z$. The maximum change in E_z over r is of order E_z and hence the maximum change in E_r over z is of order hE_z/b, which is negligible compared to E_r, and we may conclude that E_r is essentially a function of r only.

Substituting for J_r into the θ part of Equation (7.12-1), the equation for the tangential velocity becomes

$$0 = \mu_f \frac{\partial^2 v}{\partial z^2} - \sigma(E_r + vB_0)B_0 \qquad (7.12\text{-}15)$$

which can be integrated immediately (using the boundary conditions $v = 0$ at $z = -h$ and $v = r\omega$ at $z = h$, and remembering that E_r is a function of r only) to give us

$$v = \frac{E_r}{B_0}\left[\frac{\text{ch }(Mz/h)}{\text{ch } M} - 1\right] + \frac{r\omega}{2}\left[\frac{\text{ch }(Mz/h)}{\text{ch } M} + \frac{\text{sh }(Mz/h)}{\text{sh } M}\right] \qquad (7.12\text{-}16)$$

To determine $(E_r r)$, the expression for v can be combined with Ohm's law and the radial current density integrated over the surface of the cylinder whose area is $4\pi rh$. Then the total current is

$$I = \int_{-h}^{h} 2\pi r\sigma(E_r + vB_r)\,dz \qquad (7.12\text{-}17)$$

The radial electric field is, in terms of the total current,

$$E_r = \frac{IM}{4\pi\sigma h \text{ th } M} \cdot \frac{1}{r} - \tfrac{1}{2}r\omega B_0 \qquad (7.12\text{-}18)$$

Then the tangential velocity is, in terms of I,

$$v = \frac{I}{4\pi(\sigma\mu_f)^{\frac{1}{2}} \text{ th } M} \cdot \frac{1}{r}\left[\frac{\text{ch}(Mz/h)}{\text{ch } M} - 1\right] + \tfrac{1}{2}r\omega\left[\frac{\text{sh }(Mz/h)}{\text{sh } M} + 1\right] \qquad (7.12\text{-}19)$$

From Equations (7.12-13) and (7.12-18), the terminal voltage is

$$V_T = \frac{-IM}{4\pi\sigma h \text{ th } M} \ln\left(\frac{b}{a}\right) + \tfrac{1}{4}\omega B_0(b^2 - a^2) \qquad (7.12\text{-}20)$$

so that the open-circuit voltage V_{oc} is

$$V_{\text{oc}} = \tfrac{1}{4}\omega B_0(b^2 - a^2) \qquad (7.12\text{-}21)$$

and the short-circuit current I_{sc} is

$$I_{\text{sc}} = \frac{\omega B_0 \pi\sigma h(b^2 - a^2) \text{ th } M}{M \ln (b/a)} \qquad (7.12\text{-}22)$$

Then the internal resistance, which is the ratio of V_{oc} to I_{sc}, becomes

$$R_i = \frac{M \ln (b/a)}{4\pi\sigma h \text{ th } M} \qquad (7.12\text{-}23)$$

In the recess region $(a > r > 0)$ the current density is very small and the applied magnetic field is essentially zero. Therefore, the tangential component of the equation of motion in the recess is

$$\mu_f \frac{\partial^2 v}{\partial z^2} = 0 \qquad (7.12\text{-}24)$$

which has the solution (for boundary conditions $v = 0$ at $z = -L$ and $v = r\omega$ at $z = h$)

$$v = \frac{r\omega(z + h + L)}{(2h + L)} \qquad (7.12\text{-}25)$$

where L is the depth of the recess from the surface of the stator plate.

The total drag torque on the rotor can now be computed from

$$T = \int_0^b \left(\frac{\partial v}{\partial z}\right)_{z=h} 2\pi \mu_f r^2 \, dr \tag{7.12-26}$$

By using Equations (7.12-19) and (7.12-25), we can express the drag torque T as

$$T = \frac{\mu_f \omega \pi a^4}{2(2h + L)} + \frac{IM(b^2 - a^2)}{4h}\left(\frac{\mu_f}{\sigma}\right)^{\frac{1}{2}} + \frac{\mu_f M \omega \pi}{4h}(b^4 - a^4)\,\text{cth}\,M \tag{7.12-27}$$

where the first term represents the torque in the region of the recess. From Equation (7.12-27) it can be seen that in order to make the drag go to zero, the current I must be negative. This is confirmed by simple energy considerations because, when I is negative, power is supplied to the bearing from an external source. Part of this power is dissipated in the fluid as Joule heat and part of the power provides the pumping action on the fluid. The value of I' for zero torque ($T = 0$) is

$$I' = \frac{-\pi\omega(\sigma\mu_f)^{\frac{1}{2}}[2ha^4 + (2h + L)M(b^4 - a^4)\,\text{cth}\,M]}{(2h + L)(b^2 - a^2)M} \tag{7.12-28}$$

If $b \gg a$, this current can be approximated by

$$I' = -\pi\omega(\sigma\mu_f)^{\frac{1}{2}}b^2\,\text{cth}\,M \tag{7.12-29}$$

and for large values of the Hartmann number, the current approaches the value $-\pi\omega b^2(\sigma\mu_f)^{\frac{1}{2}}$.

The radial current density in the fluid can now be found from Ohm's law and Equation (7.12-19). These give us

$$J_r = \frac{IM}{4\pi h}\frac{1}{r}\frac{\text{ch}\,(Mz/h)}{\text{sh}\,M} + \frac{(\sigma\mu_f)^{\frac{1}{2}}Mr\omega}{2h}\frac{\text{sh}\,(Mz/h)}{\text{sh}\,M} \tag{7.12-30}$$

Then, from $\nabla \cdot \mathbf{J} = 0$, the axial current density J_z is

$$J_z = \omega(\sigma\mu_f)^{\frac{1}{2}}\left[\text{cth}\,M - \frac{\text{ch}\,(Mz/h)}{\text{sh}\,M}\right] \tag{7.12-31}$$

Since E_θ is zero, J_θ is simply $-\sigma u B_0$, which, like J_z, is independent of the terminal (electrical) characteristics of the bearing. J_z and J_θ go to zero at the surface of the rotor and stator plates so that circulating currents are set up within the fluid. The above functions for the current densities completely determine these circulating currents.

The viscous frictional drag torque on the rotor can be made zero by supplying electrical power from an external source so that the fluid is pumped along with the rotor. The current required to maintain zero drag is a linear function of the rotor angular velocity. If the power input is increased above that required to maintain zero drag, the device acts as a motor and energy is supplied to the rotor. When an electrical load is connected to the electrodes energy can be removed and the bearing acts as a generator. For open-circuit conditions ($I = 0$), the drag on the rotor is greater than the corresponding drag for the non-MHD bearing (for a given pressure load), because the Joule heating losses must be supplied by the mechanical power through the rotor. The efficiency of the device in any particular mode of operation can be found by considering the two dissipation effects, Joule heating and viscous shear.

7.13 AN ELECTRICALLY CONTROLLED MHD VISCOUS COUPLER

Electrical control of torque-speed characteristics can be made a feature of a viscous coupler when it consists of a conducting, incompressible, fluid film between two closely spaced, rotating, insulated plates placed in an axial magnetic field. An analysis of the two-dimensional magnetohydrodynamic flow in the film shows that the torque-speed relationship for each plate is a function of the Hartmann number M (proportional to the magnetic field) and the current density in the film. If a voltage is applied between concentric electrodes located in the film, the torque-speed relationships are functions of the applied voltage and the applied magnetic field. For large Hartmann numbers (M greater than 1) the output plate torque is linearly related to M. The overall efficiency of this coupler is, at best, slightly greater than that of the ordinary viscous coupler.

The viscous coupler geometry illustrated by Fig. 7.13-1 consists of two parallel nonmagnetic insulated plates, one of which is connected to what will be considered the input shaft rotating at an angular speed ω_1; the other is connected to an output shaft rotating at an angular speed ω_0. These shaft speeds are measured relative to the stationary outer electrode at radius $r = b$. The inner electrode at $r = a$ rotates with the input plate and is connected to the external circuitry through a slip ring. Both electrodes are assumed to be ideal conductors. The applied magnetic field B_0 is in the axial direction and is uniform over the area of the plates.

The tangential velocity is evaluated by integrating Equation (7.12-1) with the boundary conditions

$$v = r\omega_i \qquad z = h$$
$$v = r\omega_0 \qquad z = -h$$

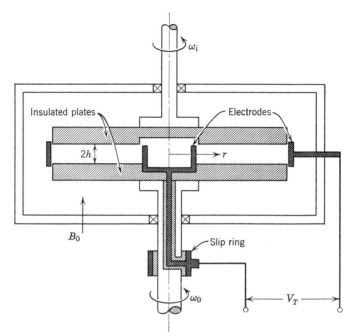

Figure 7.13-1   The magnetohydrodynamic viscous coupler.

where ω_i and ω_0 are, respectively, the angular velocities of the input and output shafts and where $2h$ is the film thickness. The result of this integration is

$$v = \frac{E_r}{B_0}\left[\frac{\operatorname{ch}(Mz/h)}{\operatorname{ch} M} - 1\right] + \frac{r(\omega_i + \omega_0)}{2\operatorname{ch} M}\operatorname{ch}(Mz/h)$$
$$+ \frac{r(\omega_i + \omega_0)}{2\operatorname{sh} M}\cdot\operatorname{sh}(Mz/h)\quad(7.13\text{-}1)$$

The total current I is

$$I = \int_{-h}^{h} 2\pi r J_r\, dz \qquad (7.13\text{-}2)$$

and substituting for J_r from Ohm's law,

$$I = 2\pi r \sigma B_0 \int_{-h}^{h}\left(\frac{E_r}{B_0} + v\right) dz \qquad (7.13\text{-}3)$$

Substituting Equation (7.13-1) for v into Equation (7.13-3) and integrating gives us

$$\frac{E_r}{B_0} = \frac{I}{4\pi(\sigma\mu_f)^{1/2}\operatorname{th} M}\left(\frac{1}{r}\right) - \frac{r(\omega_i + \omega_0)}{2} \qquad (7.13\text{-}4)$$

The tangential velocity v can be evaluated explicitly in terms of I by substituting Equation (7.13-4) into Equation (7.13-1), thus giving

$$v = \frac{I}{4\pi(\sigma\mu_f)^{\frac{1}{2}} \, \text{th} \, M} \left(\frac{1}{r} \frac{\text{ch} \, (Mz/h)}{\text{ch} \, M} - 1 \right) + \frac{r(\omega_i + \omega_0)}{2} \left[1 + \frac{\text{sh} \, (Mz/h)}{\text{sh} \, M} \right]$$

(7.13-5)

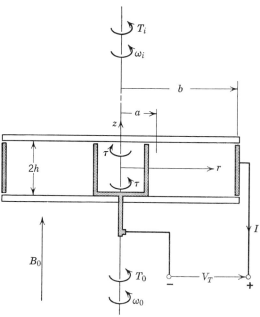

Figure 7.13-2 Diagram of shear sign conventions used to calculate torques in the magnetohydrodynamic viscous coupler.

The plate torques, which are due to viscous shear, can be calculated from the velocity gradient between the plates by assuming that the drag over the other areas of the plates and the electrodes is negligible.

The sign convention used for each plate is: angular velocity and external torque exerted on each plate are positive when their vectors are in the positively defined direction of the applied B field. Hence, when the angular velocity of a plate is positive, a positive torque means that power is going into the plate.

In accord with these definitions, which are illustrated in Fig. (7.13-2) the tangential shears on the plates are

$$\tau = \mu_f \frac{\partial v}{\partial z} \Big|_{z=\pm h}$$

(7.13-6)

and the input plate torque T_i and the output plate torque T_0 are, respectively,

$$T_i = 2\pi \int_a^b \tau r^2 \, dr = 2\pi\mu_f \int_a^b \frac{\partial v}{\partial z}\bigg|_{+h} r^2 \, dr \qquad (7.13\text{-}7)$$

and

$$T_0 = -2\pi\mu_f \int_a^b \frac{\partial v}{\partial z}\bigg|_{-h} r^2 \, dr \qquad (7.13\text{-}8)$$

From Equation (7.13-5) the normal gradient of the tangential velocity at the plates is

$$\frac{\partial v}{\partial z}\bigg|_{\pm h} = \pm \frac{IM}{4\pi(\sigma\mu_f)^{1/2}}\left(\frac{1}{r}\right) + \frac{r(\omega_i - \omega_v)}{2h} M \operatorname{cth} M \qquad (7.13\text{-}9)$$

which when substituted into Equations (7.13-7) and (7.13-8) gives for the torques

$$T_{i,0} = \frac{M(\mu_f/\sigma)^{1/2}}{4h}(b^2 - a^2)I \pm \frac{\pi\mu_f(b^4 - a^4)M \operatorname{cth} M}{4h}(\omega_i - \omega_0) \quad (7.13\text{-}10)$$

where the plus sign refers to T_i and the minus sign to T_0.

We complete our own description of this device by determining the terminal voltage from Equations (7.12-13) and (7.13-4):

$$V_T = -\left[\frac{M \operatorname{cth} M}{4\pi\sigma h} \ln (b/a)\right]I + \frac{M(\mu_f/\sigma)^{1/2}}{4h}(b^2 - a^2)(\omega_i + \omega_0) \quad (7.13\text{-}11)$$

The quantity multiplying the total current I is an apparent internal resistance, defined as the ratio of open-circuit voltage to short-circuit current.

For further analysis the terms of Equations (7.13-10) and (7.13-11) will be grouped into the following parameters: The zero Hartmann number drag coefficient D_0 is

$$D_0 = \frac{\pi\mu_f(b^4 - a^4)}{4h} \qquad (7.13\text{-}12)$$

and the zero Hartmann number internal resistance R_0 is

$$R_0 = \frac{\ln (b/a)}{4\pi\sigma h} \qquad (7.13\text{-}13)$$

A factor which is physically equivalent to the emf constant of a motor or generator can be defined as

$$K = \frac{(\mu_f/\sigma)^{1/2}}{4h}(b^2 - a^2) \qquad (7.13\text{-}14)$$

In terms of the above quantities Equations (7.13-10) and (7.13-11) become

$$T_{i,0} = \pm(M \operatorname{cth} M)D_0(\omega_i - \omega_0) + MKI \qquad (7.13\text{-}15)$$

and

$$V_T = KM(\omega_i + \omega_0) - (M \operatorname{cth} M)R_0I \qquad (7.13\text{-}16)$$

Equations (7.13-15) and (7.13-16) show that the torque and terminal voltage depend linearly on the Hartmann number for large values of M. The open-circuit torque is proportional to the slip ($\omega_i - \omega_0$) but it is multipled by ($M \operatorname{cth} M$), which means that torque control can be obtained on open circuit by varying the magnetic field, since M is proportional to B_0. A more versatile type of control is available by using an external voltage source to vary the current I, thereby controlling the torque and speed of the output shaft.

The prospect of linear control of the output torque as a function of the terminal voltage should make this type of clutch or coupler useful in servomechanism applications. However, the MHD viscous coupler has the same disadvantage as the ordinary viscous coupler, that is, relatively low efficiencies at normal operating speeds. When efficiency is not of primary importance, however, the control features of the device make its use practicable.

7.14   THE MAGNETOHYDRODYNAMIC INCLINED SLIDER BEARING WITH A TRANSVERSE MAGNETIC FIELD

The magnetohydrodynamic inclined slider bearing is analyzed under general loading conditions. In Fig. 7.14-1 the magnetic field is applied

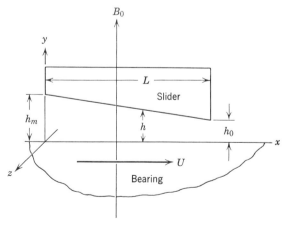

Figure 7.14-1   The inclined magnetohydrodynamic slider bearing with a transverse magnetic field.

normal to the bearing surface, and the external electrical circuit is assumed to be fixed in either the slider or bearing; the two situations are related by Lorentz transformations. It is found that significant load increases can be effected by supplying external power, and if the Hartmann number is large enough, open-circuit conditions can give rise to greatly increased load capacities. Analytical solutions are presented for large and very small values of Hartmann number.

The bearing and slider are assumed to be insulators and electrodes are assumed to be fastened to the slider forming lips or seals in the xy plane that prevent flow in the z direction. These electrodes are assumed to be perfect conductors, and a potential can be supplied to the electrodes, or power drawn off, by connecting a load resistor across them; the fluid can then act as a generator, or be pumped according to the arrangement of the external circuit. It is assumed throughout that the external electrical circuit (generator or resistor) is attached to the slider and moves with it. The slider is then the rest frame and all quantities are measured with respect to it. Later we will discuss how to transform all quantities to the frame of the bearing if the electrical circuitry is attached to that frame through sliding contacts on the electrodes attached to the slider.

If we assume that the electrodes are very good conductors compared to the fluid, it follows immediately, from the Maxwell equation $\nabla \times \mathbf{E} = 0$ and from the assumption of no variation in the z direction (infinite slider), that E_z is a constant (to be determined later). Since the electric field is irrotational, a terminal potential or voltage may be defined as

$$V_T = - \int_0^{z_0} E_z \, dz \tag{7.14-1}$$

where z_0 is the width of the slider in the z direction (normal to the direction of flow). Mathematically the slider is assumed to be infinite in the z direction, but this assumption is merely a statement that all variations in the z direction are neglected.

There will be a small (compared to B_0) magnetic field induced in the x direction; this induced field does not couple into the equation of motion in the z direction but it does produce a slight "pinch" pressure gradient across the channel. This is, however, a negligible effect. The $J_y B_z$ term is dropped from the x equation of motion and B_y is assumed constant at the value B_0, which is consistent with the assumption of negligible induced effects.

The equation of motion can then be written as

$$0 = - \frac{\partial P}{\partial x} + \mu_f \frac{\partial^2 u}{\partial y^2} - \sigma(E_z + u B_0) B_0 \tag{7.14-2}$$

Using the boundary conditions $u = U$ at $y = 0$ and $u = 0$ at $y = h(x)$, we can integrate Equation (7.14-2):

$$u = \left(U + \frac{1}{\sigma B_0^2} \frac{\partial P}{\partial x} + \frac{E_z}{B_0} \right) \left[\text{ch} \left(\frac{My}{h_0} \right) - \text{sh} \left(\frac{My}{h_0} \right) \cdot \text{cth} \left(\frac{h}{h_0} \right) \right]$$

$$+ \left(\frac{1}{\sigma B_0^2} \frac{\partial P}{\partial x} + \frac{E_z}{B_0} \right) \left[\frac{\text{sh} (My/h_0)}{\text{sh} (Mh/h_0)} - 1 \right] \quad (7.14\text{-}3)$$

where M is the Hartmann number defined as

$$M^2 = \frac{B_0^2 h_0^2 \sigma}{\mu_f}$$

Using the continuity equation, we can write the flow rate (per unit z) as

$$Q = \int_0^h u \, dy = \left(\frac{1}{\sigma B_0^2} \frac{\partial P}{\partial x} + \frac{E_z}{B_0} \right) \left[\frac{2 \, \text{ch} \, (Mh/h_0) - 2}{\text{sh} \, (Mh/h_0)} - \frac{hM}{h_0} \right] \cdot \frac{h_0}{M}$$

$$+ \frac{Uh_0}{M} \left[\frac{\text{ch} \, (Mh/h_0) - 1}{\text{sh} \, (Mh/h_0)} \right] \quad (7.14\text{-}4)$$

This equation can be used to solve for $P(x)$ if we just use the boundary conditions $P = 0$ at $x = 0, L$ to find Q and the constant of integration. It is convenient at this time to introduce the following dimensionless variables:

$$P^* = \frac{Ph_0}{L\mu_f U}$$

$$Q^* = \frac{Q}{Uh_0}$$

$$E_z^* = \frac{E_z h_0 \sqrt{\sigma/\mu_f}}{U}$$

$$x^* = \frac{x}{L}$$

$$y^* = \frac{y}{h_0}$$

$$z^* = \frac{z}{z_0}$$

$$h^* = \frac{h(x)}{h_0} = r - x^*(r - 1)$$

$$r = \frac{h_m}{h_0}$$

Equation (7.14-4) then takes the form

$$\frac{dP^*}{dx^*} = \frac{M^2\left[Q^* - \frac{1}{M}\left(\frac{\text{ch } Mh^* - 1}{\text{sh } Mh^*}\right)\right]}{\left[\frac{2}{M}\left(\frac{\text{ch } Mh^* - 1}{\text{sh } Mh^*}\right) - h^*\right]} - E_z^*M \qquad (7.14\text{-}5)$$

with the boundary conditions $P^* = 0$ at $x^* = 0, 1$. Equation (7.14-5) has general validity and is good for any variation $h(x)$, including journal bearings. The corresponding form of Reynolds' equation, obtained by differentiating (7.14-5), becomes

$$\frac{d}{dx^*}\left\{\frac{dP^*}{dx^*}\left[\frac{2}{M}\left(\frac{\text{ch } Mh^* - 1}{\text{sh } Mh^*}\right) - h^*\right]\right.$$
$$\left. + M\left(\frac{\text{ch } Mh^* - 1}{\text{sh } Mh^*}\right) + E_z^*M\right\} = 0 \qquad (7.14\text{-}6)$$

In general Equation (7.14-5) cannot be integrated analytically and an approximate solution will be constructed for large and small values of the Hartmann number M: The corresponding Reynolds' equations are

$$M \gg 1 \qquad \frac{d}{dx^*}\left[\frac{dP^*}{dx^*}\left(\frac{2}{M^2} - \frac{h^*}{M}\right) + \frac{E_z^*}{M} + 1\right] = 0 \qquad (7.14\text{-}7)$$

$$M \ll 1 \qquad \frac{d}{dx^*}\left[\frac{dP^*/dx^* - 6/h^{*2} - M^2/2 + E_z^*M}{12/h^{*3} + 2M^2/h^*}\right] = 0 \qquad (7.14\text{-}8)$$

Solution for Large Hartmann Number

For large Hartmann numbers Equation (7.14-5) takes the approximate form

$$\frac{dP^*}{dx^*} = \frac{M^2(Q^*M - 1)}{(2 - Mh^*)} - E_z^*M \qquad (7.14\text{-}9)$$

Actually this form is good for many cases of practical interest because, to engineering accuracy, M may still be as low as four or five. By integrating Equation (7.14-9), we find the flow rate:

$$Q^* = \frac{E_z^*(r - 1)}{M \ln\left[(M - 2)/(Mr - 2)\right]} + \frac{1}{M} \qquad (7.14\text{-}10)$$

and the pressure distribution is found to be

$$P^* = ME_z^*\left\{\frac{\ln\left[\dfrac{2 - Mr + Mx^*(r - 1)}{2 - Mr}\right]}{\ln\left[(M - 2)/(Mr - 2)\right]} - x^*\right\} \qquad (7.14\text{-}11)$$

Now the total current I may be found and related to the terminal potential V_T or E_z^*.

$$I = \int J_z \, dx \, dy = \int \sigma E_z \, dx \, dy + \sigma B_0 LQ \qquad (7.14\text{-}12)$$

Here the integration is over the area of the cross section of flow in the xy plane. By defining a dimensionless current and by integrating, we have:

$$I^* = \frac{I}{LU\sqrt{\mu_f \sigma}} = -V_T^* \left[\frac{r+1}{2} + \frac{r-1}{\ln \left[(M-2)/(Mr-2) \right]} \right] + 1$$

$$(7.14\text{-}13)$$

where the dimensionless terminal potential has been introduced as

$$V_T^* = -\int_0^1 E_z^* \, dz^* = V_T \frac{h_0}{z_0 U} \sqrt{\frac{\sigma}{\mu_f}} = -E_z^* \qquad (7.14\text{-}14)$$

The short-circuit current I_{sc}^* can be found from Equation (7.14-13) by setting the potential equal to zero:

$$I_{sc}^* = 1 \qquad (7.14\text{-}15)$$

And the open-circuit potential or voltage can be found by setting I^* to zero so that:

$$V_{oc}^* = -E_{zoc}^* = \frac{2 \ln \left[(M-2)/(Mr-2) \right]}{(r+1) \ln \left[(M-2)/(Mr-2) \right] + 2(r-1)} \qquad (7.14\text{-}16)$$

The internal resistance R_i can now be defined as $R_i = V_{oc}/I_{sc}$. A dimensionless resistance R_i^* can be defined as

$$R_i^* = R_i \frac{Lh_0 \sigma}{z_0} = \frac{V_{oc}^*}{I_{sc}^*} = V_{oc}^* \qquad (7.14\text{-}17)$$

By Thevenin's theorem an equivalent electric circuit can be constructed for the bearing system for the purpose of external circuit analysis. (This circuit is shown in Fig. 7.14-2.)

The total load-carrying capacity of the slider can now be found by integrating the pressure over the slider. A dimensionless load is introduced and the pressure integrated to give

$$W^* = \frac{W h_0^2}{L^2 \mu_f U} = \int_0^1 P^* \, dx^*$$

$$= M V_T^* \left\{ \frac{1}{2} + \frac{M-2}{M(r-1)} + \frac{1}{\ln \left[(M-2)/(Mr-2) \right]} \right\} \qquad (7.14\text{-}18)$$

In terms of I^* Equation (7.14-18) becomes

$$W^* = \frac{2(1 - I^*)M \ln [(M - 2)/(Mr - 2)]}{(r + 1) \ln [(M - 2)/(Mr - 2)] + 2(r - 1)}$$

$$\times \left\{\frac{1}{2} + \frac{M - 2}{M(r - 1)} + \frac{1}{\ln [(M - 2)/(Mr - 2)]}\right\} \quad (7.14\text{-}19)$$

Equation (7.14-19) thus gives us the load as a function of the Hartmann number for various values of current. Under open-circuit conditions I^* is zero and Equation (7.14-19), with I^* set to zero, gives the open-circuit performance of the bearing. (This is equivalent of course to putting V_{oc} from Equation 7.14-16 into Equation 7.14-18.)

It can be seen from Equation (7.14-18) that for a given M the load capacity is directly proportional to the terminal potential V_T^*. A positive terminal voltage is one with the positive terminal located at $z = z_0$. The current due to such an external voltage will flow in the negative z direction (from $z = z_0$ to $z = 0$). If the external voltage is positive and greater than the open-circuit value, net total current will flow

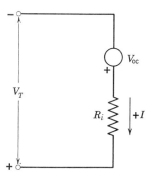

Figure 7.14-2 Equivalent electric circuit of the MHD bearing.

in the negative z direction and increase the pressurization or load. If the external terminal voltage is less than the open-circuit value, but still positive, there will still be a load that decreases in proportion to the voltage. The current will then have a net total value in the negative z direction. As the voltage goes to zero (short-circuit conditions), the load capacity goes to zero. It should be understood that if the terminal voltage is less than the open-circuit value, but positive, this condition corresponds to a resistive load being applied externally across the electrodes. If any value of potential is applied such that the terminal potential becomes negative, net current will be positive and the load capacity becomes negative, indicating cavitation. This condition requires, of course, an external potential larger than the open-circuit potential. We should also note that, although the net total current may be zero, there are circulation currents which do in fact give rise to a net force in the fluid. These circulating currents, which exist generally and under open-circuit conditions, have as their return paths the electrodes.

Figure (7.14-3) shows a plot of W^*/V_T^* versus M for various values of r. Although this curve is a complete description of the bearing performance,

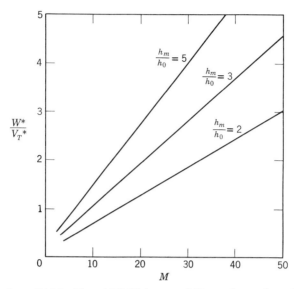

Figure 7.14-3   Plot of W^*/V_T^* versus M for various values of h_m/h_0.

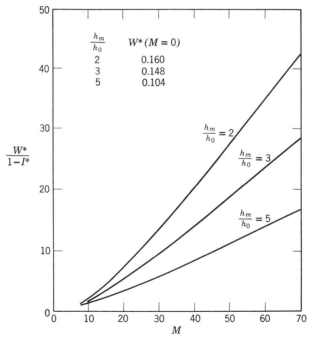

Figure 7.14-4   Plot of $W^*/(1 - I^*)$ versus M for various values of h_m/h_0.

another interesting curve is a plot of $W^*/(1 - I^*)$ for various values of r, Fig. (7.14-4). In this latter curve, if I^* is set to zero the results are for open circuit. Hence, Fig. (7.14-4) can be thought of as a plot of W^* under open-circuit conditions versus M. For large Hartmann numbers significant increases in load can be achieved even under open-circuited conditions. This is in contrast to the tangential-field case where no pressurization can be effected under open-circuit conditions.

Solution for Small Values of Hartmann Number

For M much less than unity the hyperbolic functions can be expanded in powers of M. Retention of M^2 terms leads to the following form of Equation (7.14-5):

$$\frac{dP^*}{dx^*} = -\frac{12Q^*}{h^{*3}} + \frac{6}{h^{*2}} - \frac{2Q^*M^2}{h^*} + \frac{M^2}{2} - E_z^*M \qquad (7.14\text{-}20)$$

Integration, using the proper boundary conditions, yields

$$Q^* = \frac{r(r-1)(12 - rM^2 + 2rE_z^*M)}{4r^2M^2 \ln r + 12(r^2 - 1)} \qquad (7.14\text{-}21)$$

and P^* in terms of h^* is

$$P^* = \frac{r(r-1)(12 - rM - 2rV_T^*M)}{4r^2M \ln r + 12(r^2 - 1)}\left(\frac{2M^2}{(r-1)} \ln \frac{h^*}{r} - \frac{6(r^2 - h^{*2})}{(r-1)r^2h^{*2}}\right)$$

$$+ \frac{6(r - h^*)}{(r-1)rh^*} - \left(\frac{M^2}{2} + V_T^*M\right)\left(\frac{h^* - r}{r - 1}\right) \qquad (7.14\text{-}22)$$

The load W^* becomes

$$W^* = \frac{r(r-1)(12 - rM^2 - 2rV_T^*M)}{4r^2M^2 \ln r + 12(r^2 - 1)}\left[\frac{2M^2}{(r-1)^2} \ln r - \frac{2M^2}{(r-1)} - \frac{6}{r^2}\right]$$

$$+ \frac{6 \ln r}{(r-1)^2} - \frac{6}{r(r-1)} + \frac{M^2}{4} + \frac{V_T^*M}{2} \qquad (7.14\text{-}23)$$

The electrical characteristics can be found in much the same way as those for large values of M. The current is

$$I^* = -V_T\left[\frac{r+1}{2} + \frac{M^2r^2(r-1)}{2r^2M^2 \ln r + 6(r^2 - 1)}\right]$$

$$+ \frac{Mr(r-1)(12 - rM^2)}{4r^2M^2 \ln r + 12(r^2 - 1)} \qquad (7.14\text{-}24)$$

The short-circuit current is then determined as

$$I_{sc}* = \frac{Mr(r-1)(12 - rM^2)}{4r^2M^2 \ln r + 12(r^2 - 1)} \tag{7.14-25}$$

and the open-circuit voltage as

$$V_{oc}* = \frac{Mr(r-1)(12 - rM^2)}{(r+1)[2r^2M^2 \ln r + 6(r^2 - 1)] + 2M^2r^2(r-1)} \tag{7.14-26}$$

The internal resistance is

$$R_i* = \frac{2r^2M^2 \ln r + 6(r^2 - 1)}{(r+1)[r^2M^2 \ln r + 3(r^2 - 1) + M^2r^2(r-1)]} \tag{7.14-27}$$

From Equation (7.14-23) we see that the load is no longer simply proportional to the potential for small values of M, but is a rather complex function of M and V_T*. Under open-circuit conditions little increase in load capacity occurs for such low values of M. External power must be supplied in order to effect significant rises.

Discussion and Conclusions

It is important to remember that all field quantities discussed here have been referred to the slider as a reference frame and the external potential has been assumed to be measured with respect to the slider. In practice it would be more realistic to assume that the generator, or load resistor, is fixed to the bearing and not the slider. In that case the generator or load resistor must be connected to the electrodes through contactors sliding along the electrodes affixed to the bearing slider. Alternatively, the electrodes could be affixed to the bearing surface, forming a trough through which the slider moves. In either case the analysis and conclusions are exactly the same. The only point of concern is the frame to which the power supply or resistor is attached. Under open circuit conditions the terminal voltage has one value when measured by an observer moving with the slider and another when measured by an observer moving with the bearing. If the performance characteristics are given by the condition of zero net current (for open circuit), the question of terminal potential need never arise and the problem of reference frames can be avoided. If an external potential is applied or load resistor attached to the electrodes, however, the frame of reference must be considered.

The analysis of this section is valid regardless of the frame of the external load circuit. For a given necessary potential and current in the slider frame, as indicated by the preceding analysis, the required potential in the bearing frame can be obtained as follows.

The electric fields are related by the Lorentz transformation

$$E'_z = E_z + UB. \tag{7.14-28}$$

where E'_z is the field as measured in the bearing frame. Hence it follows that

$$V'_T = V_T - UB_0 z_0 \tag{7.14-29}$$

or, in dimensionless quantities,

$$V_T^{*'} = V_T^* - M \tag{7.14-30}$$

It is interesting to note than in the slider frame W^* is directly proportional to V_T^* (for large M) and increases with M for a fixed value of V_T^*. However, for a fixed value of potential in the bearing frame $V_T^{*'}$ the load W^* increases much less rapidly with M, since $W^*/V_T^* = W^*/V_T^{*'} + M$.

7.15   THE MAGNETOHYDRODYNAMIC INCLINED SLIDER BEARING WITH A TANGENTIAL MAGNETIC FIELD

The next example which will be considered is the infinite inclined slider bearing with an externally applied uniform magnetic field that is parallel to the bearing surfaces and perpendicular to the direction of motion. The electrodes are the slider and bearing surfaces as shown in Fig. 7.15-1. This electrode geometry permits a current to flow in the y direction between the

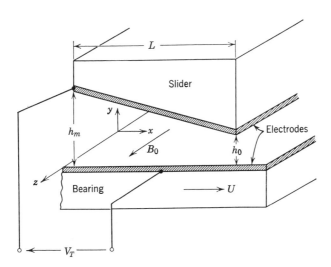

Figure 7.15-1   The inclined magnetohydrodynamic slider bearing with a tangential magnetic field.

slider and bearing. It is the interaction between this current and the applied magnetic field which gives rise to a body force in the x direction that can modify the pressure distribution in the lubricant film.

The usual lubrication assumptions are made for the incompressible flow of the lubricant: inertia is neglected, the viscosity is assumed constant, and the thickness of the film is a slowly varying function of x. It is also assumed that the current density has only a y component J_y and that induced magnetic fields (due to currents in the fluid) can be neglected since they will be several orders of magnitude smaller than the applied magnetic field. Then, from Maxwell's equations $\nabla \times \mathbf{E} = 0$ and $\nabla \cdot \mathbf{J} = 0$ and from Ohm's law it can be concluded that

$$\frac{\partial J_y}{\partial y} = 0 \qquad \frac{\partial E_y}{\partial x} = 0 \tag{7.15-1}$$

which indicates that J_y is only a function of x and that E_y is only a function of y.

The x component of the equation of motion can now be written as

$$0 = -\frac{\partial P}{\partial x} + \mu_f \frac{\partial^2 u}{\partial y^2} + J_y B_z \tag{7.15-2}$$

which can be integrated immediately for velocity since both $\partial P/\partial x$ and J_y are only functions of x. B_z, the applied magnetic field, is a constant B_0. Integrating and using the boundary conditions that $u = U$ at $y = 0$ and $u = 0$ at $y = h$ gives us

$$u = \frac{1}{2\mu_f}\left(\frac{\partial P}{\partial x} - J_y B_0\right)(y^2 - hy) + \frac{U}{h}(h - y) \tag{7.15-3}$$

The continuity equation can be expressed as

$$Q = \int_0^h u \, dy \tag{7.15-4}$$

where Q is the flow rate per unit length. Substituting Equation (7.15-3) into (7.15-4) and integrating yields

$$Q = -\frac{h^3}{12\mu_f}\left(\frac{\partial P}{\partial x} - J_y B_0\right) - \frac{Uh}{2} \tag{7.15-5}$$

Solving this expression for $\partial P/\partial x$ and integrating over the width of the slider using the boundary condition on pressure that $P = P_e$ at $x = 0$ gives us

$$P - P_e = -12\mu_f \int_0^x \left(\frac{Q}{h^3} - \frac{U}{2h^2}\right) dx + B_0 \int_0^x J_y \, dx \tag{7.15-6}$$

The film thickness h is a function of x defined by

$$h = h_m - kx \tag{7.15-7}$$

where $k = (h_m - h_0)/L$ and h_m and h_0 are the film thicknesses at $x = 0$ and $x = L$, respectively. The explicit form of J_y is not yet known and remains to be determined.

From Ohm's law the current density J_y can be expressed in terms of the electric field E_y and the velocity u. Now, because the electric field is irrotational ($\nabla \times \mathbf{E} = 0$), an electric potential difference between the slider and bearing electrodes can be defined as

$$-V_T = \int_0^h E_y \, dy \tag{7.15-8}$$

where the potential at $y = 0$ is taken to be zero. Then integrating the current density $J_y = \sigma(E_y - uB_0)$ over y, we have

$$J_y h = \sigma \int_0^h E_y \, dy - \sigma B_0 \int_0^h u \, dy \tag{7.15-9}$$

and from Equations (7.15-4) and (7.15-8) the current density becomes

$$J_y = -\frac{\sigma}{h}(B_0 Q + V_T) \tag{7.15-10}$$

To evaluate Q the additional boundary condition is needed that $P = P_e$ at $x = L$; the definite integral form of Equation (7.15-6) is

$$0 = -12\mu_f \int_0^L \left(\frac{Q}{h^3} - \frac{U}{2h^2}\right) dx + B_0 \int_0^L J_y \, dx \tag{7.15-11}$$

However, the total current per unit length can be expressed as

$$I = \int_0^L J_y \, dx \tag{7.15-12}$$

which, upon substitution into Equation (7.15-11) and evaluation of the integrals, gives for the flow rate

$$Q = \frac{h_m\left(\dfrac{h_m}{h_0} - 1\right)}{\left(\dfrac{h_m}{h_0}\right)^2 - 1} \left[U + \frac{kB_0 I h_m}{6\mu_f\left(\dfrac{h_m}{h_0} - 1\right)}\right] \tag{7.15-13}$$

Next, from Equations (7.15-10) and (7.15-12), the potential V_T can be found as a function of Q and I:

$$V_T = -\left[\frac{kI}{\sigma \ln (h_m/h_0)} + B_0 Q\right] \qquad (7.15\text{-}14)$$

Substituting this expression for V_T into Equation (7.15-10), we have

$$J_y = \frac{kI}{h \ln \left(\dfrac{h_m}{h_0}\right)} \qquad (7.15\text{-}15)$$

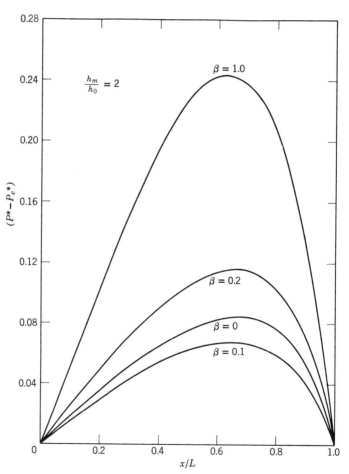

Figure 7.15-2 Plot of normalized pressure $(P - P_e)kh_m/6\mu_f U$ versus x/L for various values of β and $h_m/h_0 = 2$.

which specifies the current density J_y in terms of the total current I and also gives the functional dependence of J_y on x (since h is a function of x).

Having determined Q and J_y explicitly, we can now integrate Equation (7.15-6) and determine the pressure distribution in the fluid film. The result of this integration is:

$$P^* - P_e^* = (P - P_e)\frac{kh_m}{6\mu_f U} = \left[\left(\frac{h_m}{h} - 1\right) - \left(\frac{h_m}{h_0} - 1\right)\frac{(h_m/h)^2 - 1}{(h_m/h_0)^2 - 1}\right]$$

$$+ \beta\left[\frac{\ln(h_m/h)}{\ln(h_m/h_0)} - \frac{(h_m/h)^2 - 1}{(h_m/h_0)^2 - 1}\right] \quad (7.15\text{-}16)$$

where P^* is the normalized pressure defined by Equation (7.15-16) and β is a dimensional parameter $kh_m B_0 I/6\mu_f u$. The first term is the pressure for the non-MHD inclined slider bearing and the second term is the electromagnetic pressurization. It is important to note that pressurization is possible even if the velocity of the slider is zero. Physically this means that current from an external source is necessary if the bearing is to be electromagnetically pressurized and that the bearing acts much in the same manner as the MHD pump. The normalized pressure as a function of x/L for different values of the parameter β is shown in Fig. 7.15-2.

The load per unit length which the bearing supports is

$$W = \int_0^L (P - P_e)\,dx \quad (7.15\text{-}17)$$

and evaluation of this integral gives

$$W^* = \frac{W h_m k^2}{6\mu_f U h_0} = \left\{\frac{h_m}{h_0} \ln\left(\frac{h_m}{h_0}\right) + \left(\frac{h_m}{h_0} - 1\right) - \frac{[(h_m/h_0) - 1]^3}{(h_m/h_0)^2 - 1}\right\}$$

$$+ \beta\left\{\frac{(h_m/h_0 - 1)}{\ln(h_m/h_0)} - \frac{[(h_m/h_0) - 1]^2}{(h_m/h_0)^2 - 1} - 1\right\} \quad (7.15\text{-}18)$$

where W^* is the normalized load defined by the above equation. A plot of the normalized load versus β for various values of h_m/h_0 is shown in Fig. 7.15-3. The first term of Equation (7.15-18) is the load with no applied fields (the non-MHD case), and the second term is the electromagnetic contribution to the load capacity of the bearing. The increase in load capacity is linearly proportional to the product $B_0 I$ and, as was shown earlier, a load can be supported even if U is zero.

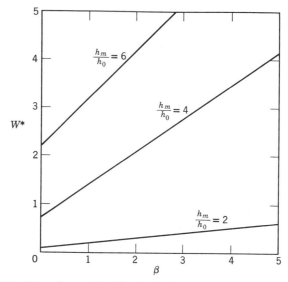

Figure 7.15-3 Plot of normalized load $Wh_mk^2/6\mu_f Uh_0$ versus β for various values of h_m/h_0.

Electrical Characteristics

Since the MHD slider bearing is an electrical device it can be described as an electrical network containing an internal resistance and voltage source as shown in Fig. 7.14-2. The voltage source arises because of the induced electric fields, which develop an electric potential between the electrodes much in the same manner as in an MHD generator. This description of the electrical characteristics of the bearing is necessary in order to determine what terminal voltage is required to maintain a given current I and hence maintain a given bearing load W.

The relationship that gives the terminal characteristics, is one between the terminal voltage V_T and the total current per unit length I. This relationship can be obtained by substituting Equation (7.15-13) for Q into Equation (7.15-14). The result is

$$V_T = -I\left(\frac{k}{\sigma \ln(h_m/h_0)} + \frac{B_0^2 h_m^2 k}{6\mu_f[(h_m/h_0)^2 - 1]}\right)$$
$$- UB_0 h_m \frac{[(h_m/h_0) - 1]}{(h_m/h_0)^2 - 1} \quad (7.15\text{-}19)$$

where the term multiplying the current is the internal resistance R_i of the bearing and where the open-circuit voltage V_{oc} is given by the second term.

It should be noted that the terminal voltage polarity is negative, which means that the electrode at $y = h$ is negative with respect to the electrode at $y = 0$. The current I is taken positive for current flow from the electrode at $y = 0$ (the bearing surface) to the electrode at $y = h$ (the slider surface) in the fluid film and this corresponds to current flow from the electrode at $y = h$ through the external circuit to the lower electrode at $y = 0$.

The preceding analysis and discussion apply when the external electrical circuit is stationary with respect to the slider and a sliding contact is made on the bearing electrode (as shown in Fig. 7.15-1). However, if the sliding contact is made at the slider electrode, and the external electrical circuit (and power supply) are stationary with respect to the bearing, the above conclusions and equations are valid except that the terminal potential is not simply as given in the previous equations. If V'_T is the terminal potential as measured in the frame of the bearing (which would then be the potential of the external power supply), then V'_T is related to V_T (which is measured in the frame of the slider) through the Lorentz transformation of the electric field

$$E_y = E'_y + UB_0 \qquad (7.15\text{-}20)$$

where E'_y is the electric field in the frame of the bearing.

Integration of Equation (7.15-20) from $y = 0$ to $y = h_s$, where h_s is the distance between the surface of the bearing and the position of the sliding contact on the slider, gives for the potential

$$V'_T = V_T - UB_0 h_s \qquad (7.15\text{-}21)$$

Equation (7.15-21) can now be combined with equation (7.15-19) to relate V'_T to the total current. This transformation of terminal potential is the only change that is necessary when the bearing acts as the stator and sliding contact is made with the slider.

As was pointed out in Section 7.11, the tangential-field bearing requires that enormous currents be supplied from an external source. Hence this type of bearing is not very practical. The problem has been presented, however, in order to illustrate the analysis of this kind of field geometry in MHD.

7.16 THE APPLICATION OF THE MHD PINCH
TO A THRUST BEARING

The calculation of a radial "pinch" forms the starting point for many problems in plasma dynamics and we will illustrate the pinch here by applying it to a specific flow geometry. From a practical standpoint the pressure generated by such a pinch is very small unless the current that interacts with its self-generated magnetic field is large. In order to get effective pinches it is often necessary to use capacitor discharges and then the pinches, because of the manner of production (and, as we shall see later, because of instabilities), are short lived. Steady-state pinches such as the one described in this section can be sustained in a stable manner, but

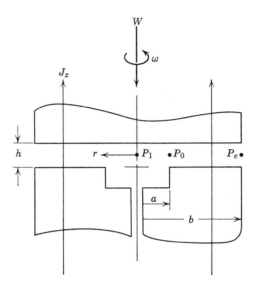

Figure 7.16-1   A pinch current flow device.

the pressures are negligible compared to those we usually associate with bearings. At any rate the following example should prove to be a useful illustration of method.

Figure 7.16-1 shows the hydrostatic thrust bearing, which may be pressurized at the center of the stator. For the purpose of analysis, it is assumed that a potential is applied between the rotor and stator and that these are both ideal conductors. Because the liquid metal lubricant is a conductor, an axial current density J_z will exist between the rotor and stator. This axial current density gives rise to a tangential magnetic field B_θ that interacts with J_z to provide a radial body force proportional to $J_z B_\theta$. This force results in a pinch effect that can increase the load capacity of the bearing.

The components of the equation of motion in cylindrical coordinates (with the usual bearing assumptions: negligible inertia, constant viscosity, and spacing h small compared to the radius b) are:

$$r: \quad 0 = -\frac{\partial P}{\partial r} + \mu_f \frac{\partial^2 u}{\partial z^2} + J_\theta B_z - J_z B_\theta$$

$$\theta: \quad 0 = \mu_f \frac{\partial^2 v}{\partial z^2} - J_r B_z + J_z B_r \qquad (7.16\text{-}1)$$

$$z: \quad 0 = -\frac{\partial P}{\partial z} + J_r B_\theta - J_\theta B_r$$

where u and v are the radial and tangential components of velocity, respectively.

The components of the current density $\mathbf{J}$ are, from Ohm's law,

$$J_r = \sigma(E_r + vB_z)$$
$$J_\theta = \sigma(E_\theta - uB_z) \qquad (7.16\text{-}2)$$
$$J_z = \sigma(E_z + uB_\theta - vB_r)$$

From Maxwell's equations it follows that $E_\theta = 0$, $E_r = 0$, and that E_z is only a function of z or a constant. In order to obtain a solution to this system of equations, we will assume that the induced fields B_z and B_r are negligible. Then it follows that $J_r = 0$, $J_\theta = 0$, and B_θ is only a function of r. We will also assume that the radial velocity u is very small so that the induced axial electric field uB_θ can be neglected. Then the axial current density J_z becomes

$$J_z = \sigma E_z \qquad (7.16\text{-}3)$$

Because $E_r = 0$ it follows from $\nabla \cdot \mathbf{J} = 0$ that $\partial J_z/\partial z = 0$ and that J_z and E_z are uniform in the fluid.

From $\nabla \times \mathbf{B} = \mu_0 \mathbf{J}$ it follows that

$$B_\theta = \frac{\mu_0 I}{2\pi b^2} \cdot r \qquad (7.16\text{-}4)$$

where I is the total current. The equations of motion are then

$$r: \quad 0 = -\frac{\partial P}{\partial r} + \mu_f \frac{\partial^2 u}{\partial z^2} - J_z B_\theta$$

$$\theta: \quad 0 = \mu_f \frac{\partial^2 v}{\partial z^2} \qquad (7.16\text{-}5)$$

$$z: \quad 0 = -\frac{\partial P}{\partial z}$$

where J_z is $I/\pi b^2$. The pressure is now only a function of r, and v is not affected by the current. The r component of Equation (7.16-5) can be integrated directly, using the boundary conditions that $u = 0$ at $z = 0, h$. This integration gives

$$u = \frac{1}{2\mu_f}\left(\frac{\partial P}{\partial r} + \alpha r\right)(z^2 - hz) \qquad (7.16\text{-}6)$$

where $\alpha = \mu_0 I^2/2\pi^2 b^4$.

From the continuity of flow rate Q there results

$$Q = \int_0^h 2\pi r u\, dz \qquad (7.16\text{-}7)$$

and integration gives

$$Q = -\frac{h^3 \pi r}{6\mu_f}\left(\frac{\partial P}{\partial r} + \alpha r\right) \qquad (7.16\text{-}8)$$

Solving for P, using the boundary conditions that $P = P_e$ at $r = b$ and $P = P_0$ at $r = a$, gives

$$P - P_e = \left(\frac{P_0 - P_e}{\ln b/a}\right)\ln\frac{b}{r} + \frac{\alpha}{2}\left[(b^2 - r^2) - \frac{b^2 - a^2}{\ln b/a}\ln\frac{b}{r}\right] \qquad (7.16\text{-}9)$$

and the rate of flow is:

$$Q = \frac{h^3 \pi}{6\mu_f \ln b/a}\left[P_0 - P_e - \frac{\alpha}{2}(b^2 - a^2)\right] \qquad (7.16\text{-}10)$$

Now the value of P_0 is undetermined and the pressure distribution in the recess ($a \geq r \geq 0$) must be found.

In the recess, u is negligible and the pressure is found from

$$\frac{\partial P}{\partial r} = -J_z B_\theta = -\alpha r \qquad (7.16\text{-}11)$$

which on integrating gives

$$P_i - P' = \frac{\alpha}{2} r^2 \qquad (a \geq r^2 \geq 0) \qquad (7.16\text{-}12)$$

where P' is the pressure in the recess and P_i is the pump pressure or pressure at $r = 0$. The value of P_0 is then found by setting $r = a$ in Equation (7.16-12) which gives

$$P_0 = P_i - \frac{\alpha}{2} a^2 \qquad (7.16\text{-}13)$$

If no external pump is provided and Q is zero, a load can still be maintained. Setting Q equal to zero in Equation (7.16-9), we have

$$P\Big|_{Q-0} - P_e = \frac{\alpha}{2}(b^2 - r^2) \qquad (7.16\text{-}14)$$

which is valid for $b \geq r \geq 0$, and the recess or step in the stator surface has no effect on the pressure distribution. The maximum pressure developed at $r = 0$ is

$$P_i\bigg|_{Q=0} - P_e = \frac{\alpha b^2}{2} = \frac{\mu_0 I^2}{4\pi^2 b^2} \qquad (7.16\text{-}15)$$

which is the normal pinch pressure.

Flow and Load Characteristics

The axial current density J_z modifies the rate of flow Q and the pressure distribution between the bearing plates. The flow rate, in terms of the pump pressure P_i and the exit pressure P_e, is found by substituting Equation (7.16-13) into Equation (7.16-10) which gives

$$Q = \frac{\pi h^3}{6\mu_f \ln b/a}\left(P_i - P_e - \frac{\alpha b^2}{2}\right) \qquad (7.16\text{-}16)$$

The pressure distribution is found to be

$$P - P_e = \left[\frac{P_i - P_e}{\ln (b/a)}\right] \ln \left(\frac{b}{r}\right) + \frac{\alpha}{2}\left[(b^2 - r^2) - \frac{b^2 \ln (b/r)}{\ln (b/a)}\right] \qquad (7.16\text{-}17)$$

which is valid for $b \geqslant r \geqslant a$. In the recess, the pressure is given by Equation (7.16-12). Evaluating $\partial P/\partial r$ from Equation (7.16-17) and substituting into Equation (7.16-6) gives for the radial velocity

$$u = \frac{1}{2\mu_f \ln (b/a)}\left[P_i - P_e - \frac{\alpha}{2} b^2\right]\left(\frac{zh - z^2}{r}\right) \qquad (7.16\text{-}18)$$

Here it should be noted that the radial profile is similar to the no-current case ($\alpha = 0$) and only the magnitude of the velocity is affected.

The load which the bearing can carry can be written in terms of the pressure as

$$W = 2\pi \int_0^a (P' - P_e)r\, dr + 2\pi \int_a^b (P - P_e)r\, dr \qquad (7.16\text{-}19)$$

Integrating, the load is

$$W = \pi \frac{(P_i - P_e)(b^2 - a^2)}{2 \ln (b/a)} + \frac{\pi \alpha b^2}{4}\left[b^2 - \frac{(b^2 - a^2)}{\ln (b/a)}\right] \qquad (7.16\text{-}20)$$

When the flow rate Q is zero, the load is

$$W\bigg|_{Q=0} = \frac{\pi \alpha b^4}{4} = \frac{\mu_0 I^2}{8\pi} \qquad (7.16\text{-}21)$$

and it is evident that the bearing can in theory support a load even when the flow rate is zero and no external pump is provided.

However, from a practical point of view the currents necessary to achieve any useful pressurization are so great that the device would probably melt. Nevertheless, the analysis presented in this section illustrates the so-called MHD "pinch" effect and forms the foundation for pinch calculations in plasma theory. The original idea of the "magnetic bottle" confinement device was based on just such a pinch.

PROBLEMS

1. Using the expressions derived in Section 7.1, show that the ratio of the electromagnetic body force per unit volume to the viscous force per unit volume in the fluid is the Hartmann number.

2. For the generalized Poiseuille flow of Section 7.1, calculate the electromagnetic power flow into the channel by means of $\int_S \mathbf{E} \times \mathbf{H} \cdot d\mathbf{S}$. How much of this power is spent in Joulean dissipation? Calculate the power used in viscous dissipation.

3. Consider the generalized Poiseuille flow of Section 7.1 as a generator of electrical power feeding a matching load and calculate the efficiency of the generator.

4. Calculate the drag on the channel walls for generalized Poiseuille flow. Put the drag in dimensionless form by dividing it by the non-MHD Poiseuille drag.

5. In Section 7.1 the channel walls were ideal insulators. Rework this section for (a) perfect conducting walls and (b) one ideal insulating wall and one perfect conducting wall. In either case, what is the effect of the load resistance?

6. Work Problems 1, 2, and 4 for the cases presented in problem 5.

7. (a) Calculate the terminal voltage for the generalized Poiseuille flow of Section 7.1 (when the external generator is not in the circuit) by using Equation (2.6-14). Do this for two different paths of integration. Integrate along the center of the channel and along the channel wall. (b) Calculate the terminal voltage by means of (2.9-5).

8. Rework Section 7.1 assuming that the top channel wall is removed.

9. Calculate the drag on the moving wall of the generalized Couette flow of Section 7.3. By Newton's third law there exists a reaction to the force moving the wall. Where is the reaction force exerted? Demonstrate that it is equal and opposite to the force moving the top plate.

10. If the distance between the fixed and the moving walls in generalized Couette flow approaches infinity, the problem of a wall dragging the surface of a very deep sea results. Keeping this in mind, find the velocity, current density, and magnetic-field profiles for a wall of finite thickness and conductivity moving normal to a uniform applied steady magnetic field and dragging the surface of a conducting sea.

11. When a hydrofoil ship skims along the sea, it passes through the Earth's magnetic field, thus acting as a generator as it travels through the vertical component of the field. The generated current completes its circuit through the hydrofoils and the sea. The interaction of this current and the vertical magnetic field produces a force which drags the sea in the direction of the ship. Make an analysis of this effect using an infinite plate (not touching the surface) traveling parallel to the surface of an infinite sea through a magnetic field normal to the plate and the surface of the sea. Assume that the electrical circuit is completed by the hydrofoils but that their viscous drag is negligible. This assumption should be investigated.

12. There is a classical problem in oceanography known as the Ekman problem. In this problem there are two forces acting on the sea, the drag of the wind on the surface and the Coriolis force. The horizontal component of the Coriolis force is proportional to $2\omega v \sin \varphi$, where ω is angular velocity of the earth, φ the latitude, and v the speed of the water. The horizontal component of the Coriolis force is the same order of magnitude as the force of the wind, except at the equator. A north wind in the southern hemisphere causes the water to flow in a southeasterly direction and in the northern hemisphere the water flow due to a north wind is in a southwesterly direction. At a depth of 75 meters and a latitude of $45°$, a 20-knot wind causes a flow of about 4% of the surface velocity. Because the sea flows through the Earth's magnetic field, an electromagnetic body force exists in addition to the Coriolis force. The electromagnetic force modifies the angle of streaming. Calculate the modification of the angle of sea drift caused by magnetohydrodynamic effects.

13. Find a general expression for the induced axial magnetic field in the MHD Couette flow problem of Section 7.3. Sketch its distribution for the open- and short-circuit cases with pressure gradient as a parameter.

14. (a) Rework the one-dimensional MHD Couette flow problem of Section 7.3 using a perfect conductor for the moving wall. (*Hint:* A finite current is allowed to flow in the moving plate.) (b) Rework the problem when the moving wall is an insulator and the bottom fixed wall is a perfect conductor.

15. Solve for the velocity and magnetic-field profiles in the open channel of Fig. P7.15-1. This channel is infinite in length and is located in a uniform, direct-current magnetic field. Assume the flow is laminar and fully developed.

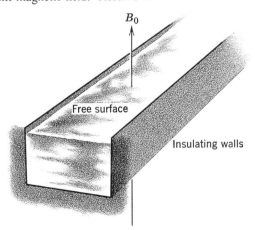

Figure P7.15-1   An open channel.

16. In the rectangular MHD channel flows considered in Chapter 7 the applied direct-current magnetic field was normal to the top and bottom walls. How would a solution be obtained if that were not the case?

17. Using the first solution of Section 7.4, solve for the velocity and magnetic-field profiles for a channel having insulating walls. (See Equations 7.4-11a and 7.4-11b.)

18. Solve for the velocity and magnetic-field profiles in channel (g) of Fig. 7.4-1.

19. Solve for the velocity and magnetic-field profiles in channel (h) of Fig. 7.4-1.

20. Which free surface channel problems are most easily solved?

21. Rework Section 7.7 using a velocity solution of the form of Equation (7.4-12a).

22. Rework Section 7.7 using a velocity solution of the form of Equation (7.4-14a).

23. Find the electric field in (a) the channel with perfectly insulating walls, and (b) the channel with perfectly conducting walls, and sketch both results.

24. For Section 7.6 find the ratio of J_y/J_z and estimate its magnitude.

25. Find the electric field in the insulating channel of Section 7.8.

26. Without solving the problem, sketch the current lines in an ideal conducting pipe of circular cross section when the conducting liquid streams axially through a transverse magnetic field.

27. A solid nonconducting cylinder of infinite length immersed in a sea of conducting liquid is placed in a uniform, steady transverse magnetic field. A

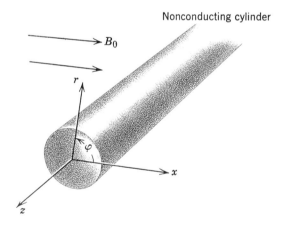

Figure P7.27-1 Flow outside a nonconducting cylinder.

pressure gradient $\partial P/\partial z$ is applied so that liquid will flow in the z direction as shown in Fig. P7.27-1. Find the velocity and magnetic-field profiles which result.

28. A conducting liquid is flowing in the axial direction between two infinitely long coaxial insulating cylinders. There exists a radial magnetic field given by $B_r = \text{const.}/r$, where r is the radius (see Fig. P7.28-1). Find the velocity and magnetic-field profiles which result. Be sure you make a limiting-case check on your solution by comparing it to short-circuited MHD Poiseuille flow. This can be done by making $r_0 \rightarrow \infty$ and simultaneously requiring that $r_0 - r_1$ remain finite.

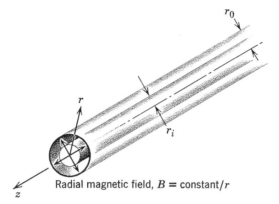

Radial magnetic field, $B = \text{constant}/r$

Figure P7.28-1   Flow in a coaxial cylinder.

29. Figure P7.29-1 shows a circular MHD Couette device similar to the Faraday disc. A shaft rotates the top plate which is an insulator. The bottom portion of the device comprises a cup holding a conducting liquid. The top plate drags

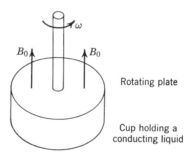

Rotating plate

Cup holding a
conducting liquid

Figure P7.29-1   A circular MHD Couette device.

the conducting liquid through the uniform axial field. Find the velocity and magnetic-field profiles in the liquid. Calculate the emf induced between the axis of the shaft and the cup.

30. Analyze the flow between two coaxial rotating cylinders with an axial magnetic field. The geometry is the same as in Fig. 7.10-1 except that the surfaces of the cylinders are the electrodes.

31. Work the problem of Section 7.12 (flow between parallel rotating disks) with a radial field instead of an axial field. The surfaces of the discs are the electrodes. Show that the tangential velocity v is

$$v = \frac{-3\sigma B_0 b}{4h} \left(\frac{V_T + \omega B_0 b h}{3\mu r^2 + \sigma B_0^2 b^2 h^2} \right)(h^2 - z^2)r + \tfrac{1}{3}r\omega(1 + z/h)$$

where $B_r = B_0 b/r$.

32. Make an energy balance of the rotating discs with an axial field (as described in Section 7.12). Account for external power into or out of the system, the Joule heat, the frictional dissipation and the mechanical shaft power.

33. Analyze the efficiency of the MHD viscous coupler of Section 7.13.

34. Calculate the frictional drag on the bearing and on the slider of the MHD bearing described in Section 7.14. Are the drag forces the same on the bearing as on the slider? Explain.

35. The device shown in Fig. P7.35-1 has been suggested as an amplifier for increasing the magnetic field of an electromagnet. Fields can be increased substantially it is claimed. Investigate the feasibility of this device. Liquid conductor is forced radially inward through a cylindrical space in which an

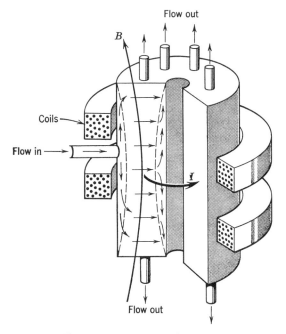

Figure P7.35-1   The hydromagnetic amplifier.

axial magnetic field is generated by external exciting coils. The induced azimuthal current in the liquid adds to the exciting field. Radial vanes are provided to prevent the fluid from spiraling and to keep it flowing generally in a radial direction. Small plenums are provided at the inlet and outlet to allow the liquid to distribute itself more evenly over the axial length of the flow region. The radial vanes are very good conductors.

36. Find the temperature distribution in the Hartmann problem assuming that the walls are held at a constant temperature T_w. Answer:

$$\theta - \theta_w = \frac{1}{M^2}\left[\frac{\text{ch}\,(2My/y_0) - \text{ch}\,2M}{\text{ch}\,M}\right]\left[2(ME_z{}^* + 1) - \frac{(ME_z{}^* + 1)^2}{4\,\text{ch}\,M}\right]$$
$$+ \tfrac{1}{2}(1 - y^2/y_0{}^2)$$

where

$$\theta = \frac{M^2 \kappa_T \mu_f T}{[y_0^2 (\partial P / \partial x)]^2}$$

$$E_z^* = \frac{E_z}{y_0 (\partial P / \partial x)} \cdot \sqrt{\sigma \mu_f}$$

37. Discuss the Couette problem of Section 7.3 if the moving top plate and the bottom plate have finite conductivity σ_T and σ_B, respectively, and thickness h_T and h_B. *Solution:* E_z is continuous and hence we have the same E_z in the fluid and plates. The total current per unit x length $\mathscr{I}$ (in the fluid) divides and returns in the two plates and any external load. In the top plate

$$J_{zT} = \sigma_T (E_z + U_0 B_0)$$

and in the bottom plate $J_{zB} = \sigma_B E_z$. In the load resistor the total current is $-E_z(2z_0)R_L$. Since $\mathscr{I}$ is defined positive in the z direction in the fluid, we must have (where l is the length of the device and $2z_0$ is its width):

$$I = \mathscr{I}l = -\sigma_B E_z h_B l - \sigma_T h_T l (E_z + U_0 B_0) - E_z(2z_0)/R_L \qquad \text{(a)}$$

$$I = \sigma y_0 l E_z + \frac{Ml}{2y_0 z_0} \sqrt{\sigma \mu_f}\, Q \qquad \text{(b)}$$

$\mathscr{I}$ is given in terms of E_z from (7.3-7b) which is still valid. Hence E_z is determined for arbitrary R_L. For short circuit, $R_L = 0$ and $E_z = 0$; for open circuit, $R_L = \infty$, but $\mathscr{I}_{oc} \neq 0$. E_{zoc} is found by equating Equation (a) to Equation (b) above. Then Equation (a) gives $\mathscr{I}_{oc}$. The student should now carry out the details. Alternatively one may begin by using $\nabla \times \mathbf{H} = \mathbf{J}$ instead of Ohm's law and eliminating E_z from the equations. Then boundary conditions of H_x must be known in terms of the total current. This is the method more useful for rectangular channels.

REFERENCES

Agarwal, J. P., Magnetohydrodynamic Effects in Lubrication, *Z.A.M.M.*, **43**, p. 181, 1963.

Chandrasekhar, S., *Hydrodynamic and Hydromagnetic Stability*, Oxford, 1961.

Chang, C. C., and T. S. Lundgren, Duct Flow in Magnetohydrodynamics, *Z. angew. Math. Phys.*, **12**, p. 100, 1961.

Elco, R. A., and W. F. Hughes, Magnetohydrodynamic Pressurization of Liquid Metal Bearings, *Wear*, **5**, p. 198. 1962.

Fucks, W., and J. Uhlenbusch, Magnetohydrodynamic Theory of Lubrication, *Phys. Fluids*, **5**, p. 498, April, 1962.

Gaylord, E. W., W. F. Hughes, and R. A. Elco., An Electrically Controlled MHD Viscous Coupler, *J. Electronics and Control*, **13**, p. 45, July, 1962.

Gold, R. R., Magnetohydrodynamic Pipe Flow, Part 1, *J. Fluid Mech.*, **13**, p. 505, 1962. This paper gives a rather complete list of references.

Hartmann, J., and F. Lazarus, Hg-Dynamics II. Experimental Investigations on the Flow of Mercury in a Homogeneous Magnetic Field, *Danske Math.-fys. Medd.*, **15**, No. 7, 1937.

Hasimoto, H., Steady Longitudinal Motion of a Cylinder in a Conducting Fluid, *J. Fluid Mech.*, **8**, p. 61, 1960.

Hughes, W. F., The Magnetohydrodynamic Finite Step Slider Bearing, *J. Basic Engineering, Trans. ASME*, **85**, p. 129, 1963.

Hughes, W. F., The Magnetohydrodynamic Inclined Slider Bearing with a Transverse Magnetic Field, *Wear*, **6**, p. 315, 1963.

Hughes, W. F., and R. A. Elco., Magnetohydrodynamic Lubrication Flow Between Parallel Rotating Disks, *J. Fluid Mech.*, **13**, p. 21, 1962.

Hughes, W. F., and R. A. Elco, Magnetohydrodynamic Journal Bearing, *J. Amer. Rocket Soc.*, **32**, p. 776, May 1962.

Kantorovich, L. V., and V. I. Krylov, *Approximate Methods of Higher Analysis*, Interscience, New York, pp. 258–304, 1958.

Kontorovich, V. M., Magnetohydrodynamics of the Ocean, *Voprosy Magnitnoy Giorodinamiki I Dinamiki Plazmy II, Izdatel'stuo* Akademii Nauk Latviyskoy SSR, Riga, 1962. (The English translation appears in ASTIA 299679, p. 161.)

Kuzma, D. C., The Magnetohydrodynamic Journal Bearing, *J. Basic Engineering, Trans. ASME*, **85**, p. 424, 1963.

Pai, S. I., Laminar Flow of an Electrically Conducting Incompressible Fluid in a Circular Pipe, *J. Appl. Phys.*, **25**, p. 1205, 1954.

Shercliff, J. A., Steady Motion of Conducting Fluids in Pipes under Transverse Magnetic Fields, *Proc. Cambridge Phil. Soc.*, **49**, p. 136, 1953.

Shercliff, J. A., Magnetohydrodynamic Pipe Flow, Part 2. High Hartmann Number, *J. Fluid Mech.*, **13**, p. 513, 1962.

Shercliff, J. A., *The Theory of Electromagnetic Flow-Measurement*, Cambridge University Press, 1962.

Singh, S. N., and G. A. Nariboli, Asymptotic Solution for the Hartmann Problem through Circular Tube, *Appl. Sci. Research*, **11b**, pp. 145–159, 1964.

Snyder, W. T., The Magnetohydrodynamic Slider Bearing, *J. Basic Engineering, Trans. ASME*, **84**, p. 197, 1962.

Tarapov, I. Ye., Problems of Lubrication in MHD, Second Conference on Theoretical and Applied MHD at Riga, June, 1960. Translated into English in: AD-299679, Foreign Technical Div., Air Force Systems Command, Wright-Patterson Air Force Base, Ohio, U.S.A.

Uflyand, Ya. S., Flow Stability of a Conducting Fluid in a Rectangular Channel in a Transverse Magnetic Field, *Soviet Phys.-Tech. Phys.*, **5**, p. 1191, 1960.

Uhlenbusch, J., and E. Fischer, Hydromagnetische Strömung in kreiszylindrischen Rohr, *Z. Physik*, **164**, p. 190, 1961.

Young, F. J., and W. F. Hughes, Session IV, Paper 1, Symposium on Magnetoplasmadynamic Elect. Power Generation, University of Durham, Newcastle upon Tyne, 1962.

Young, F. J., and J. F. Osterle, On the Load Capacity of the Hydromagnetically Lubricated Slider Bearing, *Wear*, **5**, p. 227, 1962.

8

Plane Waves in Fluids

8.1 INTRODUCTION

In Chapter 6 we mentioned one kind of wave produced by fluid-field interaction, the Alfvén wave. Now we will pursue the subject in detail and see that the Alfvén wave is just one special type of wave among many possible modes of propagation.

In this chapter we will confine ourselves to plane waves and postpone discussion of waves in bounded media (such as waveguides) until later. By a plane wave we mean one that propagates as an infinite plane in a direction perpendicular to the plane. For example, a plane wave propagating in the x direction extends infinitely in the y and z directions; no properties or characteristics of the fluid vary in the y or z directions. Although true plane waves do not exist in nature, they serve as useful idealizations in the qualitative analysis of the different types of waves that exist under various circumstances. And, on a local scale, plane waves are often an adequate representation of actual waves.

There are two distinct kinds of plane waves: transverse waves and longitudinal waves, both of which manifest themselves in classical electromagnetic theory and in classical fluid mechanics and elasticity. A transverse wave is characterized by oscillations of a parameter in a direction perpendicular to the direction of propagation, and a longitudinal wave is characterized by oscillations of a parameter in the direction of propagation. For example, an acoustic pressure wave is a longitudinal wave; the pressure variations are accompanied by oscillations of the x component of velocity (assuming propagation in the x direction). A pure torsion wave in an elastic rod is a transverse wave. As the shear stress wave propagates down the rod, the azimuthal component of velocity (perpendicular to the direction of propagation) is excited. The Alfvén wave is a transverse wave characterized by transverse velocity and magnetic field oscillations.

In electromagnetic wave propagation both transverse and longitudinal waves can exist. A transverse electromagnetic wave (sometimes denoted as a TEM wave) propagating in the x direction would have an electric field and magnetic field in the y and z directions, respectively (assuming a right-handed coordinate system) so that the flux of energy ($\mathbf{E} \times \mathbf{H}$) flows in the x direction (see Fig. 8.1-1). The relationships between E_y and H_z are then determined by Maxwell's equations. From a simple consideration of the Poynting flux ($\mathbf{E} \times \mathbf{H}$), the direction of propagation of energy must always be perpendicular to the plane defined by the $\mathbf{E}$ and $\mathbf{H}$ vectors.

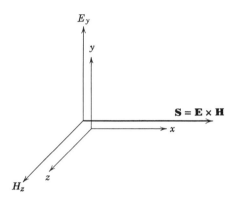

Figure 8.1-1 Propagation of an electromagnetic wave. The electric field E_y and magnetic field H_z are perpendicular and propagate in the x direction. The Poynting vector $\mathbf{S}$ must be in the direction of propagation.

However, the direction of propagation of a wave in general and its direction of energy propagation need not be colinear. Hence it is possible to speak of waves characterized by one component of the electric or magnetic field lying along the direction of propagation. Such waves are sometimes referred to as transverse magnetic (TM) and transverse electric (TE) waves, respectively. Such waves may be decomposed into a sum of plane waves.

In the study of magnetohydrodynamic waves two distinct approaches, depending on the fluid model, can be used, and we must be very careful to remember the restrictions of our model. The continuum approach is used in this chapter and applied to a liquid or homogeneous isotropic gas. In a rarefied plasma there are several new modes of wave propagation (sometimes called plasma oscillations) but these cannot be predicted by the model used here. In a dense, collision-dominated gas where the various species of particles move together without slipping, the results of the continuum theory and the more sophisticated plasma models must give the same results. However, as the gas becomes more rarefied and the various species of particles can begin to move independently, the results of plasma oscillation theory are widely different from those of the homogeneous continuum fluid model which we will now investigate.

The study of radio wave propagation in the ionosphere is one of the most important applications of plasma oscillation theory and here the continuum model gives quite diverse and incorrect results. However, for ionized gases at atmosphere pressures and for conducting liquids the continuum approach is quite good. The difference between these approaches can be seen by considering the attenuation of radio waves in an ionized gas or conducting liquid. We know that in liquids and dense gases the attenuation increases with frequency. However, the attenuation predicted by plasma oscillation theory is not so simple, and indeed only rather high (microwave) frequencies (above the plasma frequency) can penetrate the ionosphere, a result which could not be predicted from the homogeneous continuum fluid model.

Before beginning our study of plane magnetohydrodynamic waves, a few remarks concerning the role of the displacement current are necessary. In a true conductor, the conduction current completely dominates the displacement current, which may be entirely neglected. In fact, in a metal (liquid or not) the concept of displacement current even at high frequencies is really meaningless if one uses the macroscopic Maxwell equations and fluid model. In poorer conductors, however, such as ionized gases and dielectric liquids, the conduction current and displacement current may be comparable, at least at high frequencies. Hence, in general, we usually neglect the displacement current in liquid metals but retain it in gases.

Retention of the displacement current allows the description of waves (of electromagnetic nature) which propagate with phase velocities of order c (the velocity of light). If the displacement current is neglected, no such modes are predicted and phase velocities are all of the order of acoustic and Alfvén velocities.

Displacement-current effects, even though small, may sometimes be important in liquid conductors. In sea water, for instance, electromagnetic radio waves can be transmitted for very short distances. As we will see, the attenuation is so great that such transmission is important only in the case of refraction of surface waves to shallow depths beneath the surface. Powerful low frequency waves, below about 50 kilocycles, may be used in ground wave transmission over the sea and refracted downward to a submarine receiver.

When the displacement current is retained in calculations involving moving media, we must be careful to write the constitutive equations in only the rest frame of the fluid since the dielectric constant is not ϵ_0 (unless we are dealing with a gas in which case the dielectric constant may be ϵ_0). In sea water the value of the relative permittivity is about 80 and varies somewhat with frequency.

Our general method of approach to wave propagation is as follows. We begin with the basic equations, linearize with respect to small disturbances (perturbations), and investigate the propagation characteristics of these disturbances. Plane wave solutions of the form $e^{j(\omega t - kx)}$ are assumed (for propagation in the x direction), where ω is the angular frequency (in radians per second) and k is the propagation constant and is generally complex. The propagation constant k (or wave number) is related to the wave length λ as $\lambda = 2\pi/\mathrm{Re}\ k$. The dispersion relationship $\omega = \omega(k)$ is found and then the phase velocity $\omega/\mathrm{Re}\ k$, which we will denote as a, and group velocity $\partial\omega/\partial(\mathrm{Re}\ k)$ can be determined. Once these relationships have been obtained, the character of the different modes of plane wave propagation can be established. A positive real part of k indicates propagation in the positive x direction. A negative real part of k indicates propagation in the negative x direction. A positive imaginary part indicates amplification if the propagation is in the positive x direction or attenuation if the propagation is in the negative x direction. A negative imaginary part indicates attenuation if the propagation is in the positive x direction or amplification if the propagation is in the negative x direction.*

We will now investigate plane wave propagation in some detail and develop the general theory of coupled magnetohydrodynamic and magnetoacoustic wave motion in liquids and gases; we will also discuss quantitatively the role of the displacement current.

8.2   PLANE WAVES IN A PERFECT GAS

Waves in gases and liquids are similar, and their mathematical description is the same if the acoustic velocity is introduced. In our examination of wave motion in gases in this section and wave motion in liquids in Section 8.3, we will neglect the displacement current and assume the fluid to be stationary, that is, with all undisturbed quantities (before the wave

---

* The index of refraction n is defined as $n = ck/\omega$ and will be complex if k is complex. A plane wave can be written as

$$e^{j\omega(t - n_r x/c)} \cdot e^{-\omega n_i x/c}$$

where $n = n_r + jn_i$. If the group velocity is less than the phase velocity, this is referred to as ordinary dispersion. If the group velocity is greater than the phase velocity, this is referred to as anomalous dispersion.

is introduced) stationary in time and space. Later we will lift some of these restrictions to examine wave motion in moving liquids and the effect of the displacement current.

In Fig. 8.2-1 a uniform constant magnetic field $\mathbf{H}_0$ fills all space and waves are assumed to propagate in the x direction. The most general case can be considered by assuming $\mathbf{H}_0$ to have only x and y components H_{0x} and H_{0y}, respectively. This fact is obvious since the xyz triad can be rotated about the x axis until $\mathbf{H}_0$ is in the yx plane. We denote the unperturbed pressure, density, and temperature as P_0, ρ_0, and T_0, respectively.

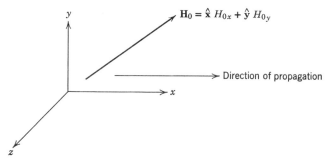

Figure 8.2-1 Propagation of a plane wave in the presence of a magnetic field. Propagation is in the x direction, and the steady magnetic field $\mathbf{H}_0$ has two components, H_{0x} and H_{0y}. This is a general case because the coordinate system can be chosen (by rotation about the x axis) so that $\mathbf{H}_0$ has only x and y components.

The steady velocity $\mathbf{V}_0$ is taken as zero. We assume that accompanying the wave are disturbances in the variables (pressure, density, and temperature) which we denote by primes so that they can be written as:

$$P = P_0 + P'$$

$$\rho = \rho_0 + \rho'$$

$$T = T_0 + T'$$

And we denote the perturbation quantities in velocity and magnetic field field as lower case so that:

$$\mathbf{V} = \mathbf{V}_0 + \mathbf{v} = \mathbf{v}$$

$$\mathbf{H} = \mathbf{H}_0 + \mathbf{h}$$

The x, y, and z components of $\mathbf{v}$ are taken as u, v, and w, respectively.

We now write the basic equations of the system in terms of the total quantities just given, linearize (by considering the first order equations), and seek solutions of the form $e^{j(\omega t - kx)}$. For example, we can write $P' = P'^* e^{j(\omega t - kx)}$, where P'^* is a phasor quantity. In general, in this chapter, phasor quantities are indicated by an asterisk. The basic equations can now be systematically listed. The continuity equation is

$$\frac{\partial \rho}{\partial t} + \nabla \cdot (\rho \mathbf{V}) = 0$$

which, when expanded, becomes

$$\frac{\partial}{\partial t} (\rho_0 + \rho') + \nabla \cdot [(\rho_0 + \rho')\mathbf{v}] = 0$$

The first-order linearized equation is

$$\frac{\partial \rho'}{\partial t} + \rho_0 \frac{\partial u}{\partial x} = 0 \tag{8.2-1}$$

where the second-order terms $(\rho'\nabla \cdot \mathbf{v} + \mathbf{v} \cdot \nabla \rho')$ have been neglected. Derivatives with respect to y and z are zero, remember, for a plane wave propagating in the x direction.

The equation of state, assuming a perfect gas, is

$$P = n\bar{R}T = \rho RT$$

where n is the number of moles per unit volume and $\bar{R}$ is the universal gas constant. Linearization yields

$$\frac{P'}{P_0} = \frac{T'}{T_0} + \frac{\rho'}{\rho_0} \tag{8.2-2}$$

We write the equation of motion with the assumption that Ohm's law $\mathbf{J} = \sigma(\mathbf{E} + \mathbf{V} \times \mathbf{B})$ is valid and the displacement current negligible. It is not necessary to assume the gas to be electrically neutral if no steady zeroth order electric field exists. Only if such a field is applied can space charge waves be generated, and then only if the relaxation time of the fluid is large compared to the period of oscillation of the waves. Only in dielectric liquids that can be charged does this effect become important and then the conductivity may be so low that displacement current must be considered. (In a statistical plasma model these observations are not correct. There the individual species of particles can move individually and space charge waves do become important.) In this chapter we will not be concerned with fluids with applied electric fields so that the problem of space charge waves does not appear.

The equations of motion for a viscous gas are

$$\rho\left[\frac{\partial \mathbf{V}}{\partial t} + (\mathbf{V} \cdot \nabla)\mathbf{V}\right] = -\nabla P + \nu\rho_0 \nabla^2 \mathbf{V}$$
$$+ (\zeta + \tfrac{1}{3}\nu\rho_0) \nabla(\nabla \cdot \mathbf{V}) + \mu(\nabla \times \mathbf{H}) \times \mathbf{H}$$

where ζ is the second coefficient of viscosity (zero for a monatomic gas), and v is the kinematic viscosity. The constitutive equation $\mathbf{B} = \mu\mathbf{H}$ has been used under the MHD approximation. Actually, of course, μ will have the value μ_0 for most fluids, but it is not necessary to make this assumption for the present calculations and we shall retain the notation μ to emphasize this fact. Linearization of the equations of motion results in the following:

$$\rho_0 \frac{\partial u}{\partial t} = -\frac{\partial P'}{\partial x} + (\zeta + \tfrac{4}{3}v\rho_0)\frac{\partial^2 u}{\partial x^2} - \mu H_{0y}\frac{\partial h_y}{\partial x} \qquad (8.2\text{-}3)$$

$$\rho_0 \frac{\partial v}{\partial t} = v\rho_0 \frac{\partial^2 v}{\partial x^2} + \mu H_{0x}\frac{\partial h_y}{\partial x} \qquad (8.2\text{-}4)$$

$$\rho_0 \frac{\partial w}{\partial t} = v\rho_0 \frac{\partial^2 w}{\partial x^2} + \mu H_{0x}\frac{\partial h_z}{\partial x} \qquad (8.2\text{-}5)$$

The energy equation for a perfect gas can be written in terms of c_P as

$$\rho c_P \frac{DT}{Dt} = \frac{DP}{Dt} + \kappa_T \nabla^2 T + \Phi + \mathbf{E'} \cdot \mathbf{J'}$$

where κ_T is the thermal conductivity and Φ the mechanical dissipation function. ($\mathbf{E'}$ and $\mathbf{J'}$ are the rest-frame values.) Linearized, the energy equation becomes (the dissipation terms are all second order)

$$\rho_0 c_P \frac{\partial T'}{\partial t} = \frac{\partial P'}{\partial t} + \kappa_T \nabla^2 T' \qquad (8.2\text{-}6)$$

If heat conduction is neglected, the gas behaves isentropically and the same results could be obtained by using the isentropic relationship $P(1/\rho)^\gamma = \text{constant}$. γ is the ratio of specific heats c_P/c_V.

The relevant Maxwell equations can be combined into the magnetic transport equation

$$\frac{\partial \mathbf{H}}{\partial t} = \eta \nabla^2 \mathbf{H} + \nabla \times (\mathbf{V} \times \mathbf{H})$$

where η is the magnetic diffusivity $1/\sigma\mu$. The constitutive equation $\mathbf{B} = \mu\mathbf{H}$ has been used implicitly here. Linearization results in

$$\frac{\partial h_x}{\partial t} = \eta \frac{\partial^2 h_x}{\partial x^2} \qquad (8.2\text{-}7)$$

$$\frac{\partial h_y}{\partial t} = \eta \frac{\partial^2 h_y}{\partial x^2} + H_{0x}\frac{\partial v}{\partial x} - H_{0y}\frac{\partial u}{\partial x} \qquad (8.2\text{-}8)$$

$$\frac{\partial h_z}{\partial t} = \eta \frac{\partial^2 h_z}{\partial x^2} + H_{0x}\frac{\partial w}{\partial x} \qquad (8.2\text{-}9)$$

The solution to the set of equations (8.2-1) through (8.2-8) has the form $e^{j(\omega t - kx)}$ and substitution of this solution into the set of equations yields the characteristic determinant. This determinant is obtained from the coefficients of the phasor quantities. The characteristic equation is obtained by setting the determinant equal to zero to yield a dispersion equation of the form $\omega(k) = 0$.

Before writing the determinant, we can make the following observations:

1. Equation (8.2-7) is uncoupled. This equation yields no information since, from $\nabla \times \mathbf{E} = -\partial \mathbf{B}/\partial t$ and the fact that no variations occur in the y or z directions, $\partial h_x/\partial t$ must be identically zero, and hence no propagation can result.

2. Equations (8.2-5) and (8.2-9) are uncoupled from the remainder of the equations and represent two transverse modes. As we shall see, if all dissipation is neglected, a single mode, an Alfvén wave, results.

3. The remaining six equations give rise to a coupled transverse and longitudinal mode system. In general, the system is fourth order in k^2, representing four types of waves (four forward and four backward). If all dissipation is neglected, the equations decouple into a first-order equation in k^2 (representing a forward and backward Alfvén wave) for the transverse mode, and a second-order system in k^2 (representing two types of magnetoacoustic waves, fast and slow) for the longitudinal modes.

We could examine each coupled set of equations separately or set up the entire determinant and then note how the coupling occurs. The entire determinant of the system has the following form.

The column heading indicates the variable whose coefficient appears in the determinant. The nonzero minors can be arranged along the main diagonal and hence are uncoupled and can each be set to zero. Let us first examine the 2 × 2 transverse wave determinant in detail.

Transverse Waves

The 2 × 2 transverse wave determinant is obtained from Equations (8.2-5) and (8.2-9) which in phasor notation become

$$j\mu H_{0x} k h_z{}^* + \nu\rho_0 k^2 w^* + j\rho_0 \omega w^* = 0 \qquad (8.2\text{-}11)$$

$$j\omega h_z{}^* + \eta k^2 h_z{}^* + jH_{0x} k w^* = 0 \qquad (8.2\text{-}12)$$

The determinantal characteristic equation is then

Variables

Equation	$h_z{}^*$	w^*	
(8.2-12)	$(j\omega + \eta k^2)$	$jH_{0x}k$	$= 0 \qquad (8.2\text{-}13)$
(8.2-11)	$j\mu H_{0x}k$	$\nu\rho_0 k^2 + j\rho_0\omega$	

By expanding, the dispersion relationship is

$$\nu\eta k^4 + [A_x{}^2 + j(\nu + \eta)\omega]k^2 - \omega^2 = 0 \qquad (8.2\text{-}14)$$

where A_x is the Alfvén speed $\sqrt{\mu/\rho_0} \cdot H_{0x}$. Equation (8.2-14) describes two modes of transverse waves, damped and dispersed by the magnetic diffusivity and fluid viscosity. These modes comprise a coupling between the ordinary Alfvén wave and viscous diffusion wave. The phase velocity could be found by forming $\omega/\mathrm{Re}\,k$, and the attenuation is given by the imaginary part of k.

If $\nu = 0$, Equation (8.2-14) becomes

$$(A_x{}^2 + j\eta\omega)k^2 - \omega^2 = 0 \qquad (8.2\text{-}14a)$$

and if $\eta = 0$, (8.2-14) becomes

$$(A_x{}^2 + j\nu\omega)k^2 - \omega^2 = 0 \qquad (8.2\text{-}14b)$$

We see that in the case of zero viscosity ($\nu = 0$), where no ordinary transverse disturbance (except an Alfvén wave) would be transmitted through the fluid, interaction with the magnetic field serves to stiffen the fluid and to give rise to a coupled damped wave. Similarly, if $\eta = 0$ ($\sigma = \infty$), no magnetic diffusion would occur; only an Alfvén wave would propagate. However, the finite viscosity gives rise to a coupled damped wave of velocity and magnetic field just as in the zero viscosity ($\nu = 0$) case above. Since the two preceding equations are identical in form, we conclude that the wave behavior with either ν or η zero is identical (except for numerical factors), serving to modify and damp the Alfvén wave. The limit of $\nu = 0$ is actually that of $Pm = 0$ (the magnetic Prandtl number is ν/η, remember) and this particular dispersion relationship will be useful later when we discuss the MHD Rayleigh problem in Chapter 9. The propagation constant k and phase velocity may be easily calculated for the case of ν or $\eta = $ zero. We find for $\nu = 0$ ($Pm = 0$):

$$k = \pm \frac{\omega}{\sqrt{2}\sqrt{A_x^4 + \eta^2\omega^2}}$$
$$\times [(\sqrt{A_x^4 + \eta^2\omega^2} + A_x^2)^{1/2} - j(\sqrt{A_x^4 + \eta^2\omega^2} - A_x^2)^{1/2}]$$

$$a = \pm \left[\frac{2(A_x^4 + \eta^2\omega^2)}{\sqrt{A_x^4 + \eta^2\omega^2} + A_x^2}\right]^{1/2} \tag{8.2-14c}$$

$$\text{Im } k = \mp \left[\frac{\omega^2(\sqrt{A_x^4 + \eta^2\omega^2} - A_x^2)}{2(A_x^4 + \eta^2\omega^2)}\right]^{1/2}$$

For $\eta = 0$ with finite ν the results are of the same form, with η replaced by ν. We note that for low frequency, $a \to A_x$, the Alfvén speed. In Section 9.6 a detailed discussion of asymptotic solutions for small Pm is given and Equation (8.2-14) is applied to some physical situations.

If H_{0x} is zero, Equation (8.2-14) becomes

$$(\eta k^2 + j\omega)(\nu k^2 + j\omega) = 0 \tag{8.2-15}$$

which is the dispersion relationship for a transverse disturbance in a viscous conducting fluid. Since k^2 is purely imaginary we recognize pure viscous diffusion waves and pure magnetic diffusion waves in which $a = \pm\sqrt{2\omega\nu}$ and $\pm\sqrt{2\omega\eta}$, respectively and $\text{Im } k = \mp\sqrt{\omega/2\nu}$ and $\mp\sqrt{\omega/2\eta}$, respectively.

If the dissipation is small and is neglected, that is, if the conductivity is taken as infinite and the viscosity as zero ($\eta \to 0$ and $\nu \to 0$), we get an ordinary Alfvén wave. Equation (8.2-14) then becomes

$$A_x^2 k^2 - \omega^2 = 0 \tag{8.2-16}$$

and hence

$$a = \left(\frac{\omega}{k}\right)_{\substack{\eta \to 0 \\ \nu \to 0}} = \pm A_x \tag{8.2-17}$$

which is a pure Alfvén wave (the plus or minus indicates a forward or backward wave, respectively) propagating along the x component of the H_0 vector.

Coupled Longitudinal Waves

The six remaining coupled equations can now be put into phasor form and the determinant of the coefficients of the variables obtained. Bypassing the details, we obtain the following determinant

			Variables				
Equation	u^*	v^*	$h_y{}^*$	P'^*	ρ'^*	T'^*	
(8.2-2)	0	0	0	$\dfrac{1}{P_0}$	$-\dfrac{1}{\rho_0}$	$-\dfrac{1}{T_0}$	
(8.2-1)	$-jk\rho_0$	0	0	0	$j\omega$	0	
(8.2-8)	$-jkH_{0y}$	jkH_{0x}	$(j\omega + k^2\eta)$	0	0	0	
(8.2-3)	$[j\omega\rho_0 +$ $(\frac{4}{3}\nu\rho_0 + \zeta)k^2]$	0	$-jk\mu H_{0y}$	$-jk$	0	0	$= 0$
(8.2-4)	0	$(j\omega\rho_0 + \nu\rho_0 k^2)$	$jk\mu H_{0x}$	0	0	0	
(8.2-6)	0	0	0	$-j\omega$	0	$(\kappa_T k^2 +$ $j\omega c_p\rho_0)$	

$$(8.2\text{-}18)$$

The expansion of the determinant can be simplified if we introduce the ordinary sonic speed a_0 $(a_0 = \sqrt{\gamma R T_0} = \sqrt{c_P(\gamma - 1)T_0})$ and the two Alfvén speeds $A_x = \sqrt{\mu/\rho_0} \cdot H_{0x}$ and $A_y = \sqrt{\mu/\rho_0} \cdot H_{0y}$. There results after a bit of algebraic manipulation:

$$\left\{ \kappa_T\left[\frac{1}{\rho_0} + j\frac{\omega}{\rho_0 P_0}(\tfrac{4}{3}\nu\rho_0 + \zeta)\right]k^4 \right.$$
$$- \left[\frac{\omega^2\kappa_T}{P_0} - j\omega c_P + \frac{\omega^2 c_P}{a_0{}^2\rho_0}(\tfrac{4}{3}\nu\rho_0 + \zeta)\right]k^2 - j\frac{\omega^3 c_P}{a_0{}^2}\right\}$$
$$\cdot \left\{\nu\eta k^4 + [A_x{}^2 + j(\nu + \eta)\omega]k^2 - \omega^2\right\}$$
$$- k^2 A_y{}^2(j\omega + \nu k^2)\left(\frac{\omega^2 c_P}{a_0{}^2} - j\frac{\omega\kappa_T k^2}{P_0}\right) = 0 \qquad (8.2\text{-}19)$$

which is the final characteristic equation for longitudinal modes. Actually, the second brace represents exactly the transverse modes and physically this means that it is in general impossible to excite longitudinal modes without exciting coupled transverse modes at the same time. However, under certain simplifying assumptions, as we shall see, the transverse-mode term here becomes a common factor of the equation and hence becomes completely uncoupled from the longitudinal modes.

This complete equation (8.2-19) represents four modes, a coupling of the basic Alfvén waves, sonic or acoustic waves, viscous diffusion, and heat conduction. The waves become entangled with dispersion and attenuation occurring and are rather difficult to interpret physically except under rather simplifying but nevertheless realistic assumptions.

Several special limiting cases can now be examined that will lend some insight into the character of these waves.

1. If A_y is zero, there is no coupling between the magnetic field and the ordinary gas dynamic waves in a viscous heat-conducting gas. Each of the braces of (8.2-19) are zero. The first represents the longitudinal acoustic wave in a viscous heat-conducting gas and the second represents precisely the coupled transverse waves described by Equation (8.2-14).

2. If both A_x and A_y are zero (no applied magnetic field), we obtain the acoustic wave and an uncoupled viscous diffusion. Explicitly, these are given by

$$\left\{ \kappa_T \left[\frac{1}{\rho_0} + j\, \frac{\omega}{\rho_0 P_0} \left(\tfrac{4}{3} \nu \rho_0 + \zeta \right) \right] k^4 - \left[\frac{\omega^2 \kappa_T}{P_0} - j\omega c_P, \right.\right.$$
$$\left.\left. + \frac{\omega^2 c_P}{a_0^2 \rho_0} \left(\tfrac{4}{3} \nu \rho_0 + \zeta \right) \right] k^2 - j\, \frac{\omega^3 c_P}{a_0^2} \right\} \cdot \left\{ \nu \rho_0 k^2 + j \rho_0 \omega \right\} = 0 \quad (8.2\text{-}20)$$

where the first brace gives the acoustic modes and the second the viscous diffusion. If heat conduction and viscosity are neglected, there results only the ordinary acoustic wave

$$a = \frac{\omega}{k} = \pm a_0 \tag{8.2-21}$$

3. If A_x is zero and all dissipation is neglected ($\eta = \zeta = \nu = \kappa_T = 0$), the ordinary acoustic wave velocity becomes modified and we get

$$a = \frac{\omega}{k} = \pm \sqrt{A_y^2 + a_0^2} \tag{8.2-22}$$

a single longitudinal mode, and no transverse modes at all.

Ideal Magnetoacoustic Waves

Perhaps the most important result in the study of MHD waves is the set of ideal magnetoacoustic waves. These coupled modes are obtained directly from Equation (8.2-19) by assuming only that all dissipation is zero, that is, $\eta = \nu = \zeta = \kappa_T = 0$. This assumption is not at all drastic. On the contrary, it is quite realistic; $\nu = \zeta = \kappa_T = 0$ is a usual assumption made in acoustic studies, and the assumption of $\eta = 0$ (that is,

$\sigma \to \infty$) is equivalent to neglecting Joulean damping—in many cases of less importance than the viscous damping. The results obtained under these assumptions can readily be given a clear physical interpretation and lend a great deal of insight into the nature of the coupling of the electromagnetic and mechanical quantities. In the study of aerodynamics and magnetogasdynamics in general, the behavior of the ideal magnetoacoustic waves is of utmost importance. Just as in conventional gasdynamics the sonic speed a_0 plays an important role, so in magnetogasdynamics the characteristic speeds of the magnetoacoustic waves are important.

Under the condition then that $\eta = \nu = \zeta = \kappa_T = 0$, the general dispersion equation (8.2-19) becomes

$$\left(a_0^2 - \frac{\omega^2}{k^2}\right)\left(A_x^2 - \frac{\omega^2}{k^2}\right) - A_y^2 \frac{\omega^2}{k^2} = 0 \qquad (8.2\text{-}23)$$

This equation can be readily solved for the phase velocity $a = \omega/k$ and we will see that two types of waves exist (since 8.2-23 is quadratic in k^2). These two waves are usually denoted as a fast wave and a slow wave whose speeds bound a_0, that is

$$a_{\text{fast}} \geqslant a_0 \geqslant a_{\text{slow}} \qquad (8.2\text{-}24)$$

Solving (8.2-23), we get

$$a_{\text{fast}} = \pm\left[\frac{A_x^2 + A_y^2 + a_0^2}{2} + \sqrt{\frac{(A_x^2 + A_y^2 + a_0^2)^2}{4} - a_0^2 A_x^2}\right]^{1/2}$$

$$a_{\text{slow}} = \pm\left[\frac{A_x^2 + A_y^2 + a_0^2}{2} - \sqrt{\frac{(A_x^2 + A_y^2 + a_0^2)^2}{4} - a_0^2 A_x^2}\right]^{1/2}$$

$$(8.2\text{-}25)$$

The plus and minus signs merely indicate a forward or backward traveling wave.

We must remember that along with the two longitudinal waves described by (8.2-25) an ideal transverse wave (in which $\nu = \eta = \zeta = \kappa_T = 0$) can also exist. This mode is given by Equation (8.2-17) and is simply a pure Alfvén wave:

$$a = \pm A_x$$

Hence we arrive at the final result that in an ideal fluid (with zero heat conductivity and infinite electrical conductivity) three types of waves can propagate, fast and slow magnetoacoustic waves (which replace the ordinary acoustic wave and are modifications of it brought about by the presence of the electromagnetic field) and a transverse Alfvén wave.

Ideal Magnetoacoustic Characteristic Surfaces

The magnetoacoustic waves in an ideal fluid of perfect conductivity can be visualized rather nicely by constructing phase velocity plots and ray-normal diagrams or characteristic surfaces.

A phase velocity plot or normal-speed locus can be constructed by plotting the magnitude of the phase velocity as the radial distance on a

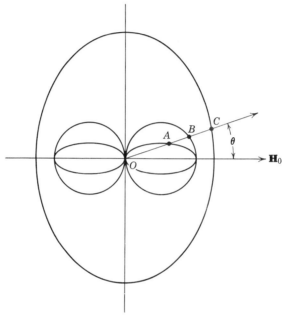

Figure 8.2-2 Construction of the phase velocity diagram. The radius vector $OABC$ represents the phase velocity of plane wave propagation in that direction (relative to $\mathbf{H}_0$). The diagram should be imagined as rotating about $\mathbf{H}_0$ to form a three-dimensional figure.

polar plot. In Fig. 8.2-2 the magnetic field is laid out along the abscissa. The curves are the loci of the radius vector whose length is the phase velocity for any direction of propagation (with respect to the direction of the magnetic field vector $\mathbf{H}_0$). For example, the arrow $OABC$ corresponds to propagation, with the applied magnetic field $\mathbf{H}$ given as $\mathbf{H} = \hat{\mathbf{x}} H_x + \hat{\mathbf{y}} H_y = \hat{\mathbf{x}} |\mathbf{H}| \cos \theta - \hat{\mathbf{y}} |\mathbf{H}| \sin \theta$ (in terms of the notation of this chapter). Vector OA represents the slow acoustic wave, OB the Alfvén wave, and OC the fast acoustic wave. Hence Equations (8.2-17) and (8.2-25) are represented completely by such phase velocity diagrams. It is understood, of course, that the entire picture must be rotated about the $\mathbf{H}$ vector (abscissa) to form a three-dimensional figure consisting of an oblate spheroid with center at O (the fast acoustic wave), two spheres tangent at O with $\mathbf{H}$ aligned along their diameters (the Alfvén waves), and two cigar-shaped surfaces meeting at O with the $\mathbf{H}$ vector aligned along their major axes (the slow acoustic waves). The magnitude of a_0 may be less than, equal to, or greater than the Alfvén velocity $A^2 = A_x^2 + A_y^2$.

Figure 8.2-2 gives the general idea, but is valid only for the case in which $a_0 > A$, the maximum Alfvén velocity. Plots for the three distinct cases of $a_0 > A$, $a_0 < A$, and $a_0 = A$ are shown in Figs. 8.2-3, 8.2-4, and 8.2-5, respectively. In each it may be noted that a wave propagating normal to the $\mathbf{H}$ field behaves as a single acoustic wave with velocity $\sqrt{a_0^2 + A^2}$. A wave propagating along the magnetic field has two uncoupled modes, the pure transverse Alfvén wave and the ordinary acoustic or sonic wave of velocity a_0. If the field is skewed, so that both an x and y component of $\mathbf{H}$ exist (remember we are considering propagation in the x direction), then all three modes manifest themselves.

Of extreme importance is the three-dimensional envelope of the ideal magnetoacoustic waves that emanate from a point source. In ordinary acoustics a point disturbance produces a spherical wave which expands outward with velocity a_0. If the point source is moving, the envelope can also be constructed. The familiar Mach cone results for supersonic motion of the source, and for subsonic motion a sphere is always the envelope. Such a diagram is known as a ray-normal diagram or characteristic surface and can be constructed for a point source of magneto-acoustic waves. The construction of such a diagram, at least for the stationary source, is not difficult.

We begin with the phase velocity diagram and imagine these diagrams rotated about the $\mathbf{H}$ vector to form three-dimensional figures. We imagine an infinite set of rays or propagation vector extending outward from the origin through the surfaces of the phase velocity figures. These rays intersect the surfaces and at every ray-surface intersection a plane perpendicular to the ray is constructed (this plane is not necessarily tangent to the surface). The envelope of all such planes constitutes the ray-normal diagram or characteristic locus and in fact defines the actual locus of the disturbances (at unit time) that originated at the same time at the origin. These diagrams are sometimes called Friedrichs' diagrams after K. O. Friedrichs, who made one of the first studies of magnetoacoustic waves. If the phase velocity diagram is plotted in meters per second, the characteristic locus would be the disturbance surface one second (or unit time) after the disturbance was initiated at the origin.

The results of the construction are obvious for the ordinary acoustic wave radiating in all directions with velocity a_0. The characteristic locus is obviously a sphere. The magnetoacoustic waves, however, generate a rather strange looking set of surfaces, unexpected perhaps, but easily constructed from Figs. 8.2-3 through 8.2-5. These results are shown in Figs. 8.2-6, 8.2-7, and 8.2-8. The large dots denoted as A represent the Alfvén wave development, merely points, out along a line aligned with the **H** vector. The fast wave generates an oblate spheroid (except under

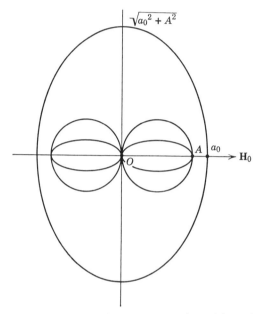

Figure 8.2-3   Phase velocity diagram or normal-speed locus for $a_0 > A$.

the condition that $a_0 = A$, Fig. 8.2-8), but the slow wave generates a rather strange cusped surface. We must imagine these figures rotated about the **H** vector to form the three-dimensional surfaces. The slow wave then looks like a pair of cones, with apexes at the origin and the bases fitted with concave covers. In the case of $a_0 = A$, these covers degenerate into the Alfvén points, and the slow wave cones become part of the fast wave spheroid, resulting in partial cusped spheroids.

It is rather difficult to visualize what the development would look like if the source were moving, but we know immediately that there are in general four distinct cases depending on where the source velocity fits among these wave characteristic velocities. Instead of merely having two cases, subsonic and supersonic flow, as in ordinary gasdynamics, we now have sub- and super-Alfvén, sub- and super-fast wave, and sub- and super-slow wave type flows, giving a total of six possibilities. Even in the

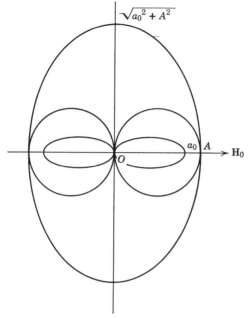

Figure 8.2-4   Phase velocity diagram or normal-speed locus for $a_0 < A$.

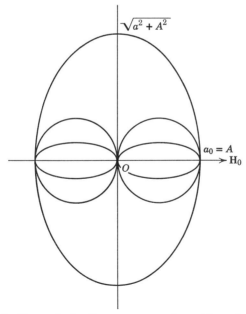

Figure 8.2-5   Phase velocity diagram or normal-speed locus for $a_0 = A$.

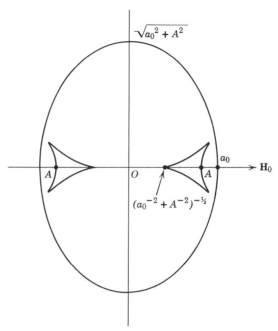

Figure 8.2-6 Characteristic surfaces or Friedrichs' diagrams for $a_0 > A$. This figure shows the development of a sound pulse in unit time from a point source at the origin O.

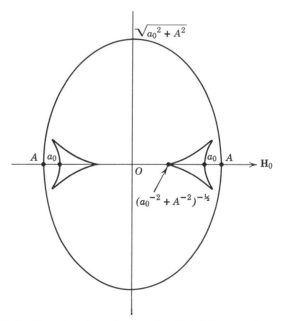

Figure 8.2-7 Characteristic surfaces or Friedrichs' diagrams for $a_0 < A$.

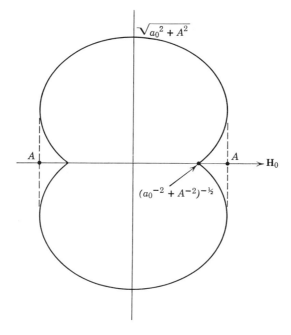

Figure 8.2-8   Characteristic surfaces or Friedrichs' diagrams for $a_0 = A$.

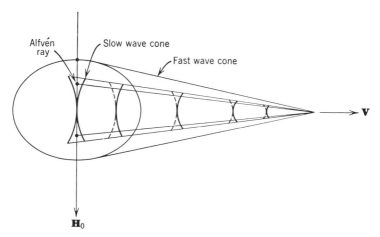

Figure 8.2-9   Development of a sound pulse from a moving source. The source moves with a velocity V greater than $a^2 + A^2$, in a direction perpendicular to the magnetic field H_0. The Alfvén waves may be rays either on the fast wave cone or imbedded in the slow wave cone, depending on whether $a_0 < A$ or $a_0 > A$, respectively.

simple case of aligned flow, where the velocity is along the magnetic field, the description of whether the flow is sub- or super-Alfvén is necessary in addition to the description sub- or super-sonic. Hence, as we shall see, it is possible to have a real flow which is supersonic, yet generate upstream wakes or disturbances by means of the Alfvén wave propagation if $A > a_0$. If $a_0 > A$, supersonic flow would, of course, not produce any upstream disturbance.

We will pursue this subject later when we discuss aerodynamics. We can mention now that for the case of source motion perpendicular to the magnetic field, the analogy of the Mach cone can be visualized. For instance, suppose that the source velocity is greater than the fast wave velocity (and hence must be greater than the slow wave velocity and the Alfvén velocity). The development might look something like that shown in Fig. 8.2-9. As long as the source velocity is perpendicular to the magnetic field, such diagrams can be constructed rather easily. If the motion has a component parallel to the magnetic field, however, the results are not so obvious, but they could be found by a careful analysis (a graphical analysis is probably easiest for quick visualization).

8.3   PLANE WAVES IN LIQUIDS

Magnetoacoustic and transverse waves, which we have just investigated in perfect gases, also exist in liquids. These waves in liquids are almost identical to those in gases; in fact, the transverse waves are exactly the same, and the ideal magnetoacoustic waves are exactly the same in terms of the appropriate sonic velocity a_0. The only differences that occur are in the general magnetoacoustic waves with dissipation included (finite η, ν, ζ, and κ_T). In liquids the energy equation becomes entirely uncoupled and represents heat conduction as a diffusion mode (that is, k^2 is entirely imaginary). Hence in liquids the energy equation is unnecessary for the discussion of magnetoacoustic waves. As with gases, liquids have a magnetic permeability of μ_0, but we can retain a general μ to emphasize the fact that the assumption of μ_0 is unnecessary to obtain our final results. In actual calculations, of course, one should remember to use the value of μ_0 for liquids. (Some newly developed colloidal suspensions do actually behave as magnetic materials, and for this reason it is useful to retain the general μ.)

We begin with the configuration shown in Fig. 8.2-1, write the basic equations, allow for small perturbations, linearize, and obtain the characteristic determinant (still neglecting displacement current). The continuity equation, equations of motion, and Maxwell's equations (and hence the magnetic transport equation) are the same for liquids and gases. Hence we retain Equations 8.2-1, 8.2-3, 8.2-4, 8.2-5, 8.2-7, 8.2-8, and 8.2-9. The equation of state can be written

$$\frac{dP}{\beta} = \frac{d\rho}{\rho} \tag{8.3-1}$$

where β is the bulk modulus. (We will neglect variations of density with temperature compared to variations with pressure.) The perturbation equation of state becomes

$$\rho_0 \frac{\partial P'}{\partial t} = \beta \frac{\partial \rho'}{\partial t} \tag{8.3-2}$$

The energy equation can be written in the form

$$\rho \frac{DU}{Dt} = -P \, \mathbf{\nabla} \cdot \mathbf{V} + \mathbf{E}' \cdot \mathbf{J}' + \Phi + \kappa_T \, \mathbf{\nabla}^2 T \tag{8.3-3}$$

The $-P\mathbf{\nabla} \cdot \mathbf{V}$ term is small and may be neglected for a liquid so that the perturbation equation becomes, approximately,

$$\rho_0 c_V \frac{\partial T'}{\partial t} = \kappa_T \frac{\partial^2 T'}{\partial x^2} \tag{8.3-4}$$

As with gases, Equation (8.2-7) is uncoupled and irrelevant. Equations (8.2-5) and (8.2-9) are coupled and yield the exact same transverse modes as were obtained for gases. Equation (8.2-14) and the conclusions relating to it are all valid for liquids.

However, the determinant for the general magnetoacoustic longitudinal modes is somewhat different because of the different equation of state and energy equation. The characteristic equation is

Equation	u^*	v^*	$h_y{}^*$	P'^*	ρ'^*	T'^*
			Variables			
(8.3-2)	0	0	0	ρ_0	$-\beta$	0
(8.2-1)	$-jk\rho_0$	0	0	0	$j\omega$	0
(8.2-8)	$-jkH_{0y}$	jkH_{0x}	$(j\omega + k^2\eta)$	0	0	0
(8.2-3)	$[j\omega\rho_0 +$ $(\frac{4}{3}\nu\rho_0 + \zeta)k^2]$	0	$-jk\mu H_{0y}$	$-jk$	0	0
(8.2-4)	0	$(j\omega\rho_0 + \nu\rho_0 k^2)$	$jk\mu H_{0x}$	0	0	0
(8.3-4)	0	0	0	0	0	$(\kappa_T k^2 +$ $j\omega c_V \rho_0)$

$$= 0$$

$$\tag{8.3-5}$$

Introducing the acoustic velocity a_0 as $a_0{}^2 = \beta/\rho_0$, we can expand the above determinant to yield

$$
\left\{ [\nu\eta k^4 + \{A_x^2 + j(\nu + \eta)\omega\}k^2 - \omega^2] \cdot \left[-jk^2 + j\frac{\omega^2}{a_0^2} + (\tfrac{4}{3}\nu\rho_0 + \zeta)\frac{k^2\omega}{a_0^2\rho_0} \right] \right.
$$
$$
\left. + \frac{\omega k^2 A_y^2}{a_0^2}(\nu k^2 + j\omega) \right\} \cdot (\kappa_T k^2 + j\omega c_V\rho_0) = 0 \quad (8.3\text{-}6)
$$

We see that this equation (except for the uncoupled right-hand bracket) has exactly the same form as Equation (8.2-19) with κ_T set to zero. (The c_P term then cancels out of (8.2-19) if κ_T is zero.) Equation (8.3-6) represents the general magnetoacoustic and coupled transverse mode in a viscous liquid of finite electrical conductivity. The terms in the right-hand bracket, which is uncoupled, represent pure heat conduction. As with gases, a purely longitudinal wave cannot be excited without exciting the coupled transverse waves, since the terms of the factor in the brace on the left represent transverse waves.

If we take the limit of zero η, ν, ζ, and κ_T (an ideal fluid with perfect conductivity), we get the ideal magnetoacoustic modes, which are identical to those in gases, that is, to those given by Equation (8.2-23), where a_0 is now the acoustic velocity in the liquid. Similarly, the phase velocity and ray-normal diagrams are the same as for gases.

8.4 PLANE WAVES INCLUDING DISPLACEMENT CURRENT

In the previous sections we have neglected the displacement current. In good conductors this assumption is a valid one, and in only relatively poor conductors at high frequencies can the displacement current become important, and even then the electromagnetic type waves introduced by this consideration may damp out quickly. Such is the case in partially ionized gases and liquids.

Consideration of the displacement current does become important in such applications as plasma diagnostics, the propagation of radio waves in the ionosphere, and dielectric liquids. In gases where the effect is important a statistical or microscopic plasma model, such as the multi-component model, is much more meaningful than the macroscopic model. This is particularly true in the ionosphere, where a continuum model becomes rather meaningless. In dense, collision-dominated gases and in liquids the macroscopic fluid model is adequate, and we will now use this model to analyze general wave motion including displacement current.

We can compare $\mathbf{J}$ (the conduction current) and the displacement current $\partial\mathbf{D}/\partial t$. The ratio of $\partial\mathbf{D}/\partial t$ to $\mathbf{J}$ is of order $\omega\epsilon\mathbf{E}^*/\sigma\mathbf{E}^*$ so that displacement current becomes important as the parameter $(\omega\epsilon/\sigma)$ approaches unity. In sea water, for instance, σ is approximately one mho per meter and κ, the relative dielectric constant, is about 80, so that $\partial \mathbf{D}/\partial t$ becomes comparable to $\mathbf{J}$ only at frequencies of about 2×10^8 cycles per second (about 200 megacycles).

In addition to considering the displacement current, we should also look into the possibility of space charge waves since the relaxation time of charge in the dielectric may be significantly large. However, we will assume that no steady electric field (of zero order) is present and that there is no steady value of space charge. Space charge effects are then second order and can be neglected.

Waves in Liquids

The equations of continuity and state are the same as (8.2-1) and (8.3-2). The equations of motion must be modified to include the displacement current effects but, as we will see, they turn out to be identical to the equations used when displacement current was neglected (8.2-3, 8.2-4, and 8.2-5). We write the total body force now as $[\mathbf{J} + (\partial \mathbf{D}/\partial t)] \times \mathbf{B}$ or simply $(\nabla \times \mathbf{H}) \times \mathbf{B}$, which is the same term used previously. There is, remember, some question as to the appropriate form of the body force when the displacement current is significant, but if we assume the Abraham tensor to give the correct result for the electromagnetic momentum, the force is as stated, conveniently yielding the same form in terms of the magnetic field regardless of the inclusion of the displacement current. To be precise, we have for the body force density, in the rest frame at least, $[\mathbf{J} \times \mathbf{B} + (\partial/\partial t)(\mathbf{D} \times \mathbf{B}) - (1/c^2)(\partial/\partial t)(\mathbf{E} \times \mathbf{H})]$, but the value of the third term compared to the second term is small, if $\epsilon \gg \epsilon_0$. Hence in dielectric fluids, where $\epsilon \gg \epsilon_0$, we retain only the first and second terms. Then to first order, $(\partial/\partial t)(\mathbf{D} \times \mathbf{B}) = (\partial \mathbf{D}/\partial t) \times \mathbf{B}$ (there is no steady $\mathbf{D}$ field) and we have from $\nabla \times \mathbf{H} = \mathbf{J} + (\partial \mathbf{D}/\partial t)$ the body force as $(\nabla \times \mathbf{H}) \times \mathbf{B}$, so that the equations of motion are identical to Equations (8.2-3), (8.2-4), and (8.2-5).

At the other extreme for gases, where $\epsilon = \epsilon_0$, there is no force at all due to displacement current and the body force is simply $\mathbf{J} \times \mathbf{B}$. We cannot write $(\nabla \times \mathbf{H}) \times \mathbf{B}$, and we cannot include $(\partial \mathbf{D}/\partial t) \times \mathbf{B}$ (for $\epsilon = \epsilon_0$) since this term is then the vacuum displacement and is exactly canceled out by the momentum term. Hence we have two extremes which we will look at in our macroscopic fluid model. (1) $\epsilon \gg \epsilon_0$ in liquids and we take the force as approximately $(\nabla \times \mathbf{H}) \times \mathbf{B}$, and (2) $\epsilon = \epsilon_0$ in gases and we take the force as $\mathbf{J} \times \mathbf{B}$, $\mathbf{J}$ being given by Ohm's law.

We can now return to our discussion of the liquid model where the energy equation is now the same as Equation (8.3-4). The magnetic transport equations are changed by the inclusion of the displacement current. The Maxwell equations are

$$\nabla \cdot \mathbf{B} = 0$$

$$\nabla \times \mathbf{E} = -\frac{\partial \mathbf{B}}{\partial t} \qquad (8.4\text{-}1)$$

$$\nabla \times \mathbf{H} = \mathbf{J} + \frac{\partial \mathbf{D}}{\partial t}$$

and Ohm's law is

$$\mathbf{J} = \sigma(\mathbf{E} + \mathbf{V} \times \mathbf{B}) \qquad (8.4\text{-}2)$$

The appropriate constitutive equations are

$$\mathbf{B} = \mu\mathbf{H}$$

$$\mathbf{D} = \epsilon\mathbf{E} + \epsilon_0(\kappa - 1)\mathbf{V} \times \mathbf{B} \qquad (8.4\text{-}3)$$

By combining these equations, we have as the appropriate magnetic transport equation including displacement current:

$$\frac{\partial \mathbf{H}}{\partial t} = \eta \, \nabla^2 \mathbf{H} + \nabla \times (\mathbf{V} \times \mathbf{H}) - \eta \, \frac{\kappa \kappa_m}{c^2} \frac{\partial^2 \mathbf{H}}{\partial t^2}$$

$$+ \eta \, \frac{\kappa_m}{c^2}(\kappa - 1) \, \nabla \times \left(\mathbf{V} \times \frac{\partial \mathbf{H}}{\partial t} + \frac{\partial \mathbf{V}}{\partial t} \times \mathbf{H} \right) \quad (8.4\text{-}4)$$

But $\mathbf{V} \times (\partial \mathbf{B}/\partial t)$ is second order and can be neglected in the first-order equation. The components (to first order) of the transport equation are as follows. The x component, which is

$$\frac{\kappa \kappa_m}{c^2} \frac{\partial^2 h_x}{\partial t^2} = \frac{\partial h_x{}^2}{\partial x^2} - \frac{1}{\eta} \frac{\partial h_x}{\partial t}$$

can be written, by using the equation $\nabla \times \mathbf{E} = -\partial \mathbf{B}/\partial t$, as

$$\frac{\partial^2 h_x}{\partial x^2} = 0 \qquad (8.4\text{-}5)$$

$$\frac{\kappa \kappa_m}{c^2} \frac{\partial^2 h_y}{\partial t^2} + \frac{1}{\eta} \frac{\partial h_y}{\partial t} = \frac{\partial^2 h_y}{\partial x^2} + \frac{1}{\eta} H_{0x} \frac{\partial v}{\partial x} - \frac{1}{\eta} H_{0y} \frac{\partial u}{\partial x}$$

$$- \frac{\kappa_m}{c^2}(\kappa - 1)\left(H_{0y} \frac{\partial^2 u}{\partial x \, \partial t} - H_{0x} \frac{\partial^2 v}{\partial x \, \partial t} \right) \quad (8.4\text{-}6)$$

$$\frac{\kappa \kappa_m}{c^2} \frac{\partial^2 h_z}{\partial t^2} + \frac{1}{\eta} \frac{\partial h_z}{\partial t} = \frac{\partial^2 h_z}{\partial x^2} + \frac{1}{\eta} H_{0x} \frac{\partial w}{\partial x} + \frac{\kappa_m}{c^2}(\kappa - 1)H_{0x} \frac{\partial^2 w}{\partial x \, \partial t} \quad (8.4\text{-}7)$$

Now Equation (8.4-5) is uncoupled and trivial. Equations (8.4-7) and (8.2-5) couple together for the transverse waves, and the remaining six equations form the longitudinal modes.

Transverse Waves in Liquids

Equations (8.4-7) and (8.2-5) give the following characteristic determinant:

Variables

Equation	w^*	$h_z{}^*$	
(8.2-5)	$(j\rho_0\omega + \nu\rho_u k^2)$	$j\mu H_{0x}k$	
(8.4-7)	$\left(\dfrac{j}{\eta}H_{0x}k - \dfrac{\kappa_m}{c^2}(\kappa - 1)H_{0x}k\omega\right)$	$\left(\dfrac{j\omega}{\eta} - \dfrac{\kappa\kappa_m}{c^2}\omega^2 + k^2\right)$	$= 0$

$$(8.4\text{-}8)$$

When expanded, the determinant yields

$$\nu\eta k^4 + \left\{A_x{}^2\left[1 + j\frac{\omega\eta\kappa_m(\kappa - 1)}{c^2}\right] + j\omega(\nu + \eta)\right\}k^2$$

$$- \omega^2\left[1 + \frac{\kappa\kappa_m\eta}{c^2}(\nu k^2 + j\omega)\right] = 0 \quad (8.4\text{-}9)$$

In the limit, as the terms involving κ and κ_m are removed (equivalent to neglecting displacement current), this equation reduces to Equation (8.2-14). (The removal of the displacement current effects in the above equation can be accomplished by the mathematical artifice of simply letting c go to infinity.) In practice, of course, the value of κ_m is essentially unity for all conducting fluids. Let us look at some special limiting cases of Equation (8.4-9).

1. If all dissipation is neglected, that is, $\nu = \eta = 0$, we get a pure Alfvén wave as before and displacement current has no effect.

2. If the viscosity ν is zero and the conductivity goes to zero, $\sigma \rightarrow 0$ so that $\eta \rightarrow \infty$; then no conduction current exists and the characteristic equation becomes

$$\left(k^2 - \frac{\kappa\kappa_m}{c^2}\omega^2\right) + k^2 A_x{}^2 \frac{\kappa_m(\kappa - 1)}{c^2} = 0 \quad (8.4\text{-}10)$$

and the phase velocity a is given by

$$a^2 = \left(\frac{\omega}{k}\right)^2 = \frac{c^2}{\kappa\kappa_m}\left[1 + \frac{A_x^2\kappa_m(\kappa - 1)}{c^2}\right] \tag{8.4-11}$$

We see that this is a pure electromagnetic wave in a material medium (where $a^2 = c^2/\kappa_m\kappa$) modified in an essentially negligible manner by the Alfvén wave. In general $A_x^2\kappa_m(\kappa - 1)/c^2 \ll 1$ so that in reality it is unlikely that the phase velocity could be significantly changed by the presence of the steady magnetic field.

3. If A_x is zero (A_y may be zero or not since its effects are uncoupled in the transverse mode), that is, if there is no applied magnetic field in the x direction, the direction of propagation, then Equation (8.4-9) takes the following form:

$$(j\omega + \nu k^2)\left[jk^2 - \omega\left(\frac{1}{\eta} + j\frac{\kappa_m\kappa\omega}{c^2}\right)\right] = 0 \tag{8.4-12}$$

The first parenthesis represents viscous diffusion of transverse disturbances, and only the second bracket is of interest here. Solving for $(\omega/\text{Re }k)$ we have

$$a = \pm\omega\sqrt{2}\left[\sqrt{\left(\frac{\omega}{c}\right)^4\kappa_m^2\kappa^2 + \left(\frac{\omega}{\eta}\right)^2} + \left(\frac{\omega}{c}\right)^2\kappa_m\kappa\right]^{-\frac{1}{2}} \tag{8.4-13}$$

which reduces to $a = \pm c/\sqrt{\kappa_m\kappa}$ as $\eta \to \infty$ (zero conductivity). For $(\omega/\eta) \gg (\omega/c)^2$, which is the case, say, for sea water at radio frequencies, $a \approx \sqrt{2\omega\eta}$ and radio waves propagate mainly by magnetic diffusion. The effect of displacement current, then, is of secondary importance here. The attenuation (imaginary part of k) can also be calculated and we obtain

$$\text{Im }k = \mp\frac{1}{\sqrt{2}}\left[\sqrt{\left(\frac{\omega}{c}\right)^4\kappa_m^2\kappa^2 + \left(\frac{\omega}{\eta}\right)^2} - \left(\frac{\omega}{c}\right)^2\kappa_m\kappa\right]^{\frac{1}{2}} \tag{8.4-14}$$

In Equation (8.4-14) the imaginary part of k is always negative for positive values of a (propagation in the positive x direction) and positive for negative values of a (propagation in the negative x direction), indicating attenuation of the wave as it travels. The attenuation of the wave increases with frequency, becoming $(\frac{1}{2}c/\eta)/\sqrt{\kappa_m\kappa}$ for large values of ω. For $(\omega/\eta) \gg (\omega/c)^2$ (sea water), $\text{Im }k \approx \sqrt{\omega/2\eta}$. Hence we do not expect radio waves to be transmitted in sea water except for very low frequencies for short distances. (Frequencies below about 50 kilocycles are used in submarine communications. The radio waves propagate as ground waves over the sea and are refracted down into the water to a depth of a few meters before becoming completely lost.)*

For the limit as $\eta \to \infty$ (zero conductivity), no damping occurs and the phase velocity a becomes simply $\pm c/\sqrt{\kappa_m \kappa}$. As $\eta \to 0$ (conductivity infinite), the damping becomes increasingly larger and in the limit no waves can penetrate into the fluid at all and there is no propagation.

Longitudinal Modes in Liquids

The remaining six equations are coupled to give the longitudinal waves with displacement current considered. The determinant is (see page 326). We will not examine these longitudinal waves in detail, but will look only at the special case of no dissipation, the ideal magnetoacoustic waves. If Equation (8.4-15) is expanded and the dissipation taken as zero, we see that all displacement terms are multiplied by η so that all these terms drop out leaving exactly the same result as we obtained neglecting the displacement current. We conclude that displacement current has no effect on the propagation of ideal magnetoacoustic waves.

The main effect of displacement current, then, is the introduction of a new transverse mode of propagation which degenerates into the classical electromagnetic wave in the absence of any applied magnetic field.

Gases

If the effect of displacement current is included in the study of waves in gases, the analysis is similar to that for liquids, but the body force term must be taken as $\mathbf{J} \times \mathbf{B}$ and not as $(\nabla \times \mathbf{H}) \times \mathbf{B}$. The reason for this is that $\epsilon = \epsilon_0$ in gases and, since $\mathbf{J}$ must be comparable to $\partial \mathbf{D}/\partial t$, the sum $[\mathbf{J} + (\partial \mathbf{D}/\partial t)]$ does not represent the actual interaction current. In detail, the force is $(\mathbf{J} \times \mathbf{B}) + (\partial/\partial t)(\mathbf{D} \times \mathbf{B}) - (1/c^2)(\partial/\partial t)(\mathbf{E} \times \mathbf{H})$. But in a

---

* We have assumed κ to be a real constant. In reality, in a conductor κ is complex and is a function of frequency, varying inversely with frequency. Hence at very high frequency the metal is actually transparent to the waves (usually the X-ray region). The critical frequency above which the material becomes transparent is known as the plasma frequency. For copper, the low frequency approximation which we have used here is valid for frequencies below about 10^6 megacycles.

We will not pursue this point here since it is of little interest in MHD. However, the behavior of rarefied gases, in which the plasma frequency may be in the microwave range, is of importance. In rarefied gases, using a microscopic model, the dielectric properties of the gas will be found as part of the general problem. Actually, $\mathbf{D} = \epsilon_0 \mathbf{E}$ in the gas, but σ will then be a tensor, giving rise to the transparent behavior above the plasma frequency. See Kittel (1956) and Feynman et al. (1964).

Variables

Equation	u^*	v^*	h_y^*	P'^*	ρ'^*	T'^*	
(8.3-2)	0	0	0	ρ_0	$-\beta$	0	
(8.2-1)	$-jk\rho_0$	0	0	0	$j\omega$	0	
(8.4-6)	$\left[-jkH_{0y} - j\eta\,\dfrac{\kappa_m}{c^2}(\kappa-1)H_{0y}k\omega\right]$	$\left[jkH_{0x} + j\eta\,\dfrac{\kappa_m}{c^2}(\kappa-1)H_{0x}k\omega\right]$	$\left[\begin{array}{c} j\omega + k^2\eta \\ -\eta\,\dfrac{\kappa\kappa_m\omega^2}{c^2} \end{array}\right]$	0	0	0	$= 0$
(3.2-3)	$[j\omega\rho_0 + (\zeta + \tfrac{4}{3}\nu\rho_0)k^2]$	0	$-jk\mu H_{0y}$	$-jk$	0	0	
(8.2-4)	0	$(j\omega\rho_0 + \nu\rho_0 k^2)$	$jk\mu H_{0x}$	0	0	0	
(8.3-4)	0	0	0	0	0	$(\kappa_T k^2 + j\omega c_v\rho_0)$	

$$(8.4\text{-}15)$$

gas $\mathbf{D} \times \mathbf{B} = (1/c^2)\mathbf{E} \times \mathbf{H}$ and the force must necessarily be written as $\mathbf{J} \times \mathbf{B}$. Physically, we can have no force due to a vacuum displacement current.

The continuity equation is the same as (8.2-1), the equation of state is the same as (8.2-2), and the energy equation is (8.2-6). However, we must now write out the Maxwell equations in full, retaining the electric field terms. It is not particularly expedient to combine these equations into a magnetic transport equation, since the electric field must now appear in the equations of motion. The relevant Maxwell equations are

$$\nabla \cdot \mathbf{B} = \nabla \cdot \mathbf{H} = 0$$

$$\nabla \times \mathbf{E} = -\frac{\partial \mathbf{B}}{\partial t} = -\mu \frac{\partial \mathbf{H}}{\partial t}$$

$$\nabla \times \mathbf{H} = \mathbf{J} + \frac{\partial \mathbf{D}}{\partial t} = \mathbf{J} + \epsilon_0 \frac{\partial \mathbf{E}}{\partial t} \qquad (8.4\text{-}16)$$

$$= \sigma(\mathbf{E} + \mathbf{V} \times \mathbf{B}) + \epsilon_0 \frac{\partial \mathbf{E}}{\partial t}$$

which, when written out in appropriate component form to first order, become

$$\frac{\partial h_x}{\partial x} = 0 \qquad (8.4\text{-}17)$$

$$\frac{\partial h_x}{\partial t} = 0 \qquad (8.4\text{-}18)$$

$$-\mu \frac{\partial h_y}{\partial t} = -\frac{\partial E_z}{\partial x} \qquad (8.4\text{-}19)$$

$$-\mu \frac{\partial h_z}{\partial t} = \frac{\partial E_y}{\partial x} \qquad (8.4\text{-}20)$$

$$0 = \sigma E_x + \epsilon_0 \frac{\partial E_x}{\partial t} - \frac{w}{\eta} H_{0y} \qquad (8.4\text{-}21)$$

$$-\frac{\partial h_z}{\partial x} = \sigma E_y + \epsilon_0 \frac{\partial E_y}{\partial t} + \frac{w}{\eta} H_{0x} \qquad (8.4\text{-}22)$$

$$\frac{\partial h_y}{\partial x} = \sigma E_z + \epsilon_0 \frac{\partial E_z}{\partial t} + \frac{1}{\eta}(uH_{0y} - vH_{0x}) \qquad (8.4\text{-}23)$$

Here the electric field components are all perturbation quantities since the steady values are zero. We do not use primes for perturbation field quantities because we wish to retain that notation for rest-frame quantities when we discuss moving fluids in the next section.

The equation of motion, combined with Ohm's law $\mathbf{J} = \sigma(\mathbf{E} + \mathbf{V} \times \mathbf{B})$, is

$$\rho\left[\frac{\partial \mathbf{V}}{\partial t} + (\mathbf{V} \cdot \nabla)\mathbf{V}\right] = -\nabla P + \nu\rho_0\nabla^2\mathbf{V} + (\zeta + \tfrac{1}{3}\nu\rho_0)\nabla(\nabla \cdot \mathbf{V})$$
$$+ \sigma(\mathbf{E} + \mathbf{V} \times \mathbf{B}) \times \mathbf{B} \quad (8.4\text{-}24)$$

so that the first-order perturbation equations of motion in component form are

$$\rho_0\frac{\partial u}{\partial t} = -\frac{\partial P'}{\partial x} + (\zeta + \tfrac{4}{3}\nu\rho_0)\frac{\partial^2 u}{\partial x^2} - \frac{1}{\eta}E_z H_{0y}$$
$$- \frac{\mu}{\eta}H_{0y}(uH_{0y} - vH_{0x}) \quad (8.4\text{-}25)$$

$$\rho_0\frac{\partial v}{\partial t} = \nu\rho_0\frac{\partial^2 v}{\partial x^2} + \frac{1}{\eta}E_z H_{0x} + \frac{\mu}{\eta}H_{0x}(uH_{0y} - vH_{0x}) \quad (8.4\text{-}26)$$

$$\rho\frac{\partial w}{\partial t} = \nu\rho_0\frac{\partial^2 w}{\partial x^2} + \frac{1}{\eta}(E_x H_{0y} - E_y H_{0x}) - \frac{w\mu}{\eta}(H_{0y}^2 + H_{0x}^2) \quad (8.4\text{-}27)$$

As before, (8.4-17) and (8.4-18) uncouple and are irrelevant. Equations (8.4-20), (8.4-21), (8.4-22), and (8.4-27) combine to give the transverse waves. The characteristic determinant is

Variables

Equation	$h_z{}^*$	w^*	$E_y{}^*$	$E_x{}^*$	
(8.4-20)	$j\mu\omega$	0	$-jk$	0	
(8.4-21)	0	$\dfrac{-H_{0y}}{\eta}$	0	$(\sigma + j\epsilon_0\omega)$	
(8.4-22)	$-jk$	$\dfrac{H_{0x}}{\eta}$	$(\sigma + j\epsilon_0\omega)$	0	$= 0$
(8.4-27)	0	$\begin{bmatrix} -\rho_0 j\omega & -\nu\rho_0 k^2 \\ \dfrac{-\mu}{\eta}(H_{0y}^2 + H_{0x}^2) \end{bmatrix}$	$\dfrac{-H_{0x}}{\eta}$	$\dfrac{H_{0y}}{\eta}$	

(8.4-28)

This then is the characteristic determinant for transverse TM waves in a viscous, electrically conducting gas in the presence of a magnetic field, with effects of displacement current included. If we leave out the displacement current terms $(j\epsilon_0\omega)$ the determinant upon expansion yields exactly Equation (8.2-14), as we would expect. Because these waves are rather important, we will compute some of their properties explicitly. By expanding the determinant, we obtain the following characteristic equation or dispersion relationship:

$$\left(j\frac{\omega}{\eta} - \frac{\omega^2}{c^2}\right)\left[(j\omega + k^2\nu)\left(k^2 - \frac{\omega^2}{c^2} + j\frac{\omega}{\eta}\right) + \frac{A_x^2}{\eta}\left(k^2 - \frac{\omega^2}{c^2}\right)\right]$$

$$- \frac{\omega^2}{c^2}\frac{A_y^2}{\eta}\left(k^2 - \frac{\omega^2}{c^2} + j\frac{\omega}{\eta}\right) = 0 \quad (8.4\text{-}29)$$

This equation is quadratic in k^2, so that there are two different types of waves or modes of propagation. The presence of two modes is due to a coupling with the viscosity ν and we can get a single mode by letting $\nu \to 0$. The value of $\omega/\mathrm{Re}\, k$ and $\mathrm{Im}\, k$ are important here and characterize the waves. These quantities can be calculated and we obtain after a little algebraic manipulation (for $\nu = 0$)

$$a = \frac{\omega}{\mathrm{Re}\, k} = \pm\frac{\omega\sqrt{2\xi}}{(\sqrt{\alpha^2 + \beta^2} + \alpha)^{1/2}} \quad (8.4\text{-}30)$$

$$\mathrm{Im}\, k = \mp\frac{(\sqrt{\alpha^2 + \beta^2} - \alpha)^{1/2}}{\sqrt{2\xi}} \quad (8.4\text{-}31)$$

where $k^2 = (\alpha - j\beta)/\xi$. The values of α, β, and ξ here are

$$\alpha = \frac{\omega^2}{\eta^2}\left(1 + \frac{A^2}{c^2}\right)\left[\frac{\omega^2}{c^2}\left(1 + \frac{A^2}{c^2}\right) + \frac{A_x^2}{\eta^2}\right] + \frac{\omega^4}{c^4}\left(\frac{\omega^2}{c^2} - \frac{A_x^2}{\eta^2}\right)$$

$$\xi = \frac{\omega^2}{\eta^2}\left(1 + \frac{A^2}{c^2}\right)^2 + \left(\frac{\omega^2}{c^2} - \frac{A_x^2}{\eta^2}\right)^2$$

$$\beta = \frac{\omega^3}{\eta^3}\left[\left(1 + \frac{A^2}{c^2}\right)^2 + \frac{\eta^2\omega^2}{c^4} - \frac{A_x^2}{c^2}\left(\frac{A^2}{c^2} + 2\right)\right]$$

where $A^2 = A_x^2 + A_y^2$.

The expression for $\mathrm{Im}\, k$ indicates damping as the wave propagates (a negative value of $\mathrm{Im}\, k$ for positive or forward traveling waves, and a positive value of $\mathrm{Im}\, k$ for a negative or backward wave). As $\eta \to 0$ ($\sigma \to \infty$) and $c \to \infty$ (that is, neglecting displacement current effects), we get simply A_x for a and $\mathrm{Im}\, k$ goes to zero. This limit gives precisely the pure Alfvén wave, as it should. From a practical standpoint, $A^2 \ll c^2$ so that A^2/c^2 may be neglected compared to unity.

Several special cases of Equation (8.4-29) are of interest and we will look at some of them now.

1. If $\mathbf{H} = 0$ (no applied magnetic field), A_x and A_y are zero, the equations of motion become completely uncoupled, and an ordinary TEM electromagnetic wave in dissipative media results. The dispersion equation obtained from Equation (8.4-29) under the condition that $\mathbf{H} = 0$ is the same as (8.4-12), that is,

$$(j\omega + \nu k^2)\left[jk^2 - \omega\left(\frac{1}{\eta} + j\frac{\omega}{c^2}\right)\right] = 0 \qquad (8.4\text{-}32)$$

Remember that $\mu = \mu_0$ and $\epsilon = \epsilon_0$ and that $c^2 = 1/\mu_0\epsilon_0$. The calculations and observations given in the previous section for liquids (Equations 8.4-13 and 8.4-14) are all valid here, including the comment on conductivity.

2. The limit as $\eta \to 0$ is not allowed here since σ must remain finite so that the conduction current is comparable to the displacement current. (Ohm's law is assumed to hold here.) Allowing $\eta \to 0$ prevents penetration of an electromagnetic wave into the fluid and no wave can propagate under such conditions.

3. $H_{0y} = 0$, and $\nu = 0$. The characteristic equation is

$$k^2\left(\omega - j\frac{A_x^2}{\eta}\right) + j\left(\frac{\omega^2}{\eta} + \frac{A_x^2\omega^2}{c^2\eta}\right) - \frac{\omega^3}{c^2} = 0 \qquad (8.4\text{-}33)$$

which is linear in k^2, indicating that only one mode is present. As $\eta \to \infty$ ($\sigma \to 0$), we get an ordinary TEM wave of velocity c. Equation (8.4-33) can be solved for the relevant parameters to give

$$a = \frac{\omega}{\text{Re } k} =$$

$$\pm \frac{\omega\sqrt{2\left(\omega^2 + \dfrac{A_x^4}{\eta^2}\right)}}{\left\{\sqrt{\dfrac{\omega^4}{c^4}\left[\omega^2 + \dfrac{A_x^2}{\eta^2}(A_x^2 + c^2)\right]^2 + \dfrac{\omega^6}{\eta^2}} + \dfrac{\omega^2}{c^2}\left[\omega^2 + \dfrac{A_x^2}{\eta^2}(A_x^2 + c^2)\right]\right\}^{1/2}} \qquad (8.4\text{-}34)$$

$$\text{Im } k =$$

$$\mp \frac{\left\{\sqrt{\dfrac{\omega^4}{c^4}\left[\omega^2 + \dfrac{A_x^2}{\eta^2}(A_x^2 + c^2)\right]^2 + \dfrac{\omega^6}{\eta^2}} - \dfrac{\omega^2}{c^2}\left[\omega^2 + \dfrac{A_x^2}{\eta^2}(A_x^2 + c^2)\right]\right\}^{1/2}}{\sqrt{2\left(\omega^2 + \dfrac{A_x^4}{\eta^2}\right)}} \qquad (8.4\text{-}35)$$

which indicates that attenuation occurs as the wave propagates. As before, $A_x^2/c^2 \ll 1$ and may in practice be neglected in comparison to unity. Equations (8.4-34) and (8.4-35) may be obtained from (8.4-30) and (8.4-31) in the limit as H_{0y} or A_y goes to zero. If we take the limit of (8.4-34) and (8.4-35) as $A_x = 0$ (no applied field at all), Equations (8.4-13) and (8.4-14) result.

4. $H_{0x} = 0$, $\nu = 0$ (only a transverse field is applied). We obtain

$$j\omega\left(j\frac{\omega}{\eta} - \frac{\omega^2}{c^2}\right)\left(k^2 - \frac{\omega^2}{c^2} + j\frac{\omega}{\eta}\right) - \frac{\omega^2}{c^2}\frac{A_y^2}{\eta}\left(k^2 - \frac{\omega^2}{c^2} + j\frac{\omega}{\eta}\right) = 0 \quad (8.4\text{-}36)$$

The phase velocity and attenuation are not given explicitly here but can be obtained from Equations (8.4-30) and (8.4-31) by taking the limit as $A_x \to 0$.

Longitudinal Waves in Gases

The remaining seven equations are coupled to give the longitudinal magnetoacoustic modes. By combining Equations (8.4-19), (8.4-23), (8.4-25), (8.4-26), (8.2-1), (8.2-2), and (8.2-6), we get the characteristic determinant as shown on page 332.

We cannot take the limit here as $\eta \to 0$ ($\sigma \to \infty$) because we have written Ohm's law as $\mathbf{J} = \sigma(\mathbf{E} + \mathbf{V} \times \mathbf{B})$ for the specification of $\mathbf{J}$. Also, we have retained displacement current so that σ must be finite and of order $\epsilon\omega$. We can, however, take the limit as $\eta \to \infty$ ($\sigma \to 0$) and get ordinary acoustic waves in a heat-conducting, viscous gas. (There can be no electromagnetic body force or coupling if $\sigma = 0$.) Moreover, it is important to remember that if we assume an ideal gas with $\nu = \zeta = \kappa_T = 0$ and $\eta \to 0$ ($\sigma \to \infty$), which necessitates dropping the displacement current term for consistency, the result, obviously, is ideal magnetoacoustic waves.

We will not expand (8.4-37) here, but if the displacement current term (in Equation 8.4-23) is dropped, the determinant must be identical to Equation (8.2-18). This fact can easily be verified by expansion of the determinant, although (8.4-37) is a seventh-order determinant it reduces to 8.2-18 under the above conditions because common factors will drop out. This expansion is left as an exercise for the ambitious reader.

8.5 TRANSVERSE WAVES IN A MOVING FLUID

So far we have confined our study to wave motion in stationary fluids. That is, there has been no steady (zeroth order) value of fluid velocity. We will now look at some of the effects that occur when the fluid is moving (with respect to the observer measuring the field quantities).

Variables

Equation	u^*	v^*	$h_y{}^*$	P'^*	ρ'^*	T'^*	$E_z{}^*$	
(8.2-2)	0	0	0	$\dfrac{1}{P_0}$	$\dfrac{-1}{\rho_0}$	$\dfrac{-1}{T_0}$	0	
(8.2-1)	$-jk\rho_0$	0	0	0	$j\omega$	0	0	
(8.4-19)	0	0	$j\mu\omega$	0	0	0	jk	
(8.4-23)	$\dfrac{H_{0y}}{\eta}$	$\dfrac{-H_{0x}}{\eta}$	jk	0	0	0	$(\sigma + j\epsilon_0\omega)$	
(8.4-25)	$\left[-\rho_0 j\omega - (\zeta + \tfrac{4}{3}\nu\rho_0)k^2\right] - \dfrac{1}{\eta}\mu H_{0y}{}^2$	$\left(\dfrac{1}{\eta}\mu H_{0x}H_{0y}\right)$	0	jk	0	0	$\dfrac{-H_{0y}}{\eta}$	$= 0$
(8.4-26)	$\left(\dfrac{1}{\eta}\mu H_{0x}H_{0y}\right)$	$\left[-\rho_0 j\omega - \nu\rho_0 k^2\right] - \dfrac{1}{\eta}\mu H_{0x}{}^2$	0	0	0	0	$\dfrac{H_{0x}}{\eta}$	
(8.2-6)	0	0	0	$-j\omega$	0	$(\kappa_T k^2 + j\omega c_P \rho_0)$	0	

$$(8.4\text{-}37)$$

Consider plane wave propagation in the x direction in a fluid with velocity V_0 in the x directon. A steady magnetic field H_{0x} (along the x axis) is present (see Fig. 8.5-1). The effect of displacement current will be included in the analysis and then limits can be taken as this effect is neglected.

As was emphasized before, if the effect of displacement current is neglected, wave behavior is exactly the same in liquids and gases. Inclusion of the displacement current leads to somewhat different results because in

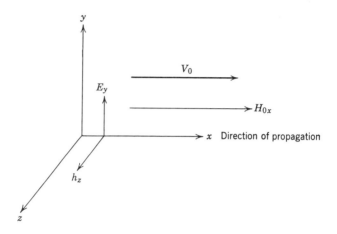

Figure 8.5-1 Propagation in a moving fluid. The fluid is moving steadily in the x direction, which is the direction of propagation. A steady magnetic field H_{0x} is applied in the x direction.

a gas (where $\epsilon = \epsilon_0$) the vacuum displacement current generates no body force, whereas in a liquid the relatively high dielectric constant may give rise to forces comparable to conduction current interaction forces. From a practical standpoint, only the propagation in gases is of real interest, since in any liquid the attenuation must be so great (under conditions where displacement current is important) that propagation phenomena are of little interest (one example, propagation in sea water, has been mentioned). For the sake of completeness, however, we will discuss liquids in this section.

One important application of propagation in moving gases is the general field of plasma diagnostics, where microwave radiation is passed through a moving gas, such as is generated in a shock tube or plasma gun, and various properties of the gas are determined by the effect of the gas on the microwave signal. We will deal with such problems in more detail presently, discussing reflection and transmission from moving plasma interfaces, etc., but first let us examine the propagation in a moving fluid without regard to the surface or boundary effects.

Gases

The relevant linearized Maxwell equations (using Ohm's law) and equations of motion are the following. (The body force is simply $\mathbf{J} \times \mathbf{B}$ and displacement current effects are included. The permittivity of a gas is essentially ϵ_0 and we write simply $\mathbf{D} = \epsilon_0 \mathbf{E}$ in any frame of reference; of course, $\mathbf{B} = \mu_0 \mathbf{H}$.)

$$\frac{\partial E_y}{\partial x} = -\mu_0 \frac{\partial h_z}{\partial t} \tag{8.5-1}$$

$$-\frac{\partial h_z}{\partial x} = \sigma E_y + \sigma w \mu_0 H_{0x} - \sigma \mu_0 V_0 h_z + \epsilon_0 \frac{\partial E_y}{\partial t} \tag{8.5-2}$$

$$\rho_0 \left(\frac{\partial w}{\partial t} + V_0 \frac{\partial w}{\partial x} \right) = \nu \rho_0 \frac{\partial^2 w}{\partial x^2} - \sigma \mu_0 E_y H_{0x}$$
$$+ \sigma \mu_0^2 V_0 h_z H_{0x} - \sigma \mu_0^2 w H_{0x}^2 \tag{8.5-3}$$

Here h_y, h_z, and E_y are the perturbation quantities. Assuming a phasor solution of the form $e^{j(\omega t - kx)}$, we obtain for the characteristic determinant the following:

Variables

Equation	w^*	h_z^*	E_y^*
(8.5-1)	0	$-j\mu_0\omega$	jk
(8.5-2)	$\dfrac{H_{0x}}{\eta}$	$-\left(jk + \dfrac{V_0}{\eta} \right)$	$(\sigma + j\epsilon_0\omega)$
(8.5-3)	$\left(-\nu\rho_0 k^2 - \dfrac{\mu_0}{\eta} H_{0x}^2 \right.$ $\left. + jV_0 k\rho_0 - j\rho_0\omega \right)$	$\dfrac{\mu_0 V_0 H_{0x}}{\eta}$	$\dfrac{-H_{0x}}{\eta}$

$$= 0$$

$$(8.5\text{-}4)$$

which upon expansion yields

$$\frac{A_x^2}{\eta}\left(k^2 - \frac{\omega^2}{c^2} \right) + (\nu k^2 - jV_0 k + j\omega)\left(k^2 + j\frac{\omega}{\eta} - j\frac{kV_0}{\eta} - \frac{\omega^2}{c^2} \right) = 0 \tag{8.5-5}$$

We note that if V_0 is zero, Equation (8.5-5) reduces to Equation (8.4-29) (with $A_y = 0$). If both V_0 and v are zero, we get Equation (8.4-33). If we neglect the effect of displacement current, set V_0 to zero, and take the limit as $v = \eta = 0$ (no dissipation), we get a pure Alfvén wave. The displacement current effect is removed by allowing c^2 to go to infinity in the preceding equation. Alternatively, if we allow the magnetic field H_{0x} to go to zero ($A_x = 0$), we get ordinary electromagnetic wave propagation in a moving dispersive medium, and an uncoupled viscous diffusion in a moving fluid.

If both the magnetic field goes to zero ($A_x = 0$) and $\eta \to \infty$ (zero conductivity), we get ordinary electromagnetic wave propagation, since the motion now has no effect, and in addition an uncoupled viscous diffusion wave in a moving fluid.

Under these conditions of complete uncoupling of the fluid and electromagnetic effects ($A_x = 0$, and $\eta \to \infty$), Equation (8.5-5) becomes

$$(j\omega + vk^2 - jkV_0)\left(k^2 - \frac{\omega^2}{c^2}\right) = 0 \qquad (8.5\text{-}6)$$

The second parenthesis is the ordinary electromagnetic wave, with phase velocity c, the velocity of light, and the first parenthesis (which is uncoupled) gives a viscous diffusion wave in a moving fluid. If v were zero (that is, if the fluid were inviscid), we would get a standing wave in the fluid. In other words, a small transverse disturbance in the fluid would move along with the fluid without dispersion or dissipation.

In general, if H_{0x} is present and η is finite, Equation (8.5-5) indicates that the viscous wave is coupled to the electromagnetic wave and will be excited whenever an electromagnetic wave is excited, and vice versa.

If the displacement current is neglected in Equation (8.5-5), we get coupled Alfvén-type waves and viscous waves. If dissipation is neglected ($\eta \to 0$ and $v \to 0$) and displacement current is neglected (ω^2/c^2 terms $\to 0$), we get pure Alfvén waves in a moving fluid. Then Equation (8.5-5) becomes

$$(A_x^2 - V_0^2)k^2 - \omega^2\left(1 - 2k\frac{V_0}{\omega}\right) = 0 \qquad (8.5\text{-}7)$$

so that

$$a = \pm\sqrt{\frac{\omega}{k}} = V_0 \pm A_x$$

which is exactly what we would expect, an Alfvén wave propagating with velocity A_x with respect to the moving fluid.

We will not attempt to discuss (8.5-5) in generality here, but the inviscid case is of interest, since most gases have small viscosity which can be neglected except in the boundary layer. In a gas ν is usually several orders of magnitude smaller than η. Setting ν to zero in (8.5-5) yields a cubic equation in k. This dispersion relationship is

$$V_0 k^3 - \left[\omega + j \frac{V_0^2}{\eta}\left(1 - \frac{A_x^2}{V_0^2}\right)\right] k^2 - \left[\left(\frac{\omega}{c}\right)^2 - 2j \frac{\omega}{\eta}\right] k V_0$$

$$+ \omega\left[\left(\frac{\omega}{c}\right)^2 - j \frac{\omega}{\eta}\left(1 + \frac{A_x^2}{c^2}\right)\right] = 0 \quad (8.5\text{-}8)$$

Since this equation is cubic in k, the forward and backward wave propagation must not be symmetric, as we would expect, because of the fluid velocity V_0 in the x direction. Two roots represent forward and backward waves, electromagnetic in nature, and the third root represents a wave with phase velocity close to V_0, that is, essentially a standing wave in the fluid. The equation becomes linear in k^2 if V_0 is set to zero, or if $\eta \to \infty$, which corresponds to setting σ, the conductivity, to zero and eliminating the fluid-field interaction.

No simple exact solution exists for Equation (8.5-8), but a rather simple approximate solution can be obtained under certain simplifying assumptions (Hughes and Young, 1964).

Liquids

For liquids, we can use the appropriate magnetic transport equation and the equations of motion. Remember that $\epsilon \neq \epsilon_0$ here and hence the constitutive equations must be written in the general form. We assume that $\epsilon \gg \epsilon_0$ so that $\mathbf{J} \times \mathbf{B} + (\partial \mathbf{P}/\partial t) \times \mathbf{B}$ is approximately $(\nabla \times \mathbf{H}) \times \mathbf{B}$. (See Section 8.4.)

The relevant equations are (8.4-4) (the transport equation) and the equations of motion. Written out in linearized form, these equations are

$$\frac{\kappa \kappa_m}{c}\frac{\partial^2 h_z}{\partial t^2} + \frac{1}{\eta}\frac{\partial h_z}{\partial t} = \frac{\partial^2 h_z}{\partial x^2} + \frac{1}{\eta} V_0 \frac{\partial h_z}{\partial x} - \frac{1}{\eta} H_{0x}\frac{\partial w}{\partial x}$$

$$+ \frac{\kappa_m(\kappa - 1)}{c^2}\left(V_0 \frac{\partial^2 h_z}{\partial x\, \partial t} - H_{0x}\frac{\partial^2 w}{\partial x\, \partial t}\right) \quad (8.5\text{-}9)$$

$$\rho_0\left(\frac{\partial w}{\partial t} + V_0 \frac{\partial w}{\partial x}\right) = \nu \rho_0 \frac{\partial^2 w}{\partial x^2} + \mu H_{0x}\frac{\partial h_z}{\partial x} \quad (8.5\text{-}10)$$

which give the characteristic determinant

Equations	Variables	
	w^*	$h_z{}^*$

$$(8.5\text{-}10)$$
$$(8.5\text{-}9)$$

$$\begin{vmatrix} (j\rho_0\omega - j\rho_0 V_0 k + \nu\rho_0 k^2) & j\mu H_{0x} \\ \left(-\dfrac{j}{\eta} H_{0x}k + \dfrac{\kappa_m(\kappa-1)}{c^2} H_{0x}k\omega\right) & \left[\dfrac{j}{\eta}\omega - \dfrac{\kappa\kappa_m\omega^2}{c^2} + k^2 + \dfrac{jkV_0}{\eta}\right. \\ & \left. -\dfrac{\kappa_m(\kappa-1)V_0 k\omega}{c^2}\right] \end{vmatrix} = 0$$

$$(8.5\text{-}11)$$

which reduces to Equation (8.4-8) for V_0 zero. We will not discuss the solution of this equation here as it is of little practical importance, except in problems involving streaming of dielectric liquids such as sea water. The expansion of the determinant yields a fourth-order equation in k, but not quadratic in k^2. If viscosity is neglected, the equation becomes cubic in k, and the remarks made concerning the analogous waves in gases are generally applicable.

8.6 INTERACTIONS AT A FLUID INTERFACE

In this section and the two that follow we will discuss the interaction of electromagnetic waves at a fluid interface in the presence of a magnetic field aligned with the direction of propagation. We are concerned with electromagnetic waves that propagate through free space and impinge on a free fluid surface that is normal to the direction of propagation (see Fig. 8.6-1). Many different arrangements may arise in actual situations, but we will confine ourselves to a few basic problems that illustrate the concepts and methods.

We will first discuss reflection and transmission at a stationary interface of a stationary fluid, and later we allow both the interface and fluid to move. The nature of the fluid need not be specified except to determine the appropriate dispersion relationship in it. The propagation constants can be retained as free variables in the calculation of interface phenomena, and only when we wish to complete the calculations and insert numbers do we need to specify the fluid and dispersion relationship. We will carry out some of the detailed calculations for a gas. Remember that we are still considering a homogeneous, isotropic fluid under the continuum model.

In Fig. 8.6-1 a TEM wave propagates in the x direction and interacts with the interface at $x = 0$. The interface lies in the yz plane. We assume an infinite expanse of fluid for $x > 0$. The field quantities are all computed with respect to a laboratory observer at rest with respect to the coordinate system and fluid.

The total wave in free space, $x < 0$, is made up of two partial waves, one forward and one backward. The forward wave is called the incident wave and the backward wave the reflected wave. The waves in the fluid are all transmitted waves. We are particularly interested in obtaining the

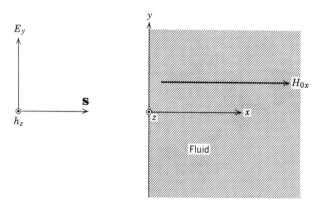

Figure 8.6-1 Interaction at a fluid interface. A conducting fluid lies to the right of the interface at $x = 0$. A steady magnetic field is applied in the x direction. The Poynting vector **S** indicates the direction of propagation. At the interface, part of the incident wave is reflected and part is transmitted.

reflection and transmission coefficients that indicate quantitatively the relative amounts of energy that are transmitted through the fluid and reflected from the interface.

From Maxwell's equations, E_y and h_z in free space are related by

$$\nabla \times \mathbf{E} = -\frac{\partial \mathbf{B}}{\partial t}$$

$$\nabla \times H = \epsilon_0 \frac{\partial \mathbf{E}}{\partial t}$$

(8.6-1)

so that the ordinary wave equations

$$\frac{\partial^2 \mathbf{E}}{\partial x^2} = \frac{1}{c^2} \frac{\partial^2 \mathbf{E}}{\partial t^2}$$

$$\frac{\partial^2 \mathbf{H}}{\partial x^2} = \frac{1}{c^2} \frac{\partial^2 \mathbf{H}}{\partial t^2}$$

(8.6-2)

are satisfied. Hence the characteristic velocity is simply c, so that in phasor form

$$\frac{E_y{}^*}{h_z{}^*} = \pm \sqrt{\frac{\mu_0}{\epsilon_0}} \tag{8.6-3}$$

The plus sign indicates a forward wave, and the minus sign indicates a backward wave. We use the subscripts i and r to indicate incident and reflected waves, respectively. Hence

$$E_{iy} = A e^{j(\omega t - \omega x/c)} \tag{8.6-4}$$

$$E_{ry} = B e^{j(\omega t + \omega x/c)} \tag{8.6-5}$$

so that in free space, $x < 0$, the total electric field is

$$E_y = A e^{j\omega(t - x/c)} + B e^{j\omega(t + x/c)} \tag{8.6-6}$$

and the total magnetic field is

$$h_z = \sqrt{\frac{\epsilon_0}{\mu_0}} \left[A e^{j\omega(t - x/c)} - B e^{j\omega(t + x/c)} \right] \tag{8.6-7}$$

The reflection coefficient is now defined in terms of the complex quantities A and B (phasors) as B/A and will be presently calculated.*

First, however, the fields in the fluid must be found. The propagation constant in the fluid we will denote as k_f and the field quantities in the fluid with a subscript f. From Equation (8.4-33) for gases or (8.4-9) for liquids we see that if the viscosity is neglected, there are two roots to k_f, a forward and backward wave. In general k_f is complex and damping occurs in the fluid. For convenience, let us assume that no backward wave exists in the fluid, that is, that the fluid extends infinitely far in the positive x directions; then no reflections can occur off the termination of the fluid to form a backward wave. (We could include the effects of such a backward wave, assuming another interface to exist at some finite positive value of x, but we would then have simultaneously to consider the interaction at this other interface, and the waves passing through again into free space. Little insight is to be gained by this additional complication, and such considerations are left as problems for the reader.) Another point to realize here is that if the viscosity is retained, there will, in general, be two forward waves in the fluid and hence two values of k_f. We will carry out the calculations assuming only one value of k_f, but will indicate what the effect of retaining two values of k_f would be.

---

* Sometimes the reflection and transmission coefficients are defined as the energy ratio in terms of the time average Poynting flux. This ratio can be related to our definitions.

The fields in the fluid can be given as

$$E_{yf} = Ce^{j(\omega t - k_f x)} \tag{8.6-8}$$

where C is the phasor amplitude. From $\nabla \times \mathbf{E} = -\partial \mathbf{B}/\partial t$, h_{zf} is

$$h_{zf} = \left(\frac{k_f}{\mu \omega}\right) Ce^{j(\omega t - k_f x)} \tag{8.6-9}$$

The transmission coefficient is defined as C/A, the ratio of the transmitted amplitude to the incident amplitude.

From the boundary condition that E_y and h_z must be continuous across the interface ($x = 0$), we can solve for the reflection and transmission coefficients. By equating E_y in the free space to E_{yf} at $x = 0$ and h_z to h_{zf} at $x = 0$, we obtain

$$A + B = C$$

$$\sqrt{\frac{\epsilon_0}{\mu_0}}(A - B) = \left(\frac{k_f}{\mu \omega}\right)C \tag{8.6-10}$$

which gives

$$\left(\frac{B}{A}\right) = \frac{\omega \kappa_m - k_f c}{\omega \kappa_m + k_f c} \tag{8.6-11}$$

$$\left(\frac{C}{A}\right) = \frac{2\omega \kappa_m}{\omega \kappa_m + k_f c} \tag{8.6-12}$$

From a practical standpoint κ_m, the relative magnetic permeability, is of course unity, and we can write

$$\left(\frac{B}{A}\right) = \frac{\omega - k_f c}{\omega + k_f c} \tag{8.6-13}$$

$$\left(\frac{C}{A}\right) = \frac{2\omega}{\omega + k_f c} \tag{8.6-14}$$

As $k_f \to \omega/c$, which is the case of the fluid behaving as free space (which would be the case if σ were zero or H_{0x} were zero so that no fluid-field interaction takes place), B/A becomes zero, and C/A becomes unity, indicating that the wave continues through the interface without interaction.

We can calculate the coefficients explicitly if k_f is known. As an example, consider an inviscid gas. k_f is given by Equations (8.4-30) and (8.4-31) as a complex number. If both $\eta = 0$ (infinite conductivity) and $H_{0x} = 0$, we get $B/A = -1$ and $C/A = 0$, which indicates that the wave does not penetrate the infinitely conducting gas, but is reflected with a $180°$ phase shift. However, if a finite value of H_{0x} is applied, even though the conductivity is infinite, a wave is transmitted into the fluid. This wave is an

Alfvén wave and we get

$$\left(\frac{B}{A}\right)_{\eta=0} = \frac{A_x - \sqrt{A_x^2 + c^2}}{A_x + \sqrt{A_x^2 + c^2}} \tag{8.6-15}$$

$$\left(\frac{C}{A}\right)_{\eta=0} = \frac{2A_x}{A_x + \sqrt{A_x^2 + c^2}} \tag{8.6-16}$$

where A_x is the Alfvén velocity $\sqrt{\mu_0 H_{0x}^2/\rho_0}$.

From a practical standpoint, $A_x^2 \ll c^2$ and the preceding equation becomes

$$\left(\frac{B}{A}\right)_{\eta=0} \simeq \frac{A_x - c}{A_x + c} \tag{8.6-17}$$

$$\left(\frac{C}{A}\right)_{\eta=0} \simeq \frac{2A_x}{A_x + c} \tag{8.6-18}$$

A_x/c is usually much less than unity so that except at high frequencies and/or large values of A_x the energy transmitted into the fluid as an Alfvén wave is small compared to the reflected energy.

In a similar manner, the appropriate values of k_f and the coefficients can be found for a liquid.

We have been concerned here with a single value of k_f for the forward wave in the fluid. If the viscosity were retained, there would have been two values of k_f and two distinct forward waves. There would then be two transmission coefficients, one for each wave. However, recall that we used the two conditions on E_y and h_z at the interface to find the two coefficients of the preceding problem. Now, since there are three coefficients to be found, three conditions at the interface must be invoked. The third condition is on the transverse velocity w. The precise condition on w at the interface depends on the particular problem, but for a viscous fluid, the shear must be zero, so that the normal derivative must be zero at the interface, $(x = 0)$. Later, when we discuss moving interfaces, we will have occasion to use a different boundary condition at the interface, one that represents an ionizing shock wave.

We should mention here that the waves in the fluid are initiated not only by the incidence of an electromagnetic wave; if a magnetic field is present so that A_x is nonzero and η is finite so that interaction occurs, the waves are initiated by physically imparting a transverse velocity to the fluid at the interface. This may be accomplished by an oscillating insulated plate, for example. Waves initiated in this way couple into the electromagnetic waves and would give rise to electromagnetic waves in free space,

$x < 0$. Later, in the chapter on transients, we will discuss in detail such fluid motion. In any case, the waves in the fluid are described by the dispersion relationships derived earlier in this chapter.

8.7   INTERACTION AT THE INTERFACE OF A MOVING FLUID IN THE PRESENCE OF A MAGNETIC FIELD

We now extend the analysis of the preceding section to allow for motion of the fluid. In Fig. 8.7-1 the fluid, which extends from the interface to the right, moves with velocity V_0 in the x direction. A magnetic field H_{0x} is applied in the x direction. The fluid is assumed to move as a whole so

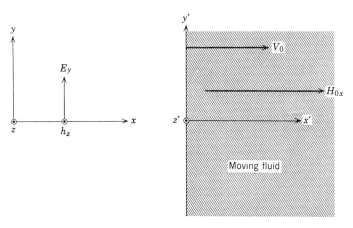

Figure 8.7-1   Interaction at a moving interface. The fluid and interface move together with velocity V_0 in the x direction in the presence of the steady magnetic field H_{0x}. The coordinate system x', y', and z' moves with the interface which is located at $x' = 0$. The coordinate system x, y, and z is located in the laboratory frame.

that the interface moves with the same velocity as the fluid. This model might represent a plasmoid in motion, or, alternatively, the motion of a radio transmitter with respect to a stationary plasma interface. The waves are assumed to be of the same type as in Section 8.6.

Since the plasma or gas is in motion with respect to the laboratory frame of reference (where the transmitter of the electromagnetic signal is located), we must be careful to denote the frame in which the fields are measured, the laboratory frame, or rest frame of the fluid. The laboratory frame is denoted as x, y, z and the rest frame of the fluid as x', y', z'. x and x' are colinear, and y and y' and z and z' are parallel. The origin of

x' is taken as the interface, and we arbitrarily say that at time $t = 0$, the interface ($x' = 0$) is coincident with the origin $x = 0$ in the laboratory frame.

We begin by analyzing the system in terms of the rest frame (as viewed by an observer moving with the fluid and interface). Then we can transform the quantities into the laboratory frame. In addition to the fields and the reflection and transmission coefficients, the frequencies of the various waves may appear different to different observers. In particular, the incident and reflected wave frequencies in free space (as measured by a laboratory observer) will appear different by the Doppler shift. We assume the transmitter to be fixed in the laboratory frame out along the negative x axis.

To an observer riding with the fluid, the dispersion relationships are exactly the same as those used in the Section 8.6. There is no way for the observer in the fluid to know he is moving (with respect to H_{0x}). We denote the propagation constant in the fluid then as k'_f which may be multivalued, depending on the nature of the fluid. The dispersion relationships developed earlier in this chapter for stationary fluids are of course applicable for computation of k'_f. For simplicity, we will neglect the backward wave here and allow only forward waves in the fluid (hence positive values of the real part of k'_f). This neglect of the backward wave is equivalent to assuming that the fluid extends from $x' = 0$ to $x' = \infty$. As mentioned before, a fluid of finite extent can easily be considered, but the other interface of a finite extent of fluid must be considered simultaneously with the interface at $x' = 0$.

Even if displacement current is considered, k'_f will have a single value (for a forward wave) if the viscosity is neglected. Hence we will neglect viscosity for now and assume that only one forward wave represented by k'_f is present in the fluid.

With respect to the fluid observer, all frequencies (the one in the fluid and the incident and reflected) are the same, ω'. This fact is obvious if we realize that the waves must match up at the interface. Hence in the fluid frame of reference the waves in free space may be written

$$E'_y = A'e^{j\omega'(t'-x'/c)} + B'e^{j\omega'(t'+x'/c)} \tag{8.7-1}$$

and

$$h'_z = \sqrt{\frac{\epsilon_0}{\mu_0}}\,[A'e^{j\omega'(t'-x'/c)} - B'e^{j\omega'(t'+x'/c)}] \tag{8.7-2}$$

and the forward wave in the fluid is

$$E'_{yf} = C'e^{j(\omega't'-k'_f x')} \tag{8.7-3}$$

$$h'_{zf} = \left(\frac{k'_f}{\mu\omega'}\right)C'e^{j(\omega't'-k'_f x')} \tag{8.7-4}$$

where we have denoted the quantities in the fluid with a subscript f. (μ is of course μ_0 for real fluids.)

In the laboratory frame we can write the free space waves as

$$E_y = Ae^{j\omega_i(t-x/c)} + Be^{j\omega_r(t+x/c)} \tag{8.7-5}$$

$$h_z = \sqrt{\frac{\epsilon_0}{\mu_0}} [Ae^{j\omega_i(t-x/c)} - Be^{j\omega_r(t+x/c)}] \tag{8.7-6}$$

and in the fluid the waves are (with respect to the laboratory observer)

$$E_{yf} = Ce^{j(\omega_T t - k_f x)} \tag{8.7-7}$$

$$h_{zf} = \left(\frac{k_f}{\mu\omega_T}\right)Ce^{j(\omega_T t - k_f x)} \tag{8.7-8}$$

where the incident wave has frequency ω_i (the frequency of the transmitter) and the reflected wave has ω_r. The frequency ω_T is that of the transmitted wave as measured in the laboratory frame. Now, A, B, C, ω_i, ω_r, and ω_T must be related to A', B', C', ω', and k'_f. The ratio ω_r/ω_i gives the Doppler shift. B/A and C/A can be found as the coefficients in the laboratory frame and B'/A' and C'/A' as the coefficients in the rest frame of the fluid. The primed and unprimed' quantities are related by the Lorentz transformations.

In the rest frame of the fluid, continuity of the fields gives

$$A' + B' = C' \tag{8.7-9}$$

$$\sqrt{\frac{\epsilon_0}{\mu_0}}(A' - B') = \frac{k'_f}{\mu\omega'}C' \tag{8.7-10}$$

which yield precisely (8.6-11) and (8.6-12), which are (for $\mu = \mu_0$)

$$\left(\frac{B'}{A'}\right) = \frac{\omega' - k'_f c}{\omega' + k'_f c} \tag{8.7-11}$$

$$\left(\frac{C'}{A'}\right) = \frac{2\omega'}{\omega' + k'_f c} \tag{8.7-12}$$

The Lorentz transformations (to relativistic accuracy) between E'_y and E_y and h'_z and h_z are

$$E'_y = \beta(E_y - \mu_0 V_0 h_z) \tag{8.7-13}$$

$$h'_z = \beta(h_z - \epsilon_0 V_0 E_y) \tag{8.7-14}$$

We retain the exact Lorentz transformation so that the final results will be valid for large values of V_0 (compared to c). In the determination of k'_f we may use nonrelativistic equations which rely on the fluid oscillation velocity being small compared to c (with respect to the rest frame), but this assumption does not invalidate the retention of high V_0 and is compatible with it. The velocity of the transmitter or plasmoid may be much higher, and is unrelated to the fluid oscillation velocities.

Now we can relate x and x', and t and t' by the Lorentz transformation as

$$x' = \beta(x - V_0 t) \tag{8.7-15}$$

$$t' = \beta\left(t - V_0 \frac{x}{c^2}\right) \tag{8.7-16}$$

In free space ($x' < 0$), with regard to 8.7-13 and 8.7-14, the transformed arguments of (8.7-1) and (8.7-2) must equal the arguments of (8.7-5) and (8.7-6). Hence

$$\omega'\left(t' - \frac{x'}{c}\right) = \omega_i\left(t - \frac{x}{c}\right)$$

$$= \omega'\beta\left(t - \frac{V_0 x}{c^2} - \frac{x}{c} + \frac{V_0 t}{c}\right) \tag{8.7-17}$$

$$\omega'\left(t' + \frac{x'}{c}\right) = \omega_r\left(t + \frac{x}{c}\right)$$

$$= \omega'\beta\left(t - \frac{V_0 x}{c^2} + \frac{x}{c} - \frac{V_0}{c} t\right) \tag{8.7-18}$$

so that we obtain

$$\omega_i = \omega'\beta\left(1 + \frac{V_0}{c}\right) \tag{8.7-19}$$

$$\omega_r = \omega'\beta\left(1 - \frac{V_0}{c}\right) \tag{8.7-20}$$

and hence

$$\frac{\omega_r}{\omega_i} = \frac{1 - V_0/c}{1 + V_0/c} \tag{8.7-21}$$

which is the Doppler shift for any value of V_0. In the nonrelativistic limit as $V_0 \ll c$, ω_r/ω_i can be approximated as

$$\frac{\omega_r}{\omega_i} \approx 1 - \frac{2V_0}{c} \tag{8.7-22}$$

If V_0 is negative (the interface approaches the transmitter) the reflected signal has an increased frequency.

In order to specify completely the fields in free space, we must find A and B in terms of A' and B'. From (8.7-13)

$$A' + B' = \beta\left[A + B - \mu_0 V_0 \sqrt{\frac{\epsilon_0}{\mu_0}}(A - B)\right] \tag{8.7-23}$$

so that by equating coefficients of A and B, we obtain

$$A' = \beta\left[1 - \frac{V_0}{c}\right]A \tag{8.7-24}$$

$$B' = \beta\left[1 + \frac{V_0}{c}\right]B \tag{8.7-25}$$

which says that $A' = A$ and $B' = B$ if $V_0 \ll c$. Equation (8.7-14) is redundant and gives the same results. In the laboratory frame, then, the reflection coefficient is (to exact relativistic order)

$$\left(\frac{B}{A}\right) = \left(\frac{B'}{A'}\right)\left(\frac{1 - V_0/c}{1 + V_0/c}\right) \approx \left(1 - \frac{2V_0}{c}\right)\frac{B'}{A'} \tag{8.7-26}$$

The only remaining task is to find the fields in the fluid. Transforming the arguments of (8.7-3) and (8.7-4) and equating them to the argument of (8.7-7), we obtain

$$(\omega't' - k'_f x') = \omega'\beta\left(t - \frac{V_0 x}{c^2}\right) - k'_f \beta(x - V_0 t)$$

$$= (\omega_T t - k_f x) \tag{8.7-27}$$

so that

$$\omega_T = \beta(\omega' + V_0 k'_f) \tag{8.7-28}$$

and

$$k_f = \beta\left(\frac{\omega' V_0}{c^2} + k'_f\right) \tag{8.7-29}$$

In general, if there is any damping in the fluid, k'_f is complex and ω_T will be complex. The imaginary part of ω_T represents temporal damping, which is to be expected since the waves in the fluid rest frame damp in space and the fluid is moving with respect to the laboratory frame.

We find C now from (8.7-13) and (8.7-14) (assuming $\mu = \mu_0$):

$$C' = \beta C\left[1 - \frac{V_0 k_f}{\omega_T}\right] = \beta C\frac{\omega'(1 - V_0^2/c^2)}{\omega' + k'_f V_0} \tag{8.7-30}$$

For $(V_0/c)^2 \ll 1$ we have simply

$$C = C'\left(1 + \frac{k'_f V_0}{\omega'}\right) \tag{8.7-31}$$

The transmission coefficient in the laboratory frame is then

$$\left(\frac{C}{A}\right) = \left(\frac{C'}{A'}\right) \cdot \left[\frac{\omega' + k'_f V_0}{\omega'(1 + V_0/c)}\right] \tag{8.7-32}$$

so that for $V_0 \ll c$ we have simply

$$\left(\frac{C}{A}\right) = \left(\frac{C'}{A'}\right)\left(1 + \frac{k'_f V_0}{\omega'}\right) \tag{8.7-33}$$

We have completely described all the fields in the fluid rest frame and in the laboratory frame and have related the various frequencies, propagation constants, and the reflection and transmission coefficients.

8.8 INTERACTION AT A MOVING INTERFACE OF A MOVING FLUID IN THE PRESENCE OF A MAGNETIC FIELD

In the last section we discussed the interaction of electromagnetic waves at the interface of a moving fluid in which the interface forming the

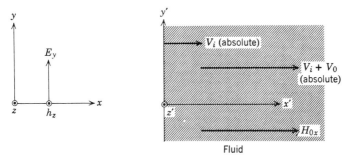

Figure 8.8-1 Interaction at a moving interface in a moving fluid. The interface located at $x' = 0$ moves with velocity V_i with respect to the laboratory frame xyz. The fluid moves with velocity V_0 with respect to the interface.

boundary of the fluid moved with the same velocity as the fluid. Now we extend that analysis to describe interaction at an interface which moves with a velocity V_i (in the x direction) which is different from the velocity of the fluid relative to the laboratory frame. We denote the velocity of the fluid relative to the interface as V_0 in the x direction, and the velocity of the fluid relative to the laboratory as $(V_i + V_0)$.

This situation, illustrated in Fig. 8.8-1, would correspond physically to interaction at an ionizing shock wave moving with a velocity different from that of the fluid behind the shock. The fluid before the shock would be un-ionized and hence would appear as free space to the electromagnetic waves. Figure 8.8-2 shows an ionizing shock wave. V_i must be negative and is denoted as V_s in the negative x direction. The fluid has velocity V_0 relative to the interface or shock front in the x' direction. The coordinate system $x'y'z'$ is attached to the shock front and is parallel to the xyz system fixed in the laboratory. The appropriate dispersion relationship in

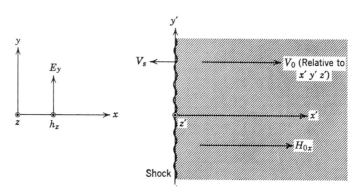

Figure 8.8-2   The moving fluid and interface problem applied to a shock wave. Figure 8.8-1 is here illustrated in terms of a moving ionizing shock wave. The shock velocity is V_s (so that $V_i = -V_s$) and the velocity of the fluid with respect to the shock wave is, as before, V_0.

the gas behind the shock front ($x' > 0$) must then be obtained by considering the gas as moving with velocity V_0 with respect to the shock frame of reference in the presence of a magnetic field H_{0x}. Such dispersion relationships have been given in Section 8.5 and can be applied here. The quantities calculated in the shock frame can then be transformed into the laboratory frame of reference.

We begin the analysis by examining the behavior of the waves in the shock frame of reference; all quantities measured in this frame are denoted by primes. Unprimed quantities denote laboratory quantities as measured by an observer fixed in the laboratory frame of reference.

With respect to the shock frame, all frequencies are ω'. The complex propagation constant k'_f may be determined from the appropriate dispersion relationship given in Section 8.5. For a gas, the equation for k'_f is cubic (if viscosity is neglected), and the roots represent two forward waves (one slow, one fast), and one backward wave (the backward mode of the fast forward wave). We will neglect the backward wave here for simplicity and compute the important parameters.

In free space (that is, $x' < 0$) with respect to the interface or shock frame of reference, the fields are

$$E'_y = A'e^{j\omega'(t'-x'/c)} + B'e^{j\omega'(t'+x'/c)} \qquad (8.8\text{-}1)$$

$$h'_z = \sqrt{\frac{\epsilon_0}{\mu_0}}\,[A'e^{j\omega'(t'-x'/c)} - B'e^{j\omega'(t'+x'/c)}] \qquad (8.8\text{-}2)$$

and in the fluids the fields are (in the shock frame)

$$E'_{yf} = C'e^{j(\omega't'-k'_{f1}x')} + D'e^{j(\omega't'-k'_{f2}x')} \qquad (8.8\text{-}3)$$

$$h'_{zf} = \left(\frac{k'_{f1}}{\mu_0\omega'}\right)C'e^{j(\omega't'-k'_{f1}x')} + \left(\frac{k'_{f2}}{\mu_0\omega'}\right)D'e^{j(\omega't'-k'_{f2}x')} \qquad (8.8\text{-}4)$$

where k'_{f1} and k'_{f2} are the propagation constants for the two forward waves in the gas.

In the laboratory frame we write the free space fields as

$$E_y = Ae^{j\omega_i(t-x/c)} + Be^{j\omega_r(t+x/c)} \qquad (8.8\text{-}5)$$

$$h_z = \sqrt{\frac{\epsilon_0}{\mu_0}}\,[Ae^{j\omega_i(t-x/c)} - Be^{j\omega_r(t+x/c)}] \qquad (8.8\text{-}6)$$

In the gas the fields are (as measured in the laboratory frame)

$$E_{yf} = Ce^{j(\omega_{T1}t-k_{f1}x)} + De^{j(\omega_{T2}t-k_{f2}x)} \qquad (8.8\text{-}7)$$

$$h_{zf} = \left(\frac{k_{f1}}{\mu_0\omega_{T1}}\right)Ce^{j(\omega_{T1}t-k_{f1}x)} + \left(\frac{k_{f2}}{\mu_0\omega_{T2}}\right)De^{j(\omega_{T2}t-k_{f2}x)} \qquad (8.8\text{-}8)$$

We see that the ω' splits into separate frequencies for each transmitted wave (with respect to the laboratory observer).

In the interface or shock frame, the boundary conditions at the interface give (using continuity of E_y and h_z at $x' = 0$)

$$A' + B' = C' + D' \qquad (8.8\text{-}9)$$

$$\sqrt{\frac{\epsilon_0}{\mu_0}}\,(A' - B') = \frac{k'_{f1}}{\mu_0\omega'}C' + \frac{k'_{f2}}{\mu_0\omega'}D' \qquad (8.8\text{-}10)$$

We see that one more boundary condition is necessary to specify the two transmission coefficients and the one reflection coefficient. The third condition is obtained by imposing the appropriate boundary condition on the oscillation velocity w (the z component of fluid velocity) at $x' = 0$. From Equations (8.5-1) and (8.5-2) the velocity w can be expressed in terms of E'_y. For inviscid flow we obtain for w

$$w = -\frac{1}{\mu_0 H_{0x}}\left\{\left[1 - \frac{V_0 k'_{f1}}{\omega'} + j\eta\left(\frac{\omega'}{c^2} - \frac{k_{f1}'^2}{\omega'}\right)\right]C'e^{j(\omega't - k'_{f1}x')}\right.$$

$$\left. + \left[1 - \frac{V_0 k'_{f2}}{\omega'} + j\eta\left(\frac{\omega'}{c^2} - \frac{k_{f2}'^2}{\omega'}\right)\right]D'e^{j(\omega't - k'_{f2}x')}\right\} \quad (8.8\text{-}11)$$

Let us consider the particular case of an ionizing shock wave to compute the proper continuity condition on w across the interface. For a supersonic V_s, which must be the case if the interface is a shock wave, the velocity w in front of the shock must be zero since there is no electromagnetic interaction there. If the fluid is inviscid, no shear can be transmitted through the fluid in back of the shock wave. Hence the velocity w must be zero at the interface. Remember, no Alfvén wave can propagate upstream because the conductivity of the fluid is zero before becoming ionized by the shock. If V_s were subsonic, or if the fluid viscosity were important, this condition on w would not be correct and a more detailed analysis would have to be made. Applying the condition that $w = 0$ at $x' = 0$ yields the condition

$$\frac{C'}{D'} = -\frac{[1 - V_0 k'_{f2}/\omega' + j\eta(\omega'/c^2 - k_{f2}'^2/\omega')]}{[1 - V_0 k'_{f1}/\omega' + j\eta(\omega'/c^2 - k_{f1}'^2/\omega')]} \quad (8.8\text{-}12)$$

Now Equations (8.8-9), (8.8-10), and (8.8-12) can be solved for B'/A', C'/A', and D'/A' to give the reflection coefficient and the two transmission coefficients respectively:

$$\frac{B'}{A'} = \frac{V_0 - c + j\eta(k'_{f1} + k'_{f2} - k'_{f1}k'_{f2}c/\omega' - \omega'/c)}{V_0 + c + j\eta(k'_{f1} + k'_{f2} + k'_{f1}k'_{f2}c/\omega' + \omega'/c)} \quad (8.8\text{-}13)$$

$$\frac{C'}{A'} = \frac{2\omega'[1 - V_0 k'_{f2}/\omega' + j\eta(\omega'/c^2 - k_{f2}'^2/\omega')]}{(k'_{f1} - k'_{f2})[V_0 + c + j\eta(k'_{f1} + k'_{f2} + k'_{f1}k'_{f2}c/\omega' + \omega'/c)]} \quad (8.8\text{-}14)$$

$$\frac{D'}{A'} = \frac{2\omega'[1 - V_0 k'_{f1}/\omega' + j\eta(\omega'/c^2 - k_{f1}'^2/\omega')]}{(k'_{f2} - k'_{f1})[V_0 + c + j\eta(k'_{f1} + k'_{f2} + k'_{f1}k'_{f2}c/\omega' + \omega'/c)]} \quad (8.8\text{-}15)$$

Now the Lorentz transformations between the field quantities measured in the interface frame and the laboratory frame can be applied to calculate the frequencies, propagation constants, and relations between A', B', C', and D', and A, B, C, and D. Equations (8.7-13), (8.7-14), (8.7-15), and (8.7-16) are valid. The velocity V_0 in these equations must be replaced by V_i or $-V_s$ if we consider a shock wave moving in the negative x direction.

Written out in full in the appropriate notation, these equations are

$$x' = \beta(x - V_i t) = \beta(x + V_s t) \tag{8.8-16}$$

$$t' = \beta\left(t - \frac{V_i x}{c^2}\right) = \beta\left(t + \frac{V_s x}{c^2}\right) \tag{8.8-17}$$

$$E'_y = \beta(E_y - \mu_0 V_i h_z) = \beta(E_y + \mu_0 V_s h_z) \tag{8.8-18}$$

$$h'_z = \beta(h_z - \epsilon_0 V_i E_y) = \beta(h_z + \epsilon_0 V_s E_y) \tag{8.8-19}$$

By a method similar to that of the preceding section, we can equate transformed exponential arguments of field quantities in the laboratory and interface frames to give

$$\omega_i = \omega'\beta\left(1 + \frac{V_i}{c}\right) = \omega'\beta\left(1 - \frac{V_s}{c}\right) \tag{8.8-20}$$

$$\omega_r = \omega'\beta\left(1 - \frac{V_i}{c}\right) = \omega'\beta\left(1 + \frac{V_s}{c}\right) \tag{8.8-21}$$

and

$$\frac{\omega_r}{\omega_i} = \frac{1 - V_i/c}{1 + V_i/c} = \frac{1 + V_s/c}{1 - V_s/c} \tag{8.8-22}$$

which is the Doppler shift for the shock wave moving with velocity V_s toward the transmitter. As $V_s/c \ll 1$, we get the familiar form

$$\frac{\omega_r}{\omega_i} \approx 1 + \frac{2V_s}{c} \tag{8.8-23}$$

In order to complete the specification in free space, we use (8.8-18) and (8.8-19) to find A and B in terms of A' and B' as

$$A' = A\beta\left[1 - \frac{V_i}{c}\right] = A\beta\left[1 + \frac{V_s}{c}\right] \tag{8.8-24}$$

$$B' = B\beta\left[1 - \frac{V_i}{c}\right] = B\beta\left[1 + \frac{V_s}{c}\right] \tag{8.8-25}$$

which reduces to $A = A'$ and $B = B'$ as $V_s/c \ll 1$. In general, the reflection coefficient is:

$$\left(\frac{B}{A}\right) = \left(\frac{B'}{A'}\right)\left(\frac{1 - V_i/c}{1 + V_i/c}\right) \approx \left(1 - \frac{2V_i}{c}\right)\frac{B'}{A'} \tag{8.8-26}$$

Now for the fluid we must equate the exponential arguments of (8.8-3) and (8.8-4) to those of (8.8-7) and (8.8-8). We obtain

$$\omega_{T1} = \beta(\omega' + k'_{f1}V_i) = \beta(\omega' - k'_{f1}V_s) \tag{8.8-27}$$

$$k_{f1} = \beta\left(\frac{\omega'V_i}{c^2} + k'_{f1}\right) = \beta\left(-\frac{\omega'V_s}{c^2} + k'_{f1}\right) \tag{8.8-28}$$

$$\omega_{T2} = \beta(\omega' + k'_{f2}V_i) = \beta(\omega' - k'_{f2}V_s) \tag{8.8-29}$$

$$k_{f2} = \beta\left(\frac{\omega'V_i}{c^2} + k'_{f2}\right) = \beta\left(-\frac{\omega'V_s}{c^2} + k'_{f2}\right) \tag{8.8-30}$$

It should be noted that ω_{T1} and ω_{T2} are now, in general, complex. The imaginary part of ω_{T1} and ω_{T2} merely represents attenuation with time (in the laboratory frame). This attenuation is easy to visualize. The fluid is moving with respect to the laboratory frame in the negative x direction and hence at any fixed value of x the fields in the fluid change as the fluid moves by (remember the fluid attenuates in space in the shock frame). Continuing the calculations, we find C and D in terms of C' and D' as we found A and B in terms of A' and B':

$$C' = \beta C\left(1 - \frac{V_i k_{f1}}{\omega_{T1}}\right) = \beta C\left(1 + \frac{V_s k_{f1}}{\omega_{T1}}\right) \tag{8.8-31}$$

$$D' = \beta D\left(1 - \frac{V_i k_{f2}}{\omega_{T2}}\right) = \beta D\left(1 + \frac{V_s k_{f2}}{\omega_{T2}}\right) \tag{8.8-32}$$

For velocities V_i (or V_s) small compared to c, these coefficients reduce to

$$C = C'\left(1 - \frac{V_s k'_{f1}}{\omega'}\right)$$
$$D = D'\left(1 - \frac{V_s k'_{f2}}{\omega'}\right) \tag{8.8-33}$$

We will not pursue the problem any further but it should be pointed out that for the shock wave situation the two transmitted waves ω_{T1} and ω_{T2} represent two entirely different types of waves. The phase velocity of ω_{T2}, the slow wave, is essentially the same as the fluid velocity in the laboratory frame and hence appears as a standing wave in the fluid and as a backward wave in the laboratory frame of reference. The absolute velocity of the gas (relative to the laboratory frame) is $V_s - V_0$ in the negative x direction. In the laboratory frame the ω_{T1} wave is a fast forward wave.

It should also be pointed out that most of the formulas of this section are relativistically correct and can be used for high values of V_i (or V_s) that approach the speed of light c. The nonrelativistic approximation enters in only when we actually compute the values of k_f, since then the nonrelativistic equations of motion are used. However, the streaming velocities of the gas (V_0) and the gas oscillation velocity w are usually low, compared to c, so that the dispersion relationships can be used regardless of the value of V_i. We can use our results confidently for high relative velocity between the transmitter and reflecting interface.

The fields and parameters can be transformed into the frame of the gas, or into any other frame moving with a general velocity $\mathbf{V}$ with respect to the observer back at the transmitter. Such transformations are left as exercises for the reader.

8.9   EXPERIMENTS—STUDIES OF MHD WAVES

In the laboratory it is difficult to carry out definitive experiments involving MHD waves. The reason for this is that the Alfvén speed is usually much smaller than the ordinary sonic speed and is consequently masked by ordinary gas dynamic effects. A quick look at the results of this chapter shows that the Alfvén and sonic speeds usually combine as their squares in determining slow and fast wave speeds. The Alfvén wave is uncoupled from the sonic wave but is usually masked by the viscous wave. Table 8.9-1 shows a few typical values and from it the difficulty in making simple laboratory experiments is obvious.

A few rather clever experiments have been carried out but were mainly concerned with torsional waves, that is, the Alfvén modes. In particular, the work of Lundquist (1949), Lehnert (1954), Jephcott and Stocker (1962), and Jameson (1964) are instructive. The work of Jameson describes experiments on standing Alfvén waves with striking agreement between theory and experiment. Longitudinal waves have been observed by Murphy (1965).

Experimentally, the field of electromagnetic wave-plasma interaction has been investigated intensively under the heading of plasma diagnostics and we refrain from discussing these problems since we are not primarily concerned with plasmas.

8.10   CONCLUSIONS

We have spent considerable time discussing wave motion in fluids from an isotropic continuum point of view. As we pointed out earlier, the

Table 8.9-1

A table of typical wave parameters in fluids

Fluid	B	P	ρ	Mean Free Path	T	A (Alfvén)	a_0 (Sonic)
Air (Sea level)	10^{-4} wb/m²	10^5 Nt/m²	1 kg/m³	6×10^{-8} m	293°K	2.5×10^{-2} m/sec	340 m/sec
Air (100 km)	10^{-4} wb/m²	3×10^{-2} Nt/m²	10^{-6} kg/m³	4×10^{-2} m	200°K	25 m/sec	280 m/sec
Solar wind (At orbit of earth)	4×10^{-10} wb/m²	2×10^{-13} Nt/m²	10^{-21} kg/m³	2.1×10^{11} m	10^5°K	3×10^3 m/sec	2×10^5 m/sec
Liquid mercury ($\sigma = 1.07 \times 10^6$ mho/m)	1 wb/m²	10^5 Nt/m²	1.355×10^4 kg/m³		293°K	7.7 m/sec	1450 m/sec
Liquid sodium ($\sigma = 2.4 \times 10^7$ mho/m)	1 wb/m²	10^5 Nt/m²	0.93×10^3 kg/m³		373°K	29.4 m/sec	2525 m/sec
Sea water	10^{-4} wb/m²	10^5 Nt/m²	1.025×10^3 kg/m³		293°K	7.8×10^{-4} m/sec	1531 m/sec
Interstellar space	10^{-10} wb/m²	1.4×10^{-15} Nt/m²	10^{-22} kg/m³			10^3 m/sec	

results of a microscopic model (treated by statistical mechanics or kinetic theory) are, in general, quite different from those obtained by a continuum approach, and it is important to examine the validity of this model for any particular physical situation. In the limit, of course, as the fluid becomes dense so that the continuum approach is valid, the statistical model yields the same results. Now let us discuss some qualitative differences between the two approaches and establish a quantitative test for the validity of the continuum model.

In ionized gases the charged particles obey the dynamical laws of motion. The particles are acted upon by the Lorentz force and collision forces. (Gravitational forces are usually negligible.) The magnetic force ($\mathbf{V} \times \mathbf{B}$) causes the particle to spiral around the magnetic lines of force with the cyclotron frequency $-qB/m$ and with a radius called the cyclotron radius.

If we use a continuum model, all physical dimensions, including wavelength, must be large compared to the mean free path. In addition, these physical dimensions (that is, wavelengths) should be small compared to the cyclotron radius. Hence in a continuum the collisions completely mask the cyclotron behavior. If the cyclotron radius is of the order of the physical dimensions, anisotropy of the gas may result, even though the mean free path is much smaller than the wavelength and the continuum theory holds.

As the wavelength, mean free path, and cyclotron radius approach one another, these motions become coupled, and resonances can occur at the cyclotron frequency. This resonance is unpredicted by the macroscopic continuum theory, and under conditions where it can occur, the macroscopic continuum theory is not applicable.

In order for the cyclotron radius to be small (of the order of micro-wavelengths), the magnetic field must be several orders of magnitude greater than the Earth's magnetic field, and only in tenuous gases in strong magnetic fields do we need to be concerned with the cyclotron radius becoming equal to the wavelength. Usually the mean free path becomes of the order of the wavelength first (as in the ionosphere) and dictates the use of a statistical model regardless of the cyclotron radius. As an example, under atmospheric conditions the ratio of the mean free path to the cyclotron radius of an electron is about 10^{-4} (for a field of 1 weber per meter^2). Considering the Earth's magnetic field ($\sim 10^{-5}$ weber per meter^2), this ratio is about 10^{-9}.

We should realize that as the frequency increases, the wavelength will eventually approach the mean free path, and then the continuum theory breaks down. At an altitude of 100 kilometers the mean free path is about 5 centimeters and we see that radio wave propagation, even at fairly low frequencies, is inadequately represented by the continuum theory. A point to remember is that in some fluids the displacement current is only of importance at high frequencies and sometimes the continuum model breaks down before such effects become important.

Another characteristic frequency of importance in rarefied gases is the plasma frequency. A rarefied gas appears transparent to waves of frequency higher than the plasma frequency and fairly opaque below it. Hence microwaves are used for transmission through the ionosphere, where low frequency waves would be reflected. The behavior of waves about the plasma frequency (there are two, one for ions and one for electrons) is unpredicted by the continuum theory, and again is of importance in tenuous gases where the continuum theory is not applicable. Physically, the plasma frequency is the frequency of oscillation of a small perturbation of charge (away from electrical neutrality) in the gas. As the gas becomes denser, the plasma frequency goes up, and in situations where the continuum theory is valid, the plasma frequency may be of the order of mega-megacycles.

For a discussion of plasma waves the reader is referred to the book by Denisse and Delcroix listed in the references at the end of this chapter.

PROBLEMS

1. The index of refraction n is defined as the ratio of a reference phase velocity to the actual phase velocity in a material medium. For electromagnetic waves the index of refraction is defined as c/a, where c is the velocity of light in vacuo. In dispersive media, at rest, where $a = c/\kappa\kappa_m$, the index of refraction is simply $\kappa\kappa_m$. Similarly, in MHD, the index of refraction can be computed on the basis of c (if displacement current is included). Interpret the physical meaning of the index of refraction in terms of your experience with light waves in refractive media such as water.

2. In Equation (8.4-28) for wave propagation in gases in the presence of a magnetic field, we see that E_x (in the direction of propagation) is excited in the gas along with the other transverse mode variables. In free space, only E_v would exist; hence the presence of the magnetic field polarizes the wave. What does the existence of E_x mean in terms of the Poynting vector? Does the Poynting vector lie in the x direction (direction of propagation)? If not, how does the energy propagate compared to the direction of the wave propagation? Does the Poynting vector really not have physical meaning unless it is integrated over a control volume?

3. In Section 8.8 we discussed plane waves impinging on an interface. The direction of propagation of the incident wave was normal to the interface. Suppose the direction of propagation of the incident wave is at an angle to the interface plane. What are the fields in free space and in the fluid? Work out the details for a stationary fluid in the presence of a magnetic field (which is perpendicular to the interface, or free surface of the fluid). Does the wave become polarized differently in the fluid?

4. Extend the above problem to the case of a moving interface.

5. Rework the example of Section 8.6 with an arbitrary orientation of the magnetic field.

6. Analyze the behavior of longitudinal waves in a moving fluid (gas or liquid) in the presence of a magnetic field arbitrarily oriented with respect to the direction of propagation. The fluid flows in the direction of propagation with steady velocity V_0. The results of this calculation are of importance in the study of traveling wave devices such as traveling wave amplifiers, where these principles are applied to electron beams.

7. In Equation (8.2-19) (longitudinal waves in a gas in the presence of a general magnetic field) let $\nu = 0$ and $\kappa_T = 0$ but retain η as a general parameter. Compute the phase velocities. Construct the ray-normal diagrams (or Friedrichs' diagrams) for this situation. This may prove difficult for all the waves, but at least try to construct the normal-speed locus.*

8. In the example of Section 8.7 we considered the interaction of an electromagnetic wave and a moving fluid with an interface. The fluid was assumed to extend from the free surface or interface to infinity in the x direction. Consider the problem of a finite extent of fluid from $x' = 0$ to, say, $x' = x'_0$. Find the waves in the fluid and in the free space, $x' < 0$ and $x' > x'_0$. See Fig. P8.8-1.

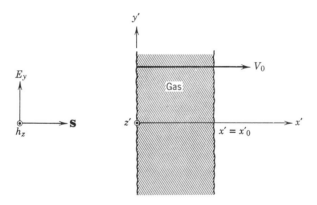

Figure P8.8-1   Interaction with a plasmoid or moving gas of finite extent in the direction of propagation.

This type of problem is important in plasma diagnostics where interaction with finite plasmoids is a primary concern. What physical properties of the plasmoid can be determined by measuring the reflection and transmission coefficients?

9. A TEM electromagnetic wave, polarized as shown in Fig. P8.9-1, propagates over the surface of the sea in a direction parallel to the surface. Since any waves in the sea damp out quickly, the depth of the sea may be considered infinite. Calculate the fields in free space over the sea, and in the sea for the

---

* For a discussion of this problem see: E. L. Resler, Jr., Some Remarks on Hydromagnetic Waves for Finite Conductivity, Revs. Modern Phys., **32** No. 4, pp. 866–867, 1960.

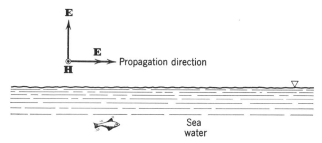

Figure P8.9-1   Propagation of waves over the sea.

case of (*a*) no applied magnetic field; (*b*) a magnetic field parallel to the surface of the sea; and (*c*) a magnetic field perpendicular to the surface of the sea. Assume the magnetic field homogeneous, and filling all space. What is the direction of the Poynting vector?

REFERENCES

Baños, Jr., A., Magneto-hydromagnetic Waves in Incompressible and Compressible Fluids, *Proc. Roy. Soc.* (London), Series A, **233**, pp. 350–366, 1955.

Bazer, J., and O. Fleischman, Propagation of Weak Hydromagnetic Discontinuities, *Phys. Fluids*, **2**, No. 4, pp. 366–378, 1959.

Brandstatter, J. J., *An Introduction to Waves, Rays, and Radiation in Plasma Media*, McGraw-Hill, New York, 1963.

Denisse, J. F., and J. L. Delcroix, *Plasma Waves*, Interscience, New York, 1963.

Feynman, R. P., R. B. Leighton, and M. Sands, *The Feynman Lectures on Physics*, Vol. II, Chapter 32, Addison-Wesley, Reading, Mass., 1964.

Friedlander, F. G., Sound Pulses in a Conducting Medium, *Proc. Cambridge Phil. Soc.*, **55**, pp. 341–367, 1959.

Friedrichs, K. O., and H. Kranzer, Notes on Magneto-Hydrodynamics, VIII, Nonlinear Wave Motion, N.Y.U. Institute of Math. Sciences Report, 0-6486, New York, 1958.

Hughes, W. F., and F. J. Young, The Interaction of Transverse Electromagnetic Plane Waves and a Moving Ionizing Shock Wave in the Presence of a Magnetic Field, *J. Fluid Mech.*, **19**, Part 1, pp. 11–20, 1964.

Jameson, A., A Demonstration of Alfvén Waves, *J. Fluid Mech.*, **19**, p. 513, 1964.

Jephcott, D. G., and P. M. Stocker, Hydromagnetic Waves in a Cylindrical Plasma: An Experiment, *J. Fluid Mech.*, **13**, p. 587, 1962.

Kittel, C., Introduction to Solid State Physics, 2nd. ed., John Wiley & Sons, New York, 1956.

Kurilko, V. I., and V. I. Miroshnichenko, Reflection of Electromagnetic Waves from a Moving Plasma, *Zh. T. F.*, **32**, p. 903, 1962. (See Soviet Phys.-Tech. Phys., **7**, p. 588, for English translation.)

Lehnert, B., Magneto-Hydrodynamic Waves in Liquid Sodium, *Phys. Rev.*, **94**, No. 4, p. 815, 1954.

Ludford, G. S. S., The Propagation of Small Disturbances in Hydromagnetics, *J. Fluid Mech.*, **5**, pp. 387–400, 1959.

Lundquist, S., Experimental Investigations of Magneto-Hydrodynamic Waves, *Phys. Rev.*, **76**, No. 12, p. 1805, 1949.

Murphy, J. H., Magnetoacoustic Waves in Waveguides, Ph.D. Thesis, Carnegie Institute of Technology, Pittsburgh, Pa., 1965.

Murphy, J. H., and W. F. Hughes, Observations on Magnetoacoustic Waves in Mercury, *Proc. IEEE*, **54**, p. 55, 1966.

Resler, Jr., E. L., Some Remarks on Hydromagnetic Waves for Finite Conductivity, *Revs. Mod. Phys.* **32**, No. 4, pp. 866–867, 1960.

Stolyarov, S. N., Reflection and Refraction of Electromagnetic Waves at a Moving Boundary, *Zh. T. F.*, **33**, p. 562, 1963. (See Soviet Phys.—Tech. Phys., **8**, p. 418, 1963, for English translation.)

9

Transient and Alternating Incompressible Viscous MHD Flow

9.1 INTRODUCTION

It is the purpose of this chapter to study the solutions to various time-varying problems. As in Chapter 7, the fluid is assumed to be electrically conducting, viscous, incompressible, and at a constant, uniform temperature, (except for Section 9.8 where thermal effects are included). It will be seen that in transient regimes the coupling between the Navier-Stokes and the Maxwell equations is stronger than it is in steady-flow problems. For magnetic Prandtl numbers of unity and/or large Hartmann numbers the coupling is very strong and the electrodynamics must be handled properly or the results will be completely wrong.

To increase our understanding of the transient electrodynamic behavior expected in MHD transient regimes, we begin with a transient problem involving the relative motion between solid conductors moving in a uniform magnetic field.

This chapter includes the development of various forms of the equations for time-varying flow in two-dimensional rectangular channels and for one-dimensional geometries. In the latter case, the concept of the Hartmann number loses meaning and is replaced by the Alfvén velocity in the dimensionless forms of the equations.

Because there are more parameters to consider in transient flow than in steady flow, this chapter cannot be as detailed as Chapter 7.

The alternating version of the MHD Poiseuille problem is treated in detail and it is seen that the nature of the return circuit affects the symmetry of the flow, which is *not* the case in the steady MHD Poiseuille problem of Section 7.1. The transient MHD Poiseuille problem is treated when the channel walls are ideal conductors. The possibility of oscillatory solutions is discussed from a physical and an analytical viewpoint.

Because it has been the subject of much consideration in the technical literature, the MHD Rayleigh problem is discussed at length, and the importance of the current return circuit is stressed because it leads to an understanding of the wave nature of the transient solution. It is shown that the sudden motion of the plate initiates an Alfvén wave in the conducting liquid which travels away from the moving plate at the Alfvén speed. The Alfvén wave is accompanied by a traveling current sheet (which provides the return path for the current generated closer to the moving plate) and a traveling vorticity sheet. When the conducting liquid is ideally conducting and inviscid, the presence of switch-on shock waves is discussed. Various limiting cases of the MHD Rayleigh problem are considered to gain a physical feeling for transient MHD flows.

The transient solution in a two-dimensional channel is given for the geometry of Section 7.7, which is considered because it leads to rather simple solutions and because the steady solutions of Section 7.7 have certain very interesting aspects. Solutions to the transient problems for the rectangular channel having all insulating or all conducting walls are not given here. These solutions are indicated by Uflyand (1962) but they are not in a very usable form.

The last section of this chapter investigates the development of one-dimensional MHD Poiseuille flow. Here the transient is not in time but in distance downstream from the fluid inlet. The problem is formidable, involving two components of velocity and the convective acceleration terms, and is solved numerically. It is seen that the entrance length decreases exponentially with the Hartmann number.

9.2 AN ELECTRODYNAMIC PLATE PROBLEM

Introduction

The solutions for the oscillating and transient motions of an infinite plate are well known for nonconducting fluids in which all electrodynamic effects are negligible (Schlichting, 1955, Chapter V). However, solutions are not common for the oscillating and transient motions and for the induced electromagnetic fields that result when an electrically conducting plate is moved through a magnetic field. It is the purpose of this section to study a typical problem which will illustrate the roles of the skin effect and the external circuit. The methods used here are essentially the ones needed for magnetohydrodynamic studies involving transients and steady oscillations of boundaries.

The Problem of Two Half-Spaces

Two electrically conducting half-spaces are separated by a distance y_0 as shown in Fig. 9.2-1. The lower half-space, initially at rest, is suddenly caused to move with a velocity V through an applied uniform magnetic field. This configuration is the limiting case of the load and generator of Fig. E2.3-2 when the bottom plate of Fig. E2.3-2 is removed. The electrode configuration connecting the top and the moving half-spaces is that of

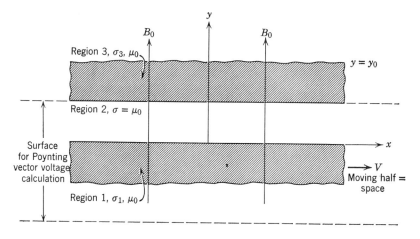

Figure 9.2-1   A half-space generator and load.

Fig. E2.3-2. The only difference between the configurations is the thickness of the plates. In Fig. 9.2-1 ideally conducting electrodes (in the xy plane) are placed at z_0 and $-z_0$, where $z_0 \gg y_0$ so that the problem is one dimensional. These electrodes provide an electrical connection between the moving half-space (generator) and the stationary half-space (load).

The object of this exercise is to find the induced electric field, the current density, the magnetic field intensity, and the terminal voltage. These are to be studied as a function of time.

Solution

By virtue of the geometry there should be no variation of the fields in x or z. Then $\nabla \times \mathbf{E} = -\mu_0(\partial \mathbf{H}/\partial t)$ dictates that H_x is the only time-dependent magnetic field induced, and $\nabla \times \mathbf{H} = \mathbf{J}$ implies that the induced electric field is in the z direction. In that case the two curl equations become

$$\frac{\partial E_{zi}}{\partial y} = -\mu_0 \frac{\partial H_{xi}}{\partial t} \tag{9.2-1}$$

and

$$-\frac{\partial H_{xi}}{\partial y} = \sigma_i(E_{zi} + V_i B_0) \tag{9.2-2}$$

where the subscript i denotes the region 1, 2, or 3, and $\sigma_2 = 0$, $V_2 = 0$, and $V_3 = 0$. It is useful to solve (9.2-2) for E_{zi}, differentiate this with respect to y, and substitute this into (9.2-1). The result is

$$\frac{\partial^2 H_{xi}}{\partial y^2} = \frac{1}{\eta_i} \frac{\partial H_{xi}}{\partial t} \quad \text{for} \quad i = 1 \text{ and } i = 3 \tag{9.2-3}$$

The second equation, useful for finding the electric field, is

$$-\frac{\partial H_{xi}}{\partial y} = (\mu_0 \eta_i)^{-1}(E_{zi} + V_i B_0) \tag{9.2-4}$$

for $i = 1$, 2, and 3, where $\eta_i = (\mu_0 \sigma_i)^{-1}$. The Laplace transform is used to solve the transient problem. The Laplace transforms of (9.2-3) and (9.2-4) are

$$\frac{d^2 h_{xi}}{dy^2} - \frac{s}{\eta_i} h_{xi} = 0 \tag{9.2-5}$$

and

$$e_{zi} = -\mu_0 \eta_i \frac{dh_{xi}}{dy} - \frac{V_i B_0}{s} \tag{9.2-6}$$

where $h_{xi}(y, s) = \int_0^\infty H_{xi}(y, t)e^{-st} dt$. These equations will be solved in regions 1 and 3. In region 2, h_{x2} is not a function of y but is a function of s only. Hence the electric field in region 2 can be found from

$$\frac{de_{z2}}{dy} = -\mu_0 s h_{x2} \tag{9.2-7}$$

Here and in the previously transformed equations it is assumed that initially the magnetic field in the x direction is zero.

The solutions derived from (9.2-5) for the magnetic field are

$$h_{x1} = C_1 e^{y\sqrt{s/\eta_1}} \tag{9.2-8a}$$

$$h_{x2} = C_1 \tag{9.2-8b}$$

$$h_{x3} = C_1 e^{(y_0-y)\sqrt{s/\eta_3}} \tag{9.2-8c}$$

In the above solutions it has been observed that h_{x1} should approach zero as $y \to -\infty$ and that h_{x3} should approach zero as $y \to \infty$. Hence two possible solutions are discarded. The constants of (9.2-8) have been adjusted so that the tangential components of the magnetic field are continuous across each boundary. The electric fields are obtained from (9.2-6) and (9.2-7) and are given by

$$e_{z1} = -\mu_0 \eta_1 C_1 \sqrt{\frac{s}{\eta_1}} \, e^{y \sqrt{s/\eta_1}} - \frac{VB_0}{s} \tag{9.2-9a}$$

$$e_{z2} = -\mu_0 s C_1 y + C_3 \tag{9.2-9b}$$

$$e_{z3} = \mu_0 \eta_3 C_1 \sqrt{\frac{s}{\eta_3}} \, e^{(y_0 - y) \sqrt{s/\eta_3}} \tag{9.2-9c}$$

where C_1 and C_3 are functions of s even though they are constants of integration. Two boundary conditions remain to be satisfied, namely, $e_{z1}(0) = e_{z2}(0)$ and $e_{z2}(y_0) = e_{z3}(y_0)$. When these boundary conditions are applied, the following system results:

$$\mu_0 \eta_1 \sqrt{\frac{s}{\eta_1}} C_1 + C_3 = -\frac{VB_0}{s}$$

$$-\left(\mu_0 s y_0 + \mu_0 \eta_3 \sqrt{\frac{s}{\eta_3}}\right) C_1 + C_3 = 0 \tag{9.2-10}$$

The constants C_1 and C_3 are given by

$$C_1 = \frac{-VB_0}{\mu_0 s(\eta_1 \sqrt{s/\eta_1} + \eta_3 \sqrt{s/\eta_3} + s y_0)} \tag{9.2-11}$$

$$C_3 = \frac{-VB_0(\eta_3 \sqrt{s/\eta_3} + s y_0)}{s(\eta_1 \sqrt{s/\eta_1} + \eta_3 \sqrt{s/\eta_3} + s y_0)} \tag{9.2-12}$$

Before going on, we express C_1 and C_3 in terms of the ratio $\sqrt{\sigma_1/\sigma_3}$ by using the relationship $\eta_3 = (\sigma_1/\sigma_3)\eta_1$. The constants become

$$C_1 = \frac{-(VB_0/y_0\mu_0)}{s^{3/2}[(\sqrt{\eta_1/y_0})(1 + \sqrt{\sigma_1/\sigma_3}) + \sqrt{s}]} \tag{9.2-13}$$

$$C_3 = \frac{-VB_0((\sqrt{\eta_1}/y_0)(\sqrt{\sigma_1/\sigma_3}) + \sqrt{s})}{s^{3/2}[(\sqrt{\eta_1/y_0})(1 + \sqrt{\sigma_1/\sigma_3}) + \sqrt{s}]} \tag{9.2-14}$$

The electric fields in regions 1 and 3 are given by (9.2-9a) and (9.2-9c). When the value of C_1 given by (9.2-13) is substituted into (9.2-9a) and (9.2-9b), the results are

$$e_{z1} = -\frac{VB_0}{s} + \frac{(VB_0\sqrt{\eta_1}/y_0)e^{(y/\sqrt{\eta_1})\sqrt{s}}}{s[(\sqrt{\eta_1}/y_0)(1 + \sqrt{\sigma_1/\sigma_3}) + \sqrt{s}]} \qquad (9.2\text{-}15)$$

$$e_{z3} = \frac{-[(VB_0\sqrt{\eta_1\sigma_1/\sigma_3})/y_0]\exp[-(y - y_0)\sqrt{s}/\sqrt{(\eta_1\sigma_1)/\sigma_3}]}{s[(\sqrt{\eta_1}/y_0)(1 + \sqrt{\sigma_1/\sigma_3}) + \sqrt{s}]} \qquad (9.2\text{-}16)$$

which should be checked for various limiting cases before the inverse Laplace transformation is made. At $t = 0^+$ the bottom plate is moving but no build-up of current density is expected in the bottom half-space at $t = 0^+$. Therefore, $\lim_{t\to 0} E_{z1}(y, t) = -VB_0$ if our solution is correct. From the initial value theorem of the Laplace transform (Churchill, 1958),

$$\lim_{t\to 0} E_{z1}(y, t) = \lim_{s\to\infty} se_{z1}(y, s)$$

which is easily calculated. Recalling that (9.2-15) is valid for $y \leq 0$ only, we see that $\lim_{s\to\infty} se_{z1}(y, s) = -VB_0$, as would be expected from physical considerations. After the bottom half-space has been moving a long time, the electric field is constant. The value it assumes depends upon the ratio σ_1/σ_3. If $\sigma_1/\sigma_3 = 0$ because σ_3 is an ideal conductor, the generator is short circuited and the electric field in it should be zero. At the other extreme there is no current flowing when $\sigma_3 = 0$, and the electric field must be $-VB_0$. From the final value theorem of the Laplace transform,

$$\lim_{t\to\infty} E_{z1}(y, t) = \lim_{s\to 0} se_{z1}(y, s) = \frac{-VB_0}{1 + \sqrt{\sigma_3/\sigma_1}} \qquad (9.2\text{-}17)$$

Hence the electric field in the bottom half-space satisfies the most easily applied limiting-case checks. The inverse Laplace transforms of (9.2-15) and (9.2-16) are most easily obtained from Churchill's table, entry 86. The electric fields in regions 1 and 3 become

$$E_{z1}^*(y^*, t^*) = -1 + (1 + \sqrt{\sigma^*})^{-1}$$

$$\times \left[\text{erfc}\left(\frac{-y^*}{2\sqrt{t^*}}\right) - (\exp\{(1 + \sqrt{\sigma^*})[(1 + \sqrt{\sigma^*})t^* - y^*]\}) \right.$$

$$\left. \times \text{erfc}\left\{(1 + \sqrt{\sigma^*})\sqrt{t^*} - \frac{y^*}{2\sqrt{t^*}}\right\}\right] \qquad (9.2\text{-}18)$$

and

$$E_{z3}^*(y^*, t^*) = \frac{\sqrt{\sigma^*}}{1 + \sqrt{\sigma^*}}$$

$$\times \left[\operatorname{erfc}\left(\frac{y^* - 1}{2\sqrt{\sigma^* t^*}}\right) - \left(\exp\left\{(1 + \sqrt{\sigma^*})\left[(1 + \sqrt{\sigma^*})t^* + \frac{y^* - 1}{\sqrt{\sigma^*}}\right]\right\}\right) \right.$$

$$\left. \times \operatorname{erfc}\left\{(1 + \sqrt{\sigma^*})\sqrt{t^*} + \frac{y^* - 1}{\sqrt{\sigma^* t^*}}\right\}\right] \quad (9.2\text{-}19)$$

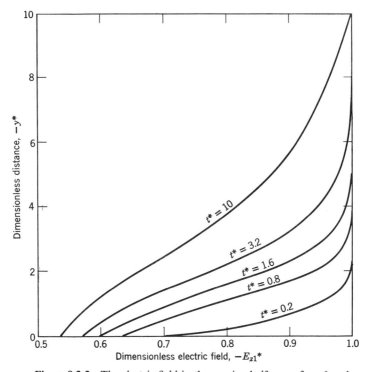

Figure 9.2-2   The electric field in the moving half-space for $\sigma^* = 1$.

where $y^* = y/y_0$, $t^* = \eta_1 t/y_0^2$, $E_{z1}^* = E_{z1}/(VB_0)$, and $\sigma^* = \sigma_1/\sigma_3$. The normalized electric field in the moving half-space is plotted in Fig. 9.2-2 for $\sigma^* = 1$. Here it is clear that the normalized electric field at any station y^* gradually increases from -1 to -0.5 as the normalized time goes from zero to infinity. Since this is a diffusion process, it is not very meaningful to search for time constants or characteristic speeds, but it is important to understand that at stations on surface more than two-thirds of the transient in the electric field is over when $t^* = 0.5$, whereas at $y^* = -2$, two-thirds of the transient is not over until $t^* = 10$.

It is easy to let the spacing between the half-spaces approach zero. When $y_0 \to 0$, there results from (9.2-18) and (9.2-19)

$$E_{z1}(y, t) = -VB_0 + \frac{VB_0}{1 + \sqrt{\sigma^*}} \operatorname{erfc}\left(\frac{-y}{2\sqrt{\eta_1 t}}\right) \qquad (9.2\text{-}20a)$$

and

$$E_{z3}(y, t) = -\frac{VB_0\sqrt{\sigma^*}}{1 + \sqrt{\sigma^*}} \operatorname{erfc}\left(\frac{y}{2\sqrt{\eta_1 \sigma^* t}}\right) \qquad (9.2\text{-}20b)$$

As $\operatorname{erfc}(0) = 1$, it is clear that $E_{z1}(0, t) = E_{z3}(0, t)$, as should be the case for two half-spaces in electrical contact.

It is especially important to study the behavior of the electric field in the moving half-space when the conductivity of the stationary half-space is infinite and $y_0 = 0$. By the initial value theorem, we obtain from (9.2-15) (letting $y_0 \to 0$ first)

$$\lim_{\substack{t \to 0 \\ \sigma_3 \to \infty}} E_{z1}(y, t) = VB_0\left(-1 + \lim_{s \to \infty} e^{y\sqrt{s/\eta_1}}\right) = \begin{array}{ll} -VB_0 & \text{for } y < 0 \\ 0 & \text{for } y = 0 \end{array}$$

$$(9.2\text{-}21)$$

Because $\sigma_3 \to \infty$, this is called a short-circuit case.

The Terminal Voltage

The terminal voltage is easily calculated by means of (2.9-5). In order to utilize this method, the total current flowing in the stationary half-space must be found. From (9.2-2) it is clear that

$$j_{z3}(y, s) = \frac{1}{\mu_0 \eta_3} e_{z3}(y, s) \qquad (9.2\text{-}22)$$

and therefore the total current is given by

$$i(s) = 2x_0 C_1 \sqrt{\frac{s}{\eta_3}} \int_y^\infty e^{(y_0 - y)\sqrt{s/\eta_3}} \, dy = 2x_0 C_1 \qquad (9.2\text{-}23)$$

where $2x_0$ is the width of the half-spaces in the x direction. The integral $\int_{-z_0}^{z_0} \int_{-x_0}^{x_0} e_{z3} h_{x3} \, dx \, dz$ results from the left side of (2.9-5) since the component of the Poynting vector normal to the other surface located in the xz plane at $y = -\infty$ is zero. The only contribution to the Poynting flux is normal to the surface of the stationary half-space having a length in the x direction of $2x_0$. Then from (2.9-5) there results

$$v_T(s)i(s) = \int_{-z_0}^{z_0} \int_{-x_0}^{x_0} e_{z3}(y_0, s)h_{x3}(y_0, s)\, dx\, dz \qquad (9.2\text{-}24a)$$

which is evaluated by means of (9.2-23), (9.2-9c), and (9.2-8c). The resulting equation is solved for $v_T(s)$:

$$v_T(s) = \frac{-2x_0\sqrt{\sigma^*}VB_0\sqrt{\eta_1}/y_0}{s[(\sqrt{\eta_1/y_0})(1 + \sqrt{\sigma^*}) + \sqrt{s}]} \qquad (9.2\text{-}24b)$$

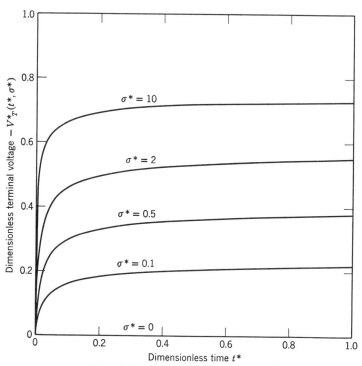

Figure 9.2-3   The terminal voltage transient.

and is easily checked for limiting cases. Clearly,

$$\lim_{t \to 0} V_T(t) = 0 \qquad \text{and} \qquad \lim_{t \to \infty} V_T(t) = \frac{-2x_0VB_0}{1 + \sqrt{1/\sigma^*}}$$

The inverse Laplace transform of (9.2-24b) is

$$V_T^*(t^*) = \frac{-\sqrt{\sigma^*}}{1 + \sqrt{\sigma^*}}\{1 - e^{t^*(1+\sqrt{\sigma^*})^2}\ \mathrm{erfc}\,[(1 + \sqrt{\sigma^*})\sqrt{t^*}]\} \qquad (9.2\text{-}24c)$$

where the dimensionless terminal voltage is $V_T^* = V_T/(2x_0VB_0)$.

The normalized terminal voltage of this configuration is shown in Fig. 9.2-3. Curves ranging from open- to short-circuit conditions are given. As expected, the short-circuit case ($\sigma^* = 0$) yields zero terminal voltage at all times, even though E_{z1} is not zero. The open circuit yields a normalized terminal voltage of unity for all time. Later we will discuss the rise of the open-circuit voltage from zero to unity. The voltage versus time curves are characterized by a normalized time constant of about 0.01, regardless of the value of σ^*.

The Oscillating Half-Space

If the lower half-space oscillates at an angular frequency of ω, the alternating-current phasor solutions indicated by bars can be obtained from the Laplace transformed solutions by replacing s by $j\omega$, except for the driving function VB_0/s, which is replaced by $\bar{V}B_0$, where $\bar{V}$ is the root mean square half-space velocity. Then the electric fields of (9.2-15) and (9.2-16) become

$$\bar{e}_{z1} = -\bar{V}B_0\left[1 - \frac{e^{(y/\delta)(1+j)}}{1 + \sqrt{\sigma^* + (1 + j)y_0/\delta}}\right] \tag{9.2-25a}$$

$$\bar{e}_{z3} = \frac{-\bar{V}B_0\sqrt{\sigma^*}}{1 + \sqrt{\sigma^* + (1 + j)y_0/\delta}} \exp\left[-(y - y_0)\frac{1 + j}{\delta\sqrt{\sigma^*}}\right] \tag{9.2-25b}$$

where $\delta = \sqrt{2\eta_1/\omega}$ and is commonly called the skin depth. The physical significance of δ is easily illustrated by inspecting the magnitude of the current density in the moving half-space. Since $\bar{J}_{z1} = \sigma_1(\bar{e}_{z1} + \bar{V}B_0)$, the magnitude of the current density is given by

$$|\bar{J}_{z1}| = \frac{\bar{V}B_0 e^{y/\delta}}{(1 + \sqrt{\sigma^* + y_0/\delta})^2 + y_0^2/\delta^2} \tag{9.2-25c}$$

Here we observe that when $y = -\delta$, the magnitude of the current density is one-eth the magnitude of the surface current density. It is useful to remember that the magnitude of the current density does not diminish to one per cent of its surface value until a depth of about $4\frac{1}{2}$ skin depths is attained. The phasor value of the terminal voltage is easily obtained from (9.2-24b). It becomes

$$\bar{V}_T = \frac{-2x_0\sqrt{\sigma^*}\,\bar{V}B_0}{1 + \sqrt{\sigma^* + y_0/\delta} + j(y_0/\delta)} \tag{9.2-26}$$

which indicates that as the skin depth goes to zero, or as the frequency increases to infinity, the amplitude of the terminal voltage decreases toward zero.

Discussion

The situation just treated is a generalization of Example 2.4. Therefore, it is interesting to examine the problem of the half-spaces qualitatively. When $\sigma^* = \infty$, we are dealing with the open-circuit case in which a conducting half-space moves through a uniform magnetic field. In Example 2.4 an open-circuited conducting filament, rather than a half-space, moves through the magnetic field. In both cases the electric field in the laboratory (stationary half-space) frame must be zero at the time the movement is initiated. If the motion begins at $t = 0$, at $t = 0^+$ the electric field in the frame of the moving conductor must be given by $E'_{z1} = VB_0$ everywhere in the moving conductor. At first glance, this seems contrary to the limiting-case checks of (9.2-15). However, (9.2-15) is derived from Maxwell's equations and Ohm's law, the latter being good in quasi-static situations only. In reality the electric field E'_{z1}, which occurs in the moving conductor just after the motion starts, causes a charge separation. Positive and negative charges flow to opposite ends of the moving half-space, as was the case in Example 2.4. These charges set up a field which reduces E'_{z1} to zero in the moving conductor. Then in the laboratory frame, $E_{z1} = -VB_0$. This initial portion of the transient occurs very fast and is not present in the solution based on Ohm's law. The initial portion of the transient might possibly be handled by treating the free charge in the conductor as a three-component fluid comprising electrons, ions, and neutrals. Where the stationary slab is a conductor, the initial portion of the transient is similar to the transient just described. After the initial portion of the transient is over, the solutions derived here apply.

We have considered the solution to the alternating-current case. This solution has the advantage of not involving the complications of the inverse Laplace transform. For alternating-current it might be said that the "electromagnetic boundary layer" extends 4.6 skin depths into the conductor.

9.3 TIME-VARYING TWO-DIMENSIONAL MHD CHANNEL FLOW

Introduction

We now establish equations that describe a wide class of transient and alternating flows of incompressible, viscous, electrically conducting fluid. It is assumed that the flow has only one component of velocity which is normal to the steady, uniform applied magnetic field. This section, done in cartesian coordinates, is applicable to transient and oscillating plate problems and is easily extended to other systems of coordinates. The equations derived here apply in one- and two-dimensional channels. The driving functions may be moving channel walls, time-varying potentials, time-varying load resistors, or time-varying pressure gradients. Although the alternating-current steady-state problems can be solved in most cases, the transient solutions to the same problems may be exceedingly difficult mathematically. For this reason, the equations are not derived in generalized orthogonal coordinates.

In certain equations the pressure gradient is a function of time and the velocity flows axially. In these equations it is assumed that the piston or pistons causing the time-varying pressure gradient are located very far from the region where the velocity is axial. Nearer the pistons the fluid has vorticity which couples to the pressure through viscosity causing damped pressure waves. At a sufficient distance from the pistons, as will be discussed in Chapter 13, the vorticity wave damps out and the flow becomes unidirectional.

Development of the Equations

It is assumed that the only component of velocity is in the x direction. Therefore, $v = 0$, $w = 0$, and, by the equation of continuity, u is a function of y, z, and t only. However complicated the velocity, it will interact with the transverse magnetic field and generate currents mutually perpendicular to the transverse magnetic field and the velocity. These currents will interact with the transverse magnetic field causing a body force to be exerted on the fluid. They will also generate an axial magnetic field. The situation is very similar to steady MHD channel flow and is modified by time derivatives in the Navier-Stokes and Maxwell equations. Assuming $\partial/\partial x$ of all quantities (except pressure) is zero, Maxwell's $\nabla \times \mathbf{H}$ equation becomes

$$\hat{x}\left(\frac{\partial H_z}{\partial y} - \frac{\partial H_y}{\partial z}\right) + \hat{y}\frac{\partial H_x}{\partial z} - \hat{z}\frac{\partial H_x}{\partial y}$$
$$= \hat{x}\sigma E_x + \hat{y}\sigma(E_y - uB_z) + \hat{z}\sigma(E_z + uB_y) \quad (9.3\text{-}1)$$

From (9.3-1) it is clear that the flow of the fluid does not contribute to the x component of current density. Maxwell's $\nabla \times \mathbf{E}$ equation yields

$$\hat{x}\left(\frac{\partial E_z}{\partial y} - \frac{\partial E_y}{\partial z}\right) + \hat{y}\frac{\partial E_x}{\partial z} - \hat{z}\frac{\partial E_x}{\partial y}$$
$$= -\hat{x}\mu_0\frac{\partial H_x}{\partial t} - \hat{y}\mu_0\frac{\partial H_y}{\partial t} - \hat{z}\mu_0\frac{\partial H_z}{\partial t} \quad (9.3\text{-}2)$$

and the Navier-Stokes equation becomes

$$\rho \frac{\partial u}{\partial t} = -\frac{\partial P}{\partial x} + \mu_f \nabla^2 u + B_y \frac{\partial H_x}{\partial y} + B_z \frac{\partial H_x}{\partial z} \tag{9.3-3a}$$

$$0 = -\frac{\partial P}{\partial y} - B_x \frac{\partial H_x}{\partial y} - B_z \left(\frac{\partial H_z}{\partial y} - \frac{\partial H_y}{\partial z} \right) \tag{9.3-3b}$$

$$0 = -\frac{\partial P}{\partial z} + B_y \left(\frac{\partial H_z}{\partial y} - \frac{\partial H_y}{\partial z} \right) - B_x \frac{\partial H_x}{\partial z} \tag{9.3-3c}$$

From (9.3-3b) $\partial^2 P/\partial x \, \partial y = 0$ and from (9.3-3c) $\partial^2 P/\partial x \, \partial z = 0$, which is satisfied when $\partial P/\partial x$ is a constant. In the class of problems now considered, $\partial P/\partial x$ may assume various values depending on the configuration. Equations (9.3-3b) and (9.3-3c) are useful for finding $\partial P/\partial y$ and $\partial P/\partial z$ after the magnetic fields have been found. Either B_z or B_y can be assumed to be the applied magnetic induction. In this derivation, we let $B_z = 0$ and investigate B_y under that condition. When $B_z = 0$, the z component of (9.3-2) implies that E_x is a function of z and/or t, a constant, or zero. From the x component of (9.3-1)

$$-\frac{\partial H_y}{\partial z} = \sigma E_x \tag{9.3-4}$$

and from the y component of (9.3-2)

$$\frac{\partial E_x}{\partial z} = -\mu_0 \frac{\partial H_y}{\partial t} \tag{9.3-5}$$

which indicates that E_x and H_y can be found without knowing u, H_x, E_y, or E_z. Because $\partial B_x/\partial x = 0$ and $B_z = 0$, the $\nabla \cdot \mathbf{B} = 0$ equation indicates that B_y is a function of z and/or t, a constant, or zero. Here we choose $B_y = B_0$, a constant which is the applied magnetic induction. Then by (9.3-4) E_x must be zero. The equations which must be solved to determine u, H_x, and E_z become

$$-\frac{\partial H_x}{\partial y} = \sigma(E_z + B_0 u) \tag{9.3-6a}$$

$$\frac{\partial E_z}{\partial y} - \frac{\partial E_y}{\partial z} = -\mu_0 \frac{\partial H_x}{\partial t} \tag{9.3-6b}$$

$$\sigma E_y = \frac{\partial H_x}{\partial z} \tag{9.3-6c}$$

$$\rho \frac{\partial u}{\partial t} = -\frac{\partial P}{\partial x} + \mu_f \nabla^2 u + B_0 \frac{\partial H_x}{\partial y} \tag{9.3-6d}$$

It is easy to combine (9.3-6a), (9.3-6b), and (9.3-6c) to obtain

$$\nabla_T^2 H_x = \sigma\mu_0 \frac{\partial H_x}{\partial t} - \sigma B_0 \frac{\partial u}{\partial y} \qquad (9.3\text{-}7)$$

where $\nabla_T^2 = \partial^2/\partial y^2 + \partial^2/\partial z^2$. This relationship is the one obtained in Section 6.4:

$$\sigma\mu_0 \frac{\partial \mathbf{H}}{\partial t} = \nabla^2 \mathbf{H} + \sigma \nabla \times (\mathbf{V} \times \mathbf{B}) \qquad (9.3\text{-}8a)$$

It is interesting to inspect this equation by using the vector identity

$$\nabla \times (\nabla \times \mathbf{B}) = \mathbf{V}\nabla \cdot \mathbf{B} - \mathbf{B}\nabla \cdot \mathbf{V} + (\mathbf{B} \cdot \nabla)\mathbf{V} - (\mathbf{V} \cdot \nabla)\mathbf{B} \qquad (9.3\text{-}8b)$$

in which the first two terms vanish because $\nabla \cdot \mathbf{B} = 0$, and, since the fluid is incompressible, $\nabla \cdot \mathbf{V} = 0$. Since $\mathbf{V} = \hat{x}u$, $\mathbf{B} = \hat{x}B_x + \hat{y}B_0$, and $\partial/\partial x = 0$, $\nabla \times (\mathbf{V} \times \mathbf{B})$ becomes $\hat{x}B_0(\partial u/\partial y)$, which agrees with (9.3-7). This could have been obtained without the preceding considerations. However, there is no way of knowing from (9.3-8a) that the assumptions are consistent with all of the other MHD equations.

The simultaneous solution of (9.3-6d) and (9.3-7), subject to the appropriate initial and boundary conditions, yields u and H_x. E_y, E_z, J_y, and J_z can be found with the aid of (9.3-6a), (9.3-6b), and (9.3-6c).

Dimensionless Forms of the Equations

The magnetic field H_x and the x component of the velocity u are both functions of y, z, t, $\partial P/\partial x$, ρ, μ_f, μ_0, σ, and B_0. By the Buckingham pi theorem (Birkhoff, 1960), Equations (9.3-6b) and (9.3-7) can be expressed in terms of 7 independent dimensionless variables. It would be desirable to use dimensionless coordinates for y, z, and t. The spatial coordinates should be normalized by the use of the channel dimensions. For example, if y_0 is the height of the channel, the choice of the dimensionless coordinates might be $y^* = y/y_0$ and $z^* = z/y_0$. The familiar Hartmann number $M = y_0 B_0 \sqrt{\sigma/\mu_f}$ is also a useful dimensionless parameter which is directly proportional to the applied magnetic induction. The most obvious way of normalizing the velocity and the magnetic field is to choose $u^* = u/[(y_0^2/\mu_f)(\partial P/\partial x)]$ and $H_x^* = H_x/[y_0^2\sqrt{\sigma/\mu_f}(\partial P/\partial x)]$ which is useful providing $\partial P/\partial x \neq 0$. The ratio of viscous diffusivity to magnetic diffusivity, the magnetic Prandtl number $Pm = \mu_f\sigma\mu_0/\rho$, may also be useful. To complete our selection of 7 dimensionless variables, we can express time as $t^* = t/(y_0^2\rho/\mu_f)$. New dimensionless variables can be generated by making products of the independent quantities given above. For example, $\bar{t}^* = t^*/Pm = t/(y_0^2\sigma\mu_0)$, which is not independent of t^*.

When $\partial P/\partial x = 0$, it is obvious that $H^* = H_x/(B_0/\mu_0)$, but the means of normalizing the velocity is not so clear. Some possible choices for u^* are $\mu/(\mu_f/y_0\rho)$, $u/(1/y_0\sigma\mu_0)$, and $u/(B_0/\sqrt{\mu_0\rho})$. The last of these is the ratio of the velocity of the fluid to the Alfvén speed discussed in Chapter 8. The introduction of the Alfvén speed allows time to be normalized as $t^* = t/(y_0\sqrt{\mu_0\rho}/B_0)$. Other normalizations of time involving the magnetic induction can be made. However, it is not useful to have the magnetic field appear in too many of the dimensionless variables.

When $\partial P/\partial x \neq 0$, an attractive set of dimensionless variables is $y^* = y/y_0$, $z^* = z/y_0$, $t^* = t/(y_0^2\rho/\mu_f)$, $M = y_0B_0\sqrt{\sigma/\mu_f}$, $Pm = \mu_f\sigma\mu_0/\rho$, $u^* = u/[(y_0^2/\mu_f)(\partial P/\partial x)]$, and $H^* = H_x/[y_0^2\sqrt{\sigma/\mu_f}(\partial P/\partial y)]$. Under these substitutions (9.3-6d) and (9.3-7) become

$$\frac{\partial^2 u^*}{\partial y^{*2}} + \frac{\partial^2 u^*}{\partial z^{*2}} + M\frac{\partial H^*}{\partial y^*} = 1 + \frac{\partial u^*}{\partial t^*} \tag{9.3-9a}$$

and

$$\frac{\partial^2 H^*}{\partial y^{*2}} + \frac{\partial^2 H^*}{\partial z^{*2}} + M\frac{\partial u^*}{\partial y^*} = Pm\frac{\partial H^*}{\partial t^*} \tag{9.3-9b}$$

which have the advantage of containing the magnetic induction in only one dimensionless parameter. The other dimensionless parameter, Pm, is the ratio of fluid to magnetic diffusivity (the magnetic Prandtl number). This particular choice of dimensionless variables, however, is useful only when $\partial P/\partial x$ is constant in time or when $\partial P/\partial x$ varies sinusoidally. Then the rms velocity and magnetic field are normalized with respect to the rms pressure gradient. In doing phasor calculations, it must be remembered that the resulting unity on the right-hand side of (9.3-9a) is the driving function.

Where the pressure gradient may be zero, a possible choice of dimensionless variables is $y^* = y/y_0$, $z^* = z/y_0$, $t^* = t/(y_0^2\rho/\mu_f)$, $H^* = H_x/(B_0/\mu_0)$, $u^* = u/(\mu_f/y_0\rho)$, $G^* = (y_0^3\rho/\mu_f^2)(\partial P/\partial x)$, $M = y_0B_0\sqrt{\sigma/\mu_f}$, and $Pm = \mu_f\sigma\mu_0/\rho$. Under these substitutions (9.3-6d) and (9.3-7) become

$$\frac{\partial^2 u^*}{\partial y^{*2}} + \frac{\partial^2 u^*}{\partial z^{*2}} + \frac{M^2}{Pm}\frac{\partial H^*}{\partial y^*} = G^* + \frac{\partial u^*}{\partial t^*} \tag{9.3-10a}$$

$$\frac{\partial^2 H^*}{\partial y^{*2}} + \frac{\partial^2 H^*}{\partial z^{*2}} + Pm\frac{\partial u^*}{\partial y^*} = Pm\frac{\partial H^*}{\partial t^*} \tag{9.3-10b}$$

This form of the equations of transient MHD channel flow contains three dimensionless parameters. However, when the pressure gradient is zero, only M and Pm remain. Hence, by using the systems of (9.3-9) or (9.3-10), we can write the equations of transient MHD channel flow with the aid of only two parameters. For example, if the contours of constant velocity were examined at a preassigned time, contours for all combinations of M and Pm would have to be exhibited. Hence the introduction of time to the problem has greatly complicated the solution by introducing the new variable t^* and the new parameter Pm.

There are cases where no characteristic dimension exists, as in a semi-infinite sea. Then the Hartmann number of the other variables and parameters of (9.3-9a), (9.3-9b), (9.3-10a), and (9.3-10b) lose physical significance. In these cases a possible choice of dimensionless variables is $y^* = y/(v/A)$, $z^* = z/(v/A)$, $t^* = t/(v/A^2)$, $H^* = H/H_0$, $u^* = u/A$, $G^* = (v/\rho A^3)(\partial P/\partial x)$, and $Pm = \sigma\mu_0 v = v/\eta$, where A is the Alfvén speed $(A = H_0(\mu_0/\rho)^{1/2})$. Equations (9.3-6d) and (9.3-7) would then become

$$\frac{\partial^2 u^*}{\partial y^{*2}} + \frac{\partial^2 u^*}{\partial z^{*2}} + \frac{\partial H^*}{\partial y^*} = G^* + \frac{\partial u^*}{\partial t^*} \qquad (9.3\text{-}11a)$$

and

$$\frac{\partial^2 H^*}{\partial y^{*2}} + \frac{\partial^2 H^*}{\partial z^{*2}} + Pm\frac{\partial u^*}{\partial y^*} = Pm\frac{\partial H^*}{\partial t^*} \qquad (9.3\text{-}11b)$$

These equations are especially useful in the analysis of flow in semi-infinite regions. They may seem simpler than (9.3-10a) and (9.3-10b) because of the absence of the Hartmann number. However, the above choice has the disadvantage of the magnetic field appearing in five rather than two of the variables.

Boundary and Initial Conditions

When the boundaries are either perfect conductors or insulators, the boundary conditions presented in Section 7.4 apply. If the boundary is an imperfect conductor, the Maxwell equations must be solved in the imperfect conductor as well as in the conducting fluid subject to the electromagnetic boundary conditions discussed in Sections 2.5 and 7.2.

In addition to the boundary conditions, initial conditions on velocity and magnetic field must be known for all y^* and z^* at the time the transient is initiated.

9.4 OSCILLATING MHD ONE-DIMENSIONAL POISEUILLE FLOW

Introduction

In this section the steady alternating flow of an electrically conducting liquid is investigated. The fluid is located in the channel sketched in Fig. 7.1-1 and is driven by two oscillating pistons. The pistons are located at $x = \pm x_0$, where $x_0 \gg y_0$, and are oscillating in phase so that they do not compress the liquid. Near the pistons there are x and y components of velocity. The y component exists because the fluid very near the pistons must move with a very flat velocity profile, which becomes modified by the viscous forces at greater distances from the pistons. At very large distances from the pistons, the flow becomes fully developed and the y component becomes negligible compared to the x component of velocity. We will consider the MHD Poiseuille flow between two infinite planes and solve for the case where the pistons are located far from the region of interest. Under these assumptions, this problem is similar to one involving the oscillation in the x direction of the infinite plates with electrically conducting, viscous fluid between them. The latter problem is not free of the y component of velocity at $x = \pm x_0$ either. Although steady-state development problems are treated later in this chapter, a discussion of the development problem arising from the oscillating pistons is deferred until Chapter 13 because it involves the study of the propagation of pressure waves which are coupled (through the viscosity) at the boundaries to vorticity waves.

In the investigation of one-dimensional oscillating MHD Poiseuille flow it is very important to consider the external electrical circuit since it can destroy the symmetry of the velocity profile. Although this is not possible in the case of steady flow, it occurs in oscillating flow because of spatial variations in the electric field induced by an oscillating magnetic field. In alternating-current and transient problems the electric field is *never* zero everywhere in the conducting fluid, not even in the short-circuited case. For example, in Section 9.2 the terminal voltage was zero in the short-circuited case but the electric field was not zero everywhere in the moving medium. In alternating-current problems, however, certain components of the electric field may be zero along the boundaries of a generator so that no real Poynting flux passes from the generator to the load in the short-circuit case.

The problem of the flow of an electrically conducting fluid between two oscillating flat plates is treated by M. M. Staniśić et al. (1962). In their analysis the electric field is set to zero everywhere and the influence of the external circuit is not even mentioned.

A theoretical treatment of the problem to be considered here, given by Étienne Crausse et al. (1964), is valid for cases in which $Pm \ll 1$, a condition usually found in the laboratory. This investigation gives the amplitude of the mean velocity of the conducting fluid and its phase angle as a function of channel width, frequency, and kinematic viscosity for various Hartmann numbers.

In another paper (Causse et al., 1964) these quantities are measured experimentally in a tube of insulating material approximately 1 meter long.

The tube is of rectangular cross section having dimensions of 0.88 mm × 6.50 mm and is filled with mercury. The difference between the theoretical and experimental curves is about 10% for the mean velocity and the agreement is very good between the phase angle curves. Such a disparity between the theoretical and the experimental results are to be expected because the experimental tube has a width-to-height ratio of about 1/7. Ideally the ratio should be smaller, or the solution to the two- rather than the one-dimensional problem should be compared to the experimental results.

We seek a more general solution, valid for any choice of parameters, which holds between insulating planes and accounts for an external electrical circuit. Our analysis deals with the one-dimensional analogue of an alternating-current generator in general. Solutions are sought for the velocity profile, the induced axial magnetic field, the induced current density, the terminal voltage and the internal impedance of the device, and the volumetric flow rate.

Solution

The phasor equations for the velocity and the magnetic field obtained from (9.3-9a) and (9.3-9b) by assuming all quantities vary as $e^{j\omega^* t^*}$ are given by

$$\frac{d^2 u^*}{dy^{*2}} + M \frac{dH^*}{dy^*} = 1 + j\omega^* u^* \tag{9.4-1a}$$

and

$$\frac{d^2 H^*}{dy^{*2}} + M \frac{du^*}{dy^*} = j\omega^* Pm H^* \tag{9.4-1b}$$

where $\omega^* = \omega y_0^2 \rho / \mu_f$ and ω is the angular frequency at which the pressure gradient is varied. When (9.4-1a) and (9.4-1b) are combined, we have

$$\left\{ \frac{d^4}{dy^{*4}} - [M^2 + j\omega^*(1 + Pm)] \frac{d^2}{dy^{*2}} - \omega^{*2} Pm \right\} \begin{bmatrix} u^* \\ H^* \end{bmatrix} = \begin{bmatrix} -j\omega^* Pm \\ 0 \end{bmatrix} \tag{9.4-1c}$$

The solution for u^* is obtained by solving (9.4-1c). In its most general form,

$$u^* = \bar{C}_1 \, \mathrm{ch} \, p_1 y^* + \bar{C}_2 \, \mathrm{ch} \, p_2 y^* + \bar{C}_3 \, \mathrm{sh} \, p_1 y^* + \bar{C}_4 \, \mathrm{sh} \, p_2 y^* + \frac{j}{\omega^*} \tag{9.4-2}$$

where p_1 and p_2 are obtained from

$$p^4 - [M^2 + j\omega^*(1 + Pm)]p^2 - \omega^{*2} Pm = 0 \tag{9.4-3a}$$

The solution to this equation is given by

$$p_{1,2}^2 = \tfrac{1}{2}[M^2 + j\omega^*(1 + Pm)$$

$$\pm \sqrt{M^4 - \omega^{*2} + 2\omega^* Pm - \omega^{*2} Pm^2 + j2\omega^* M^2(1 + Pm)}] \tag{9.4-3b}$$

The characteristic equation (9.4-3a) is equivalent to dispersion relationship (8.2-14) which implies coupling between the ordinary Alfvén and viscous diffusion waves. (8.2-14) can be reduced to (9.4-3a) by letting $k = p/y_0$ and $H_{0x} = B_0/\mu_0$ and by introducing M, ω^*, and Pm. After a moderate amount of manipulation $p_{1,2}$ can be reduced to

$$p_{1,2} = \tfrac{1}{2}[\sqrt{M^2 + j\omega^*(1 + \sqrt{Pm})^2} \pm \sqrt{M^2 + j\omega^*(1 - \sqrt{Pm})^2}] \quad (9.4\text{-}3c)$$

and the real and imaginary parts of $p_{1,2}$ are given by

$$\text{Re } p_{1,2} = \frac{1}{2\sqrt{2}}\left[\sqrt{\sqrt{M^4 + \omega^{*2}(1 + \sqrt{Pm})^4} + M^2}\right.$$
$$\left. \pm \sqrt{\sqrt{M^4 + \omega^{*2}(1 - \sqrt{Pm})^4} + M^2}\right] \quad (9.4\text{-}3d)$$

$$\text{Im } p_{1,2} = \frac{1}{2\sqrt{2}}\left[\sqrt{\sqrt{M^4 + \omega^{*2}(1 + \sqrt{Pm})^4} - M^2}\right.$$
$$\left. \pm \sqrt{\sqrt{M^4 + \omega^{*2}(1 - \sqrt{Pm})^4} - M^2}\right] \quad (9.4\text{-}3e)$$

where Re and Im denote the real and imaginary parts, respectively. In the very important case where $Pm \ll 1$, as in mercury $Pm \simeq 10^{-7}$, p_1 and p_2 are given by

$$p_1 = \sqrt{M^2 + j\omega^*} \quad (9.4\text{-}3f)$$

$$p_2 = j\omega^*\sqrt{Pm}/(M^2 + j\omega^*)^{1/2} \quad (9.4\text{-}3g)$$

Before solving for the magnetic field, we will satisfy the boundary conditions on velocity at the channel walls. These conditions are $u^*(1) = u^*(-1) = 0$, and they are satisfied when

$$\bar{C}_2 = -\bar{C}_1 \frac{\text{ch } p_1}{\text{ch } p_2} - \frac{j}{\omega^* \text{ ch } p_2} \quad \text{and} \quad \bar{C}_4 = -\bar{C}_3 \frac{\text{sh } p_1}{\text{sh } p_2} \quad (9.4\text{-}4)$$

Therefore u^* may be rewritten as

$$u^* = \frac{j}{\omega^*}\left(1 - \frac{\text{ch } p_2 y^*}{\text{ch } p_2}\right) + C_1(\text{ch } p_2 \text{ ch } p_1 y^* - \text{ch } p_1 \text{ ch } p_2 y^*)$$
$$+ C_2(\text{sh } p_2 \text{ sh } p_1 y^* - \text{sh } p_1 \text{ sh } p_2 y^*) \quad (9.4\text{-}5)$$

where C_1 and C_2 are new constants which must be evaluated by using the magnetic field boundary conditions. The magnetic field can be found by solving (9.4-1a) for $\partial H^*/\partial y^*$. This is integrated and the constant of integration is set to zero in order to satisfy (9.4-1c). The resulting solution is

$$H^* = \frac{-j(j\omega^* - p_2^{\ 2})\ \text{sh}\ p_2 y^*}{\omega^* M p_2 \qquad \text{ch}\ p_2}$$

$$+ \frac{C_1}{M}\left(\frac{j\omega^* - p_1^{\ 2}}{p_1}\ \text{ch}\ p_2\ \text{sh}\ p_1 y^* - \frac{j\omega^* - p_2^{\ 2}}{p_2}\ \text{ch}\ p_1\ \text{sh}\ p_2 y^*\right)$$

$$+ \frac{C_2}{M}\left(\frac{j\omega^* - p_1^{\ 2}}{p_1}\ \text{sh}\ p_2\ \text{ch}\ p_1 y^* - \frac{j\omega^* - p_2^{\ 2}}{p_2}\ \text{sh}\ p_1\ \text{ch}\ p_2 y^*\right) \quad (9.4\text{-}6)$$

The constants C_1 and C_2 depend upon the return circuit. If the return circuit is symmetrical, the magnetic field must be antisymmetric. In that case, C_2 would be zero. If the return circuit is located entirely below the channel, as in Fig. 7.1-1, the magnetic field at $y^* = 1$ would be zero. At the same time the magnetic field at $y^* = -1$ would be $\mathscr{I}^*$. Here $\mathscr{I}^*$ is the dimensionless rms current per unit length of x dimension and $\mathscr{I}^* = \mathscr{I}/[y_0^2\sqrt{\sigma/\mu_f}(\partial P/\partial x)]$. In order to treat the general return circuit case, let the magnetic field at $y^* = -1$ be given by

$$H^*(-1) = \frac{(1 + \alpha)}{2}\mathscr{I}^* \qquad -1 \le \alpha \le 1 \qquad (9.4\text{-}7a)$$

where α is the return circuit symmetry parameter. By Ampere's circuital law, $H^*(-1) - H^*(1) = \mathscr{I}^*$ and therefore

$$H^*(1) = -\left(\frac{1 - \alpha}{2}\right)\mathscr{I}^* \qquad (9.4\text{-}7b)$$

When $\alpha = 1$, the return circuit is entirely below the channel. A symmetrical return circuit exists when $\alpha = 0$, and when $\alpha = -1$, the return circuit is entirely above the channel. Using (9.4-7a) and (9.4-7b) as boundary conditions yields solutions for C_1 and C_2. The velocity and the magnetic field are given by

$$u^* = \left(\frac{\text{ch}\ p_2\ \text{ch}\ p_1 y^* - \text{ch}\ p_1\ \text{ch}\ p_2 y^*}{\dfrac{j\omega^* - p_1^{\ 2}}{p_1}\ \text{ch}\ p_2\ \text{sh}\ p_1 - \dfrac{j\omega^* - p_2^{\ 2}}{p_2}\ \text{ch}\ p_1\ \text{sh}\ p_2}\right)$$

$$\times \left[-\frac{M\mathscr{I}^*}{2} + \frac{j(j\omega^* - p_2^{\ 2})}{\omega^* p_2}\ \text{th}\ p_2\right]$$

$$+ \frac{\text{sh}\ p_2\ \text{sh}\ p_1 y^* - \text{sh}\ p_1\ \text{sh}\ p_2 y^*}{\dfrac{j\omega^* - p_1^{\ 2}}{p_1}\ \text{sh}\ p_2\ \text{ch}\ p_1 - \dfrac{j\omega^* - p_2^{\ 2}}{p_2}\ \text{sh}\ p_1\ \text{ch}\ p_2} \cdot \frac{M\alpha\mathscr{I}^*}{2}$$

$$+ \frac{j}{\omega^*}\left(1 - \frac{\text{ch}\ p_2 y^*}{\text{ch}\ p_2}\right) \qquad (9.4\text{-}8a)$$

and

$$H^* = \frac{-j(j\omega^* - p_2^{\ 2})\ \text{sh}\ p_2 y^*}{\omega^* M p_2}\ \frac{}{\text{ch}\ p_2}$$

$$+ \frac{\left\{\left[-\dfrac{\mathscr{I}^*}{2} + \dfrac{j(j\omega^* - p_2^{\ 2})\ \text{th}\ p_2}{\omega^* M p_2}\right]\left(\dfrac{j\omega^* - p_1^{\ 2}}{p_1}\ \text{ch}\ p_2\ \text{sh}\ p_1 y^* - \dfrac{j\omega^* - p_2^{\ 2}}{p_2}\ \text{ch}\ p_1\ \text{sh}\ p_2 y^*\right)\right\}}{\dfrac{j\omega^* - p_1^{\ 2}}{p_1}\ \text{ch}\ p_2\ \text{sh}\ p_1 - \dfrac{j\omega^* - p_2^{\ 2}}{p_2}\ \text{ch}\ p_1\ \text{sh}\ p_2}$$

$$+ \frac{\dfrac{j\omega^* - p_1^{\ 2}}{p_1}\ \text{sh}\ p_2\ \text{ch}\ p_1 y^* - \dfrac{j\omega^* - p_2^{\ 2}}{p_2}\ \text{sh}\ p_1\ \text{ch}\ p_2 y^*}{\dfrac{j\omega^* - p_1^{\ 2}}{p_1}\ \text{sh}\ p_2\ \text{ch}\ p_1 - \dfrac{j\omega^* - p_2^{\ 2}}{p_2}\ \text{sh}\ p_1\ \text{ch}\ p_2} \cdot \frac{\alpha \mathscr{I}^*}{2}$$

$$(9.4\text{-}8b)$$

The dimensionless current density J_z^* is given by $J_z^* = -\partial H^*/\partial y^*$ and is easily obtained from (9.4-8b). The dimensionless current density in the channel is

$$J_z^* = \frac{j(j\omega^* - p_2^{\ 2})\ \text{ch}\ p_2 y^*}{\omega^* M}\ \frac{}{\text{ch}\ p_2}$$

$$+ \frac{\left\{\left[\dfrac{\mathscr{I}^*}{2} - \dfrac{j(j\omega^* - p_2^{\ 2})\ \text{th}\ p_2}{\omega^* M p_2}\right][(j\omega^* - p_1^{\ 2})\ \text{ch}\ p_2\ \text{ch}\ p_1 y^* - (j\omega^* - p_2^{\ 2})\ \text{ch}\ p_1\ \text{ch}\ p_2 y^*]\right\}}{\dfrac{j\omega^* - p_1^{\ 2}}{p_1}\ \text{ch}\ p_2\ \text{sh}\ p_1 - \dfrac{j\omega^* - p_2^{\ 2}}{p_2}\ \text{ch}\ p_1\ \text{sh}\ p_2}$$

$$- \frac{(j\omega^* - p_1^{\ 2})\ \text{sh}\ p_2\ \text{sh}\ p_1 y^* - (j\omega^* - p_2^{\ 2})\ \text{sh}\ p_1\ \text{sh}\ p_2 y^*}{\dfrac{j\omega^* - p_1^{\ 2}}{p_1}\ \text{sh}\ p_2\ \text{ch}\ p_1 - \dfrac{j\omega^* - p_2^{\ 2}}{p_2}\ \text{sh}\ p_1\ \text{ch}\ p_2} \cdot \left(\frac{\alpha \mathscr{I}^*}{2}\right)$$

$$(9.4\text{-}9)$$

When the return circuit has infinite impedance, no current flows and $\mathscr{I}^* = 0$. The current density becomes an even function of y^*, the induced magnetic field becomes antisymmetric, and the velocity profile assumes symmetry. It is a good check on the validity of the solution to observe that (9.4-8b) yields $H^*(1) = H^*(-1) = H^*(0) = 0$ in the open-circuit case. This must be true because no alternating current flows in the load circuit.

The terminal voltage can be calculated from the Poynting vector as derived in Section 2.9. By (2.9-5) in its phasor form the dimensionless terminal voltage $V_T{}^* = V_T/[(2y_0z_0/\sqrt{\sigma\mu_f})(\partial P/\partial x)]$ becomes

$$V_T{}^* = \frac{1}{I^*}\int_{S^*}(\mathbf{E}^* \times \bar{\mathbf{H}}^*)\cdot d\mathbf{S}^* \qquad (9.4\text{-}10)$$

where I^* is the total dimensionless current flowing through the electrodes and $I^* = I/[2x_0y_0{}^2\sqrt{\sigma/\mu_f}(\partial P/\partial x)]$, where $2x_0$ is the length of the electrodes in the x direction. The bar denotes the complex conjugate. The surface of integration encloses the channel. The only contributions to the Poynting vector occur on xz planes at $y^* = \pm 1$. It is not necessary to calculate the electric field for all y^* because at $y^* = \pm 1$, $E_z{}^* = J_z{}^*$ because of the no-slip boundary condition on the velocity. By using (9.4-10), (9.4-9), and (9.4-8b), we can write the dimensionless terminal voltage as

$$V_T{}^* = \frac{-j(j\omega^* - p_2{}^2)}{\omega^* M}$$

$$+ \frac{\left[-\dfrac{\mathscr{I}^*}{2} + \dfrac{j(j\omega^* - p_2{}^2)\,\text{th }p_2}{\omega^* M p_2}\right](p_2{}^2 - p_1{}^2)\,\text{ch }p_1\,\text{ch }p_2}{\dfrac{j\omega^* - p_1{}^2}{p_1}\,\text{ch }p_2\,\text{sh }p_1 - \dfrac{j\omega^* - p_2{}^2}{p_2}\,\text{ch }p_1\,\text{sh }p_2}$$

$$- \frac{\alpha^2 \mathscr{I}^*}{2}\cdot\frac{(p_2{}^2 - p_1{}^2)\,\text{sh }p_1\,\text{sh }p_2}{\dfrac{j\omega^* - p_1{}^2}{p_1}\,\text{sh }p_2\,\text{ch }p_1 - \dfrac{j\omega^* - p_2{}^2}{p_2}\,\text{sh }p_1\,\text{ch }p_2} \qquad (9.4\text{-}11)$$

The open-circuit voltage is derived from (9.4-11) by letting $\mathscr{I}^* = 0$. The result is

$$V_{oc}{}^* = \frac{-j(j\omega^* - p_2{}^2)(j\omega^* - p_1{}^2)}{\omega^* M}$$

$$\cdot \frac{\left(\dfrac{\text{th }p_1}{p_1} - \dfrac{\text{th }p_2}{p_2}\right)}{\dfrac{j\omega^* - p_1{}^2}{p_1}\,\text{th }p_1 - \dfrac{j\omega^* - p_2{}^2}{p_2}\,\text{th }p_2} \qquad (9.4\text{-}12a)$$

which should exhibit some of the characteristics found for direct-current Hartmann flow in Section 7.1. In order to check (9.4-12a), as well as (9.4-11), (9.4-9), (9.4-8b), and (9.4-8a), it is convenient to let the frequency approach zero.

At zero frequency the open-circuit voltage given by (9.4-12a) should be the same as that given by (7.1-13) for one-dimensional MHD Poiseuille flow. As the frequency approaches zero, $p_1^2 \to M^2$, $p_2^2 = -\omega^{*2}Pm/M^2$, ch $p_2 \to 1$, and sh $p_2 \to p_2$. Therefore,

$$\lim_{\omega^* \to 0} V_{oc}^* = \frac{1}{M}\left(1 - \frac{M}{\text{th } M}\right) \tag{9.4-12b}$$

which is in agreement with (7.1-13). It is left as an exercise for the reader to make the zero frequency limiting-case check on the velocity, magnetic field, and current density.

It is also important to check the expression for the velocity as electrical conductivity of the fluid approaches zero. It is easy to show that

$$\lim_{\substack{M \to 0 \\ Pm \to 0}} u^* = \frac{1}{j\omega^*}\left(\frac{\text{ch } y^*\sqrt{j\omega^*}}{\text{ch }\sqrt{j\omega^*}} - 1\right) \tag{9.4-13}$$

which is the solution to the non-MHD problem. This solution can be obtained by solving (9.4-1a) when $M = 0$.

The short-circuit current per unit length is obtained from (9.4-11) by setting the terminal voltage to zero and solving for $\mathscr{I}^*$. This procedure yields

$$\mathscr{I}_{sc}^* = \cfrac{\cfrac{2j(j\omega^* - p_2^2)(j\omega^* - p_1^2)}{\omega^*M(p_2^2 - p_1^2)}\left(\cfrac{\text{th } p_1}{p_1} - \cfrac{\text{th } p_2}{p_2}\right)}{1 + \cfrac{\cfrac{j\omega^* - p_1^2}{p_1}\text{th } p_1 - \cfrac{j\omega^* - p_2^2}{p_2}\text{th } p_2}{\cfrac{j\omega^* - p_1^2}{p_1}\text{th } p_2 - \cfrac{j\omega^* - p_2^2}{p_2}\text{th } p_1}\alpha^2\,\text{th } p_1\,\text{th } p_2} \tag{9.4-14}$$

which reduces to the dimensionless form of (7.1-14) when $\omega^* \to 0$. The internal electrical impedance exhibited by this configuration is given by the ratio of the open-circuit voltage to the short-circuit current. From the ratio of (9.4-12a) to (9.4-14) there results

$$Z_i^* = \cfrac{\cfrac{p_2^2 - p_1^2}{2}\left[1 + \cfrac{\cfrac{j\omega^* - p_1^2}{p_1}\text{th } p_1 - \cfrac{j\omega^* - p_2^2}{p_2}\text{th } p_2}{\cfrac{j\omega^* - p_1^2}{p_1}\text{th } p_2 - \cfrac{j\omega^* - p_2^2}{p_2}\text{th } p_1}\alpha^2\,\text{th } p_1\,\text{th } p_2\right]}{\cfrac{j\omega^* - p_1^2}{p_1}\text{th } p_1 - \cfrac{j\omega^* - p_2^2}{p_2}\text{th } p_2} \tag{9.4-15}$$

where $Z_i{}^*$ is the dimensionless internal impedance. When $\omega^* \to 0$, this result agrees with the dimensionless form of (7.1-16). It is important to realize that the symmetry of the return circuit influences the internal impedance of the device.

The dimensionless rms flow rate is defined as $Q^* = \int_{-1}^{1} u^* \, dy^*$. The integration of u^* from (9.4-8a) yields

$$Q^* = \frac{2j}{\omega^*}\left(1 - \frac{\text{th } p_2}{p_2}\right)$$

$$+ \frac{2\left[-\dfrac{M \mathscr{I}^*}{2} + \dfrac{j(j\omega^* - p_2{}^2)\,\text{th } p_2}{\omega^* p_2}\right]\left(\dfrac{\text{th } p_1}{p_1} - \dfrac{\text{th } p_2}{p_2}\right)}{\dfrac{j\omega^* - p_1{}^2}{p_1}\,\text{th } p_1 - \dfrac{j\omega^* - p_2{}^2}{p_2}\,\text{th } p_2} \tag{9.4-16}$$

It is easy to demonstrate that

$$\lim_{\substack{M \to 0 \\ Pm \to 0}} Q^* = \frac{2}{j\omega^*}\left(\frac{\text{th } \sqrt{j\omega^*}}{\sqrt{j\omega^*}} - 1\right) \tag{9.4-17a}$$

which is the result for non-MHD flow. When the frequency approaches zero, the flow rate derived here should approach that of one-dimensional Poiseuille flow. When this is done for (9.4-16), we have

$$\lim_{\omega^* \to 0} Q^* = \frac{(2 + M \mathscr{I}^*)\left(\dfrac{\text{th } M}{M} - 1\right)}{M \, \text{th } M} \tag{9.4-17b}$$

which agrees with (7.1-26).

Discussion

In Fig. 9.4-1 we show the magnitude of the dimensionless flow rate and its phase angle as a function of frequency. The effect of the magnetic field upon the magnitude of the dimensionless flow rate is seen in Fig. 9.4-2. Here we see that the dimensionless flow rate is influenced greatly by the Hartmann number at low values of dimensionless frequency. For $\omega^* > 15$ the influence of M is not so strong. For $M = 10$ we see that the dimensionless flow rate decreases very slowly with frequency. In Fig. 9.4-3 the influence of the magnetic Prandtl number upon the magnitude of the dimensionless flow rate is given for $\omega^* = 13$. It is interesting to notice that there is an optimum magnetic Prandtl number which maximizes the magnitude of the flow rate. In general, for each different value of ω^* there is a different value of optimum magnetic Prandtl number. We leave further investigations of this effect to the reader.

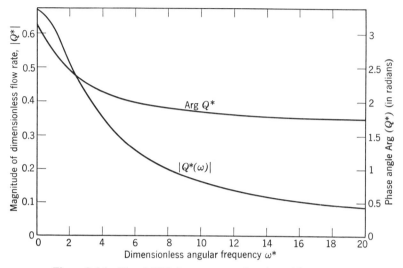

Figure 9.4-1   Non-MHD flow rate as a function of frequency.

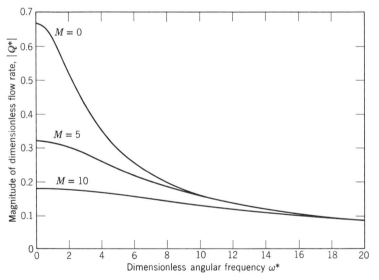

Figure 9.4-2   The flow rate as a function of frequency for various Hartmann numbers and $Pm = 0$.

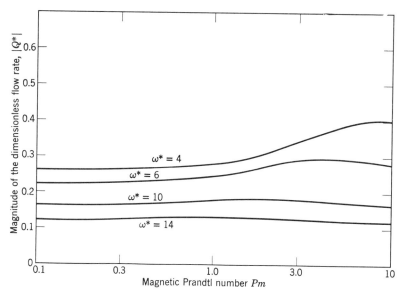

Figure 9.4-3   Flow rate versus magnetic Prandtl number.

9.5 TRANSIENT MHD ONE-DIMENSIONAL POISEUILLE FLOW

Introduction

When we realize that one-dimensional MHD Poiseuille flow is an idealization of a two-dimensional problem involving an external electrical circuit and a magnet, it is easy to imagine many circumstances which cause transients. If the device under consideration is an MHD generator or a motor running in its steady state, a transient will occur if the electrical or mechanical load is changed or if the applied magnetic field is altered. When a pressure gradient is applied to the system (originally at rest), a start-up transient occurs which depends upon the values of the applied magnetic field and the electrical loading. Practical questions, involving the advisability of starting up an MHD generator under load or how long to wait after start-up to apply the load, are part of the class of problems of interest in this section. F. H. Shair (1963) attempts to answer some of these questions by solving the transient problem of MHD Couette flow in a short-circuited configuration. However, his analysis assumes the electric field is zero everywhere, which is clearly not the case in unsteady flow. The electric field rises very quickly (as was discussed in Section 9.2) and tends to retard current flow at the beginning of the start-up transient.

Hence the initial portions of the transient in velocity may be unaffected by the electromagnetic body force. When the electric field is neglected, the resulting solution corresponds, in general, to some other situation in which a variable external electrical source is included in the external electrical circuit.

The problem of switching on the magnetic field involves not only the external electrical circuit of the generator but also the external magnetic circuit and is not treated here. The larger the magnetic field and its attendant stored energy the slower must be the increase, especially if a superconducting magnet is used. In superconducting magnets the time rate of change of the magnetic field must not be too large or a catastrophic change from the superconducting to normal state may occur. This is partly due to the decrease in current-carrying capacity with increasing frequency which is experienced by superconductors (Young and Schenk, 1964).

Ludford (1959) has obtained an exact solution for the nonstationary flow of an electrically conducting fluid dragged along by uniformly moving, ideally conducting parallel walls in the presence of a transverse magnetic field. His analysis is equivalent to the short-circuit case presented in this section.

We will solve the start-up transient flow of a conducting, incompressible, viscous fluid between parallel, perfectly conducting walls of infinite extent. Throughout the duration of the transient, a steady transverse magnetic field is applied, and, at time $t = 0$, a constant pressure gradient is suddenly applied to the channel. This might be achieved by the action of a piston at $x = -\infty$ and the solution is subject to the limitations discussed in the introduction to Section 9.4. The geometry of the problem is given in Fig. 7.1-1 and we assume that the external circuit is absent since the conducting walls are the return current paths. The method of solution presented here can be used to solve the whole class of MHD one-dimensional transient regimes which occur when the mechanical loading is suddenly altered. However, in these problems the transverse magnetic field must be held constant.

Solution

The transient problem of the initiation of flow between parallel plates is often solved by means of the Laplace transform. This transform is used to eliminate time from the equations and thereby reduce them to ordinary differential equations in distance. After the differential equation in distance is solved subject to the proper boundary conditions, time is reintroduced by the inverse Laplace transform. From Section 9.4 we see that the inversion may be a formidable task. In the special case of an electrically short-circuited channel, rather complicated results (which do not neglect the electric field) have been obtained by the Laplace transform method (Chekmarev, 1960).

It is easier to transform with respect to distance and solve an ordinary differential equation in time. The method used might be called the finite sinusoid transform method. Here it is assumed that

$$u^* = u_{ss}^* + \sum_{n=0}^{\infty} U_n(t^*) \cos \lambda y^* \qquad (9.5\text{-}1a)$$

and

$$H_x^* = H_{ss}^* + \sum_{n=0}^{\infty} h_n(t^*) \sin \lambda y^* \qquad (9.5\text{-}1b)$$

where $\lambda = (2n + 1)\pi/2$, $u_{ss}^* = (1/M + \mathscr{I}_{sc}^*/2)(\text{ch } My^* - \text{ch } M)/\text{sh } M$, $H_{ss}^* = y^*/M - (1/M + \mathscr{I}_{sc}^*/2) \text{ sh } My^*/\text{sh } M$, and $\mathscr{I}_{sc}^*$ is the total dimensionless steady-state short-circuit current flowing in the fluid. One-half of $\mathscr{I}_{sc}^*$ returns in each of the ideally conducting walls. The notation of Section 9.4 is used here for all quantities. When the assumed solutions given by (9.5-1a) and (9.5-1b) are substituted into (9.3-9a) and (9.3-9b), we have

$$-\lambda^2 U_n + M\lambda h_n = \frac{dU_n}{dt^*} \qquad (9.5\text{-}2a)$$

$$-\lambda^2 h_n - M\lambda U_n = Pm \frac{dh_n}{dt^*} \qquad (9.5\text{-}2b)$$

These equations can easily be combined to yield

$$\left[Pm \frac{d^2}{dt^{*2}} + \lambda^2(1 + Pm)\frac{d}{dt^*} + \lambda^2(\lambda^2 + M^2) \right] \begin{bmatrix} U_n \\ h_n \end{bmatrix} = 0 \quad (9.5\text{-}2c)$$

which is easy to solve. The solution is

$$U_n = C_1 e^{m_1 t^*} + C_2 e^{m_2 t^*} \qquad (9.5\text{-}2d)$$

where

$$m_{1,2} = \frac{-\lambda^2(1 + Pm) \pm \sqrt{\lambda^4(1 + Pm)^2 - 4Pm\lambda^2(\lambda^2 + M^2)}}{2Pm} \qquad (9.5\text{-}2e)$$

Before relating h_n to the solution for U_n, we should study (9.5-2e), for it implies the existence of an oscillatory transient. In non-MHD viscous flow the corresponding solution is aperiodic. If $4Pm(\lambda^2 + M^2) > \lambda^2(1 + Pm)^2$, the solution is oscillatory. It is clear that $Pm = 1$ will make the solution oscillatory for all values of λ and M. However, in the laboratory $Pm \ll 1$. In that case the condition becomes $M > \lambda/(2\sqrt{Pm})$. For the lowest harmonic and $Pm = 10^{-7}$, the Hartmann number must be greater than 2500 for an oscillatory solution to exist. As the solutions are not usually oscillatory, they are presented first in exponential form and can easily be converted to sinusoids when desired. By substituting U_n into (9.5-2a), we obtain the magnetic solution

$$h_n = \frac{1}{M}\left(\frac{\lambda^2 + m_1}{\lambda} C_1 e^{m_1 t^*} + \frac{\lambda^2 + m_2}{\lambda} C_2 e^{m_2 t^*}\right) \qquad (9.5\text{-}2f)$$

To complete the solution, $U_n(0)$ and $h_n(0)$ are used to evaluate C_1 and C_2. $U_n(0)$ and $h_n(0)$ are obtained from (9.5-1a) and (9.5-1b) and depend upon $u^*(y^*, t^* = 0)$ and $h^*(y^*, t^* = 0)$. Under general initial conditions the solutions become

$$U_n(t^*) = \frac{\begin{aligned}[(\lambda^2 + m_2)U_n(0) - M\lambda h_n(0)]e^{m_1 t^*} \\ - [(\lambda^2 + m_1)U_n(0) - M\lambda h_n(0)]e^{m_2 t^*}\end{aligned}}{m_2 - m_1} \qquad (9.5\text{-}3a)$$

$$h_n(t^*) = \frac{\begin{aligned}(\lambda^2 + m_1)[(\lambda^2 + m_2)U_n(0) - M\lambda h_n(0)]e^{m_1 t^*} \\ - (\lambda^2 + m_2)[(\lambda^2 + m_1)U_n(0) - M\lambda h_n(0)]e^{m_2 t^*}\end{aligned}}{\lambda M(m_2 - m_1)} \qquad (9.5\text{-}3b)$$

where $\sum_{n=0}^{\infty} U_n(0) \cos \lambda y^* = -u_{ss}^*$ and $\sum_{n=0}^{\infty} h_n(0) \sin \lambda y^* = -H_{ss}$ because $u^*(y^*, t^* = 0)$ and $H_x^*(y^*, t^* = 0)$ are zero. In the more general case the values of $U_n(0)$ and $h_n(0)$ are found from

$$u^*(y^*, t^* = 0) - u_{ss}^* = \sum_{n=0}^{\infty} U_n(0) \cos \lambda y^*$$

and

$$H_x^*(y^*, t^* = 0) - H_{ss}^* = \sum_{n=0}^{\infty} h_n(0) \sin \lambda y^*$$

where $u^*(y^*, t^* = 0)$ and $H_x^*(y^*, t^* = 0)$ are the initial conditions. A Fourier expansion is used to evaluate $U_n(0)$ and $h_n(0)$. The results are

$$U_n(0) = \frac{2M^2\left(\dfrac{1}{M} + \dfrac{\mathscr{I}_{sc}^*}{2}\right)}{\text{th } M} \cdot \frac{(-1)^n}{\lambda(\lambda^2 + M^2)} \qquad (9.5\text{-}3c)$$

and

$$h_n(0) = -\frac{2(-1)^n}{M\lambda^2} + \frac{2M\left(\dfrac{1}{M} + \dfrac{\mathscr{I}_{sc}^*}{2}\right)}{\text{th } M} \cdot \frac{(-1)^n}{\lambda^2 + M^2} = \frac{-M}{\lambda} U_n(0) \quad (9.5\text{-}3d)$$

The solution is completed and in summary the velocity $u^*(y^*, t^*)$ and the magnetic field $H_x^*(y^*, t^*)$ are given by (9.5-1a) and (9.5-1b), respectively. These expressions contain $U_n(t^*)$ and $h_n(t^*)$ which are found in (9.5-3a) and (9.5-3b). The remaining variables $m_{1,2}$, $U_n(0)$, and $h_n(0)$ are given in (9.5-2e), (9.5-3c), and (9.5-3d), respectively. It is important to check so complicated a result. By letting $M \to 0$, $u^*(y^*, t^*)$ is checked. In that case

$$\lim_{M \to 0} u_{SS} = \tfrac{1}{2}(y^{*2} - 1) \tag{9.5-4a}$$

$$\lim_{M \to 0} m_1 = -\lambda^2 \tag{9.5-4b}$$

$$\lim_{M \to 0} m_2 = -\frac{\lambda^2}{Pm} \tag{9.5-4c}$$

and it is easy to show that

$$\lim_{M \to 0} u^*(y^*, t^*) = \tfrac{1}{2}(y^{*2} - 1) + 2 \sum_{n=0}^{\infty} \frac{(-1)^n e^{-\lambda^2 t^*}}{\lambda^3} \cos \lambda y^* \tag{9.5-4d}$$

which is indeed the solution to the non-MHD problem. The transient flow rate $Q^*(y^*, t^*) = 2\int_0^1 u^*(y^*, t^*)\, dy^*$ is given by

$$Q^*(y, t^*) = 2\left(\frac{1}{M} + \frac{\mathscr{I}_{SC}^*}{2}\right)\left(\frac{1}{M} - \frac{1}{\text{th } M}\right) + 2 \sum_{n=0}^{\infty} \frac{(-1)^n U_n(t^*)}{\lambda} \tag{9.5-5}$$

The total current flowing in the liquid is time dependent. The total dimensionless current (as both quantities are dimensionless $I^* = \mathscr{I}^*$) is $I^* = -2\int_0^1 (\partial H_x^* / \partial y^*)\, dy^* = -2H_x^*(y^* = 1, t^*)$ since $H_x^*(y^* = 0, t^*) = 0$ in the symmetrical load case considered here. Therefore, $I^*(t^*)$ is given by

$$I^*(t^*) = \mathscr{I}_{SC}^* - 2 \sum_{n=0}^{\infty} (-1)^n h_n(t^*) \tag{9.5-6}$$

and it is clear that $\lim_{t^* \to \infty} I^* = \mathscr{I}_{SC}^*$. The total steady-state short-circuit current, obtained from (7.1-19), is given by

$$I_{SC}^* = \frac{2}{M}\left(\frac{\text{th } M}{M} - 1\right) \tag{9.5-7}$$

Approximate Solution for $Pm \ll 1$

In the terrestrial laboratory, Pm is usually small compared to unity for liquid metals. In that case, the solutions simplify greatly. When $Pm \ll \lambda^2/4M^2$, the characteristic roots m_1 and m_2 become $m_1 = -(\lambda^2 + M^2)$ and $m_2 = -\lambda^2/Pm$. $U_n(t^*)$ and $h_n(t^*)$ are calculated from (9.5-3a) and (9.5-3b) $(m_2 \gg m_1)$. Thus

$$U_n(t^*) = U_n(0)e^{-(\lambda^2 + M^2)t^*} \tag{9.5-8a}$$

and

$$h_n(t^*) = -\frac{M}{\lambda}U_n(0)e^{-(\lambda^2 + M^2)t^*} \tag{9.5-8b}$$

and we are led to the following solution for the velocity:

$$u^* = \left(\frac{1}{M} + \frac{\mathscr{I}_{sc}^*}{2}\right)\left[\frac{\text{ch } My^* - \text{ch } M}{\text{sh } M}\right.$$
$$\left. + \frac{2M^2}{\text{th } M}\sum_{n=0}^{\infty}\frac{(-1)^n e^{-(\lambda^2+M^2)t^*}}{\lambda(\lambda^2 + M^2)}\cos \lambda y^*\right] \tag{9.5-9}$$

This solution is the one obtained by neglecting the electric field and is valid as long as $Pm \ll \pi^2/16M^2$. The assumption of zero electric field, however, completely hides the oscillatory nature of the velocity transient. The corresponding solution for the induced magnetic field is given by

$$H^* = \frac{y^*}{M} - \left(\frac{1}{M} + \frac{\mathscr{I}_{sc}^*}{2}\right)\left[\frac{\text{sh } My^*}{\text{sh } M}\right.$$
$$\left. - \frac{2M^3}{\text{th } M}\sum_{n=0}^{\infty}\frac{(-1)^n e^{-(\lambda^2+M^2)t^*}\sin \lambda y^*}{\lambda^2(\lambda^2 + M^2)}\right] \tag{9.5-10}$$

Oscillatory Solution

When $4Pm(\lambda^2 + M^2) > \lambda^2(1 + Pm)^2$, the solutions become oscillatory and it is convenient to express the results in sinusoidal form. The expressions (9.5-1a), (9.5-1b), (9.5-5), and (9.5-6) for the velocity, induced magnetic field, flow rate, and electrical current are still valid provided the sinusoidal form of $U_n(t)$ and $h_n(t)$ are used. These forms are

$$U_n(t^*) = \left\{U_n(0)\cos \beta t - \frac{[(\alpha + \lambda^2)U_n(0) - M\lambda h_n(0)]\sin \beta t^*}{\beta}\right\}e^{\alpha t^*}$$
$$\tag{9.5-11a}$$

$$h_n(t^*) = \left\{h_n(0)\cos \beta t^* - \frac{[(\alpha + \lambda^2)^2 + \beta^2]U_n(0) - M\lambda(\alpha + \lambda^2)h_n(0)}{\beta\lambda M}\right.$$
$$\left. \times \sin \beta t^*\right\}e^{\alpha t^*} \tag{9.5-11b}$$

where

$$\alpha = \frac{-\lambda^2(1 + Pm)}{2Pm} \tag{9.5-11c}$$

and

$$\beta = \frac{\sqrt{4Pm\lambda^2(\lambda^2 + M^2) - \lambda^4(1 + Pm)^2}}{2Pm} \tag{9.5-11d}$$

The period of the oscillation is given by

$$T = \frac{4\pi Pm}{\lambda\sqrt{4Pm^2(\lambda^2 + M^2) - \lambda^2(1 + Pm)^2}} \tag{9.5-12}$$

For example, when $Pm = 1$, the period is $T_{Pm=1} = 4/[(2n + 1)M]$. Assuming that high harmonics damp out quickly yields an approximate period of $4/M$. Hence it is seen that the frequency varies in proportion to the Hartmann number.

Discussion

The transient velocity profile is presented in Fig. 9.5-2 for $M = 5$ and $Pm = 10^{-7}$. When this is compared to the non-MHD result of Fig. 9.5-1, it becomes clear that the application of the magnetic field speeds up

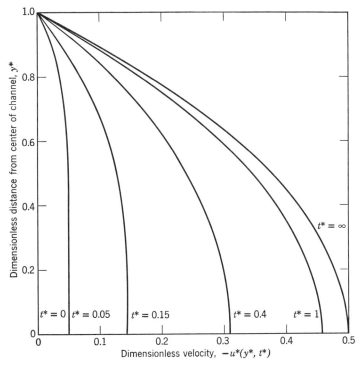

Figure 9.5-1   Transient velocity profiles for $M = Pm = 0$.

the transient. When $M = 5$, the transient lasts about one-tenth as long as it does in the non-MHD case. This comes about because the MHD velocity profile in the steady state is flattened by the electromagnetic body force. In the case of low magnetic Prandtl number ($Pm = 10^{-7}$), the electric field does not oppose the development of the electric current

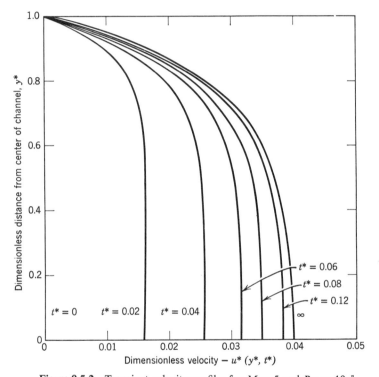

Figure 9.5-2   Transient velocity profiles for $M = 5$ and $Pm = 10^{-7}$.

density significantly. Figures 9.5-3 and 9.5-4 illustrate the build-up of the magnetic field when (1) $M = 0.001$ and $Pm = 10^{-7}$, and (2) $M = 5$ and $Pm = 10^{-7}$. Figure 9.5-5 shows the ratio $Q^*(t^*, M)/Q^*(\infty, M)$ versus time for Hartmann numbers of 0, 3, 5, and 10 when the magnetic Prandtl number is very small. These curves are expected in liquid metals for $Pm \simeq 10^{-7}$. Figure 9.5-6 gives the transient total current for various Hartmann numbers. The largest steady value of current is attained when $M = 1.65$, as was the case in Section 7.1.

When $Pm = 1$, the curves are oscillatory because the induced electric field inhibits the flow of current when the transient is first initiated. For example, in Fig. 9.5-7 the velocity rises quickly to a large value because the electromagnetic body force is weak. For $Pm = 1$ and $M = 5$, the center line velocity reaches more than thrice its steady-state value when $t^* = 0.2$. However, in Fig. 9.5-8 the induced magnetic field reaches its peak at $t^* = 0.38$. Between $t^* = 0.2$ and 0.38 the electromagnetic body force is large enough to retard the fluid considerably. As the fluid is

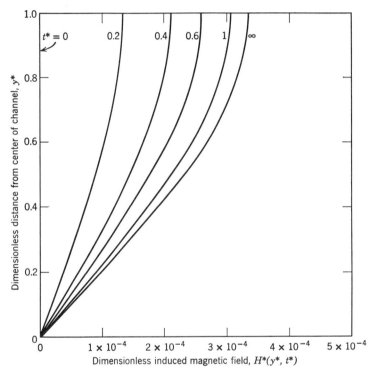

Figure 9.5-3   Transient magnetic-field profiles for $M = 0.001$ and $Pm = 10^{-7}$.

retarded, the electromagnetic body force weakens until the pressure gradient again becomes effective. The fluid then accelerates in the presence of a weak electromagnetic body force. As time progresses, the electromagnetic body force becomes steady, as does the velocity profile. The transient flow rate curves are given in Figs. 9.5-9 and 9.5-10. It is interesting to note that the flow rate actually reverses sign when $M = 10$ and $Pm = 1$. The transient current curves are given for $Pm = 1$ and $Pm = 0.1$ in Figs. 9.5-11 and 9.5-12 for $M = 1.65$, 5, and 10. Here, the oscillations fade more quickly for $Pm = 0.1$ than for $Pm = 1$. The period of the oscillations is close to the value predicted by (9.5-12) when $n = 0$.

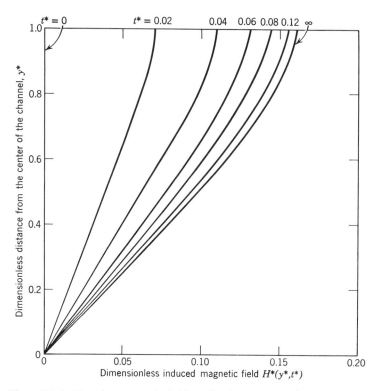

Figure 9.5-4   Transient magnetic-field profiles for $M = 5$ and $Pm = 10^{-7}$.

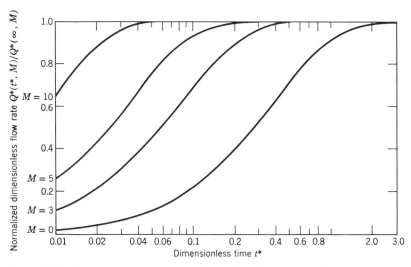

Figure 9.5-5   Flow rate versus time for $Pm = 10^{-7}$ for various Hartmann numbers.

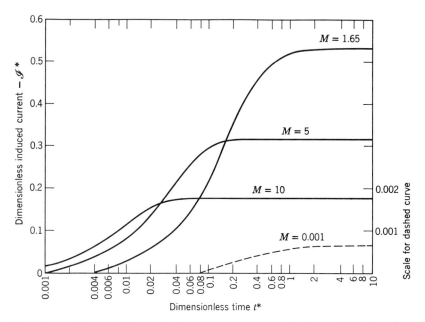

Figure 9.5-6 The total dimensionless current transient for $Pm = 10^{-7}$ at various Hartmann numbers.

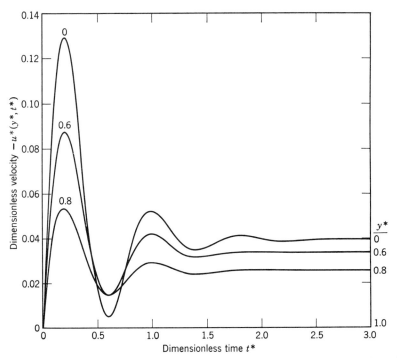

Figure 9.5-7 Plot of dimensionless velocity versus time at various positions for $Pm = 1$, $M = 5$.

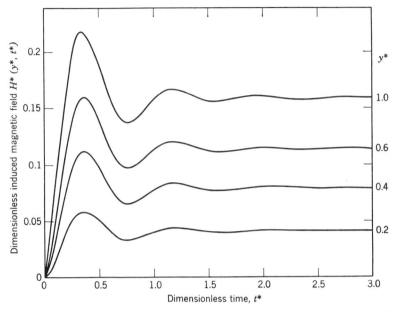

Figure 9.5-8 Plot of dimensionless induced magnetic field versus time at various positions for $Pm = 1$ and $M = 5$.

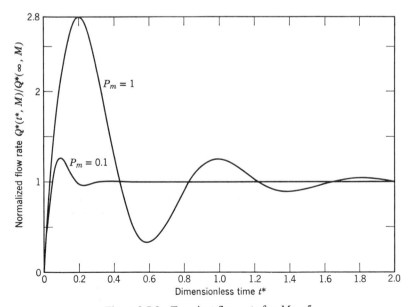

Figure 9.5-9 Transient flow rate for $M = 5$.

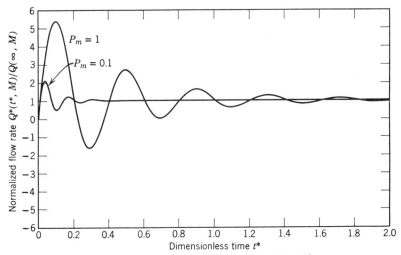

Figure 9.5-10 Transient flow rate for $M = 10$.

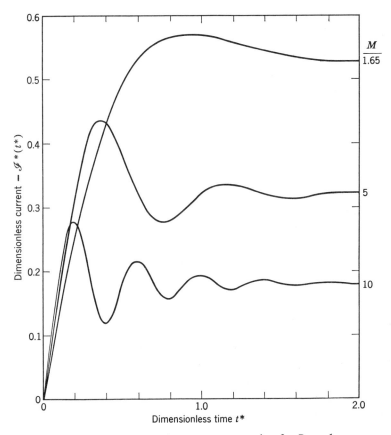

Figure 9.5-11 The transient current versus time for $Pm = 1$.

Although the form of solution used in this section is not valid for a channel with insulating walls, it is valid for conducting walls containing current sources. If each of the walls contains a direct-current source of value $\mathscr{I}_w^*/2$ applied simultaneously with the pressure gradient, all the expressions derived here are valid if $\mathscr{I}_{sc}^*$ is replaced by the resulting

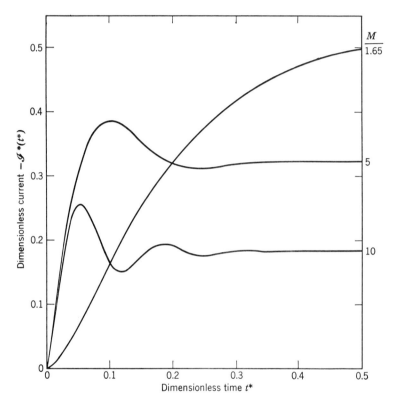

Figure 9.5-12   The transient current versus time for $Pm = 0.1$.

steady-state current $\mathscr{I}_{ss}^*$.   Hence $\mathscr{I}_w^* = \mathscr{I}_{ss}^* - \mathscr{I}_{sc}^*$ which means that no current flows if $\mathscr{I}_w^* = -\mathscr{I}_{sc}^*$. The transient velocity profiles for this case are given in Fig. 9.5-13 for $Pm = 10^{-7}$. The transient ends quicker in this case than in Fig. 9.5-2 because the current supplied from the current sources produces an accelerating body force that aids the pressure gradient. As the flow builds up, the body force diminishes, leaving a steady Hartmann velocity profile. Although the steady-state result obtained by forcing the steady-state current to be zero is identical to

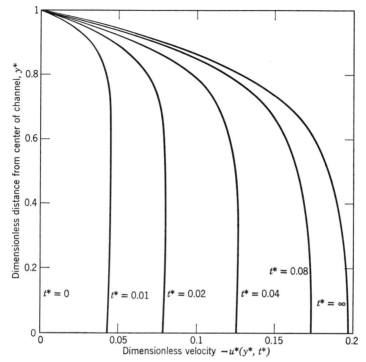

Figure 9.5-13   Transient velocity profiles for $M = 5$ and $Pm = 10^{-7}$.

open-circuited MHD Poiseuille flow between insulating walls, the transitory behavior is not valid for a channel with insulating walls. Transients in insulating one-dimensional channels are treated in the literature (see Regirer, 1959, and Young and Rouleau, 1965).

9.6 THE RAYLEIGH PROBLEM IN MAGNETOHYDRODYNAMICS

Introduction

The classical Rayleigh problem (1911) studies the motion of an infinitely extended, incompressible, viscous fluid in response to an infinite flat plate suddenly set in motion along its own plane. This problem is of particular interest in conjunction with the formation of a boundary layer at the leading edge of a semi-infinite plate moving through a fluid. To obtain the magnetohydrodynamic extension of this problem (see Fig. 9.6-1) a uniform magnetic field H_0 is applied normal to the moving plate, which may be a

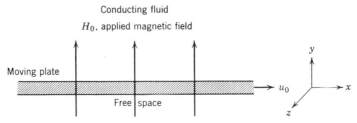

Figure 9.6-1 The hydromagnetic Rayleigh problem.

conductor or an insulator. Magnetic fields in other directions do not alter the flow. A very good qualitative discussion of this problem, including a survey of the earlier work done on it, is given by Dix (1963).

The MHD Rayleigh problem is straightforward in comparison to many of those so far considered. However, difficulties arise from two sources: the mathematics involved and the infinite geometry. Since the problem is usually solved by the aid of the Laplace transform, the inverse transform may not be obtainable in tabulated functions. The more basic difficulty arises when the role of the return circuit for the current is not fully appreciated. Rossow (1957) shows the electromagnetic body force to be a retarding force while Chang and Yen (1959) mention the role of the electromagnetic body force as an accelerating force. The electromagnetic force can act as either, depending upon the configuration. The confusion resulting from considering infinite geometries without using them as

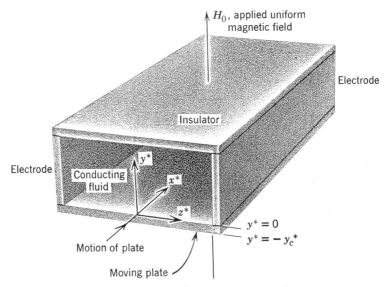

Figure 9.6-2 The MHD Couette problem.

limiting cases of finite configurations is very great. In this section the
MHD Rayleigh problem of Fig. 9.6-1 is treated as the limiting case of the
MHD Couette problem of Fig. 9.6-2. The traveling wave nature of
the transient is given special attention. When the insulator, electrodes,
and moving plate of Fig. 9.6-2 become semi-infinite, the MHD Couette
problem becomes the MHD Rayleigh problem. The bottom plate is
assumed to be a half-space of arbitrary conductivity and the electrical load
is omitted so that all the current generated in either the plate or the fluid
must find its return circuit in the fluid.

The results, valid for arbitrary plate conductivity, are studied for zero
and infinite plate conductivity. When the plate is an insulator, it propels
the fluid near it by viscous forces. In the region where viscous forces drive
the fluid, the electromagnetic body force retards the fluid. However,
beyond the viscous layer there exists an Alfvén region where the total
current generated in the viscous layer finds its return path. In this region
the electromagnetic body force propels the fluid and carries the transient
(at the Alfvén speed) to an ever-increasing distance from the insulating
plate.

When the semi-infinite plate is an ideal conductor, the plate generates
an electrical current which returns in the fluid, thereby propeling the fluid
and reducing the viscous drag. In this case, the viscous drag vanishes for
large values of time. However, the plate is retarded by an electromagnetic
body force which becomes constant for large values of time.

Special attention is given to various limiting cases and to the investigation of the steady-state solutions. It is shown that no disparity exists
between the steady-state solution and the limit of the transient solution
as the value of time approaches infinity.

Steady Solution

Here we consider the semi-infinite configuration obtained as a limiting
case of Fig. 9.6-2 as $y_c{}^*$, z^*, and x^* are increased without bound. The
moving plate has a conductivity σ_c and the fluid has a conductivity σ_f.
The subscripts f and c are used to denote quantities evaluated in the
conducting fluid and the moving plate, respectively.

As there is no characteristic dimension in the fluid, the most suitable
set of dimensionless equations is given by (9.3-11a) and (9.3-11b). In
the steady state these equations become

$$\frac{d^2 u_{ss}{}^*}{dy^{*2}} + \frac{dH_{ss}{}^*}{dy^*} = 0 \tag{9.6-1a}$$

$$-\frac{dH_{ss}{}^*}{dy^*} = E_{ss}{}^* + Pmu_{ss}{}^* \tag{9.6-1b}$$

where E_{ss}^* (as was discussed in Section 9.3) is not a function of y^* because $\partial/\partial x^* = 0$ and $E_{ss}^* = (\sigma v/AH_0)E_{ss}$, where A is the Alfvén speed. In the conducting fluid, the equation of the dimensionless velocity is obtained by substituting $\partial H_{ss}^*/\partial y^*$ given by (9.6-1b) into (9.6-1a). The resulting equation is

$$\frac{d^2 u_{ssf}^*}{dy^{*2}} - Pm u_{ssf}^* = E_{ssf}^* \qquad (9.6\text{-}2a)$$

which admits to the solution

$$u_{ssf}^* = \frac{-E_{ssf}^*}{Pm} + Ce^{-y^*\sqrt{Pm}} \qquad (9.6\text{-}2b)$$

The other solution has been discarded because u_{ssf}^* must remain finite at $y^* = \infty$. At $y^* = 0$, the fluid obeys the no-slip condition, and thus $u_{ssf}^*(y^* = 0) = u_0^*$. ($u_0^*$ is the dimensionless plate velocity.) When we evaluate C, u_{ssf}^* becomes

$$u_{ssf}^* = \frac{-E_{ssf}^*}{Pm} + \left(u_0^* + \frac{E_{ssf}^*}{Pm} \right) e^{-y^*\sqrt{Pm}} \qquad (9.6\text{-}2c)$$

By integrating (9.6-1b), we obtain the dimensionless magnetic field in the fluid. Since the field at $y^* = \infty$ is zero, the field is given by

$$H_{ssf}^* = C_1 + \frac{1}{\sqrt{Pm}} (Pm u_0^* + E_{ssf}) e^{-y^*\sqrt{Pm}} \qquad (9.6\text{-}3)$$

The electric field is continuous across the boundaries. Hence the dimensionless electric field is different in each medium. The dimensionless electric field is given by

$$E_{ssc}^* = \frac{\sigma_c}{\sigma_f} E_{ssf}^* \qquad (9.6\text{-}4)$$

and the magnetic Prandtl number in the moving plate becomes $Pm_c = Pm\sigma_c/\sigma_f$. The induced magnetic field in the moving plate is obtained from the equation

$$-\frac{dH_{ssc}^*}{dy^*} = \frac{\sigma_c}{\sigma_f} (E_{ssf}^* + Pm u_0^*) \qquad (9.6\text{-}5a)$$

The solution to (9.6-5a) is

$$H_{ssc}^* = C_2 - \frac{\sigma_c}{\sigma_f} (E_{ssf}^* + Pm u_0^*) y^* \qquad (9.6\text{-}5b)$$

where C_1 and C_2 are constants which must be obtained from the boundary conditions.

The only boundary condition not yet satisfied is the continuity of the tangential magnetic field at the interface between the fluid and the moving semi-infinite solid. This condition becomes $H^*_{ssc}(0) = H^*_{ssf}(0)$. Hence

$$C_2 = C_1 + \frac{1}{\sqrt{Pm}}(Pmu_0{}^* + E^*_{ssf}) \tag{9.6-6}$$

and H^*_{ssc} becomes

$$H^*_{ssc} = C_1 + (E^*_{ssf} + Pmu_0{}^*)\left(\frac{1}{\sqrt{Pm}} - \frac{\sigma_c}{\sigma_f}y^*\right) \tag{9.6-7}$$

All the boundary conditions have been used, but C_1 and E^*_{ssf} remain to be determined. When $\sigma_c \neq 0$, it is clear that $E^*_{ssf} = -Pmu_0{}^*$, for the induced magnetic field must remain finite. It might seem reasonable to set C_1 equal to zero by claiming that C_1 represents an externally applied magnetic field in the steady-state solution. Since the geometry is infinite in the y^* direction, a true steady state can never be attained. Although the fluid velocity may be constant for any finite value of y^*, there will always be transients at $y^* = t^*$ which produce currents. These currents, in turn, might give rise to the magnetic field represented by C_1. Hence we write two forms of the "steady solutions" and leave the constants C_1 and E^*_{ssf} undetermined, for they depend upon the current returning at very large values of y^*. Hence, for $\sigma_c = 0$ the solutions are given by (9.6-2c), (9.6-3), and

$$H^*_{ssc} = C_1 + \frac{1}{\sqrt{Pm}}(E^*_{ssf} + Pmu_0^*) \tag{9.6-8}$$

In the case of a conducting moving plate, $\sigma_c \neq 0$, and the velocity and the induced magnetic fields are given by

$$u^*_{ssf} = u_0{}^* \tag{9.6-9a}$$

$$H^*_{ssf} = C_1 \tag{9.6-9b}$$

The induced magnetic field in the moving plate is given by $H^*_{ssc} = C_1$ when y^* and σ_c remain finite. When the moving plate has infinite conductivity, $H^*_{ss}{}^*$ will be equal to C_1 at the surface of the plate and will jump to zero in the interior of the plate. The attendant current sheet has its return path somewhere in the conducting fluid (its location is discussed later) and interacts with the applied magnetic induction to help accelerate the fluid at ever-increasing values of y^*. The current loop so formed produces a negative value for C_1.

Transient Solution for a Solid Half-Space Moving through an Infinite Sea of Conducting Liquid

To minimize the mathematical difficulties which arise in the inversion of the solutions, it is assumed that a semi-infinite sea of viscous, electrically conducting fluid is located in the region $y^* > 0$. The rest of the space ($y^* < 0$) is filled with a solid material of conductivity σ_c. A constant magnetic induction B_0 is applied in the y^* direction and at dimensionless time $t^* = 0$ the semi-infinite solid is given a dimensionless velocity $u_0{}^*$. Equations (9.3-11a) and (9.3-11b) are Laplace transformed with respect to dimensionless time and become

$$\frac{d^2U^*}{dy^{*2}}(s, y^*) - sU^*(s, y^*) = -\frac{dh^*}{dy^*}(s, y^*) \qquad (9.6\text{-}10a)$$

$$\frac{d^2h^*}{dy^{*2}}(s, y^*) - Pmsh^*(s, y^*) = -Pm\frac{dU^*}{dy^*}(s, y^*) \qquad (9.6\text{-}10b)$$

where initially $H^*(t = 0, y^*) = u^*(t = 0, y^*) = 0$ and s is the dimensionless complex frequency. In the moving half-space, the dimensionless magnetic diffusion equation applies. It is given by

$$\frac{d^2h_c{}^*}{dy^{*2}}(s, y^*) - Pm_csh_c{}^*(s, y^*) = 0 \qquad (9.6\text{-}10c)$$

where Pm_c is the magnetic Prandtl number of the moving solid. The appropriate boundary conditions are $U^*(s, 0) = u_0{}^*/s$, $U^*(s, \infty) = 0$, $h^*(s, \infty) = 0$, $h_c{}^*(s, -\infty) = 0$, and $h^*(s, 0) = h_c{}^*(s, 0)$ and

$$\alpha \left.\frac{dh^*(s, y^*)}{dy^*}\right|_{y^*=0} = \left.\frac{dh_c{}^*(s, y^*)}{dy^*}\right|_{y^*=0}$$

is a consequence of the continuity of the tangential electric field and $\alpha = \sigma_c/\sigma_f$. When Equations (9.6-10a) and (9.6-10b) are combined, we have

$$\left\{\frac{d^4}{dy^{*4}} - [s(1 + Pm) + Pm]\frac{d^2}{dy^{*2}} + Pms^2\right\}\begin{bmatrix}U^* \\ h^*\end{bmatrix} = 0 \quad (9.6\text{-}11)$$

which is equivalent to the dispersion equation given by (8.2-14). By using the boundary conditions at $y^* = \pm\infty$, it is easy to show that

$$U^*(s, y^*) = C_1e^{-\lambda_1y^*} + C_2e^{-\lambda_2y^*} \qquad (9.6\text{-}12a)$$

$$h^*(s, y^*) = \frac{\lambda_1{}^2 - s}{\lambda_1}C_1e^{-\lambda_1y^*} + \frac{\lambda_2{}^2 - s}{\lambda_2}C_2e^{-\lambda_2y^*} \qquad (9.6\text{-}12b)$$

$$h_c{}^*(s, y^*) = C_3e^{\sqrt{Pm_cs}\,y^*} \qquad (9.6\text{-}12c)$$

where $\lambda_{1,2}$ is given by

$$\lambda_{1,2} = \tfrac{1}{2}[\sqrt{Pm + s(1 + \sqrt{Pm})^2} \pm \sqrt{Pm + s(1 - \sqrt{Pm})^2}] \quad (9.6\text{-}12d)$$

The roots $\lambda_{1,2}$ are similar to $p_{1,2}$ obtained in Equation (9.4-5), as would be expected. The application of the boundary conditions to (9.6-12a), (9.6-12b), and (9.6-12c) yields the following system of equations:

$$C_1 + C_2 = \frac{u_0^*}{s} \quad (9.6\text{-}13a)$$

$$\frac{\lambda_1^2 - s}{\lambda_1} C_1 + \frac{\lambda_2^2 - s}{\lambda_2} C_2 - C_3 = 0 \quad (9.6\text{-}13b)$$

$$\alpha(\lambda_1^2 - s)C_1 + \alpha(\lambda_2^2 - s)C_2 + \sqrt{Pm_c}sC_3 = 0 \quad (9.6\text{-}13c)$$

The solutions to the system of equations resulting from the application of the boundary conditions are given by

$$C_1 = \frac{u_0^*\sqrt{Pm/s}(\lambda_2^2 - s)(\lambda_1 + \sqrt{\alpha s})}{\Delta} \quad (9.6\text{-}14a)$$

$$C_2 = \frac{-u_0^*\sqrt{Pm/s}(\lambda_1^2 - s)(\lambda_2 + \sqrt{\alpha s})}{\Delta} \quad (9.6\text{-}14b)$$

$$C_3 = \frac{u_0^*\sqrt{\alpha}Pm\sqrt{Pm + s(1 - \sqrt{Pm})^2}}{\Delta} \quad (9.6\text{-}14c)$$

where

$$\Delta = -\sqrt{Pms}\sqrt{Pm + s(1 - \sqrt{Pm})^2}$$

$$\times [s(1 + \sqrt{Pm}) + \sqrt{\alpha}s\sqrt{Pm + s(1 + \sqrt{Pm})^2}]$$

$$= (\lambda_2 - \lambda_1)[(\lambda_1\lambda_2 + s) + \sqrt{\alpha}s(\lambda_1 + \lambda_2)]\sqrt{Pms} \quad (9.6\text{-}14d)$$

In obtaining these relationships, various easily derived properties of products, sums, differences, etc. of λ_1 and λ_2 must be used. It is unfortunate that the inverse Laplace transforms of U^*, h^*, and h_c^* cannot easily be obtained in general. We will consider two cases of interest that can be inverted in terms of tabulated functions. The first is for a magnetic Prandtl number of 1.

Insulator Case $(Pm = 1, \alpha = 0)$

When $Pm = 1$, C_1, C_2, C_3, λ_1, λ_2, and Δ simplify to the following:

$$\lambda_{1,2} = \tfrac{1}{2}(\sqrt{1 + 4s} \pm 1) \tag{9.6-15a}$$

$$\Delta = -\sqrt{s}(2s + \sqrt{\alpha s}\sqrt{1 + 4s}) \tag{9.6-15b}$$

$$C_1 = \frac{u_0^*}{4\sqrt{s}} \frac{(1 - \sqrt{1 + 4s})(1 + \sqrt{1 + 4s} + 2\sqrt{\alpha s})}{\Delta} \tag{9.6-15c}$$

$$C_2 = \frac{u_0^*}{4\sqrt{s}}(1 + \sqrt{1 + 4s})(1 - \sqrt{1 + 4s} - 2\sqrt{\alpha s})\,\Delta \tag{9.6-15d}$$

$$C_3 = \frac{u_0^* \sqrt{\alpha}}{\Delta} \tag{9.6-15e}$$

Here the magnetic Prandtl number is unity, and the Laplace-transformed velocity and magnetic fields are obtained by substituting the expressions of (9.6-15a, b, c, and d) into (9.6-12a, b, and c). When the moving half-space is an insulator and $\alpha = 0$, the result is

$$U^*(s, y^*) = \frac{u_0^*}{2s} [e^{(-y^*/2)(1+\sqrt{1+4s})} + e^{(-y^*/2)(-1+\sqrt{1+4s})}] \tag{9.6-16a}$$

$$h^*(s, y^*) = \frac{u_0^*}{2s} [e^{(-y^*/2)(1+\sqrt{1+4s})} - e^{(-y^*/2)(-1+\sqrt{1+4s})}] \tag{9.6-16b}$$

and

$$h_c^* = 0 \tag{9.6-16c}$$

The solution to this problem has been given (approximately) as a limiting case of a problem with cylindrical symmetry by Carrier and Greenspan, 1960. The inverse Laplace transforms of (9.6-16a) and (9.6-16b) are given by

$$u^*(t^*, y^*) = \frac{u_0^*}{4}\left[(1 + e^{y^*})\operatorname{erfc}\left(\frac{y^* + t^*}{2\sqrt{t^*}}\right)\right.$$
$$\left. + (1 + e^{-y^*})\operatorname{erfc}\left(\frac{y^* - t^*}{2\sqrt{t^*}}\right)\right] \tag{9.6-17a}$$

and

$$H^*(t^*, y^*) = \frac{u_0^*}{4}\left[(e^{y^*} - 1)\operatorname{erfc}\left(\frac{y^* + t^*}{2\sqrt{t^*}}\right)\right.$$
$$\left. + (1 - e^{-y^*})\operatorname{erfc}\left(\frac{y^* - t^*}{2\sqrt{t^*}}\right)\right] \tag{9.6-17b}$$

which comprises the superposition of two diffusing Alfvén waves having decaying amplitudes. It is very interesting to examine these solutions for large values of time. To accomplish this, we let s become much smaller than unity in (9.6-16a) and (9.6-16b). The inverse Laplace transforms of the resulting equations are valid for $t^* \gg 1$. Allowing $s \ll 1$ in (9.6-16a) and (9.6-16b) yields

$$U^*(s, y^*) = \frac{u_0^*}{2s} (e^{-y^*} + 1)e^{-y^* s} \qquad (9.6\text{-}18a)$$

$$h^*(s, y^*) = \frac{u_0^*}{2s} (e^{-y^*} - 1)e^{-y^* s} \qquad (9.6\text{-}18b)$$

The dimensionless current density and electric field are given by

$$j^*(s, y^*) = \frac{u_0^*}{2s} (e^{-y^*} - s)e^{-y^* s} \qquad (9.6\text{-}18c)$$

$$e^*(s, y^*) = \frac{-u_0^*}{2s} (1 + s)e^{-y^* s} \qquad (9.6\text{-}18d)$$

The inverse Laplace transforms of (9.6-18a through d), valid for large t^*, are given by

$$u^*(t^*, y^*) = \frac{u_0^*}{2} (1 + e^{-y^*}) \qquad \text{for} \quad 0 \le y^* \le t^*$$
$$= 0 \qquad \text{for} \quad y^* \ge t^* \qquad (9.6\text{-}18e)$$

$$H^*(t^*, y^*) = \frac{-u_0^*}{2} (1 - e^{-y^*}) \qquad \text{for} \quad 0 \le y^* \le t^*$$
$$= 0 \qquad \text{for} \quad y^* \ge t^* \qquad (9.6\text{-}18f)$$

$$J^*(t^*, y^*) = \frac{u_0^*}{2} [e^{-y^*} - \delta(y^* - t^*)] \qquad \text{for} \quad 0 \le y^* \le t^*$$
$$= 0 \qquad \text{for} \quad y^* \ge t^* \qquad (9.6\text{-}18g)$$

and

$$E^*(t^*, y^*) = \frac{-u_0^*}{2} [1 + \delta(y^* - t^*)] \qquad \text{for} \quad 0 \le y^* \le t^*$$
$$= 0 \qquad \text{for} \quad y^* \ge t^* \qquad (9.6\text{-}18h)$$

where $\delta(y^* - t^*)$ is a traveling Dirac δ-function having the properties: (1) $\delta(x) = 0$ for $x \ne 0$, (2) $\delta(x) \to \infty$ for $x = 0$, and (3) $\int_{-\infty}^{\infty} \delta(x)\, dx = 1$. These solutions are shown in Fig. 9.6-3. From (9.6-18e through h) it is clear that a true steady state is never approached because a wavefront traveling at unit dimensionless velocity (which is the Alfvén speed) propagates to ever-increasing distances from the source of disturbance. Behind the wavefront ($y^* < t^*$) is a steady-state solution of the form obtained in (9.6-2c) and (9.6-3). The steady-state solutions of (9.6-2c) and (9.6-3) were not complete because E_{ss}^* and C_1 were not known. In order to obtain the steady portions of (9.6-18e) and (9.6-18f) from (9.6-2c) and (9.6-3), we must assume $E_{ss}^* = C_1 = -u_0^*/2$. Ordinarily E_{ss}^* would be

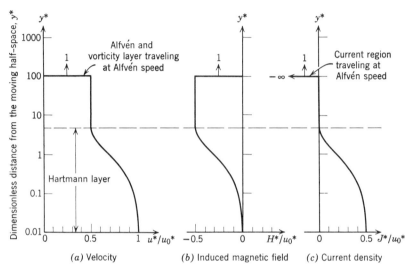

Figure 9.6-3 The transient-velocity, induced magnetic-field, and current-density profiles for $Pm = 1$, $\alpha = 0$, and $t^* \gg 1$.

found by requiring no net flow of current in the z direction, since the current is generated and must return in the fluid when it is driven by an insulator. In the steady-solution part of this section the application of this condition would yield $E_{ss}^* = -u_{ss}^*/Pm$. In the steady state, we might suspect $C_1 = 0$, unless an external field were applied in the x direction. The apparent disparity between the constants E_{ss}^* and C_1 derived from the limiting process of the transient solutions and the constants E_{ss}^* and C_1 obtained from the purely steady-state solution does not indicate that the true steady-state solution cannot be obtained from the transient solutions. This question has been the subject of much discussion in the literature. (See Stewartson, 1960 for references.) From our analysis it is seen that the transient never ends in the infinite geometry even though a steady-state solution exists near the moving solid half-space. The layer in which the steady-state solution exists is called the "Hartmann layer," (Bryson and Rosciszewski, 1962). The constants of integration in the "Hartmann layer" depend upon the transients which are occurring just beyond the "Hartmann layer." To illustrate this, we consider the dimensionless electric current density of (9.6-18g). In the Hartmann layer the steady current is $J^*(y^*) = (u_0^*/2)e^{-y^*}$ and therefore the total current (per unit x width) is $\mathscr{I} = u_0^*/2$. This current returns in the current sheet at $y^* = t^*$. The returning current density is $(-u_0^*/2)\delta(y^* - t^*)$ which can be integrated over y^* to show that all the current returns in the current sheet. Hence the steady magnetic field in the Hartmann layer is produced by currents generated by the moving fluid in the Hartmann layer. These currents complete their circuit in a current sheet which propagates in the y^* direction at the Alfvén speed. Actually, the current sheet extends over a region called the Alfvén layer and has a finite rather than infinite current density. However, to the first approximation, the Alfvén layer appears to have zero thickness.

Hence it is seen that no inconsistencies exist between the transient solution, its limiting value for large t^*, and the steady-state solution derived without regard to how the steady-state solution is approached in time.

From Figs. 9.6-4a through d, it is clear that for $t^* > 25$ the velocity and the field in the Hartmann layer obey the steady portions of the solutions given by (9.6-18e) and (9.6-18f). The layer extends from $y^* = 0$ to about $y^* = 5$, when $t^* = 9$. In the Hartmann layer the viscous shear force is balanced by the electromagnetic body force. Outside the Hartmann layer Alfvén waves propagate with time-dependent velocities and amplitudes that approach those given by (9.6-18e through h) for large t^*.

The curves of Figs. 9.6-4a through d are obtained directly from (9.6-17a) and (9.6-17b), whereas the curves of Figs. 9.6-3a through c are approximations to (9.6-17a) and (9.6-17b). The approximate solution, which holds very well in the Hartmann layer, discloses the wave nature of the Alfvén region but indicates that the Alfvén region ends abruptly. It is clear from Figs. 9.6-4a through d that the Alfvén region does not end in a discontinuity. Instead, the edges of the Alfvén region become more diffuse as it travels along. The region in which $u^*(t^*, y^*)/u_0^*$ decays from 0.495 to 0.005 is called the Alfvén layer. From Figs. 9.6-4a through d it is clear that the center of the Alfvén layer travels at the Alfvén speed (unit dimensionless velocity) and the thickness of the layer increases in proportion to the square root of its distance from the moving half-space. The dimensionless thickness of the Alfvén layer, δ_A^*, is given by

$$\delta_A^* = 3.1\sqrt{y^*} \tag{9.6-18i}$$

and the dimensionless thickness δ_H^* of the Hartmann layer is about 4.6.

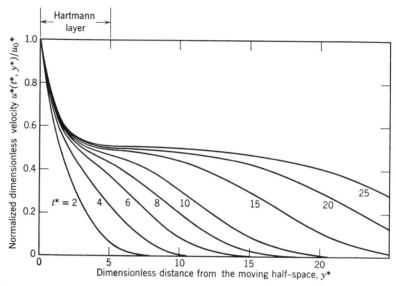

Figure 9.6-4a   The velocity distribution as a function of time when $\alpha = 0$ (insulator case) and $Pm = 1$.

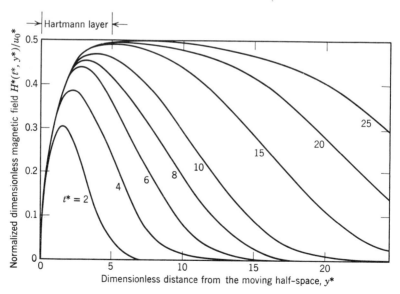

Figure 9.6-4b   The magnetic field distribution as a function of time when $\alpha = 0$ and $Pm = 1$.

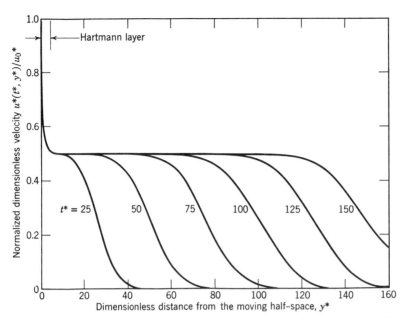

Figure 9.6-4c The velocity distribution as a function of time when $\alpha = 0$ (insulator case) and $Pm = 1$.

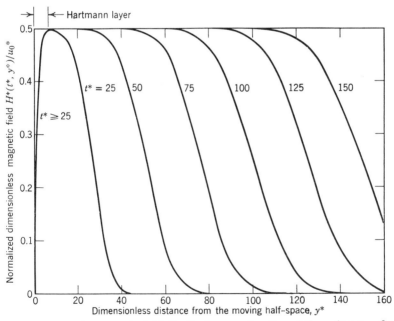

Figure 9.6-4d The magnetic field distribution as a function of time when $\alpha = 0$ and $Pm = 1$.

411

When Figs. 9.6-4a through d are plotted on semilog paper, the Alfvén layer appears to get smaller as the wave travels along.

When $v \to 0$ (but Pm remains unity), an interesting limiting case exists which can be obtained from (9.6-16a) and (9.6-16b) by changing them to their dimensional form and letting $v \to 0$. Physically, this is the case of an inviscid, superconducting liquid. The results of this limiting process are

$$U(s, y) = \frac{u_0}{2s} e^{-sy/A} \tag{9.6-19a}$$

and

$$h^*(s, y) = \frac{-u_0}{2sA} e^{-sy/A} \tag{9.6-19b}$$

The inverse Laplace transforms of (9.6-19a) and (9.6-19b) are given by

$$u(t, y) = \frac{u_0}{2} \quad \text{for} \quad 0 \le y \le At$$

$$= 0 \quad \text{for} \quad y \ge At \tag{9.6-19c}$$

$$H^*(t, y) = \frac{-u_0}{2A} \quad \text{for} \quad 0 \le y \le At$$

$$= 0 \quad \text{for} \quad y \ge At \tag{9.6-19d}$$

This is known as a switch-on shock wave and is discussed in detail in Chapter 10. (The magnetic field changes its direction and magnitude across the shock front and thus is *not* a rotational discontinuity.) The plots of (9.6-19c) and (9.6-19d) are given in Fig. 9.6-5. A layer of fluid beginning an infinitesimal distance beyond the fluid-solid interface has a velocity of one-half the velocity of the solid, and the thickness of the layer increases at At. (Here the thickness of the Hartmann layer has been reduced to ϵ, where $\epsilon \to 0$.) Beyond the moving layer, the fluid is at rest and the region of the discontinuity of the fluid velocity travels at A, the Alfvén speed. The induced dimensionless magnetic field is $-u_0/2A$ in the region $y \le At$, where the fluid moves and is zero outside that region. Thus there are two current sheets resulting from the discontinuities in the induced magnetic field. One is located at $y = 0$ in the liquid, flows in the z direction, and exerts a body force which prevents the fluid velocity from being the plate velocity. The other current sheet, directed in the negative z direction and traveling in the y direction at the Alfvén speed, exerts a body force which accelerates the fluid in the x direction. The y component of this body force causes no fluid motion since it is balanced by the fluid pressure gradient which occurs at $y = At$. The pressure gradient exists because the magnetic field is not the same for $y > At$ and $y < At$. In this limiting case, it is assumed that the no-slip boundary condition is observed at the interface between the inviscid, perfectly conducting liquid and the moving insulator. If slip occurs, no fluid motion will result and no current sheet will be generated to sustain and propagate the motion.

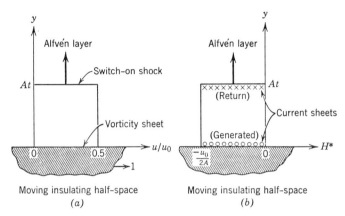

Fgiure 9.6-5 The velocity and magnetic field distribution for $v = \eta = \alpha = 0$. (A is the Alfvén speed).

It is important to understand this example, for it is the electromagnetic body force, caused by the interaction of the applied magnetic field and the diffusing currents, which propels the fluid outside the Hartmann layer.

Insulator Case ($Pm \ll 1, \alpha = 0$)

Regardless of the value of Pm, the roots λ_1 and λ_2 possess certain useful properties. For further analysis, it is convenient to state certain easily derived relationships of general validity. They are

$$\lambda_1 \lambda_2 = s\sqrt{Pm} \tag{9.6-20a}$$

$$\lambda_1{}^2 + \lambda_1{}^2 = s(1 + Pm) + Pm \tag{9.6-20b}$$

$$\lambda_1{}^2 - \lambda_2{}^2 = \sqrt{s^2(1 - Pm) + 2sPm(1 + Pm) + Pm^2} \tag{9.6-20c}$$

and

$$(\lambda_1{}^2 - s)(\lambda_2{}^2 - s) = -sPm \tag{9.6-20d}$$

For $P_m \ll 1$, it is clear from (9.6-12d) that

$$\lambda_1 = \sqrt{s + Pm} \tag{9.6-21a}$$

The easiest way to obtain the appropriate value of λ_2 is to substitute the approximate value of λ_1 (from 9.6-21a) into the exact relationship of (9.6-20a). Solving this for λ_2 yields

$$\lambda_2 = \frac{s\sqrt{Pm}}{\sqrt{s + Pm}} \tag{9.6-21b}$$

which is as good an approximation as (9.6-21a). Here extreme care is exercised to avoid placing hidden restrictions on the values of s for which the expressions are valid. It is obvious that for $Pm \ll 1$

$$\lambda_1{}^2 - s = Pm \tag{9.6-21c}$$

In order to obtain $\lambda_2{}^2 - s$, it is advisable to combine (9.6-21c) with the exact relationship given by (9.6-20d) so that

$$\lambda_2{}^2 - s = -s \tag{9.6-21d}$$

which may seem strange because it implies $\lambda_2{}^2 = 0$. A more exact analysis would include another term, $s^2 Pm/(s + Pm)$, which is the approximate value of $\lambda_2{}^2$. Thus in (9.6-21d) $\lambda_2{}^2$ is discarded as being small compared to $-s$ for all values of s. The constants C_1 and C_2 given by (9.6-14a) and (9.6-14b) are easily evaluated by using (9.6-21a, b, c, and d). C_1 and C_2 are given by

$$C_1 = \frac{u_0{}^*}{s} \tag{9.6-22a}$$

$$C_2 = \frac{u_0{}^* Pm^{3/2}}{s(s + Pm)} \tag{9.6-22b}$$

When C_1 and C_2 are substituted into (9.6-12a) and (9.6-12b), we have

$$U^*(s, y^*) = \frac{u_0{}^*}{s}\left[e^{-y^*\sqrt{s+Pm}} + \frac{Pm^{3/2}}{s + Pm}\, e^{(-y^* s\sqrt{Pm}/\sqrt{s+Pm})} \right] \tag{9.6-23a}$$

and

$$h^*(s, y^*) = \frac{u_0{}^* Pm}{s\sqrt{s + Pm}}\, [e^{-y^*\sqrt{s+Pm}} - e^{(-y^* s\sqrt{Pm}/\sqrt{s+Pm})}] \tag{9.6-23b}$$

It is interesting to express (9.6-23a) and (9.6-23b) in a form valid for $s \ll Pm$. For $s \ll Pm$ the velocity and induced magnetic field become

$$U^*(s, y^*) = \frac{u_0{}^*}{s}\left[e^{-y^*\sqrt{Pm}\left(1 + \frac{s}{2\,Pm}\right)} + \sqrt{Pm}\, e^{-y^* s} \right] \tag{9.6-23c}$$

and

$$h^*(s, y^*) = \frac{u_0^* \sqrt{Pm}}{s} [e^{-y^* \sqrt{Pm}\left(1 + \frac{s}{2Pm}\right)} - e^{-y^* s}] \qquad (9.6\text{-}23d)$$

The dimensionless current density, obtained directly from the differentiation of (9.6-12b) and expressed for $s \ll Pm$, is given by

$$j^*(s, y^*) = u_0^* Pm \left[\frac{1 + s/\sqrt{Pm}}{s} e^{-y^* \sqrt{Pm}\left(1 + \frac{s}{2\,Pm}\right)} - \frac{e^{-y^* s}}{\sqrt{Pm}}\right] \qquad (9.6\text{-}23e)$$

This procedure is used to avoid losing any quantities involving the first power of s. If the approximate result of (9.6-23d) is used to obtain the current density, the result is inaccurate.

In contrast to the solutions of (9.6-23a and b), it is easy to obtain the inverse Laplace transforms of (9.6-23c through e). They are

$$u(t^*, y^*) = u_0^* \left[e^{-y^* \sqrt{Pm}} g\left(t^* - \frac{y^*}{2\sqrt{Pm}}\right) + \sqrt{Pm}\, g(t^* - y^*)\right] \qquad (9.6\text{-}25a)$$

$$H^*(t^*, y^*) = u_0^* \sqrt{Pm} \left[e^{-y^* \sqrt{Pm}} g\left(t^* - \frac{y^*}{2\sqrt{Pm}}\right) - g(t^* - y^*)\right] \qquad (9.6\text{-}25b)$$

$$J^*(t^*, y^*) = u_0^* \sqrt{Pm} \left\{e^{-y^* \sqrt{Pm}} \left[g\left(t^* - \frac{y^*}{2\sqrt{Pm}}\right)\right.\right.$$
$$\left.\left. + \frac{1}{\sqrt{Pm}} \delta\left(t^* - \frac{y^*}{2\sqrt{Pm}}\right)\right] - \frac{1}{\sqrt{Pm}} \delta(t^* - y^*)\right\} \qquad (9.6\text{-}25c)$$

where $g(t - \tau)$ is the unit step function defined by $g(t - \tau) = 1$ for $t \geq \tau$ and $g(t - \tau) = 0$ for $t < \tau$. The solutions just derived for large t^* comprise the superposition of fast and slow waves. The fast waves travel at the Alfvén speed A and the slow waves travel at $2\sqrt{Pm}A$. The slow wave term in the velocity solution is another form of the Hartmann layer described previously. The other term is an Alfvén wave of small amplitude which acts as a precursor to the even smaller (for large t^*) amplitude slow wave. This is illustrated by Fig. 9.6-6, constructed for $t^* = 400$ and $Pm = 0.01$. From this figure it is clear that the slow wave has a very small amplitude, $u_0^* e^{-8}$. The amplitude of the fast wave is 0.1. The slow wave modifies the solutions to a negligible extent. However, it seems to indicate that the Alfvén wave portion of the solution is established before the Hartmann layer becomes steady. Regardless of the effect of the slow wave, the Alfvén wave solution is necessary to provide a return circuit for

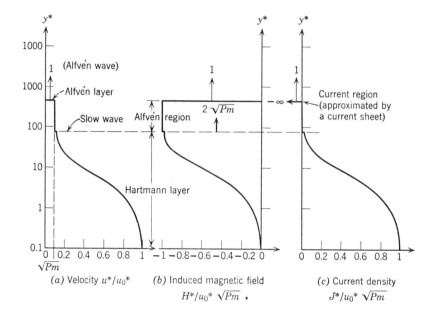

(a) Velocity u^*/u_0^* (b) Induced magnetic field
$H^*/u_0^* \sqrt{Pm}$,

(c) Current density
$J^*/u_0^* \sqrt{Pm}$

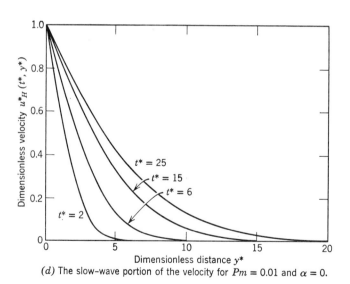

(d) The slow-wave portion of the velocity for $Pm = 0.01$ and $\alpha = 0$.

Figure 9.6-6   The transient solution for $t^* = 400$, $Pm = 0.01$, and $\alpha = 0$.

the current generated in the Hartmann layer. The current sheet traveling with the slow speed is a result of the mathematical approximations. The discontinuities in the velocity and magnetic field actually are smooth variations comprising an Alfvén layer.

Although the general inverse transforms of (9.6-23a) and (9.6-23b) are difficult to obtain, the inversion of the slow wave or Hartmann layer portion of the solution is straightforward. The inverse Laplace transform of the first term of (9.6-23a) is given by

$$u_H{}^*(t^*, y^*) = \frac{u_0{}^*}{2}\left[e^{y^*\sqrt{Pm}} \operatorname{erfc}\left(\frac{y^* + 2\sqrt{Pm}t^*}{2\sqrt{t^*}}\right)\right.$$

$$\left. + e^{-y^*\sqrt{Pm}} \operatorname{erfc}\left(\frac{y^* - 2\sqrt{Pm}t^*}{2\sqrt{t^*}}\right)\right] \quad (9.6\text{-}25d)$$

where $u_H{}^*(t^*, y^*)$ is the slow wave portion of the velocity solution, valid for all y^* and t^* (see Fig. 9.6-6). It is clear that the components of the slow wave solution propagate at a speed of $\pm 2\sqrt{Pm}A$. This solution is very large in magnitude, near the moving half-space, compared to the fast wave solution. As shown by Equation (9.6-25a) the slow wave solution attenuates with increasing time and distance until the fast wave solution is dominant. Since the fast wave discontinuity in the magnetic field provides the return circuit for the currents generated in the Hartmann layer, the fast wave solution propagates unattenuated for large t^* and y^*.

Ideal Conductor Case ($Pm = 1$, $\alpha = \infty$)

Equations (9.6-15a through e) are applicable to this case. Taking the limit of those expressions as $\alpha \to \infty$ yields

$$U^*(s, y^*) = \frac{u_0{}^*}{2}\left[\frac{\begin{array}{l}-(1 - \sqrt{1 + 4s})e^{(-y^*/2)(1+\sqrt{1+4s})}\\ \quad + (1 + \sqrt{1 + 4s})e^{(-y^*/2)(-1+\sqrt{1+4s})}\end{array}}{s\sqrt{1 + 4s}}\right] \quad (9.6\text{-}26a)$$

$$h^*(s, y^*) = -\frac{u_0{}^*}{2}\left[\frac{\begin{array}{l}(1 - \sqrt{1 + 4s})e^{(-y^*/2)(1+\sqrt{1+4s})}\\ \quad + (1 + \sqrt{1 + 4s})e^{(-y^*/2)(-1+\sqrt{1+4s})}\end{array}}{s\sqrt{1 + 4s}}\right] \quad (9.6\text{-}26b)$$

$$h_c{}^*(s, y^*) = \lim_{\alpha \to \infty} -\frac{u_0{}^* e^{y^*\sqrt{\alpha s}}}{s\sqrt{1 + 4s}} = \frac{-u_0{}^*}{s\sqrt{1 + 4s}} \quad \text{for} \quad y^* = 0$$

$$= 0 \qquad \text{for} \quad y^* < 0 \qquad (9.6\text{-}26c)$$

which can be inverted easily. The induced magnetic field in the moving conducting half-space is zero except at $y^* = 0$. The inverse Laplace transform of (9.6-26a) and (9.6-26b) yields

$$u^*(t^*, y^*) = \frac{u_0^*}{2}\left[\text{erfc}\left(\frac{y^* + t^*}{2\sqrt{t^*}}\right) + \text{erfc}\left(\frac{y^* - t^*}{2\sqrt{t^*}}\right)\right] \quad (9.6\text{-}27a)$$

$$H^*(t^*, y^*) = \frac{u_0^*}{2}\left[\text{erfc}\left(\frac{y^* + t^*}{2\sqrt{t^*}}\right) - \text{erfc}\left(\frac{y^* - t^*}{2\sqrt{t^*}}\right)\right] \quad (9.6\text{-}27b)$$

and

$$H_c^*(t^*, 0) = -u_0^* \, \text{erf}\left(\tfrac{1}{2}\sqrt{t^*}\right) \quad (9.6\text{-}27c)$$

which is the set of solutions given by Chang and Yen (1959). The solutions for velocity and induced field plotted in Figs. 9.6-7a through d comprise the superposition of diffusing Alfvén waves, as was the case when an insulating plate caused the flow. From Figs. 9.6-7a through d it is seen that the Hartmann layer extends to near the Alfvén layer when the moving half-space is an ideal conductor. The dimensionless thickness of the Alfvén layer in this case is given by $\delta_A^* = 7\sqrt{y^*}$. Once again the center of the Alfvén layer propagates with the Alfvén speed.

It is interesting to inspect the steady solutions that occur when $t^* \gg 1$. To accomplish this, we let $s \ll 1$ in (9.6-26a) and (9.6-26b) and take the inverse Laplace transform. The results are

$$u^*(t^*, y^*) = u_0^*[1 - e^{-t^*/2}(1 - e^{-y^*})]g(t^* - y^*)$$
$$\approx u_0^* g(t^* - y^*) \quad (9.6\text{-}28a)$$

$$H^*(t^*, y^*) = -u_0^*[1 - e^{-t^*/2}(1 + e^{-y^*})]g(t^* - y^*)$$
$$\approx -u_0^* g(t^* - y^*) \quad (9.6\text{-}28b)$$

and

$$J^*(t^*, y^*) = -u_0^*[(1 - e^{-y^*})e^{-t^*/2}g(t^* - y^*) + \delta(t^* - y^*)]$$
$$\approx -u_0^* \delta(t^* - y^*) \quad (9.6\text{-}28c)$$

where $g(t^* - y^*)$ and $\delta(t^* - y^*)$ are the unit step function and the Dirac δ-function, each traveling at unity dimensionless speed (Alfvén speed). For large values of $t^*(t^* \gg 1)$, the velocity, induced magnetic field, and the current density become constants in the Hartmann layer. The outer boundary of the Hartmann layer propagates with the Alfvén speed as shown in Fig. 9.6-8. A current sheet or layer in the Alfvén layer (between the Hartmann layer and the undistributed fluid) provides a return path for the current generated in the moving conducting half-space. As previously discussed, the transient is never terminated and hence the steady-state solutions are influenced by the transients occurring at $y^* = t^*$. The

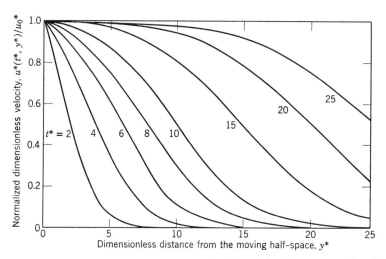

Figure 9.6-7a   The velocity distribution as a function of time for $\alpha = \infty$ (conducto case) and $Pm = 1$.

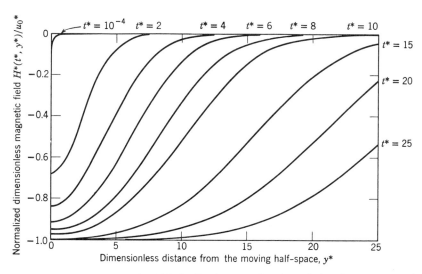

Figure 9.6-7b   The magnetic field distribution as a function of time for $\alpha = \infty$ and $Pm = 1$.

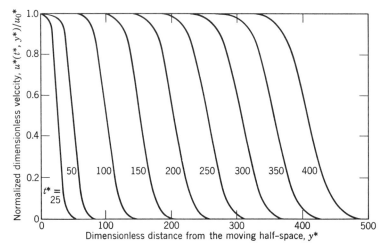

Figure 9.6-7c   The velocity distribution as a function of time for $\alpha = \infty$ and $Pm = 1$.

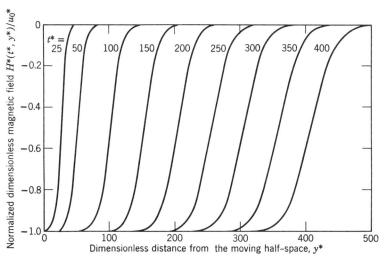

Figure 9.6-7d   The magnetic field distribution as a function of time for $\alpha = \infty$ and $Pm = 1$.

"steady-state" solutions obtained here when $t^* \to \infty$ agree with those derived in (9.6-9a) and (9.6-9b). In that derivation, C_1 could not be found. From (9.6-28b) it is seen that $C_1 = -u_0^*$.

When $\nu = 0$ and $Pm = 1$, it is easy to show that the velocity and induced magnetic field of (9.6-26a) and (9.6-26b) become

$$U(s, y) = \frac{u_0}{s} e^{-ys/A} \tag{9.6-29a}$$

and

$$h^*(s, y) = \frac{-u_0}{sA} e^{-ys/A} \tag{9.6-29b}$$

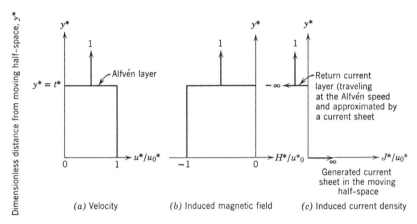

Figure 9.6-8 The velocity, induced magnetic-field, and current-density profiles valid for $Pm \leq 1$, $Pmt^* \gg 1$, and $\alpha = \infty$.

The inverse Laplace transforms of these are given by

$$u(t, y) = u_0 \quad \text{for} \quad 0 \leq y \leq At \tag{9.6-30a}$$
$$= 0 \quad \text{for} \quad y \geq At$$

and

$$H^*(t, y) = \frac{-u_0}{A} \quad \text{for} \quad 0 \leq y \leq At$$
$$= 0 \quad \text{for} \quad y \geq At \tag{9.6-30b}$$

which are plotted in Fig. 9.6-9.

This solution is similar to the one obtained for the flow of an inviscid, ideally conducting fluid driven by an insulating moving half-space. Physically, the only difference between the two problems is the location of one of the current sheets. In the insulator-driven case the current sheets are located at $y = 0^+$ (in the fluid) and at $y = At$; in the ideal-conductor case the current sheets are located at $y = 0^-$ (in the semi-infinite half-space) and at $y = At$. The location of the current sheet at the origin greatly influences the flow. In the insulator-driven flow, the interaction of the current sheet and the applied magnetic field exerts a retarding force on the fluid. In the conductor-driven flow the retarding force is exerted on the moving conducting half-space and hence the fluid velocity is twice as great.

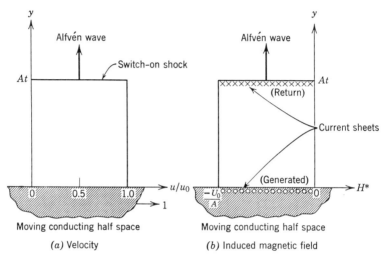

Figure 9.6-9   The velocity and magnetic field distribution for $\nu = \eta = 0$ and $\alpha = \infty$.

The Ideal Conductor Case ($Pm \ll 1$, $\alpha = \infty$)

When the solid moving half-space is an ideal conductor and $Pm \ll 1$, (9.6-12a) and (9.6-12b) must be treated very carefully as $Pm \to 0$ and $\alpha = \infty$. Our analysis will be aided if we use the exact expressions given by (9.6-20a through d) and the approximate expressions valid for $Pm \ll 1$ given by (9.6-21a through d). By using the relationships (9.6-12b), (9.6-14a), and (9.6-14b) and by letting $\alpha \to \infty$, we can obtain

$$U^* = \frac{u_0^*}{s + Pm}\left[e^{-y^*\sqrt{s+Pm}} + \frac{Pm}{s}e^{(-y^*s\sqrt{Pm}/\sqrt{s+Pm})}\right] \qquad (9.6\text{-}31a)$$

$$h^* = \frac{Pm u_0^*}{s + Pm}\left[\frac{e^{-y^*\sqrt{s+Pm}}}{\sqrt{s+Pm}} - \frac{\sqrt{s+Pm}}{s\sqrt{Pm}}e^{(-y^*s\sqrt{Pm}/\sqrt{s+Pm})}\right] \qquad (9.6\text{-}31b)$$

where (9.6-31a) and (9.6-31b) are good for all values of s.

It is easy to show from (9.6-31a) that $\lim_{t^* \to \infty} u^*(t^*, y^*) = u_0^*$ and $\lim_{t^* \to \infty} u^*(t^*,$ $y^* = 0) = u_0^*$, as should be the case. In the case of the magnetic field,

$$\partial h^*/\partial y^*\big|_{y^* = 0} = 0 \qquad \text{and} \qquad \lim_{t^* \to \infty} H^*(t^*, y^*) = -u_0^*$$

Since the solutions of (9.6-31a) and (9.6-31b) are valid for $Pm \ll 1$ but difficult to invert for all values of s, it is interesting to find $h^*(s, y^* = 0)$

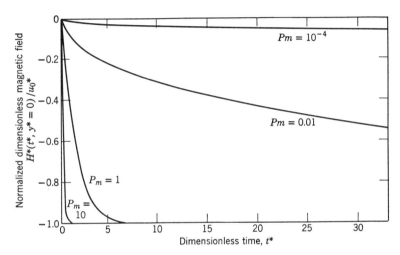

Figure 9.6-10   The magnetic field at the moving ideal conductor as a function of time for various magnetic Prandtl numbers.

and perform the inverse Laplace transform of it. The Laplace transform of the induced magnetic field at the interface $y^* = 0$ is given by

$$h^*(s, 0) = Pmu_0^* \left[\frac{1}{(s + Pm)^{3/2}} - \frac{1}{s\sqrt{s + Pm\sqrt{Pm}}} \right] \qquad (9.6\text{-}32a)$$

and its inverse Laplace transform is

$$H^*(t^*, y^* = 0) = u_0^* \left[2Pm e^{-Pmt^*} \sqrt{\frac{t^*}{\pi}} - \text{erf}\left(\sqrt{Pmt^*}\right) \right] \qquad (9.6\text{-}32b)$$

This is plotted in Fig. 9.6-10 and shows how decreasing the magnetic Prandtl number increases the time necessary for the magnetic field transient to be completed at the moving half-space.

For $s \ll Pm$ Equations (9.6-31a) and (9.6-31b) become

$$U^* = u_0^* \left(\frac{e^{-y^* \sqrt{s+Pm}}}{s + Pm} + \frac{e^{-y^* s}}{s} \right) \tag{9.6-33a}$$

and

$$h^* = u_0^* \left[\frac{Pm e^{-y^* \sqrt{s+Pm}}}{(s + Pm)^{3/2}} - \frac{e^{-y^* s}}{s} \right] \tag{9.6-33b}$$

where the first term of the expressions is left in its original form. The inverse Laplace transforms of these expressions are

$$u^*(t^*, y^*) = u_0^* \left[e^{-Pm t^*} \operatorname{erfc} \frac{y^*}{2\sqrt{t^*}} + g(t^* - y^*) \right] \tag{9.6-33c}$$

and

$$H^*(t^*, y^*) = u_0^* \left\{ Pm \, e^{-Pm t^*} \left[2 \sqrt{\frac{t^*}{\pi}} \, e^{-y^*/4t^*} \right. \right.$$
$$\left. \left. - y^* \operatorname{erfc} \left(\frac{y^*}{2\sqrt{t^*}} \right) \right] - g(t^* - y^*) \right\} \tag{9.6-33d}$$

where $g(t^* - y^*)$ is the traveling unit step function and the terms not involving $g(t^* - y^*)$ are valid for all t^*. The step function terms are valid for $Pm t^* \gg 1$, in which case the velocity and induced field are best expressed as

$$u^*(t^*, y^*) = u_0^* g(t^* - y^*) \tag{9.6-33e}$$

$$H^*(t^*, y^*) = -u_0^* g(t^* - y^*) \tag{9.6-33f}$$

Hence, when $Pm t^* \gg 1$, the velocity and induced magnetic-field profiles are steady near the moving conducting half-space. But at distances such that $y^* \gg Pm^{-1}$ there is still fluid and no magnetic field. The boundary between the undisturbed and the steady velocity regions propagates in the y^* direction at unity dimensionless speed or in terms of dimensional velocity, the Alfvén speed. The Laplace-transformed current density, found by differentiating (9.6-12b), is given by

$$j^* = \frac{Pm u_0^*}{s + Pm} (e^{-y^* \sqrt{s+Pm}} - e^{(-y^* s \sqrt{Pm})/\sqrt{s+Pm}}) \tag{9.6-34a}$$

and is valid for all s. The inverse Laplace transform is taken in the manner previously described. The result is

$$J^*(t^*, y^*) = Pm u_0^* \left[e^{-Pm t} \operatorname{erfc} \frac{y^*}{2\sqrt{t^*}} - \frac{1}{Pm} \delta(t^* - y^*) \right] \tag{9.6-34b}$$

Here the first term is valid for all time and the second term is valid for $Pmt^* \gg 1$. Thus for $Pmt^* \gg 1$ the dimensionless current density becomes

$$J^*(t^*, y^*) = -u_0^* \delta(t^* - y^*) \qquad (9.6\text{-}34c)$$

where $\delta(t^* - y^*)$ is a traveling Dirac δ-function.

Forces Acting on the Moving Half-Space

The shear force exerted upon the wall by the fluid is given by

$$F_{sh}^*(s) = \frac{\partial U^*}{\partial y^*}(s, y^*) \Big|_{y^*=0} \qquad (9.6\text{-}35a)$$

The shear force is obtained by differentiating (9.6-12a) with respect to y^*:

$$F_{sh}^*(s) = -\frac{(1 + \sqrt{Pm})\sqrt{\alpha s} + \sqrt{Pm + s(1 + \sqrt{Pm})^2}}{s(1 + \sqrt{Pm}) + \sqrt{\alpha s}\sqrt{Pm + s(1 + \sqrt{Pm})^2}} u_0^* \qquad (9.6\text{-}35b)$$

The inverse Laplace transform of (9.6-35b) can be found for any α. Here we find the inverse Laplace transform for the cases of $\alpha = 0$ and $\alpha = \infty$. For $\alpha = 0$, (9.6-35b) becomes

$$F_{sh}^*(s) = -\frac{u_0^*}{s}\sqrt{s + \frac{Pm}{(1 + \sqrt{Pm})^2}} \qquad (9.6\text{-}35c)$$

which has the inverse Laplace transform of

$$f_{sh}^*(t^*) = -u_0^* \left\{ \frac{e^{(-Pmt^*)/(1+\sqrt{Pm})^2}}{\sqrt{\pi t^*}} + \frac{\sqrt{Pm}}{1 + \sqrt{Pm}} \, \text{erf} \, \frac{\sqrt{Pmt^*}}{1 + \sqrt{Pm}} \right\} \qquad (9.6\text{-}35d)$$

When $Pm = 0$, the shear force is given by

$$\lim_{Pm \to 0} f_{sh}^*(t^*) = -\frac{u_0^*}{\sqrt{\pi t^*}} \qquad (9.6\text{-}35e)$$

This result is useful, since it is convenient to plot $f_{sh}^*(t^*, Pm)/f_{sh}^*(t^*, Pm = 0)$. This curve is given in Fig. 9.6-11.

When the flow is driven by an ideal conductor, the Laplace-transformed shear force is given by

$$F_{sh}^*(s) = \frac{-u_0^*}{\sqrt{s + Pm/(1 + \sqrt{Pm})^2}} \qquad (9.6\text{-}36a)$$

The inverse Laplace transform of (9.6-36a) is

$$f_{sh}^*(t^*) = -\frac{u_0^* e^{(-Pmt^*)/(1+\sqrt{Pm})^2}}{\sqrt{\pi t^*}} \qquad (9.6\text{-}36b)$$

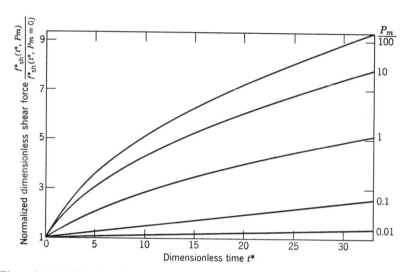

Figure 9.6-11 The shear force on the insulating plate versus time for various magnetic Prandtl numbers.

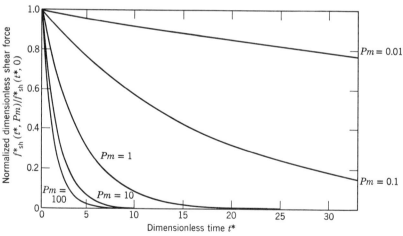

Figure 9.6-12 Shear force on the conducting plate as a function of time for various values of magnetic Prandtl number.

which is plotted on Fig. 9.6-12. The electromagnetic force on the conducting plate is

$$F_{em}*(s) = -\int_{-\infty}^{0} j*B* \, dy* = -\int_{-\infty}^{0} j* \, dy* \qquad (9.6\text{-}36c)$$

because $B* = 1$. This expression can be simplified by recognizing $j* = -\partial H*/\partial y*$. Then

$$F_{em}*(s) = \int_{H_c^*(-\infty)}^{H_c^*(0)} dH* = H_c(0) \qquad (9.6\text{-}36d)$$

which is obtained from (9.6-12c). For any value of the half-space con-

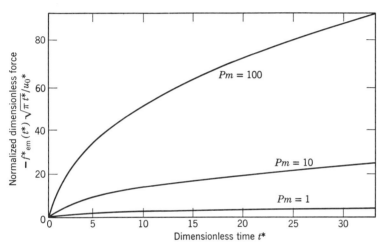

Figure 9.6-13 The electromagnetic force on the conducting plate versus time for $Pm = 1$, 10, and 100.

ductivity, the electromagnetic force is given by

$$F_{em}*(s) = \frac{-u_0* Pm\sqrt{\alpha}}{\sqrt{Pms}[s(1 + \sqrt{Pm}) + \sqrt{\alpha}s\sqrt{Pm} + s(1 + \sqrt{Pm})^2]} \qquad (9.6\text{-}36e)$$

which reduces to zero for an insulator. For an ideal conductor

$$F_{em}*(s) = \frac{-u_0*\sqrt{Pm}}{s\sqrt{Pm} + s(1 + \sqrt{Pm})^2} \qquad (9.6\text{-}36f)$$

which has an inverse Laplace transform of

$$f_{em}*(t*) = \frac{-u_0* Pm}{1 + \sqrt{Pm}} \, \text{erf} \, \frac{\sqrt{Pmt*}}{1 + \sqrt{Pm}} \qquad (9.6\text{-}36g)$$

The electromagnetic force on the ideal conducting half-space is plotted in Fig. 9.6-13. We can see that lowering the magnetic Prandtl number causes the duration of the transient to increase. This is consistent with the transient behavior of the magnetic field at the boundary between the fluid and the moving half-space. The plot of Fig. 9.6-13 is normalized so that it can be compared to Fig. 9.6-12.

9.7 TRANSIENT MHD FLOW IN A RECTANGULAR CHANNEL WITH CONDUCTING WALLS PERPENDICULAR TO THE APPLIED MAGNETIC FIELD

The most easily solved two-dimensional channel problem is given in Section 7.7, Fig. 7.7-1. In that channel the two conducting walls are perpendicular and the two insulating walls are parallel to the applied magnetic field. We now want to study the transient that occurs when the pressure gradient is applied to the configuration of Fig. 7.7-1; we assume that the applied magnetic field is steady and the incompressible, electrically conducting fluid filling the channel is at rest initially. At $t^* = 0$ a pressure gradient appears which accelerates the fluid. Here we assume the driving piston is at $x^* = -\infty$, as we did in Sections 9.3, 9.4, and 9.5.

The methods of solving for transient regimes are similar to the methods used in Chapter 7 except that now we must deal with the complexity introduced by time variation. The remarks of Section 7.4 apply, nevertheless, and the unsteady problems associated with channels a, b, d, g, and h of Fig. 7.4-1 can be solved with simple Fourier series solutions. Channel d is considered because of the very interesting results obtained in its steady solution.

We begin the solution by using the velocity and magnetic field given by Equations (9.3-9a) and (9.3-9b). The velocity must be zero along the boundaries at all values of time. The magnetic boundary conditions are given by (7.4-10a) and (7.4-10b). The four boundary conditions on velocity are (here $k = z_0/y_0$)

$$u^*(\pm 1, z^*, t^*) = u^*(y^*, \pm k, t^*) = 0 \qquad (9.7\text{-}1a)$$

and the four boundary conditions on the induced magnetic field are

$$\frac{\partial H^*}{\partial y^*}(\pm 1, z^*, t^*) = \frac{\partial H^*}{\partial y^*}(y^*, \pm k, t^*) = 0 \qquad (9.7\text{-}1b)$$

Two initial conditions are necessary for the solution. They are

$$u^*(y^*, z^*, 0) = H^*(y^*, z^*, 0) = 0 \qquad (9.7\text{-}1c)$$

Then the induced magnetic field $H^*(y^*, z^*, 0)$ is zero because no field can be induced until the fluid flows. In order to satisfy (9.7-1b), we assume

$$H^*(y^*, z^*, t^*) = \sum_{m=1,3,5\cdots}^{\infty} \sum_{n=1,3,5\cdots}^{\infty} h_{m,n}(t^*) \sin \frac{n\pi y^*}{2} \cos \frac{m\pi z^*}{2k} \quad (9.7\text{-}2)$$

and in order to satisfy (9.7-1a), we assume

$$u^*(y^*, z^*, t^*) = \sum_{m=1,3,5\cdots}^{\infty} \sum_{n=1,3,5\cdots}^{\infty} u_{m,n}(t^*) \cos \frac{n\pi y^*}{2} \cos \frac{m\pi z^*}{2k} \quad (9.7\text{-}3)$$

which are the forms of the solutions to the steady problem studied in Section 7.7. When the assumed solutions are substituted into (9.3-9a) and (9.3-9b), we have

$$\sum_{m=1,3,5\cdots}^{\infty} \sum_{n=1,3,5\cdots}^{\infty} \left[\frac{du_{m,n}(t^*)}{dt^*} + \frac{\pi^2}{4}\left(n^2 + \frac{m^2}{k^2}\right)u_{m,n}(t^*) - \frac{n\pi}{2} M h_{m,n}(t^*) \right]$$
$$\cdot \cos \frac{n\pi y^*}{2} \cos \frac{m\pi z^*}{2k} = -1 \quad (9.7\text{-}4)$$

and

$$Pm \frac{dh_{m,n}(t^*)}{dt^*} + \frac{\pi^2}{4}\left(n^2 + \frac{m^2}{k^2}\right)h_{m,n}(t^*) + \frac{n\pi}{2} M u_{m,n}(t^*) = 0 \quad (9.7\text{-}5)$$

The right-hand side of (9.7-4) can be expressed as

$$-1 = \frac{-16}{\pi^2} \sum_{m=1,3,5\cdots}^{\infty} \sum_{n=1,3,5\cdots}^{\infty} \frac{\sin \frac{n\pi}{2} \sin \frac{m\pi}{2} \cos \frac{n\pi y^*}{2} \cos \frac{m\pi z^*}{2k}}{mn} \quad (9.7\text{-}6)$$

This relationship allows the simplification of (9.7-4):

$$\frac{du_{m,n}(t^*)}{dt^*} + \frac{\pi^2}{4}\left(n^2 + \frac{m^2}{k^2}\right)u_{m,n}(t^*) - \frac{n\pi}{2} M h_{m,n}(t^*)$$
$$= -\frac{16}{\pi^2 mn} \sin \frac{n\pi}{2} \sin \frac{m\pi}{2} \quad (9.7\text{-}7)$$

To complete the solution, (9.7-5) and (9.7-7) must be solved simultaneously and subjected to the initial conditions of (9.7-1c). These equations can be easily combined to yield

$$\left\{ Pm \frac{d^2}{dt^{*2}} + \frac{(1+Pm)\pi^2}{4}\left(n^2 + \frac{m^2}{k^2}\right)\frac{d}{dt^*} + \left[\frac{\pi^2}{4}\left(n^2 + \frac{m^2}{k^2}\right) \right]^2 \right.$$
$$\left. + \frac{n^2\pi^2 M^2}{4} \right\} \begin{bmatrix} u_{m,n}(t^*) \\ h_{m,n}(t^*) \end{bmatrix} = \begin{bmatrix} \dfrac{-4}{mn}\left(n^2 + \dfrac{m^2}{k^2}\right)\sin\dfrac{n\pi}{2}\sin\dfrac{m\pi}{2} \\[2mm] \dfrac{8M}{\pi m}\sin\dfrac{n\pi}{2}\sin\dfrac{m\pi}{2} \end{bmatrix} \quad (9.7\text{-}8)$$

The solution to (9.7-8) for velocity is

$$u_{m,n}(t^*) = \frac{-16(n^2 + m^2/k^2)\sin(n\pi/2)\sin(m\pi/2)}{\pi^2 mn[(\pi^2/4)(n^2 + m^2/k^2)^2 + M^2 n^2]} + C_1 e^{p_1 t^*} + C_2 e^{p_2 t^*}$$

(9.7-9)

where p_1 and p_2 are given by

$$p_{1,2} = \frac{-(1+Pm)\frac{\pi^2}{4}\left(n^2+\frac{m^2}{k^2}\right) \pm \left\{\left[(1-P_m)\frac{\pi^2}{4}\left(n^2+\frac{m^2}{k^2}\right)\right]^2 - n^2\pi^2 PmM^2\right\}^{\frac{1}{2}}}{2Pm}$$

(9.7-10)

which can become complex when the proper value of Hartmann number is chosen. Since a complex value for $p_{1,2}$ implies the existence of an oscillatory transient, the conditions for the complex roots are studied. When

$$M^2 > \left[\frac{(1-Pm)\pi/4(n^2 + m^2/k^2)}{n\sqrt{Pm}}\right]^2$$

(9.7-11)

$p_{1,2}$ becomes complex. Then for $Pm = 1$, all the solutions are oscillatory but damped. For $Pm \gg 1$, this condition becomes

$$M^2 > \frac{Pm\pi^2}{16n^2}\left(n^2 + \frac{m^2}{k^2}\right)^2$$

or, for the lowest mode to be damped oscillatory, $M^2 > Pm(\pi^2/16)(1 + 1/k^2)^2$. If $Pm = 20$ and $k^2 = 10$, then M must exceed 0.966 if a damped oscillatory solution is to be obtained. In the terrestrial laboratory $Pm \simeq 10^{-7}$, in which case (9.7-11) yields $M > [\pi(n^2 + m^2/k^2)]/4n\sqrt{Pm}$. These results agree with those obtained in Section 9.5 and indicate how the width-to-height factor k influences the nature of the transient (height is measured in the y^* direction). Increasing k leads to oscillatory solutions at lower Hartmann numbers and decreasing k has the opposite effect. For liquid metals, only very large Hartmann numbers ($M > 2500$) yield damped oscillatory solutions.

The solution for $h_{m,n}(t^*)$ is obtained by solving (9.7-7) for $h_{m,n}(t^*)$ and substituting in values of $u_{m,n}(t^*)$ given by (9.7-9). The result is

$$h_{m,n}(t^*) = \frac{32M\sin(n\pi/2)\sin(m\pi/2)}{m\pi^3[(\pi^2/4)(n^2 + m^2/k^2)^2 + n^2M^2]}$$

$$+ \frac{2C_1}{Mn\pi}\left[p_1 + \frac{\pi^2}{4}\left(n^2 + \frac{m^2}{k^2}\right)\right]e^{p_1 t^*}$$

$$+ \frac{2C_2}{Mn\pi}\left[p_2 + \frac{\pi^2}{4}\left(n^2 + \frac{m^2}{k^2}\right)\right]e^{p_2 t^*}$$

(9.7-12)

Both the velocity and the induced magnetic field are initially zero and therefore $h_{m,n}(t^* = 0) = 0$ and $u_{m,n}(t^* = 0) = 0$. Hence C_1 and C_2 are found by solving the system

$$C_1 + C_2 = -u_{m,n}^{ss}$$

$$\alpha_1 C_1 + \alpha_2 C_2 = -h_{m,n}^{ss} \tag{9.7-13}$$

which follows from letting $t^* = 0$ in (9.7-9) and (9.7-12). Here the steady coefficients $u_{m,n}^{ss}$ and $h_{m,n}^{ss}$ are the first terms on the right side of (9.7-9) and (9.7-12), respectively;

$$\alpha_1 = (2/Mn\pi)[p_1 + (\pi^2/4)(n^2 + m^2/k^2)]$$

and

$$\alpha_2 = (2/Mn\pi)[p_2 + (\pi^2/4)(n^2 + m^2/k^2)]$$

The solutions to the system of (9.7-13) are

$$C_1 = \frac{h_{m,n}^{ss} - \alpha_2 u_{m,n}^{ss}}{p_2 - p_1} \cdot \frac{n\pi}{2} M \tag{9.7-14a}$$

and

$$C_2 = -\frac{h_{m,n}^{ss} - \alpha_1 u_{m,n}^{ss}}{p_2 - p_1} \cdot \frac{n\pi}{2} M \tag{9.7-14b}$$

The constants C_1 and C_2 are substituted into (9.7-9) and (9.7-12). Then $u_{m,n}(t^*)$, obtained from (9.7-9), is substituted into (9.7-3) to yield the final result for the velocity:

$$u^*(y^*, z^*, t^*) = \sum_{m=1,3,5\cdots}^{\infty} \sum_{n=1,3,5\cdots}^{\infty} (u_{m,n}^{ss} + C_1 e^{p_1 t^*} + C_2 e^{p_2 t^*})$$

$$\times \cos\frac{n\pi y^*}{2} \cos\frac{m\pi z^*}{2k} \tag{9.7-15a}$$

and similarly the induced magnetic field is given by

$$H^*(y^*, z^*, t^*) = \sum_{m=1,3,5\cdots}^{\infty} \sum_{n=1,3,5\cdots}^{\infty} (h_{m,n}^{ss} + \alpha_1 C_1 e^{p_1 t^*} + \alpha_2 C_2 e^{p_2 t^*})$$

$$\times \sin\frac{n\pi y^*}{2} \cos\frac{m\pi z^*}{2k} \tag{9.7-15b}$$

where

$$u_{m,n}^{ss} = \frac{-16(n^2 + m^2/k^2)\sin(n\pi/2)\sin(m\pi/2)}{\pi^2 mn[(\pi^2/4)(n^2 + m^2/k^2)^2 + M^2 n^2]} \qquad (9.7\text{-}15c)$$

$$h_{m,n}^{ss} = \frac{32M\sin(n\pi/2)\sin(m\pi/2)}{m\pi^3[(\pi^2/4)(n^2 + m^2/k^2)^2 + M^2 n^2]} = \frac{-2mMu_{m,n}^{ss}}{\pi(n^2 + m^2/k^2)}$$

$$(9.7\text{-}15d)$$

$$\alpha_1 = \frac{2}{Mn\pi}\left[p_1 + \frac{\pi^2}{4}\left(n^2 + \frac{m^2}{k^2}\right)\right] \qquad (9.7\text{-}15e)$$

$$\alpha_2 = \frac{2}{Mn\pi}\left[p_2 + \frac{\pi^2}{4}\left(n^2 + \frac{m^2}{k^2}\right)\right] \qquad (9.7\text{-}15f)$$

and $p_{1,2}$, C_1, and C_2 are obtained from (9.7-10), (9.7-14a), and (9.7-14b), respectively. The solutions given here are complicated but they obey the initial and boundary conditions and can be easily used for computations. The volumetric flow rate is defined as

$$Q^*(t^*) = 4\int_0^1\int_0^k u^*(y^*, z^*, t^*)\,dz^*\,dy^*$$

Hence the volumetric flow rate becomes

$$Q^*(t^*) = \frac{16k}{\pi^2}\sum_{m=1,3,5\cdots}^{\infty}\sum_{n=1,3,5\cdots}^{\infty}\frac{(u_{m,n}^{ss} + C_1 e^{p_1 t^*} + C_2 e^{p_2 t^*})}{mn}$$

$$\times \sin\frac{m\pi}{2}\sin\frac{n\pi}{2} \qquad (9.7\text{-}15g)$$

In the approximate solution, when $Pm \ll 1$, p_2, which is negative, becomes very large in magnitude since it varies as Pm^{-1}. p_1 becomes independent of Pm and is given by

$$p_1 = -\frac{n^2 M^2 + (\pi^2/4)(n^2 + m^2/k^2)^2}{n^2 + m^2/k^2} \qquad (9.7\text{-}16a)$$

and

$$C_1 = -u_{m,n}^{ss} \qquad (9.7\text{-}16b)$$

when $Pm \ll 1$. Therefore, the solutions for the velocity and the induced field become

$$u^*(y^*, z^*, t^*) = \sum_{m=1,3,5\cdots}^{\infty}\sum_{n=1,3,5\cdots}^{\infty}$$

$$\times \left\{1 - \exp\left[-\frac{n^2 M^2 + (\pi^2/4)(n^2 + m^2/k^2)^2}{n^2 + m^2/k^2}t^*\right]\right\}$$

$$\times u_{m,n}^{ss}\cos\frac{n\pi y^*}{2}\cos\frac{m\pi z^*}{2k} \qquad (9.7\text{-}17a)$$

and

$$H^*(y^*, z^*, t^*) = \sum_{m=1,3\,5\cdots}^{\infty} \sum_{n=1,3\,5\cdots}^{\infty}$$

$$\times \left\{ 1 - \exp\left[-\frac{n^2 M^2 + (\pi^2/4)(n^2 + m^2/k^2)^2}{n^2 + m^2/k^2} t^* \right] \right\}$$

$$\times u_{m,n}^{ss} \sin\frac{n\pi y^*}{2} \cos\frac{m\pi z^*}{2k} \qquad (9.7\text{-}17\text{b})$$

which are valid solutions for $Pm \ll 1$ provided the Hartmann number does not exceed $\pi(1 + k^{-2})/(4\sqrt{Pm})$. When the Hartmann number does exceed this value, oscillatory solutions exist, as was discussed earlier. The approximate solutions could have been obtained directly by setting Pm to zero in the original partial differential equations. However, that solution fails to disclose the possibility of oscillatory solutions.

It is interesting to examine the time constant for any particular mode of the transient. It is given by

$$\tau_{m,n}^* = \frac{n^2 + m^2/k^2}{n^2 M^2 + (\pi^2/4)(n^2 + m^2/k^2)^2}. \qquad (9.7\text{-}18)$$

Here we can see that $\tau_{m,n}^*$ decreases rapidly as M is increased, as was the case in the infinite channel of Section 9.5.

In Fig. 9.7-1 the ratio of the dimensionless flow rate at the dimensionless time t^* to the dimensionless flow rate at $t^* = \infty$ is plotted for the non-magnetohydrodynamic case. The same plot is given in Fig. 9.7-2 when $M = 5$ and $Pm = 10^{-7}$. Here it is clear that the magnetic field has caused the steady state to arrive more quickly than in the nonmagnetohydro-dynamic case. The curves of Figs. 9.7-1 and 9.7-2 exhibit time constants given approximately by (9.7-18). In the nonmagnetohydrodynamic regime the time constant increases monotonically with increasing values of k. In the magnetohydrodynamic case of Fig. 9.7-2 the behavior of the constant is not as simple; it is small for small values of k, then it increases to a maximum at $k \simeq 0.68$ and diminishes thereafter until it approaches a value of 0.036 as $k \to \infty$. Actually, for $k \geq 9$ the transients fall close to the curve of $k = \frac{1}{3}$ in Fig. 9.7-2. It is easy to show from Equation (9.7-18) that the maximum value of $\tau_{1,1}^*$ is given when

$$k = \left(\frac{2M}{\pi} - 1\right)^{-1/2} \qquad (9.7\text{-}19)$$

in which case $\tau_{1,1\max}^* = (\pi M)^{-1}$. The time constant does not increase further because the electromagnetic body force becomes stronger as k increases and dominates the viscous forces that tend to increase the time

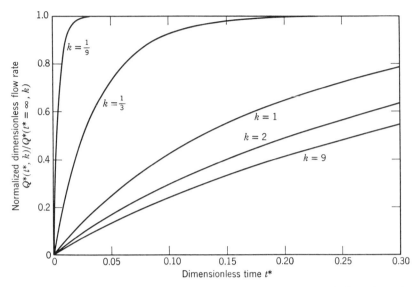

Figure 9.7-1 Normalized dimensionless flow rate versus dimensionless time for various values of k when $M = 0$.

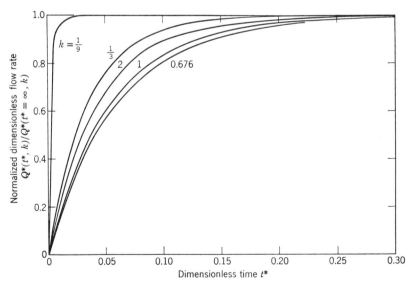

Figure 9.7-2 Normalized dimensionless flow rate versus dimensionless time for various values of k when $M = 5$ and $Pm = 10^{-7}$.

constant. The $k = \frac{1}{3}$ curve of Fig. 9.7-2 which approximates the $k = \infty$ case is valid for a one-dimensional channel between ideally conducting walls. This curve is the same as that for $M = 5$ in Fig. 9.5-5, where the infinite ideally conducting wall channel is considered.

9.8   THE DEVELOPMENT OF MHD POISEUILLE FLOW IN AN INFINITE CHANNEL

Introduction

In the situations examined so far, there have been no axial variations in any quantity except pressure. At the beginning of a channel or at the place where two channels converge, the flow is not fully developed and hence the velocity profile changes as a fluid particle goes downstream. The velocity and temperature profiles may change in various locations along the channel. The change can be caused by anything that is not the same for all stations upstream and downstream. For example, a post passing through the channel causes disturbances both upstream and downstream from the post location. If the applied magnetic field is not identical at all axial locations, the velocity profile exhibits axial variations. Locales where the profiles change with respect to position are called development regions. A standard development region is observed when a fluid with uniform velocity and temperature profiles enters a channel. The fluid must travel a certain distance from the entrance before the velocity and temperature profiles become fixed. This distance is designated as the development length. The section of the channel through which the fluid passes while it is readjusting its profile is termed the development or entrance region.

It is the purpose of this section to determine the velocity and temperature profiles in the entrance development region for laminar magnetohydrodynamic flow between parallel insulating plates with a constant transverse applied magnetic field.

Although many solutions are available for fully developed flows, only a few people have dealt with the development problem. Schlichting (1934), following the original Blasius (1908) technique for a flat plate, obtained the velocity profile for the entrance region by means of a matching process between an upstream and a downstream solution to the differential equations describing the system.

Bodoia and Osterle (1961) solved the entry problem by means of a finite-difference procedure and obtained results that differed from Schlichting's solution. Bodoia and Osterle had two explanations for this discrepancy. First, there was always a discontinuity introduced at the point where the upstream and downstream solutions are matched. Second, Schlichting's assumption, that the second derivative of the forward velocity with respect to the cross channel position variable was zero, was incorrect. The average discrepancy was around 5%.

Shercliff (1953, 1956) developed approximate methods for solving the magnetohydrodynamic entry problem in circular-pipe flow-meters but did not arrive at velocity profiles explicitly. Approximate and numerical solutions to the MHD development problem have been presented by several authors. Cess and Roidt (1962) adapted the Schlichting method to this problem, and Moffatt (1964) used a momentum integral method based upon the assumption of a Hartmann velocity profile. The solution discussed here follows the method of Bodoia and Osterle and is the one used by Shohet, Osterle, and Young (1962). The results of Shohet et al. are complemented by a similar numerical method used by Hwang and Fan (1963).

This section deals with the velocity and temperature profiles in the entrance region for laminar magnetohydrodynamic flow. The applied magnetic field is constant and uniform. The velocity and temperature profiles are initially flat upon entering the channel. The equations of this system are placed in finite difference form and solved numerically for various Hartmann, Prandtl, and Eckert numbers and values of electric field.

Representation of the Problem

The parallel plate is shown in Fig. 9.8-1. The channel, of height $2a$ and width d, has an arbitrary length, but one that must be long compared with

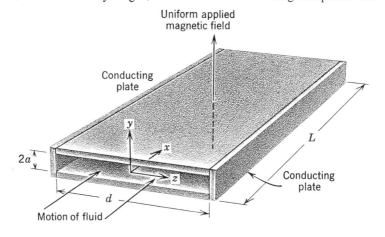

Figure 9.8-1   The development region.

the development length and the height. The fluid enters the channel on the left in this figure. A coordinate system is placed on the channel with the origin at the center of the channel at the entrance. The variable y increases in an upward direction, and the variable z increases perpendicularly to both x and y so as to form a right-handed coordinate system. The velocity and temperature profiles develop toward the direction of increasing x.

The external magnetic field is applied in the positive y direction from the bottom to the top of the channel.

Two perfectly conducting plates are then placed in planes parallel to the xy plane at distances of $(\frac{1}{2})d$ and $(-\frac{1}{2})d$ from the origin. These plates enclose the outside of the channel, and, if d is sufficiently large they will not affect the velocity and temperature profile development at the middle of the channel, as was demonstrated in Chapter 7.

The channel walls, which are at a distance of a and $-a$ from the origin, will affect the profile development. These walls may be at any constant temperature not necessarily that of the fluid.

Basic Equations

The equations of incompressible MHD channel flow describe this problem. In contrast to the fully developed flows earlier, in this problem the derivatives with respect to x are not zero, the y component of velocity is not zero, and the convective acceleration terms must not be neglected. Hence the fluid-dynamic continuity equation is needed to relate the x and y components of velocity. Since the temperature of the fluid is not held constant, an energy equation is necessary to relate the temperature of the fluid to viscous and Joulean dissipation. These equations are combined with Ohm's law and Maxwell's $\nabla \times \mathbf{H} = \mathbf{J}$ equation to obtain a solution to the development problem.

We will assume that there are no applied (external) magnetic fields other than one in the y direction and that there will be no variation of any quantities and no motion in the z direction at any time. We will regard the problem as time independent and the fluid as incompressible, non-magnetic, in laminar flow, and no fluid loss through the external boundaries.

All electrical, mechanical, and thermal coefficients determined by the gross properties of the fluid, walls, etc., will be considered constant. The usual dissipation, velocity, and thermal boundary-layer assumptions will be made.

The magnetic Reynolds number in terms of the entry length is assumed to be small, thus allowing us to keep the magnetic field in the y direction uniform and much larger than any fields in the other coordinate directions.

The equations resulting from the preceding assumptions are as follows:

$$\frac{\partial u}{\partial x} + \frac{\partial v}{\partial y} = 0 \tag{9.8-1}$$

$$\rho\left(u\frac{\partial u}{\partial x} + v\frac{\partial u}{\partial y}\right) = -\frac{\partial p}{\partial x} + \mu_f\frac{\partial^2 u}{\partial y^2} - \sigma E_z B_y - \sigma u B_y^2 \tag{9.8-2}$$

$$\rho c_P\left(u\frac{\partial T}{\partial x} + v\frac{\partial T}{\partial y}\right) = \kappa_T\frac{\partial^2 T}{\partial y^2} + \frac{J_z^2}{\sigma} + \mu_f\left(\frac{\partial u}{\partial y}\right)^2 \tag{9.8-3}$$

where p is the pressure, J the current density, σ the electrical conductivity, κ_T the thermal conductivity, ρ the mass density, μ_f the viscosity, c_P the specific heat, and T the temperature.

From the Maxwell equation relating the curl of the electric field to the time rate of change of the magnetic field, it can be shown that E_z does not vary with x and y and so must be a constant. It can be shown that E_y becomes zero because $J_y = 0$ and $B_z = 0$. The Maxwell equation $\nabla \cdot \mathbf{B} = 0$ is useful for finding out how much the applied magnetic field is perturbed by the development regime.

A set of dimensionless variables may now be introduced as follows:

$$U = \frac{u}{u_0} \qquad X = \frac{\mu_f x}{a^2 \rho u_0} \qquad M = B_y a\sqrt{\frac{\sigma}{\mu_f}}$$

$$V = \frac{a\rho v}{\mu_f} \qquad Y = \frac{y}{a} \qquad \text{Pr} = \frac{\mu c_P}{\kappa_T} \tag{9.8-4}$$

$$\Theta = \frac{T - T_{\text{in}}}{T_w - T_{\text{in}}} \qquad P = \frac{p}{\rho u_0^2} \qquad \text{Ek} = \frac{u_0^2}{c_P(T_w - T_{\text{in}})}$$

where T_w is the wall temperature, T_{in} the entrance temperature, and M, Pr, Ek are the Hartmann, Prandtl, and Eckert numbers, respectively.

The determining equations are then:

$$U\frac{\partial U}{\partial X} + V\frac{\partial U}{\partial Y} = -\frac{\partial P}{\partial X} + \frac{\partial^2 U}{\partial Y^2} - M^2 U + V_T^* M^2 \tag{9.8-5}$$

$$\frac{\partial U}{\partial X} + \frac{\partial V}{\partial Y} = 0 \tag{9.8-6}$$

$$U\frac{\partial \Theta}{\partial X} + V\frac{\partial \Theta}{\partial Y} = \frac{1}{\text{Pr}}\frac{\partial^2 \Theta}{\partial Y^2} + \text{Ek}\left(\frac{\partial V}{\partial Y}\right)^2 + \text{Ek}(U^2 - 2V_T^* U + V_T^{*2})M^2 \tag{9.8-7}$$

$$V_T^* = -\frac{E_z}{B_y u_0} = -E_z^*$$

We should note at this point that we assume that the entrance values of velocity and temperature are constant for $X < 0$.

Finite-Difference Solution

Following the method of Bodoia and Osterle, we introduce a mesh network across the range of the problem (see Fig. 9.8-2). The finite-difference approximations to the derivatives in (9.8-5), (9.8-6), and (9.8-7) are shown as follows:

Momentum Equation.

$$\frac{\partial U}{\partial X} = \frac{U(j+1, k) - U(j, k)}{\Delta X} \qquad \frac{\partial P}{\partial X} = \frac{P(j+1) - P(j)}{\Delta X}$$

$$\frac{\partial U}{\partial Y} = \frac{U(j+1, k+1) - U(j+1, k-1)}{2\,\Delta Y}$$

$$\frac{\partial^2 U}{\partial Y^2} = \frac{U(j+1, k+1) - 2U(j+1, k) + U(j+1, k-1)}{(\Delta Y)^2}$$

Energy Equation.

$$\frac{\partial \Theta}{\partial X} = \frac{\Theta(j+1, k) - \Theta(j, k)}{\Delta X}$$

$$\frac{\partial \Theta}{\partial Y} = \frac{\Theta(j+1, k+1) - \Theta(k+1, j-1)}{2\,\Delta Y}$$

$$\frac{\partial^2 \Theta}{\partial Y^2} = \frac{\Theta(j+1, k+1) - 2\Theta(j+1, k) + \Theta(j+1, k-1)}{(\Delta Y)^2}$$

Continuity Equation.

$$\frac{\partial U}{\partial X} = \frac{U(j+1, k+1) + U(j+1, k)}{2\,\Delta X} - \frac{U(j, k+1) + U(j, k)}{2\,\Delta X}$$

$$\frac{\partial V}{\partial Y} = \frac{V(j+1, k+1) - V(j+1, k)}{\Delta Y}$$

The finite-difference approximations are not perfectly symmetrical, nor are they of the same form in all equations. We do this in order to insure stability of the computer solution and to enable the equations to be uncoupled from each other. All of these forms approach the real derivative if a small mesh spacing is used.

From the last three expressions, we can see that (9.8-7) is the only expression involving the temperatures and therefore may be solved separately from (9.8-5) and (9.8-6). This is done by determining an additional equation involving only unknowns that appear in (9.8-5) and then

440   THE ELECTROMAGNETODYNAMICS OF FLUIDS

uncoupling Equation (9.8-7) from (9.8-6). This additional equation, or equation of constraint, may be obtained by solving (9.8-6) to obtain the velocity at the wall, $V(j + 1, N + 1)$, which is zero, in terms of the center line velocity $V(j + 1, 0)$, which is also zero. The resulting equation is

$$U(j + 1, 0) + 2\sum_{k=1}^{N} U(j + 1, k) = U(j, 0) + 2\sum_{k=1}^{N} U(j, k) \quad (9.8\text{-}8)$$

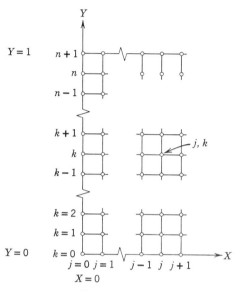

Figure 9.8-2   Mesh network.

A set of simultaneous equations of (9.8-5) together with (9.8-8) may be written. One equation can be formed about each mesh point in a column as shown:

$$U(j + 1, 0) + 2U(j + 1, 1) + 2U(j + 1, 2) + \cdots$$

$$= U(j, 0) + 2\sum_{k=1}^{N} U(j, k)$$

$$\beta_0 U(j + 1, 0) + (\alpha_0 + \gamma_0)U(j + 1, 1) + \xi P(j + 1) = \phi_0$$

$$\alpha_1 U(j + 1, 0) + \beta_1 U(j + 1, 1) + \gamma_1 U(j + 1, 2) + \xi P(j + 1) = \phi_1$$

$$\alpha_2 U(j + 1, 1) + \beta_2 U(j + 1, 2) + \gamma_2 U(j + 1, 3) + \xi P(j + 1) = \phi_2$$

$$\cdot$$
$$\cdot$$
$$\cdot$$

$$\alpha_N U(j + 1, N - 1) + \beta_N U(j + 1, N) + \xi P(j + 1) = \phi_N$$

where

$$\alpha_k = \left[(\Delta Y)^{-2} + \frac{V(j, k)}{2\,\Delta Y}\right] \qquad \gamma_k = \left[(\Delta Y)^{-2} - \frac{V(j, k)}{2\,\Delta Y}\right]$$

$$\beta_k = -\left[2(\Delta Y)^{-2} + \frac{U(j, k)}{\Delta X} + M^2\right] \qquad \xi = -\frac{1}{\Delta X}$$

$$\phi_k = -\left\{\frac{P(j) + [U(j, k)]^2}{\Delta X} + V_T{}^*M^2\right\}$$

This set of equations can be solved either simultaneously or by means of matrix inversion and multiplication. Substitution of the newly found axial velocities (U's) together with those in the preceding column into Equation (9.8-6) determines the new transverse velocities (V's).

The set of velocities are now placed into a set of finite-difference equations written about each mesh point in a column for (9.8-7):

$$\bar{\beta}_0\Theta(j + 1, 0) + (\bar{\alpha}_0 + \bar{\gamma}_0)\Theta(j + 1, 1) = \bar{\phi}_0$$

$$\bar{\alpha}_1\Theta(j + 1, 0) + \bar{\beta}_1\Theta(j + 1, 1) + \bar{\gamma}_1\Theta(j + 1, 2) = \bar{\phi}_1$$

$$\bar{\alpha}_2\Theta(j + 1, 1) + \bar{\beta}_2\Theta(j + 1, 2) + \bar{\gamma}_2\Theta(j + 1, 3) = \bar{\phi}_2$$

$$\cdot$$
$$\cdot$$
$$\cdot$$

$$\bar{\alpha}_N\Theta(j + 1, N - 1) + \bar{\beta}_N\Theta(j + 1, N) = \bar{\phi}_N - \bar{\gamma}_N$$

where

$$\bar{\alpha}_k = \left[\frac{1}{\Pr(\Delta Y)^2} + \frac{V(j, k)}{2\,\Delta Y}\right]$$

$$\bar{\gamma}_k = \left[\frac{1}{\Pr(\Delta Y)^2} - \frac{V(j, k)}{2\,\Delta Y}\right]$$

$$\bar{\beta}_k = -\left[\frac{2}{\Pr(\Delta Y)^2} + \frac{U(j, k)}{\Delta X}\right]$$

$$\bar{\phi}_k = -\left\{\frac{\Theta(j, k)U(j, k)}{\Delta X} + \text{Ek } M^2[U(j + 1, k) - V_T{}^*]^2\right.$$

$$\left. + \text{Ek}\left[\frac{U(j + 1, k + 1) - U(j + 1, k - 1)}{2\,\Delta Y}\right]^2\right\}$$

The same techniques used to solve the momentum equation may be used to solve this set of equations.

Results and Conclusions

In Figs. 9.8-3a, b, and c the dimensionless velocity versus the dimensionless distance from the entrance of the channel is plotted at various stations across the channel for $M = 0$, 4, and 9, and it is clear that the Hartmann number greatly influences the development of MHD Poiseuille flow. The value of the electric field does not affect the velocity development, since the component of the electromagnetic body force due to the electric field is constant across the channel. Table 9.8-1 presents the development lengths

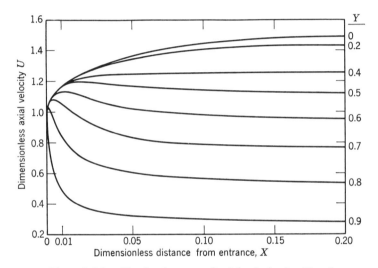

Figure 9.8-3a   The development of axial velocity for $M = 0$.

obtained by various researchers. Here the development length is taken as the value of X at which the center line velocity (for $Y = 0$) equals 99% of the fully developed center line velocity.

The results of Shohet et al. can be fitted with the equation

$$X_d = 0.267e^{-M/3} \tag{9.8-9}$$

in the region $2 \leq M \leq 9$. Here X_d is the length (measured from the entrance) the fluid must travel along the xz plane located at $y = 0$ before it attains 99% of its fully developed velocity. Hence the applied transverse magnetic field shortens the development length just as it shortened the transients of Sections 9.5 and 9.7. However, the effect of M is not as strong in the development problem as it is in the transient phenomena.

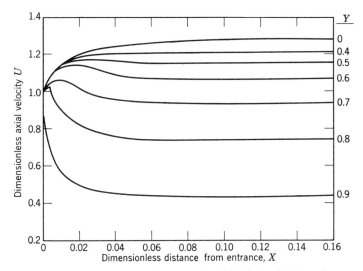

Figure 9.8-3b   The development of axial velocity for $M = 4$.

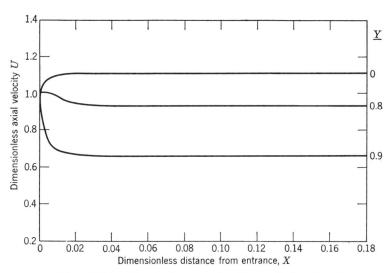

Figure 9.8-3c   The development of axial velocity for $M = 9$.

Table 9.8-1

Hartmann Number M	Development Length X	Investigators
0	0.16	Schlichting
0	0.176	Bodoia and Osterle
0	0.182	Roidt and Cess
0	0.169	Hwang and Fan
2	0.137	Shohet, Osterle, and Young
4	0.0668	Roidt and Cess
4	0.07	Shohet, Osterle, and Young
4	0.0752	Hwang and Fan
7	0.025	Shohet, Osterle, and Young
9	0.0129	Shohet, Osterle, and Young

Figure 9.8-4 shows temperature development for $M = 4$, $Pr = 0.1$, $Ek = 1.0$, and $V_T{}^* = 0$. Since there are many parameters to vary in the consideration of temperature development, it is necessary to inspect many combinations of them. The results of such a procedure are given in Table 9.8-2. It is interesting to notice in Fig. 9.8-4 that for $X < 0.038$ the fluid is cooler than the walls and heat flows toward the center of the channel from the walls. Around $X = 0.038$, the temperature gradient loses its y component. At $X = 0.038$, heat flows from the fully developed

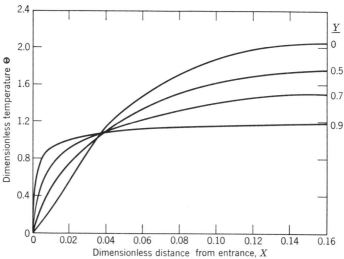

Figure 9.8-4   Temperature development for $M = 4.0$, $Pr = 0.1$, $Ek = 1.0$, and $V_T{}^* = 0$.

Table 9.8-2

Effects on velocity profile due to increase in parameters

Parameter	Effects
Hartmann number	Flattens velocity profile
	Decreases development length
	Increases pressure gradient
	Increases temperature
Electric field	No effect on velocity profile
	Increases pressure gradient
	Increases temperature
Prandtl number	Increases temperature
Eckert number	Increases temperature

region toward the development region. For $X > 0.038$, heat flows toward the walls and toward the development region.

The electric field does affect the pressure gradient. Figure 9.8-5 shows the pressure versus axial distance for a constant Hartmann number M with various values of V_T^*. The initial drop in pressure occurs regardless of the mode of operation of the device, due to the presence of high wall shear caused by the large velocity gradients at the walls.

Table 9.8-2 summarizes the effects upon the velocity profile, pressure, and temperature in the device for an increase in each essential parameter.

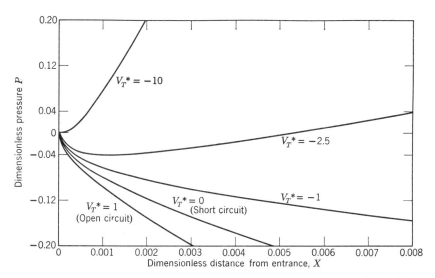

Figure 9.8-5 Pressure development with $M = 4.0$, $V_T^* = 1, 0, -1, -2.5, -10$.

PROBLEMS

1. Show that the magnitude of the time rate of change of total current in either of the half-spaces of Fig. 9.2-1 is given by

$$\frac{dI(t)}{dt} = \frac{VB_0}{\mu_0 y_0} e^{(1+\sqrt{\sigma^*})^2(\eta_1 t/y_0^2)} \operatorname{erfc}\left[(1 + \sqrt{\sigma^*})\sqrt{\frac{t\eta_1}{y_0^2}}\right]$$

where

$$\sigma^* = \frac{\sigma_1}{\sigma_3}$$

2. Derive equations in circular cylindrical coordinates corresponding to (9.3-11a) and (9.3-11b).

3. An electrically conducting fluid fills the space between two insulators located in xz planes. The plates are oscillating sinusoidally (in phase) in the x direction. A uniform direct-current magnetic field is applied in the y direction. Electrodes (in the xy plane) located at $\pm z_0$ are provided so that electrical power can be extracted. Here $z_0 \gg y_0$, where y_0 is the distance between the insulating walls. The problem to be solved is like the one in Section 9.4, except that here the motion is caused by the moving walls. Calculate the velocity profile and the steady alternating current flowing in the electrical load. Find the internal impedance of this generator.

4. In Section 9.4 oscillations in a one-dimensional channel were considered. Rework that problem for a two-dimensional insulating channel similar to the channel of Section 7.5.†

5. Rework Problem 3 for a two-dimensional channel with insulating walls.†

6. Rework Section 9.4 for a channel with ideal conducting walls.

7. Work the transient build-up of fluid flow in the cylindrical configuration of Section 7.8 when (1) the magnetic Prandtl number Pm is unity and (2) $Pm \ll 1$.†

8. (a) A semi-infinite half-space is filled with viscous, electrically conducting fluid. The configuration is almost the limiting case of Fig. 9.6-2 when x^*, y^*, and z^* dimensions become very large. However, in this problem the moving plate is absent and hence there is a free surface at $y^* = 0$. The fluid is driven by a step function of current which is suddenly passed through the fluid from one electrode to the other in the z^* direction, as shown in Fig. P9.8-1. Before the current step is obtained from the current source, a constant, uniform magnetic field is assumed to exist in the y^* direction. Show that for Pm (using the notation of Section 9.6) the fluid velocity is given by

$$u^*(t^*, y^*) = \frac{\mathscr{I}^*}{2}\left[-\operatorname{erfc}\left(\frac{y^* + t^*}{2\sqrt{t^*}}\right) + \operatorname{erfc}\left(\frac{y^* - t^*}{2\sqrt{t^*}}\right)\right]$$

where $\mathscr{I}^*$ is the dimensionless applied current per unit width of the x direction. Here $\mathscr{I}^* = \mathscr{I}/H_0$. (*Hint:* The inverse Laplace transforms used in Section 9.6 may be useful.) (b) Investigate the limiting case of this problem in which $\nu = \eta = 0$. Sketch your results in the form of Fig. 9.6-5, clearly designating Alfvén waves, switch-on shocks, and vorticity and current sheets. (c) In the general case where $Pm \neq 1$, it is difficult to find the velocity distribution as

† For hints, see Uflyland, 1962.

a function of time. However, at $y^* = 0$ it is fairly easy to find a solution. Show that

$$u^*(t^*, y^* = 0) = \mathscr{I}^* \, \mathrm{erf} \, \frac{\sqrt{Pmt^*}}{1 + \sqrt{Pm}}$$

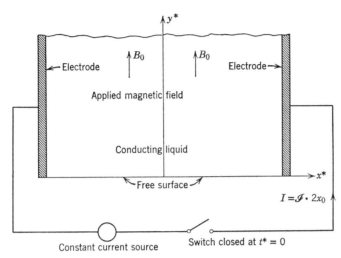

Figure P9.8-1   The free surface Rayleigh problem of Problem 8.

9. Mercury flows in a 3-cm wide channel at an average speed of 1 cm/sec. The pipe is in a transverse magnetic field of 100 gauss. What is the development length in this case?

10. Rework the problem of Section 9.7-5 for a pipe circular cross section.

11. How would you determine the open circuit voltage in the development channel of Section 9.8? *Hint:* The value of E_z^* at open circuit $= 1$; you must integrate the current throughout the entire channel and set the total external current to zero in order to find V_{oc}. If the channel is very long can you use the solutions to the Hartmann problem directly for the electrical characteristics? This procedure would be valid if the fully developed region were much longer than the development length. Does the open circuit voltage depend on the velocity profile, or just the flow rate?

REFERENCES

Birkhoff, G., *Hydrodynamics*, Revised ed., Princeton University Press, 1960.

Blasius, H., Grenzschichten in Flüssigkeiten mit kleiner Reibung, *Z. Math. u. Phys.*, **56**, p. 1, 1908. Also *NACA Tech. Memo.* No. 1256.

Bodoia, J. R., and J. F. Osterle, Finite Difference Analysis of Plane Poiseuille and Couette Flow Developments, *Appl. Sci. Research*, **A10**, p. 265, 1961.

Bryson, A. E., and J. Rosciszewski, Influence of Viscosity, Fluid Conductivity, and Wall Conductivity in the Magnetohydrodynamic Rayleigh Problem, *Phys. Fluids*, **5**, p. 175, 1962.

Carrier, G. F., and H. P. Greenspan, The Time-Dependent Magnetohydrodynamic Flow Past a Flat Plate, *J. Fluid Mech.*, **7**, p. 22, 1960.

Causse, Rene, Étienne Crausse, Yves Poirier, and Charles Vivès, Magnetohydrodynamique. Étude expérimentale des oscillations forcées sinusoïdales d'un liquide électroconducteur dans un tube rectiligne de section rectangulaire en présence d'un champ magnétique transversal, *C. R. Acad. Sc.*, Paris, **258**, Group 2, pp. 1399–1401, 1964.

Chang, C. C., and J. T. Yen, Rayleigh's Problem in Magnetohydrodynamics, *Phys. Fluids*, **2**, pp. 393–403, 1959.

Chekmarev, I. B., Nonstationary Flow of a Conducting Fluid in a Flat Tube in the Presence of a Transverse Magnetic Field, *Soviet Phys.—Tech. Phys.*, **5**, pp. 313–319, 1960.

Churchill, R. V., *Operational Mathematics*, McGraw-Hill, New York, 1958.

Crausse, Étienne, Yves Poirier, and Charles Vivès, Magnetohydrodynamique. Étude théorique des oscillations forcées sinusoïdales entre plans parallèles indéfinis d'un liquide électroconducteur, en présence d'un champ magnétique transversal, *C. R. Acad. Sc.*, Paris, **258**, Group 2, pp. 809–812, 1964.

Dix, D. M., The Magnetohydrodynamic Flow Past a Non-Conducting Flat Plate in the Presence of a Transverse Magnetic Field, *J. Fluid Mech.*, **15**, pp. 449–476, 1963.

Hwang, C. L., and L. T. Fan, Finite Difference Analysis of Laminar Magneto-Hydrodynamic Flow in Entrance Region of Flat Rectangular Duct, *Appl. Sci. Research* **10B**, p. 329, 1963.

Ludford, G. S. S., Rayleigh's Problem in Hydromagnetics: The Impulse Motion of a Pole-Piece, *Arch. Rat. Mech. Anal.*, **3**, pp. 14–27, 1959.

Moffatt, W. C., An Analysis of MHD Channel Entrance Flows Using the Momentum Integral Method, Tech. Rep. MIT-35-P, Project SQUID, University of Virginia, April, 1964.

Lord Rayleigh, On the Motion of Solid Bodies through Viscous Liquid, *Phil. Mag.*, Series VI, **21**, pp. 697–711, 1911.

Regirer, S. A., *Inzh.-Fiz. Zh.*, **2**, No. 8, p. 43, 1959.

Roidt, M., and R. D. Cess, An Approximate Analysis of Laminar Magnetohydrodynamic Flow in the Entrance Region of a Flat Duet, *Trans. ASME, J. Appl. Mech.*, Series E, **84**, p. 171, 1962.

Rossow, V. J., On Flow of Electrically Conducting Fluids over a Flat Plate in the Presence of a Transverse Magnetic Field, Natl. Advisory Comm. Aeronaut. Tech. Note No. 3971, 1957.

Schlichting, H., Laminare Kanaleinlaufströmung, *Z. angew. Math. u. Mech.*, **14**, p. 368, 1934.

Schlichting, H., *Boundary Layer Theory*, McGraw-Hill, New York, 1955.

Shair, F. H., The Transient Interaction of a Transverse Magnetic Field with Fluid in Couette Flow, NASA Technical Information Series N63-13559, Code 3, 1963.

Shercliff, J. A., Steady Motion of Conducting Fluids in Pipes under Transverse Magnetic Fields, *Proc. Cambridge Phil Soc.*, **49**, p. 136, 1953.

Shercliff, J. A., A Flow of Conducting Fluids in Circular Pipes under Transverse Magnetic Fields, *J. Fluid Mech.*, **1**, p. 644, 1956.

Shohet, J. L., J. F. Osterle, and F. J. Young, Velocity and Temperature Profiles for Laminar Magnetohydrodynamic Flow in the Entrance Region of a Plane Channel, *Phys. Fluids*, **5**, p. 545, 1962.

Stanišić, M. M., B. H. Fetz, H. P. Mickelson, Jr., and F. M. Czumak, On the Flow of a Hydromagnetic Fluid between Two Oscillating Flat Plates, *J. Aerospace Sciences*, **29**, pp. 116–117, 1962.

Stewartson, K., Motion of Bodies through Conducting Fluids, *Rev. Modern Phys.*, **32,** No. 4, p. 855, 1960.

Uflyand, Ya. S., Certain Questions in the Unsteady Flow of a Conducting Fluid through a Tube of Constant Cross Section in a Transverse Magnetic Field, *Soviet Phys.—Tech. Phys.*, **6,** pp. 1031–1038, 1962.

Young, F. J., and H. L. Schenk, Critical Alternating Currents in Superconductors, *J. Appl. Phys.*, **35,** Part 2, pp. 980–981, 1964.

Young, F. J., and W. T. Rouleau, Pressure Surges in Magnetoviscous Flow, *J. Basic Engineering*, **87,** pp. 478–483, 1965.

10

Discontinuities and Shock Waves

10.1 INTRODUCTION

Just as in ordinary fluid mechanics, various types of discontinuities can occur in magnetohydrodynamic flow, but there are more types of discontinuities in magnetohydrodynamics than in ordinary gas dynamics. There are two general classes of discontinuities in ordinary gas dynamics, the tangential discontinuity and the shock wave. In MHD both classes appear and in addition a third, the rotational discontinuity.

A tangential discontinuity is characterized by the fact that there is no flux of fluid through it; the shock wave does have a flux of fluid through its surface, that is, a normal component of fluid velocity exists.

In ordinary gas dynamics there are two types of tangential discontinuities. One, called a contact surface, has different values of density and temperature (but the same pressure) across the interface. The tangential velocity (tangent to the interface) is continuous across the interface. Such contact surfaces occur, for example, at the trailing edge of a supersonic airfoil. The interface between two immiscible fluids is a simple example of a contact surface. The second type of tangential discontinuity allows the tangential velocity to be discontinuous across the interface. This discontinuity is an unstable situation and generates a turbulent layer that broadens downstream. The vortex sheet behind a subsonic airfoil is an example of this type of discontinuity. Both types diffuse and weaken because of the dissipative effects in the fluid.

In ordinary gas dynamics there is no basic difference between a normal shock and an oblique shock. The normal components of velocity in an oblique shock satisfy the normal shock relationships, and the tangential velocity components are continuous.

In MHD there can exist three types of discontinuities, the two types of tangential discontinuities which occur in ordinary gas dynamics and in addition a new type called a rotational discontinuity. This rotational discontinuity is characterized by a rotation of the tangential component of both the magnetic field and the fluid velocity across the interface, but the fluid properties remain unchanged across it. The rotational discontinuity propagates with the Alfvén speed (in terms of the normal magnetic field) so that there is a flux of fluid through this type of discontinuity.

In MHD flow we can classify shock waves as normal and oblique. A normal MHD shock is one in which the magnetic field is always tangent to the shock surface but the fluid velocity may or may not be normal to the shock surface. The tangential component of velocity is continuous through the shock in a normal MHD shock, so that the normal MHD shock includes both the ordinary gas dynamic normal and oblique shocks. (The rotational discontinuity is not a special case of the MHD normal shock since a normal component of magnetic field must be present.)

The more general oblique MHD shock is one in which both normal and tangential components of the magnetic field exist. The velocity may or may not have tangential components and, in fact, the tangential velocity is not necessarily continuous through the shock. In the oblique MHD shock the magnetic field and velocity may change magnitude and direction through the shock. The general mathematical analysis of the oblique shock configuration yields as special case solutions all the possible MHD discontinuities and MHD shocks as well as the results of ordinary gas dynamics.

If the magnetic field is normal to the shock (and no tangential component of magnetic field exists), no interaction takes place and the ordinary gas dynamic relationships (for a normal or oblique shock) hold. A rotational discontinuity may propagate under such conditions, and a transverse component of magnetic field is generated behind the shock. However, such a discontinuity will broaden and die out unless the electrical conductivity is infinite.

As we will see, there are three distinct types of oblique MHD shocks (in addition to the three discontinuities), which we identify as fast, intermediate, and slow. There are four subtypes of intermediate waves, so that in all there are six distinct possibilities for the general normal MHD shock. For any given set of imposed physical conditions only certain shock solutions are admissible. A rather complete classification of MHD shocks has been made by Bazer and Ericson (1959) and Shercliff (1960).

We now discuss in detail the quantitative character of these MHD shocks.

10.2   NORMAL MHD SHOCKS

We begin our study with a simple special case, the normal MHD shock, and in the next section we will take up the general MHD shock problem of which the analysis in this section is a special case. The normal MHD shock is one in which the magnetic field, on both sides of the shock, is parallel to the shock surface. The velocity may be oblique, but the tangential component is continuous through the shock and uncoupled from the other equations. The normal MHD shock, then, is a generalization of the ordinary gas dynamic oblique shock with a tangential magnetic field.

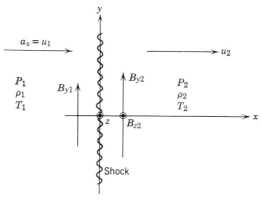

Figure 10.2-1   The normal shock shown at rest in the shock frame of reference. The upstream quantities are denoted as ( )₁ and the downstream quantities as ( )₂.

Figure 10.2-1 shows the physical configuration in a frame of reference stationary with respect to the shock. The subscript $(\ )_1$ indicates upstream quantities, and the subscript $(\ )_2$ indicates downstream quantities. The coordinates system x, y, z is attached to the shock and indicates the shock wave frame of reference. The upstream magnetic field is taken as B_{y1} and the downstream field is B_{y2}. (We will show that B_z is zero downstream if we assume it zero upstream, as we do by orienting our coordinate system appropriately.) The x component of upstream fluid velocity u_1 is denoted as a_s, the shock propagation velocity; the x component of fluid velocity downstream is u_2. In an absolute frame of reference at rest with respect to the gas upstream, the shock propagates into the still gas with velocity a_s, and the gas behind the shock wave flows (in the same direction as the shock) propagates with velocity $(a_s - u_2)$. As the shock becomes weaker and approaches a sonic wave, $(a_s - u_2)$ becomes zero. Figure 10.2-2 shows such a moving shock.

We do not distinguish between **B** in the shock frame of reference and in the laboratory frame of reference since we assume $|V|^2/c^2 \ll 1$ and use the MHD approximations. However, we can if we wish always work in the shock frame of reference, without making such assumptions, and later transform to any other frame of reference. We begin in the shock frame then and look for the property changes across the shock and the possible values of shock velocity a_s.

Referring to Fig. 10.2-1, we will write the momentum, continuity, energy, and magnetic transport equations in differential form and integrate

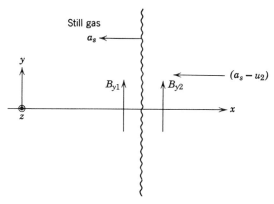

Figure 10.2-2   The absolute frame of reference showing the normal shock moving with speed a_s into still gas.

them through the shock, obtaining relationships between the properties before $(\ )_1$ and after $(\ )_2$ the shock. Alternatively, we could write control volume equations on a thin slab of volume enclosing the shock wave and make use of the electromagnetic stress tensor. For the sake of illumination we will derive the equations by this latter method in a later section (10.6).

We will use the shorthand notation $[Q]$ to mean $Q_2 - Q_1$ in order to express conservation equations across the shock.

Continuity is

$$\frac{\partial}{\partial x}(\rho u) = 0 \qquad (10.2\text{-}1)$$

which when integrated between states 1 and 2 becomes

$$\rho_1 a_s = \rho_2 u_2 = m \qquad (10.2\text{-}2)$$

or, in the canonical form,

$$[\rho u] = 0 \qquad (10.2\text{-}3)$$

Here m stand for the mass flow rate, a constant.

The x component of motion is (see Equation 6.4-9)

$$\rho u \frac{\partial u}{\partial x} = -\frac{\partial P}{\partial x} + (\tfrac{4}{3}\mu_f + \zeta)\frac{\partial^2 u}{\partial x^2} - \frac{1}{2\mu}\frac{\partial}{\partial x}(B_y{}^2) \tag{10.2-4}$$

which when integrated becomes

$$\left[\rho u^2 + P + \frac{1}{2\mu}B_y{}^2\right] = 0 \tag{10.2-5}$$

(B_{z2} will be zero since B_{z1} is taken as zero and B_{z2} must be zero to satisfy the magnetic transport equations below.) The y and z momentum equations are uncoupled and yield no useful information. Hence v and w are continuous through the shock wave and do not enter into the formulation.

It is convenient to use the magnetic transport equation in order to eliminate the necessity of introducing the full Maxwell equations. From (6.4-11),

$$0 = \eta \frac{\partial^2 B_y}{\partial x^2} - u \frac{\partial B_y}{\partial x} - B_y \frac{\partial u}{\partial x} \tag{10.2-6}$$

which integrates to

$$[uB_y] = 0 \tag{10.2-7}$$

since

$$\int_1^2 \frac{\partial^2 B_y}{\partial x^2} = \frac{\partial B_y}{\partial x}\bigg|_1^2 = 0$$

(B_y is constant outside the transition region of the shock layer.) From the y and z momentum equations, v and w are continuous so that the z component of magnetic transport equation says that $B_z =$ constant $= 0$.

The energy equation may be written conveniently for our purpose as follows. From Equation (5.10-7)

$$m\left[\frac{P}{\rho} + U + \frac{u^2}{2}\right] = \int_1^2 \mathbf{E} \cdot \mathbf{J}\, dx \tag{10.2-8}$$

Where U is the specific internal energy. The heat conduction term drops out since we integrate between states of zero gradients and heat conduction along the shock layer is neglected. The dissipation function integrates out with the shear stress term and the details are left as an exercise for the student. The integrals can be evaluated as follows. $\mathbf{J}' = \mathbf{J}$ and $\mathbf{E}' = \mathbf{E} + \mathbf{V} \times \mathbf{B}$ so that

$$\int_1^2 \mathbf{E} \cdot \mathbf{J}\, dx = \int_1^2 [\mathbf{E}' \cdot \mathbf{J}' - (\mathbf{V} \times \mathbf{B}) \cdot (\nabla \times \mathbf{H})]\, dx \tag{10.2-9}$$

But $\mathbf{H} = H_y \hat{y}$ and H_y only varies in the x direction so that

$$\int_1^2 - (\mathbf{V} \times \mathbf{B}) \cdot (\nabla \times \mathbf{H}) \, dx = -\int_1^2 \frac{u}{\mu} B_y \frac{\partial B_y}{\partial x} \, dx$$

But from (10.2-7) uB_y is a constant so that the above integral becomes

$-\left.\dfrac{uB_y^2}{\mu}\right|_1^2$. The integrals $\int_1^2 \mathbf{E}' \cdot \mathbf{J}' \, dx$ (Joulean dissipation) is zero if we

assume the shock to be of infinitesimal thickness which is exact only if $\sigma \to \infty$. Thus we have for the energy equation

$$\left[\frac{P}{\rho} + U + \frac{u^2}{2} + \frac{B_y^2}{\rho u}\right] = 0 \tag{10.2-10}$$

By using the relationships $\gamma = c_P/c_V$ and $R = c_P - c_V$ with the perfect gas law $P = \rho RT$, we obtain finally

$$\left[\frac{P}{\rho}\left(\frac{\gamma}{\gamma - 1}\right) + \frac{u^2}{2} + \frac{B_y^2}{\rho\mu}\right] = 0 \tag{10.2-11}$$

The four equations (10.2-3), (10.2-5), (10.2-7), and (10.2-11) constitute the normal shock relationships for a perfect gas. We can think of these equations as giving the four unknowns P_2, ρ_2, u_2, and B_{y2} in terms of P_1, ρ_1, a_s, and B_{y1}. Of course, T_2 can be found from the gas law once P_2 and ρ_2 are known. Alternatively, we can think of u_2, or the shock strength (of, say, ρ_2/ρ_1 or P_2/P_1) as given and the other downstream ( )$_2$ properties and the shock speed a_s as being unknowns. There is only one solution to these equations, that is, one type of shock wave.

There are two important points to note here. One is that B_x must be zero in this type of shock. If a B_x and B_y were present, the situation would be more complicated (as we will see in the next section). The other point is that there has been an assumption about electrical conductivity. A current sheet exists in the shock layer in order to effect the change in B_y and in order for this layer to be infinitesimally thin the conductivity must be infinite. However, if the conductivity is finite (not ∞), so that Joulean dissipation can occur, the shock wave thickness becomes spread out and a precise shock layer may not be as well defined as in the infinite conductivity shock. We will briefly discuss the nature of the interior of the shock in a later section.

The shock velocity a_s may be written in terms of the density ratio ρ_2/ρ_1 as

$$a_s^2 = \frac{2}{\gamma + 1} \frac{a_1^2 + A_1^2[1 + (1 - \gamma/2)(\rho_2/\rho_1 - 1)]}{\rho_1/\rho_2 - [(\gamma - 1)/(\gamma + 1)]} \tag{10.2-12}$$

where a_1 is the ordinary sonic velocity upstream and A_1 is the upstream

Alfvén velocity $\sqrt{B_{y1}^2/\mu\rho_1}$. As A_1 goes to zero, we get the shock velocity of ordinary gas dynamics. We see that the shock velocity is increased by the presence of the magnetic field (for a given shock strength); as $\rho_2/\rho_1 \rightarrow 1$, we get $a_s^2 = a_1^2 + A_1^2$, the magnetosonic velocity in a perpendicular field.

Some other results of interest are

$$P_2 - P_1 = a_s^2\rho_1\left(1 - \frac{\rho_1}{\rho_2}\right) + \frac{B_{y1}^2}{2\mu}\left(1 - \frac{\rho_2^2}{\rho_1^2}\right) \qquad (10.2\text{-}13)$$

We can solve for u_2/a_s in terms of upstream properties. Then

$$\left(\frac{u_2}{a_s}\right) = \frac{1}{2}\left(\frac{\gamma - 1}{\gamma + 1} + \frac{2\gamma P_1}{(\gamma + 1)\rho_1 a_s^2} + \frac{A_1^2\gamma}{(\gamma + 1)a_s^2}\right)$$

$$+ \frac{1}{2}\left[\left(\frac{\gamma - 1}{\gamma + 1} + \frac{2\gamma P_1}{(\gamma + 1)\rho_1 a_s^2} + \frac{A_1^2\gamma}{(\gamma + 1)a_s^2}\right)^2 + \frac{4(2 - \gamma)}{\gamma + 1}\frac{A_1^2}{a_s^2}\right]^{1/2} \qquad (10.2\text{-}14)$$

As $A_1 \rightarrow 0$, we get the ordinary gas dynamic equation, of course.

We can express our relationships in terms of an appropriate Mach number if we wish. The (transverse) magnetosonic velocity here is $\sqrt{a_1^2 + A_1^2}$ so that the appropriate magnetosonic Mach number is $M_t^2 = a_s^2/(a_1^2 + A_1^2)$, where the subscript t is used to indicate a transverse field (to the direction of motion). Equation (10.2-12) can then be written

$$M_t^2 = \frac{2}{\gamma + 1}\frac{1 + \dfrac{A_1^2}{a_1^2 + A_1^2}\left(1 - \dfrac{\gamma}{2}\right)\left(\dfrac{\rho_2}{\rho_1} - 1\right)}{\dfrac{\rho_1}{\rho_2} - \dfrac{\gamma - 1}{\gamma + 1}} \qquad (10.2\text{-}15)$$

As $\rho_2/\rho_1 \rightarrow 1$, we see that $M_{t1} \rightarrow 1$, which is what we would expect.

For a given value of $a_s^2 > a_1^2$, the effective Mach number M_{t1} may be $\gtrless 1$, depending on the value of A_1. The larger the value of A_1 the lower the value of M_{t1}. For $M_{t1} < 1$, no shock can occur; at $M_{t1} = 1$ we have a magnetosonic wave; and for $M_{t1} > 1$ there exists the possibility of a shock. For $a_s^2 < a_1^2$ no shock can occur for any value of A_1. Therefore, as the field is increased beyond a critical point, no shock can occur, for a given upstream velocity a_s; $0 < A_1^2 < a_s^2 - a_1^2$ for a shock to occur. (From 10.2-14 it can be shown that if A_1 is such as to make $M_{t1} < 1$, even though $a_s > a_1$, a_s/u_2 will be < 1, which is impossible since it would imply a rarefaction shock.)

We have not yet mentioned the return path for the current sheet flowing in the shock, which is not a problem in a truly infinite configuration but which may be of importance in a practical situation. As an example, consider a piston generating a shock wave between two parallel planes as shown in Fig. 10.2-3. The piston and gas behind the shock have velocity $(a_s - u_2)$. The current in the shock front flows back through the walls or in a sheath and through the piston face to form a complete circuit. A

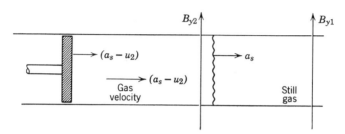

Figure 10.2-3 A piston generating a normal shock in a tube. The surface currents in the shock must return through the piston face.

simpler model to understand is one for axial symmetry, such as a shock in a coaxial tube with a radial magnetic field, or a bow shock in front of a projectile or missile with a radial magnetic field. In such cases the current would flow in closed, concentric, circular loops in the shock.

10.3 OBLIQUE SHOCKS AND DISCONTINUITIES

We now extend our analysis to the general oblique MHD shock of which the preceding MHD shock will be a special case. By an oblique shock we mean one in which the applied upstream magnetic field has both a component tangent to the shock front and a component normal to the shock front. Figure 10.3-1 shows the shock frame of reference. We can choose our coordinate system such that the upstream magnetic field $\mathbf{B}_1$ has only an x and y component B_{x1} and B_{y1}, respectively. A downstream z component B_{z2} may exist. There will in general be three components of the fluid velocity in front of and behind the shock. (In the ordinary gas dynamic shock, and in the normal MHD shock, v and w, the tangential components of velocity, are continuous through the shock.)

As before, we write the conservation equations across the shock. The [ ] is used as before to indicate the difference across the shock wave.

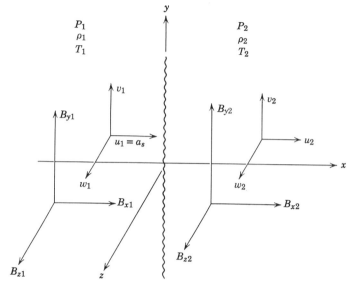

Figure 10.3-1 The rest frame of the oblique shock showing the jump in various quantities. The shock lies in the yz plane.

Continuity

$$[\rho u] = 0 \tag{10.3-1}$$

Momentum

$$\left[\rho u^2 + P + \frac{1}{2\mu}(B_y^2 + B_z^2 - B_x^2) \right] = 0 \tag{10.3-2}$$

$$\left[\rho u v - \frac{1}{\mu} B_x B_y \right] = 0 \tag{10.3-3}$$

$$\left[\rho u w - \frac{1}{\mu} B_x B_z \right] = 0 \tag{10.3-4}$$

Magnetic Transport

$$[B_x] = 0 \tag{10.3-5}$$

$$[u B_y - v B_x] = 0 \tag{10.3-6}$$

$$[u B_z - w B_x] = 0 \tag{10.3-7}$$

Energy (by referring to 10.2-8 and using 10.3-6 and 10.3-7)

$$\left[\frac{P}{\rho}\left(\frac{\gamma}{\gamma - 1} \right) + \tfrac{1}{2}(u^2 + v^2 + w^2) \right.$$
$$\left. + \left(\frac{B_y^2 + B_z^2}{\rho\mu} \right) - \frac{B_x(v B_y + w B_z)}{\rho u \mu} \right] = 0 \tag{10.3-8}$$

By transforming to a coordinate system moving with velocity v_1 and w_1 parallel to the shock surface, it is possible to simplify the expressions somewhat. The final results are the same but v_1 and w_1 in the new coordinate system are then zero. This transformation is often made in the literature on shock waves.

Furthermore, from (10.3-2), (10.3-3), and (10.3-4) it follows that (if $B_x \neq 0$) a coordinate system can always be chosen such that $\mathbf{V}$ is parallel to $\mathbf{B}$ on each side of the shock.

Three special cases can be considered immediately.

1. $B_x = 0$. Here we have exactly the normal shock of the previous section, and v and w are continuous and uncoupled.

2. $B_y = B_z = 0$. There is no coupling at all and we get the ordinary gas dynamic oblique shock. (There is a special solution where B_y and B_z are zero on one side of the shock and not on the other. This type of wave is called a switch-on or switch-off shock and is discussed later.)

3. As the strength of the shock goes to zero, $\rho_2/\rho_1 \rightarrow 1$, and we get the ideal magnetoacoustic waves of Chapter 8. Although we have not introduced the conductivity σ explicitly, so that there is no assumption as to the value of σ, as we let the wave become weaker and broader our equations are valid only for infinite conductivity. Finite conductivity tends to broaden the shock wave but as long as it is thin enough to be called a shock we need not specify σ.

Let us now examine the general oblique shock. There are various ways of classifying the general solutions. One is to separate the solutions for $m = 0$ and $m \neq 0$. The former (for $m = 0$) are called discontinuities (contact or tangential), and the latter (for $m \neq 0$) are shocks. One particular solution for $m \neq 0$ is not a true shock (since no density change occurs across it) but is what we call a rotational discontinuity.

Before we examine these solutions in detail, let us see how the rotational discontinuity arises. By combining Equations (10.3-5), (10.3-7), and (10.3-4) (from 10.3-5 $B_{x1} = B_{x2}$ and $B_{z1} = 0$, remember), we have

$$u_2 m B_{z2} = \frac{1}{\mu} B_x^2 B_{z2} \tag{10.3-9}$$

Hence either $B_{z2} = 0$ (in which case $w_1 = w_2$) or $B_x^2 = u_2 m \mu$. The first case, $B_{z2} = 0$, corresponds to the true shock wave solutions, and the special solution $B_x^2 = u_2 m \mu$ corresponds to the rotational discontinuity if we require that $[\rho] = 0$. From the shock equations it follows immediately that if $B_x^2 = u_2 m \mu$,

$$a_s^2 = u_2^2 = \frac{1}{\mu} \frac{B_x^2}{\rho_1} = A_1^2 = A_2^2 \tag{10.3-10}$$

which is precisely the Alfvén velocity. From this solution it follows that

$$[T] = [\rho] = [P] = 0 \tag{10.3-11}$$

$$[B_z] = B_{z2} = (w_2 - w_1)\sqrt{\rho\mu} = [w]\sqrt{\rho\mu} \tag{10.3-12}$$

$$[B_y] = B_{y2} - B_{y1} = [v]\sqrt{\rho\mu} = (v_2 - v_1)\sqrt{\rho\mu} \tag{10.3-13}$$

$$[B_y^2 + B_z^2] = (B_{y2}^2 + B_{z2}^2 - B_{y1}^2) = 0 \tag{10.3-14}$$

so that the rotational discontinuity might be thought of as a large amplitude Alfvén wave. We will come back to this wave a little later.

Discontinuities. Let us look into the discontinuity solutions for $m = 0$ and list the possibilities for the types of discontinuities other than true shock waves.

1. Contact surface: $m = 0$, $B_x \neq 0$. It follows from the conservation equations that $[B_y] = 0$, $[v] = 0$, and $[P] = 0$. However, $[\rho] \neq 0$ and $[T] \neq 0$. This discontinuity is known as a "contact surface" and is the same type that occurs in ordinary gas dynamics. The jump of density and temperature can have any value (consistent with the equation of state).

2. Tangential discontinuity: $m = 0$, $B_x = 0$. The conservation equations become

$$P_2 - P_1 + \frac{1}{2\mu}(B_{y2}^2 - B_{y1}^2) = 0 \tag{10.3-15}$$

$$\begin{aligned} [v] &\neq 0 \\ [B_y] &\neq 0 \\ [\rho] &\neq 0 \\ [T] &\neq 0 \end{aligned} \tag{10.3-16}$$

which is an MHD tangential discontinuity. In ordinary fluid mechanics the pressure difference across the discontinuity would be zero, but here it is given by (10.3-15). The values given in (10.3-16) are arbitrary and can have any values imposed by the physical situation. (Of course P, ρ, and T are related by the equation of state.) It is interesting to note that if $B_x \neq 0$, such a discontinuity cannot be maintained.

3. Rotational discontinuity: $m \neq 0$, $[v] \neq 0$, $[P] = [\rho] = [T] = 0$. For the rotational discontinuity, which was discussed earlier, all the mechanical thermodynamic properties are continuous.

From (10.3-12), (10.3-13), and (10.3-14) it follows that the magnitude of the tangential velocity and tangential magnetic field are both constant across the rotational discontinuity; hence the magnitude of the total velocity vector and magnetic field vector are constant across the discontinuity. Since the magnitudes of the y and z components change, the velocity and magnetic vector must rotate (about the x axis) through the surface. Furthermore, since the change in B_z, $[B_z]$, is proportional to $[w]$ and since $[B_y]$ is proportional to $[v]$ (by the same proportionality constant), it is possible to choose a coordinate system moving parallel to the surface such that the velocity and magnetic vector are parallel to each other on each side of the discontinuity.

A contact surface in ordinary fluid mechanics may be stable or unstable (Rayleigh instability). In any case, the temperature discontinuity will tend to diffuse away due to heat conduction even though the density discontinuity may be stable. The tangential discontinuity in ordinary fluid mechanics is an unstable phenomenon and will quickly develop into a turbulent layer that diffuses away.

The same observations about the contact surface are valid in MHD. The tangential discontinuity, however, may be stabilized by the magnetic field. If the conductivity is infinite, the discontinuity may become completely stable, but the effect of finite conductivity would be to broaden the discontinuity and eventually dissipate it. This type of instability has been investigated by Syrovatskii (1953) and the reader is referred to that original work or to the résumé by Landau and Lifshitz (1960).

10.4 OBLIQUE SHOCK SOLUTIONS

The true oblique shocks are characterized by $m \neq 0$ and $[P] \neq 0$. Equations (10.3-1) through (10.3-8) constitute the basic shock conservation equations. By combining these equations with the fact that $B_{z2} = 0$ and $w_1 = w_2$ (which follows from 10.3-9), we can simplify the shock relationships into the following five equations:

$$\rho_1 a_s = \rho_2 u_2 = m \qquad (10.4\text{-}1)$$

$$m(u_2 - a_s) + (P_2 - P_1) + \frac{1}{2\mu}(B_{y2}{}^2 - B_{y1}{}^2) = 0 \qquad (10.4\text{-}2)$$

$$m(v_2 - v_1) - \frac{B_x}{\mu}(B_{y2} - B_{y1}) = 0 \qquad (10.4\text{-}3)$$

$$(v_2 - v_1)B_x - u_2 B_{y2} + a_s B_{y1} = 0 \qquad (10.4\text{-}4)$$

$$\left(\frac{P_2}{\rho_2} - \frac{P_1}{\rho_1}\right)\frac{\gamma}{\gamma - 1} + \frac{1}{2}(u_2{}^2 + v_2{}^2 - a_s{}^2 - v_1{}^2)$$
$$+ \frac{B_{y2}{}^2}{\rho_2\mu} - \frac{B_{y1}{}^2}{\rho_1\mu} - \frac{B_x}{\mu m}(v_2 B_{y2} - v_1 B_{y1}) = 0 \quad (10.4\text{-}5)$$

these describe the general oblique shock (except for the rotational discontinuity in which $[P] = 0$).

In general, there are three possible types of shocks, that is three shock velocities (a_s) for any given shock strength (as determined by ρ_2/ρ_1, say). These shocks can be called fast, slow, and intermediate, because in the limit of zero strength they reduce to the fast and slow magnetoacoustic waves and the Alfvén wave.

In principle, if all the properties, fields, and velocities are known at state 1 (upstream), they can be found at state 2 (downstream) for each of the three possible shocks. In other words, the downstream state is not unique, but triple valued.

We can find a_s (and characterize the shock by this value) in terms of upstream properties and the shock strength ρ_2/ρ_1. But first let us derive some useful preliminary relationships.

We know that $B_{x1} = B_{x2}$, $B_{z2} = B_{z1} = 0$, and $w_1 = w_2$. Hence $\mathbf{B}_1$ and $\mathbf{B}_2$ and the normal to the shock surface lie in a common plane. From (10.4-3) and (10.4-4) we obtain

$$B_{y2} = B_{y1} \frac{(a_s^2 - A_{x1}^2)}{(a_s u_2 - A_{x1}^2)} \tag{10.4-6}$$

$$v_2 - v_1 = \frac{A_{x1} A_{y1}(a_s - u_2)}{(a_s u_2 - A_{x1}^2)} \tag{10.4-7}$$

where $A_{x1}^2 = B_{x1}^2/\rho_1\mu$ and $A_{y1}^2 = B_{y1}^2/\rho_1\mu$. These equations have meaning only if $(a_s u_2 - A_{x1}^2) \neq 0$. If

$$(a_s u_2 - A_{x1}^2) = 0 \tag{10.4-8}$$

we have what are known as switch-on shocks, which will be discussed presently. In the switch-on shock B_{y2} and v_2 may be finite even though $B_{y1} = v_1 = 0$.

Let us confine ourselves for the moment to the case $(a_s u_s - A_{x1}^2) \neq 0$, which corresponds to the regular MHD true shocks. Under the condition (10.4-8), Equations (10.4-1) through (10.4-5) may be solved for a_s^2 in terms of ρ_2/ρ_1 to give

$$\left[a_s^2 - \frac{\gamma + 1}{2} a_s^2 \left(1 - \frac{\rho_1}{\rho_2} \right) - a_1^2 \right] \left(a_s^2 \frac{\rho_1}{\rho_2} - A_{x1}^2 \right)^2$$

$$- a_s^2 A_{y1}^2 \left\{ a_s^2 \left[1 - \frac{\gamma + 2}{2} \left(1 - \frac{\rho_1}{\rho_2} \right) + \frac{\gamma}{2} \left(1 - \frac{\rho_1}{\rho_2} \right)^2 \right] \right.$$

$$\left. + \frac{\gamma + 1}{2} A_{x1}^2 \left(1 - \frac{\rho_1}{\rho_2} \right) - A_{x1}^2 \right\} = 0 \tag{10.4-9}$$

This equation is a cubic in a_s^2. The roots must be all real and positive, and a_s itself must be positive (for $\rho_1/\rho_2 < 1$). By examining the behavior of this cubic, we can see that as $a_s^2 \to \infty$, the cubic expression $\to \infty$. As $a_s^2 \to 0$, the expression goes to $-a_1^2 A_{x1}^2$. Hence there must be either one or three positive roots to a_s^2 if we require that they be real. In order for there to be three positive roots, we obtain a restriction on ρ_2/ρ_1 and actually obtain a maximum value which it can attain:

$$\frac{\rho_2}{\rho_1} < \frac{\gamma + 1}{\gamma - 1} \tag{10.4-10}$$

which is the same as the ordinary gas dynamic shock bound.

As $\rho_2/\rho_1 \to 1$, Equation (10.4-9) becomes identical to the ideal magneto-acoustic dispersion relationship and the three roots become, as we said, the velocities of the fast, slow, and Alfvén sonic disturbances. The reader may wonder why the ideal magnetosonic disturbances apply to gases with infinite electrical and thermal conductivity and zero viscosity; while in the shock equations we made no explicit assumption about conductivity or viscosity. The answer is that as long as the shock wave remains infinitesimally thin our analysis is exact. As the dissipation becomes stronger, the shock broadens and weakens as it propagates. As the shock becomes weak and sonic, it is no longer a surface of discontinuity with uniform properties in front and back of a "thin" layer, and our equation of motion and energy equation must take into account dissipation processes.

Fast and Slow Shocks. The following conclusions may be drawn from an examination of the shock equations. We use the notation: a_{fast} for fast magnetosonic velocity, and a_{slow} for slow magnetosonic velocity (see Chapter 8). For a fast shock:

1. State 1 (upstream) $\quad a_s > a_{\text{fast } 1} \qquad\qquad$ (10.4-11)

2. State 2 (downstream)

$$a_{\text{fast } 2} > u_2 > A_{x2} \tag{10.4-12}$$

For a slow shock:

1. State 1 (upstream) $\quad A_{x1} > a_s > a_{\text{slow } 1} \qquad$ (10.4-13)

2. State 2 (downstream) $\quad a_{\text{slow } 2} > u_2 \qquad$ (10.4-14)

For a detailed derivation of these inequalities the reader is referred to the work of Bazer and Ericson (1959) and Shercliff (1960). We see that in a fast shock the normal velocity jumps from supersonic to subsonic relative to the fast magnetosonic velocity and that in a slow shock it jumps from supersonic to subsonic relative to the slow magnetosonic velocity. In the fast shock the values of a_s and u_2 are both super-Alfvén and in the slow shock a_s and u_2 are both sub-Alfvén.

Across a fast shock the direction of **B** is rotated away from the normal and in a slow shock **B** is rotated toward the normal. The same statement holds for the velocity vector **V** across the two types of shocks.

The magnitudes of the tangential magnetic field $|B_y|$ and the tangential velocity $|v|$ rise across a fast shock and drop across a slow shock. It can also be shown that across both a fast and slow shock the sign of B_y does not change. This fact can be readily seen from Equation (10.4-6), although Friedrichs and Kranzer (1958) indicate incorrectly that B_y may actually reverse across a slow shock. The reversal may occur across a rotational discontinuity only.

Where B_y is created or wiped out across a shock, we have the extreme cases of a fast and slow shock, respectively, named switch-on and switch-off shocks, respectively, by Friedrichs and Kranzer (1958).

Switch-On and Switch-Off Shocks. The switch-on and switch-off shocks are extreme cases of the fast and slow shocks, respectively. In a switch-on shock a transverse component of magnetic field B_{y2} appears on the downstream side of the shock and is absent upstream. We saw an example of a switch-on shock in Section 9.6, (Fig. 9.6-5). In a switch-off shock B_y appears on the upstream side but is erased on the downstream side. Let us return to Equations (10.4-6) and (10.4-7) and examine the solution satisfied by the condition $(a_s u_2 - A_{x1}^2 = 0)$.

From (10.4-1) we obtain

$$u_2^2 = A_{x2}^2 \qquad a_s^2 = A_{x1}^2 \left(\frac{\rho_2}{\rho_1} \right) \tag{10.4-15}$$

From (10.4-6), then, either $B_{y1} = 0$ (a switch-on shock) or $a_s^2 - A_{x1}^2 = 0$ (a rotational discontinuity).

The condition $B_{y1} = 0$ satisfies both (10.4-6) and (10.4-7). B_{y2} and $(v_2 - v_1)$ are indeterminant but must be such as to satisfy the energy equation (10.3-8). One possible solution is (if $\rho_1 = \rho_2$) simply a rotational discontinuity with $a_s = u_2 = A_1 = A_2$. The question arises, are other solutions possible with a finite pressure and density change across the shock? We must remove the restrictions that $w_1 = w_2$ and that $B_{z2} = 0$ (since they were imposed only on solutions in which $u_2 \neq A_{x2}$.) (Remember we have already considered the case of $u_2 = A_{x2}$ and $\rho_1 = \rho_2$, the rotational discontinuity.) By combining the energy equation and the x momentum (10.3-2 and 10.3-8) and by using the condition that $\rho_2/\rho_1 > 1$, we can show that a solution exists only if $A_{x1} > a_1$, that is, the Alfvén speed exceeds the sonic speed. Furthermore, $a_s > A_{x1} > a_1$.

The so-called switch-off shock is an extreme type of slow shock in which $B_{y2} = 0$. From (10.4-6) it follows that $a_s = A_{x1}$. The tangential magnetic field exists upstream $(B_{y1} \neq 0)$ but $B_{y2} = B_{z2} = 0$. From Equations

(10.4-6) and (10.4-7), $a_s u_2 - A_{x1}^2 \neq 0$ now as in a switch-on shock. A consideration of the x momentum and energy equations shows that downstream of the switch-off shock $u_2 <$ both a_2 and A_{x2}.

From (10.4-11) through (10.4-14) the character of the switch shocks can be summed up as follows. On the side of the shock where the field is normal the velocity equals the local Alfvén velocity, and on the side where a tangential field exists a_{fast} is the greater of a or A_x and a_{slow} the lesser. Upstream of the switch-on shock, $a_s > A_{x1} > a_1$, and downstream of a switch-off shock $a_s <$ both a_2 and A_{x2}. Behind the switch-off shock either a_2 or A_{x2} may be the greater, although if $A_{x2} > a_2$, the shock can occur only if the strength exceeds a critical value. If $A_{x2} < a_2$, there is no restriction on the strength. We will not go into a proof of these statements but they will become clearer when we show the Rayleigh line for the shock processes. For a detailed discussion of these points the reader is referred to the work of Friedrichs and Kranzer (1958) and Shercliff (1960).

It is interesting to note that the switch-on and switch-off shocks can be represented by states of zero y momentum if we choose a coordinate system moving parallel to the surface such that $v_1 = 0$ in a switch-on shock and $v_2 = 0$ in a switch-off shock, that is

$$mv_1 - \frac{B_{x1}B_{y1}}{\mu} = mv_2 - \frac{B_{x2}B_{y2}}{\mu} = 0$$

This representation will be useful when we show the shocks on a Rayleigh line diagram.

Intermediate Shocks. The third root of Equation (10.4-9) represents an intermediate shock. In the limit as $\rho_2/\rho_1 \to 1$ (sonic wave) we get $a_s = A_x$, transverse Alfvén wave.

It can be shown that in all intermediate shocks the upstream velocity is above the local Alfvén velocity and downstream below the local Alfvén velocity. This observation and a graphical picture can be deduced from the Rayleigh line representation of the shocks. We will show this approach, following Shercliff (1960), in the next section.

In the limit as the y momentum goes to zero (switch-on and switch-off shocks replace the fast and slow waves, respectively), the intermediate shock goes to one of four possible solutions depending on upstream conditions and strength of the shock. These possibilities are:

1. If $v = B_y = 0$ on both sides, we get an ordinary shock.

2, 3. If v and $B_y \neq 0$ on one side but zero on the other, the intermediate shock coincides with the switch-on or switch-off shock.

4. A rotational discontinuity is possible since y momentum $= 0$ is consistent with this type of discontinuity.

10.5   THE RAYLEIGH LINE DIAGRAM

The oblique shock processes may be visualized on a generalized Rayleigh line diagram, which shows in a graphical and easy-to-remember manner the various possible shock transitions. Following the analysis of Shercliff (1960), we will outline the construction of the Rayleigh line and point out the various transitions discussed in the preceding section.

The generalized Rayleigh line is defined as the locus of constant generalized momentum and mass flux. For convenience we denote the x and y components of generalized momentum (to within a constant) as F_x and F_y, so that

$$F_x = P + \rho u^2 + \frac{1}{2\mu} B_y^2$$

$$F_y = \rho u v - \frac{B_x B_y}{\mu} = - \frac{B_x B_{y1}}{\mu} \tag{10.5-1}$$

The coordinate system is taken so that $v_1 = 0$. By (10.3-2) F_x is equal to the x momentum plus the constant $B_x^2/2\mu$, so that F_x and F_y are conserved across the shock. The Rayleigh line can be defined then as the locus of constant F_x, F_y, m, and B_x, subject to the magnetic transport equation (10.4-4).

It is convenient to express F_x in terms of P and ρ and examine the family of Rayleigh lines P versus ρ for fixed values of F_x, m, and B_x for various values of $|F_y|$. These diagrams were first discussed by Germain (1959) but were analyzed in detail by Shercliff (1960). We obtain after combining (10.5-1) with (10.4-4)

$$F_x = P + m^2 \tau + \frac{F_y^2 B_x^2}{2\mu m^4} (\tau - \tau_0)^{-2} \tag{10.5-2}$$

where $\tau = 1/\rho$ and $\tau_0 = B_x^2/\mu m^2$ (a constant, the specific volume at the Alfvén speed).

The family of Rayleigh lines, as shown in Fig. 10.5-1, may be deduced from Equation (10.5-2). There are two distinct cases:

$$(a)\ \ F_x > B_x^2/\mu \qquad \text{and} \qquad (b)\ \ F_x < B_x^2/\mu$$

The branches are denoted as fast if $u > A_x$ and slow if $u < A_x$. The $F_y = 0$ line consists of two parts, the straight line $F_x = P + m^2\tau$ ($B_y = 0$, the ordinary Rayleigh line) and the straight vertical line $\tau = \tau_0$. $|F_y|$ increases downward in (a) of Fig. 10.5-1. The fast branch Rayleigh line disappears (falls into the τ axis) as $F_y^2 \geq 8\mu(F_x - B_x^2/\mu)^3/27B_x^2$ and the slow branch disappears as $F_y^2 \geq 2B_x^2 F_x/\mu$. The fast or slow branch disappears as $F_x < 4B_x^2/\mu$ or $F_x > 4B_x^2/\mu$, respectively. A shock state is inaccessible unless it falls on the diagram so that the above inequalities can actually provide physical bounds on the states.

A more useful and informative Rayleigh line plot is the Ts diagram, on which the various shock transitions are graphically depicted. Points representing end states across a shock on the Rayleigh line diagram must be states that are related by the energy equation, (10.4-5) for a perfect gas (and with a larger value of specific entropy s downstream than upstream).

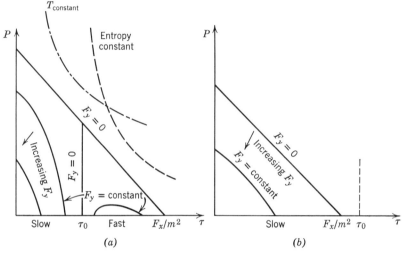

Figure 10.5-1 Rayleigh lines for given (F_x, B_x, m) and various F_y on the $P\tau$ plane. (a) $F_x > B_x^2/\mu$, (b) $F_x < B_x^2/\mu$.

This energy equation does not include dissipative effects and hence must be used only for thin shock layers and isentropic waves. As the shock becomes sonic, using this energy equation implies that the wave is isentropic—the same situation as in ordinary gas dynamics. The energy equation as expressed in (10.4-5) is actually the conservation of total enthalpy including electromagnetic effects and will be referred to as such.

We show the Ts diagrams in Fig. 10.5-2 and indicate shock transitions as arrows satisfying entropy increases. We will not go into detail but the topological properties of the diagrams may be inferred from Fig. 10.5-1 and the basic conservation equations.

In Fig. 10.5-2, (a) is for $F_x > B_x^2/\mu$ and $\tau^* > \tau_0$; and (b) is for $F_x > B_x^2/\mu$ but $\tau^* < \tau_0$. τ^* is the specific volume $(1/\rho)$, where $u =$ sonic velocity (which is a_{slow}, a_{fast}, or A_x). The condition on τ^* relative to τ_0 may be translated into a condition on F_x if we specify the equation of state

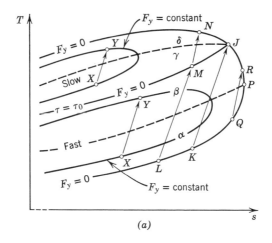

(a)

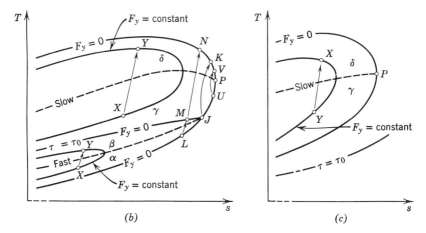

(b)   (c)

Figure 10.5-2   Rayleigh lines for given (F_x, B_x, m) and various F_y on the Ts plane.
(a) $F_x > B_x^2/\mu$, $\tau^* > \tau_0$, (b) $F_x > B_x^2/\mu$, $\tau^* < \tau_0$, (c) $F_x < B_x^2/\mu$.

for the gas. For a perfect gas, $\tau^* > \tau_0$ is equivalent to $F_x > (\gamma + 1)B_x^2/\gamma\mu$. In Fig. 10.5-2, (c) is for $F_x < B_x^2/\mu$. The line $F_y = 0$ consists of the ordinary Rayleigh line and the branch corresponding to $\tau = \tau_0$. Point P is the point of maximum entropy, where $u = $ ordinary sonic velocity a and $\tau = \tau^*$. The difference between (a) and (b) is in the relative positions of points P and J (where $u = A_x$ and $\tau = \tau_0$). The line $\tau = \tau_0$ ($F_y = 0$) divides the Rayleigh plot into two branches, a fast and slow line. As $|F_y|$ increases, these branches recede toward the ordinate and disappear, as was indicated in Fig. 10.5-1.

Fast and Slow Shocks. Depending on the branch, the shock is denoted as fast or slow. Lines $X \rightarrow Y$ indicate possible fast and slow shocks. In (*c*) only slow shocks are possible. The character of the shocks has been discussed in the preceding section. As the total enthalpy increases (for a fixed B_x and m), the point X moves to the right along the Rayleigh line. X and Y finally coincide at the extrema, which are points of maximum entropy and maximum total enthalpy. These points represent the fast and slow sonic waves that are isentropic. (We may neglect dissipative effects here, remember, as the shock weakens and becomes a sound wave.) Here $u = a_{\text{slow}}$ or a_{fast}. The dotted lines are the loci of these sonic points for variable $|F_y|$.

The line of the sonic-point loci and the line $\tau = \tau_0$ divide the Rayleigh loops into four distinct regions. The following inequalities, can be established which characterize these regions, and allow the conclusions which were presented in the preceding section. The four regions α, β, γ, and δ are:

$$(\alpha) \qquad u > a_{\text{fast}}$$

$$(\beta) \qquad a_{\text{fast}} > u > A_x$$

$$(\gamma) \qquad A_x > u > a_{\text{slow}} \qquad\qquad (10.5\text{-}3)$$

$$(\delta) \qquad a_{\text{slow}} > u$$

We observe immediately that u jumps from supersonic to subsonic (relative to the slow and fast sonic speeds) in slow and fast shocks, respectively, but u remains below or above the Alfvén speed in slow and fast shocks, respectively.

Switch-on and Switch-Off Shocks.   The switch-on and switch-off shocks are seen to be the extreme case as $F_y \rightarrow 0$ of the fast and slow shocks, respectively. The $L \rightarrow M$ shock is a switch-on and $M \rightarrow N$ shock a switch-off shock. The point J limits the values of F_x, m, B_x, and energy. The values of F_x, m, and B_x fix the point J. Then only values of total enthalpy less than its value at J will permit switch-on or switch-off shocks. As the total energy increases to its limit (at point J) in (*a*) of Fig. 10.5-2 for switch-on shocks, the corresponding switch-off shocks weaken and disappear. The converse occurs in (*b*). The velocities on each side of these shocks have been discussed in the preceding section and should become clear now with reference to the Rayleigh line.

The point M itself represents a large-amplitude Alfvén wave or rotational discontinuity (called by Shercliff an Alfvén shock).

Starting to the right of K in (*a*) or J in (*b*), shocks can only develop as $Q \rightarrow R$ or $U \rightarrow V$ and are simply ordinary shocks (since $B_y = 0$).

Intermediate Shocks. The intermediate shocks are those that join points on different branches of a Rayleigh line, as shown in Fig. 10.5-3. We number the states 1, 2, 3, 4 in order of increasing density and a shock must proceed from a lower- to a higher-numbered state. One and 2 are fast, 3 and 4 are slow. The fast shock is $1 \rightarrow 2$ and the slow shock $3 \rightarrow 4$. Shocks $1 \rightarrow 3$, $1 \rightarrow 4$, $2 \rightarrow 3$, and $2 \rightarrow 4$ are intermediate. Upstream in an

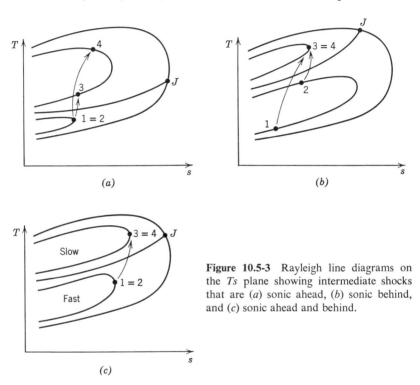

Figure 10.5-3 Rayleigh line diagrams on the *Ts* plane showing intermediate shocks that are (*a*) sonic ahead, (*b*) sonic behind, and (*c*) sonic ahead and behind.

intermediate shock the velocity is above the local Alfvén velocity, and downstream it is below the Alfvén velocity. As can be seen from Fig. 10.5-3, the upstream or the downstream states may be sonic, but one of them must be sonic—otherwise the shock would have to be a slow or fast shock. One special case is that of sonic conditions both upstream and downstream, as shown in Fig. 10.5-3(*c*).

In the limit as $F_y \rightarrow 0$ the intermediate shocks become: $2 \rightarrow 3$, the rotational discontinuity; $1 \rightarrow 3$, the switch-on; $1 \rightarrow 4$, the ordinary; and $2 \rightarrow 4$, the switch-off.

Some Concluding Remarks. It has been pointed out earlier that, just as in ordinary gas dynamics, in MHD as the pressure ratio becomes infinite, the density ratio remains finite, and for a perfect gas this limit for a normal MHD shock is the same as in ordinary gas dynamics. This behavior can be seen by examining Fig. 10.5-1.

As the total enthalpy is lowered, the pressure will eventually approach zero on the upstream side, giving rise to a strong shock. As the total enthalpy is further lowered, the states 1, 2, 3, and 4 vanish in that order as the pressure correspondingly falls to zero. Hence certain of the six possible shocks (for a given F_x, F_y, B_x, and m) may be impossible because the total enthalpy is too low, just as certain shocks are impossible because the total enthalpy is too high (as can be seen by looking at the Rayleigh line plots).

We have given a brief outline of the Rayleigh line characterization of the MHD shocks. These diagrams should serve as a visual map of the possible shock transitions and simplify the rather complex relationships between ordinary and MHD shocks.

10.6   STRESS TENSOR FORMULATION

The shock conservation equations may be formulated by using the electromagnetic stress tensor instead of directly integrating the differential equations through the shock. The final equations are identical to (10.3-1) through (10.3-8), and using the stress tensor provides a quick path to the equations. The first paper to discuss the hydromagnetic shock wave (de Hoffman and Teller, 1950) was formulated in terms of the stress tensor. Their analysis included relativistic effects, and the continuity across the shock of the four-dimensional energy-momentum-stress tensor provided the basic principle. We confine ourselves here to the nonrelativistic analysis but in Appendix 2 the four-dimensional formulation is briefly discussed.

Consider the control volume enclosing the shock (Fig. 10.6-1). The continuity equation is the same as (10.3-1), of course. We use the electromagnetic stress tensor T_{ij} discussed in Chapter 3. The electromagnetic stresses are shown acting on the surfaces of the control volume. As before, we choose our coordinate system so that $B_{z1} = 0$. The momentum balance, where $\mathbf{F}$ is the total external force on the fluid in the control volume, is

$$\mathbf{F} = \int_A \rho(\mathbf{V} \cdot d\mathbf{A})\mathbf{V} \qquad (10.6\text{-}1)$$

T_{xx} is given by

$$T_{xx} = \frac{B_x^{\,2} - B_y^{\,2} - B_z^{\,2}}{2\mu} \qquad (10.6\text{-}2)$$

so that the x-momentum equation is

$$(\rho_2 u_2^2 - \rho_1 a_s^2) + (P_2 - P_1) + \left(\frac{B_{x1}^2 - B_{y1}^2}{2\mu}\right)$$

$$- \left(\frac{B_{x2}^2 - B_{y2}^2 - B_{z2}^2}{2\mu}\right) = 0 \quad (10.6\text{-}3)$$

which is identical to (10.3-2).

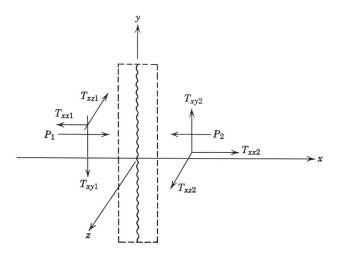

Figure 10.6-1   A control volume around the shock front showing the stresses.

$T_{xy} = (1/\mu)B_x B_y$ so that we obtain for the y-momentum equation

$$(\rho_2 u_2 v_2 - \rho_1 a_s v_1) + \frac{1}{\mu}(B_{x2}B_{y2} - B_{x1}B_{y1}) = 0 \qquad (10.6\text{-}4)$$

which is identical to (10.3-3). Similarly, for the z momentum we obtain exactly (10.3-4).

We will not go through the details, but Equation (5.4-1), applied to the control volume, can be cast into (10.3-8) (remember that $\mathbf{E} \cdot \mathbf{J} = \mathbf{E'} \cdot \mathbf{J'} + \mathbf{V} \cdot (\mathbf{J} \times \mathbf{B})$. The Poynting theorem may be used to transform $\mathbf{E'} \times \mathbf{H'}$ in terms of $\mathbf{E'} \cdot \mathbf{J'}$ and the mechanical energy equation (5.10-2) may be combined with it to yield a volume integral in terms of $\mathbf{E} \cdot \mathbf{J}$).

The magnetic transport equations are obtained in the same manner as in Section 10.3.

10.7 SHOCK STRUCTURE

We do not propose to discuss MHD shock structure in detail but will merely mention some of the general characteristics of the shocks. Of particular interest are the works of Marshall (1955) and Ludford (1959).

In the analysis of MHD shocks in this chapter we did not explicitly assume anything about the electrical conductivity of the fluid. However, in the energy equation, the assumption was made that the shock front was essentially an infinitesimally thin sheet if the conductivity were not infinite. Hence our results hold exactly only insofar as the shock front is thin, unless all dissipation is negligible in which case all the equations are exact. Hence, when the sonic limit was taken, the assumption of infinite conductivity (zero dissipation) was implied. We conclude that our shock analysis is exact only for infinite conductivity, but the results should be at least approximately correct even for finite conductivity so long as the shock front is narrow.

In general the shock structure may be divided into three classes:

1.   For high electrical conductivity the shock front is a thin layer of the order of magnitude of several mean free paths. The magnetic field, velocity, and gas properties change through this thin layer. The results of this chapter apply to this case.

2.   If the conductivity is low and the magnetic field larger than a critical value (which depends on the shock strength), the shock front is wide and all variables change gradually across the shock.

3.   If the conductivity is low and the magnetic field smaller than this critical value, a sharp, well-defined shock occurs in pressure but the magnetic field, velocity, density, and temperature change slowly through a wide region before the shock. Eventually, of course, as the conductivity and/or magnetic field go to zero, there is no interaction and an ordinary sharp gas dynamic shock occurs.

10.8 CONCLUSIONS

We have presented the theory behind magnetohydrodynamic shocks in a general oblique magnetic field. The Rayleigh line was introduced as an aid to visualizing the shock processes and presenting the results in a simple form.

Very few experimental investigations of true MHD shocks have been fruitful. The experiments of Patrick (1959) showed a fair agreement between experimental and calculated shock speeds. More recent experiments of various types have been made by Camac et al. (1962) and Vlases (1963, 1964).

Another relevant problem is that of the behavior of an ionizing shock wave. In this case the fluid in front of the shock is nonconducting, but behind the shock the fluid is ionized and conducting. Since the chemical reaction times are usually long compared to the time of travel through the shock front, such a shock wave is essentially unaffected by the magnetic field. We will not go into this type of shock here, but the reader is referred to the work of Kulikovskii and Lyubimov (1959), Helliwell (1962, 1963), and C. K. Chu (1964).

The formation of a MHD shock on the nose of a missile can be examined by the methods discussed in this chapter. However, the behavior of the flow behind the shock may affect the shock itself if $\mathbf{J} \times \mathbf{B}$ forces exist behind the shock. Whether or not such forces exist depends on the configuration and return circuits if electrodes are present. In an axial symmetric flow the azimuthal electric field may be zero and then the current density behind the shock would be $\sigma(\mathbf{V} \times \mathbf{B})$. Such a body force could bend the shock away from or toward the body. Such problems will be discussed in detail in Chapter 12. Attached shocks on a missile have been analyzed by Cabannes (1960) and Cowley (1963).

PROBLEMS

1. Derive the hydraulic jump conditions for MHD open-channel flow.
2. Derive the inequalities of Equation (10.5-2).
3. In Problem 8 of Chapter 9 let the fluid conductivity be infinite. Discuss the resulting shock waves.
4. Derive equation 10.2-10 in detail paying particular attention to the mechanical dissipation function.

REFERENCES

GENERAL

Akhiezer, A. J., et al., The Stability of Shock Waves in Magnetohydrodynamics, *Soviet Phys.*-J.E.T.P., **35** (8), p. 507, 1959.

Anderson, J. E., *Magnetohydrodynamic Shock Waves*, The M.I.T. Press, Cambridge, Mass., 1963.

Bazer, J., and W. B. Ericson, Hydromagnetic Shocks, *Astrophys. J.*, **129**, p. 758, 1959.

Bianco, E., H. Cabannes, and J. Kuntzmann, Curvature of Attached Shock Waves in Steady Axially Symmetric Flow, *J. Fluid Mech.*, **7**, Part 4, p. 610, 1960.

Cabannes, H., *Rech. Aero*, **71**, p. 3, 1959.

Cabannes, H., Attached Stationary Shock Waves in Ionized Gases, *Rev. Mod. Phys.*, **32**, p. 973, 1960.

Cole, J. D., Magnetohydrodynamic Waves, in *The Magnetohydrodynamics of Conducting Fluids*, edited by D. Bershader, Stanford University Press, Stanford, California, 1959.

Cowley, M. D., On Plane Flow of a Gas with Finite Electrical Conductivity in a Strong Magnetic Field, *J. Fluid Mech.*, **15**, p. 577, 1963.

de Hoffman, F., and E. Teller, Magneto-hydrodynamic Shocks, *Phys. Rev.*, **80**, No. 4, p. 692, 1950.

Friedrichs, K. O., and H. Kranzer, Notes on Magneto-Hydrodynamics, VIII, Nonlinear Wave-Motion, N.Y.U. Institute of Math. Sci. Rep. NYO-6486, 1958.

Germain, P., O.N.E.R.A. (France) Publication No. 97, 1959.

Helfer, L., Magneto-Hydrodynamic Shock Waves, *Astrophys. J.* **117**, p. 177, 1953.

Iordanskii, S. V., *Akad. Nauk S.S.S.R.* Doklady, **121**, p. 610, 1958 (in Russian only).

Landau, L. D., and E. M. Lifshitz, *Electrodynamics of Continuous Media*, Addison-Wesley, Reading, Mass., 1960, pp. 224–233.

Liubarskii, G. I., and R. V. Polovin, Simple Magnetoacoustic Waves; Impossibility of Rarefaction Shock Waves in Magnetohydrodynamics, J.E.T.P., **35**, pp. 509, 510, 1958. English translation: *Soviet Phys.*, J.E.T.P., p. 361, 1959.

Lust, R., Magneto-hydrodynamische Stosswellen in einem Plasma unendlicher Leitfahigkeit, *Z. Naturforsch.*, **8a**, p. 277, 1953.

Lust, R., Stationare Magneto-hydrodynamische Stosswellen beliebiger Starke, *Z. Naturforsch.*, **10a**, p. 125, 1955.

Polovin, R. V., Shock Waves in Magnetohydrodynamics, *Soviet Phys.—Uspekhi*, **3**, p. 677, 1961.

Shercliff, J. A., One-dimensional Magnetogasdynamics in Oblique Fields, *J. Fluid Mech.*, **9**, p. 481, 1960.

Syrovatskii, S. I. (See *Electrodynamics of Continuous Media* by Landau and Lifshitz, Addison-Wesley, Reading, Mass., 1960, for a review of the stability analysis.)

Syrovatskii, S. I., The Stability of Tangential Discontinuities in a Magnetohydrodynamic Medium, J.E.T.P., **24**, p. 622, 1953.

Syrovatskii, S. I., The Stability of Shock Waves in Magnetohydrodynamics, *Soviet Phys.*, J.E.T.P., **35** (8), p. 1024, 1959.

Ionizing Shocks

Chu, C. K., Dynamics of Ionizing Shock Waves: Shocks in Transverse Magnetic Fields, *Phys. Fluids*, **7**, p. 1349, 1964.

Helliwell, J. B., Gas-Ionizing Shock and Combustion Waves in Magnetogasdynamics, *J. Fluid Mech.*, **14**, p. 405, 1962.

Helliwell, J. B., Gas-Ionizing Shock Waves with Oblique Fields, *Phys. Fluids*, **6**, p. 1516, 1963.

Helliwell, J. B., and D. C. Pack, Magneto-Gas-Dynamic Shock Waves in a Gas with Variable Conductivity, *Phys. Fluids*, **5**, p. 738, 1962.

Kulikovskii, A. G., and G. A. Lyubimov, Gas-Ionizing Magnetohydrodynamic Shock Waves, *Akad Nauk. S.S.S.R. Doklady*, **129**, p. 52, 1959. English translation: *Soviet Phys.—Doklady*, **4**, p. 1185, 1960.

Kulikovskii, A. G., and G. A. Lyubimov, The Simplest Problems Concerning Gas-Ionizing Shock Waves in an Electromagnetic Field, *Akad. Nauk. S.S.S.R. Doklady*, **129**, p. 525, 1959. English translation: *Soviet Phys.—Doklady*, **4**, p. 1195, 1960.

Kulikovskii, A. G., and G. A. Lyubimov, On Gas-Ionizing Magnetohydrodynamic Shock Waves, *Rev. Mod. Phys.*, **32**, p. 977, 1960.

SHOCK STRUCTURE

Bleviss, Z. O., A Study of the Structure of the Magnetohydrodynamic Switch-on Shock in Steady Motion, *J. Fluid Mech.*, **5**, p. 67, 1959.

Germain, P., Structure of Shock Waves in Magneto-Fluid Dynamics, *Rev. Mod. Phys.*, **32**, p. 951, 1960.

Kulikovskii, A. G., and G. A. Lyubimov, See references in preceding section.

Ludford, G. S. S., The Structure of a Hydromagnetic Shock in Plane Steady Motion, *J. Fluid Mech.*, **5**, p. 67, 1959.

Marshall, W., The Structure of Magneto-Hydrodynamic Shock Waves, *Proc. Roy. Soc.* (London), **A233**, p. 367, 1955.

Todd, L., Evolution of the Trans-Alfvénic Normal Shock in a Gas of Finite Electrical Conductivity, *J. Fluid Mech.*, **18**, p. 321, 1964.

EXPERIMENTAL

Camac, M., A. R. Kantrowitz, M. M. Litvak, R. M. Patrick, and H. E. Petschek, *Nucl. Fusion Suppl.*, Part 2, p. 423, 1962.

Patrick, R. M., High-Speed Shock Waves in a Magnetic Annular Shock Tube, *Phys. Fluids*, **2**, p. 589, 1959.

Vlases, G. C., Experiments in a Cylindrical Magnetic Shock Tube, *J. Fluid Mech.*, **16**, No. 82, 1963.

Vlases, G. C., Experiments on Magnetohydrodynamic Shock Waves, *Phys. Fluids*, **7**, No. 8, p. 1358, 1964.

Wilson, C. R., and M. Sugiura, Hydromagnetic Waves Generated by the July 9, 1962 Nuclear Weapons Test as Observed at College, Alaska, *J. Geophys. Research*, **68**, p. 3149, 1963.

11

One-Dimensional Compressible Flow

11.1 INTRODUCTION

In this chapter we will develop some of the basic ideas of one-dimensional magnetogasdynamic (MGD) compressible flow, an understanding of which is vital to the study of MGD generators, accelerators, and magneto-aerodynamics. Compressible flows are usually divided into two arbitrary categories: (1) one-dimensional flow, such as plane wave motion and channel flow, and (2) two- and three-dimensional flow, such as boundary layer flow and aerodynamic flow.

There are two distinct physical situations commonly classified as one-dimensional flow. One is the true one-dimensional flow associated with plane waves and shock waves (see Chapters 8 and 10). The other is the quasi-one-dimensional flow occurring in channels of slowly varying cross section. Channel flow is not one-dimensional in the true sense because assumptions must be made about the wall effects so that properties may be averaged over the cross section of the channel. Even after averaging, and after the flow variables have been assumed to be functions of only one coordinate, there are still important differences between the true one-dimensional flow and channel flow.

As we have seen, the important characteristic speeds in true one-dimensional flow (plane waves) are the magnetosonic speeds (of which there are generally three types). However, in channel flow (for σ finite) the characteristic speed is simply the ordinary sonic speed a unless the conductivity σ is infinite in which case the magnetosonic speeds become relevant.

Since we have already discussed plane waves and shocks, we will now concentrate on quasi-one-dimensional channel flow. We will consider flow through a straight channel of varying area, then point out some applications to generators and accelerators, and finally we will discuss some special flow problems, such as the vortex generator.

11.2 ONE-DIMENSIONAL CHANNEL FLOW

A detailed study of this type of flow is vital for an understanding of many practical devices, such as the MGD generator and accelerator. A rectangular channel is shown schematically in Fig. 11.2-1. The electrodes, assumed to be perfect conductors, form two opposite sides of the channel. The other two sides are insulators. The cross-sectional area A ($A = lh$) is a slowly varying function of x. This area variation may be achieved by varying the spacing between the insulating walls or the spacing between the electrodes, or both. As we will see, the electric field E_z will be constant over z and y and can vary only with x (along the channel). However,

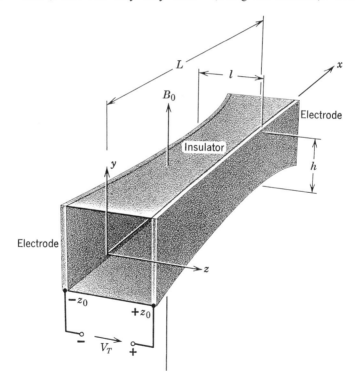

Figure 11.2-1 The quasi-one-dimensional channel. The channel is formed of opposite electrode and insulating walls. The spacing h and l may both vary with x.

since the electrodes are perfect conductors, the terminal potential V_T between the electrodes must be the same between any point on one electrode and any point on the other electrode. From $V_T = -\int_{-z_0}^{+z_0} E_z \, dz =$ constant, we have

$$E_z = -\frac{V_T}{2z_0} = -\frac{V_T}{l(x)} \tag{11.2-1}$$

so that E_z varies inversely with l (the spacing between the electrodes), which may be any given function of x. Hence, for a given $A(x)$, E_z may be a constant along the channel if the area change is brought about entirely by insulator spacing $h(x)$, or E_z may be a function of x if l is a function of x.

The channel of this configuration is actually a MGD generator or pump, depending on whether a load resistor or external generator is connected across the electrodes. The operation of either device is characterized by the value of V_T (or E_z). The analysis of the two modes of operation is exactly the same and whether we call the device a generator or pump (accelerator) depends on the value of V_T or the electric field E_z. Later we will classify the flow according to the value of E_z.

As in ordinary gas dynamics, the boundary layer effects are assumed negligible but may be taken into account in an approximate fashion by a frictional pressure drop.

The question now arises, what effect does the quasi-one-dimensional assumption have on the induced magnetic field? If the channel were of uniform cross section so that the velocity were exactly axial with zero transverse components, the only induced magnetic field would be in the x (axial) direction and would not interact with the flow (except to provide an uncoupled pinch pressure effect across the channel). This same situation occurred in the uniform cross section channels with incompressible flow discussed in Chapter 7. If the channel area changes with x, then small transverse velocity components exist. These velocity components will be much smaller than the main flow velocity (in the x direction) by virtue of the quasi-one-dimensional assumption; namely v and $w \ll u$. The transverse velocities do couple into the main flow in the same way as in the rectangular channel development flow discussed in Chapter 9. However, this interaction will be neglected here because v, $w \ll u$.

We need not assume that Rm (the magnetic Reynolds number) is small since the induced field H_x, although it may actually be large compared to the applied magnetic field, does not couple into the main flow as long as v and $w \ll u$.

A complete general solution to the channel flow problem will not be possible, but a first integral, an expression for du/dx, and the Mach number ($M = u/a$, where a is the ordinary sonic speed $\sqrt{\gamma RT}$) can be readily obtained. These first integrals yield important qualitative information about the flow and allow a quantitative classification of various flow regimes—that is, classification according to whether the flow accelerates, decelerates, chokes, etc. for varying initial flow conditions and channel configurations, and depending on whether the local flow is subsonic or supersonic. The behavior of the flow in the vicinity of $M = 1$ is particularly interesting and some observations about the possibilities of MHD shock waves can be made.

Under open-circuit conditions the total external current is zero but the current density J_z is not necessarily zero everywhere and may form circulating loops (through the electrodes). This is the case if the velocity u varies with x. Then in parts of the channel J_z is positive (in the $+z$ direction) and in other parts negative.

Under any condition other than open circuit the induced magnetic field H_x will depend on the configuration of the external return circuit—the load or generator. We will not be concerned with the exact form of H_x here since it is uncoupled from the main flow equations. Furthermore, in cases of practical importance—where the channel acts as a pump or generator—$H_x \ll H_0$ (the applied field) and $Rm \ll 1$ so that the pinch pressure effect is negligible anyway. When we consider MHD shock waves in a channel, it is easier to discuss a normal MHD shock with the magnetic field parallel to the shock front ($\mathbf{B} \perp$ to u) than it is to consider the general oblique MHD shock with components of magnetic field both parallel to and normal to the shock. If $H_x \ll H_0$, then the normal MHD shock analysis is approximately correct. Remember there is only one type of normal MHD shock (a modification of the ordinary gas dynamic shock) but there are three distinct oblique MHD shocks.

The basic channel flow equations can be obtained by averaging the continuity, motion, energy, and field equations across the channel. We assume steady flow, σ to be a scalar,* and a perfect gas. The equations are:

Continuity

$$\frac{d}{dx} (\rho u A) = 0 \tag{11.2-2}$$

Motion

$$\rho u \frac{du}{dx} = -\frac{dP}{dx} + (\mathbf{J} \times \mathbf{B})_x \tag{11.2-3}$$

---

* σ may be a function of x (because of temperature variations, say). Only when we integrate the equations must we specify σ as constant or a given function of x.

Energy (from 5.10-8)

$$\rho u \frac{dh_0}{dx} = \rho u \left[c_P \frac{dT}{dx} + u \frac{du}{dx} \right] = \mathbf{E} \cdot \mathbf{J} + Q \qquad (11.2\text{-}4)$$

where Q is the heat transfer rate, per unit volume, to the gas through the channel walls. Q then is the heat transfer per unit length of the channel divided by the cross-sectional area. This term is obtained by neglecting the heat conduction (in the gas) along the channel and lumping transverse conduction through the walls into this one term, which may be positive or negative, of course, depending on whether heat is added to or removed from the channel.

State

$$P = \rho RT \qquad (11.2\text{-}5)$$

Ohm's law

$$\mathbf{J} = \sigma(\mathbf{E} + \mathbf{V} \times \mathbf{B}) \qquad (11.2\text{-}6)$$

We have already pointed out that E_z must be a constant over the cross section (and may vary with x if the spacing between the electrodes varies). E_x and E_y must be zero (from $\nabla \times \mathbf{E} = 0$) under the one-dimensional approximation. Hence the only component of current is $J_z = \sigma(E_z + uB_0)$ and the basic equations become, in terms of $E_z(x)$,

$$\rho u A = m \qquad \text{(a constant)} \qquad (11.2\text{-}7)$$

$$\rho u \frac{du}{dx} = -\frac{dP}{dx} - \sigma(E_z + uB_0)B_0 \qquad (11.2\text{-}8)$$

$$\rho u \left(c_P \frac{dT}{dx} + u \frac{du}{dx} \right) = \sigma(E_z + uB_0)E_z + Q \qquad (11.2\text{-}9)$$

$$P = \rho RT \qquad (11.2\text{-}10)$$

In general now, both E_z and B_0 could be functions of x. In cases of most practical interest B_0 would be a constant and the electrodes would be parallel, thus making E_z constant. The four equations (11.2-7) to (11.2-10) allow a solution, in principle, for P, T, u, and ρ for a given $A(x)$, $\sigma(x)$, $E_z(x)$, and $B_0(x)$. After we find $u(x)$, we can relate the current density J_z and the total current I (which flows through the external circuit) to E_z and V_T, the terminal potential. The problem is solved once we know the terminal characteristics. Such calculations were treated in detail in Chapter 7.

We begin by eliminating T between (11.2-9) and (11.2-10). Then, using (11.2-7) and (11.2-8) to eliminate dP/dx and $d\rho/dx$, we find for the acceleration du/dx:

$$\frac{du}{dx} = \frac{\dfrac{u}{A}\left(\dfrac{dA}{dx}\right) - \dfrac{\gamma - 1}{\gamma}\dfrac{Q}{P} - \dfrac{\sigma B_0^2}{P}\left(u + \dfrac{E_z}{B_0}\right)\left(u + \dfrac{\gamma - 1}{\gamma}\cdot\dfrac{E_z}{B_0}\right)}{(M^2 - 1)} \qquad (11.2\text{-}11)$$

where $\gamma = c_P/c_V$ and $M = u/a$, the ordinary Mach number. This equation is significant in determining the behavior of the flow. For a given B_0 and E_z the acceleration can be found for a given (dA/dx), Mach number, and rate of heat addition. This type of analysis is the same as in ordinary gas dynamics except that now we have the additional electro-magnetic term, which can have either sign depending on the sign of E_z and the particular value of u. We will examine this equation in detail presently.

Another equation of interest, which must be considered together with (11.2-11), is the expression dM/dx. From (11.2-11) and (11.2-9) we obtain

$$\frac{dM}{dx} = \frac{1}{(M^2 - 1)}\left\{\left(1 + \frac{\gamma - 1}{2}M^2\right)\frac{M}{A}\frac{dA}{dx} - \frac{\gamma - 1}{\gamma}\cdot\frac{1 + \gamma M^2}{2}\cdot\frac{Q}{aP}\right.$$
$$\left. - \left(1 + \frac{\gamma - 1}{2}M^2\right)\frac{\sigma B_0^2}{aP}\left(u + \frac{E_z}{B_0}\right)\left[u + \frac{(1 + \gamma M^2)(\gamma - 1)}{2\gamma + (\gamma - 1)M^2\gamma}\cdot\frac{E_z}{B_0}\right]\right\}$$
$$(11.2\text{-}12)$$

Now there are two distinct types of flow to consider, positive and negative E_z. If E_z is positive, the terminal potential V_T is negative and must be maintained by an external voltage source. The electromagnetic body force decelerates the gas. If E_z is negative, the terminal potential V_T is positive and the channel acts as a generator (feeding an external load) or as a pump (the electromagnetic body force acts to accelerate the gas) in which case an external voltage source must be supplied. Under short-circuit conditions, $E_z = V_T = 0$, and under open circuit the potential must be such as to make the total current zero. The total current I can be written

$$I = \int_0^L h\sigma(E_z + uB_0)\,dx \qquad (11.2\text{-}13)$$

where L is the length of the channel in the x direction. Even if I is zero (open circuit), u may vary along the channel (as well as E_z) so that J_z may have different signs in parts of the channel, the current thus circulating around through the electrodes. However, we may speak of local conditions (at a given x) and examine the sign of J_z locally. (E_z will always have the same sign throughout the channel.)

We can now verify our statements about E_z. In a local sense, for positive u the effect of the body force (but not including the Joule heating effect) can be classified as follows:

1. If $(\mathbf{J} \times \mathbf{B}) > 0$, acceleration or pumping mode. $J_z < 0$, $E_z < -uB_0$, $|E_z| > uB_0$. The body force tends to accelerate the flow. Power must be fed from an external voltage source.

2. If $(\mathbf{J} \times \mathbf{B}) < 0$, generator mode (flow decelerated). $J_z > 0$, $0 > E_z > -uB_0$. E_z must be less than zero. ($E_z = 0$ corresponds to short-circuit conditions). Under open-circuit conditions, $E_z = -uB_0$. Hence E_z must lie between these values in order for power to be fed to an external load.

3. If $(\mathbf{J} \times \mathbf{B}) < 0$, negative pumping mode (decelerator). $J_z > 0$, $E_z > 0$. Here external power must be fed from an external voltage source (of opposite polarity to case 1 above) so that the electromagnetic body force tends to decelerate the flow.

Figure 11.2-2 shows a diagram of the cross section of the channel with polarity indicated. It is clear that the sign on E_z alone is not enough to indicate the effect of the electromagnetic body force. Furthermore, the local behavior of the flow may be different from the average overall effect. That is, the device must act entirely as a ·decelerator (positive E_z), or if E_z is negative, it can act as a generator-decelerator-pump in some combination along the length, or entirely as a generator, or entirely as a pump.

It is convenient to show the range of E_z in a graphical manner, comparing it to uB_0. This is the most useful way of classifying the flow. Figure 11.2-3 shows a plot of E_z with the three flow regimes discussed above. In order to solve the basic equations we need to distinguish between positive and negative E_z. For the cases of most practical interest (generators, positive pumps, and flow meters), E_z is negative and V_T positive. By examining (11.2-11), we see that the two products in the electromagnetic term each can be zero for certain values of positive u (if E_z is negative) and the net electromagnetic term can change sign depending on the relative size of u and E_z/B_0. For positive E_z the electromagnetic term is always the same sign and influences the flow in the same manner as does heat addition. One very important point should now be made clear. We have classified E_z according to the direction of the body force. However, the net effect of the electromagnetic interaction for E_z negative is not indicated by the body force alone. Heat is added to the gas by Joulean dissipation $(\mathbf{E'} \cdot \mathbf{J'})$ which modifies the action of the body force. Let us look at this problem in detail.

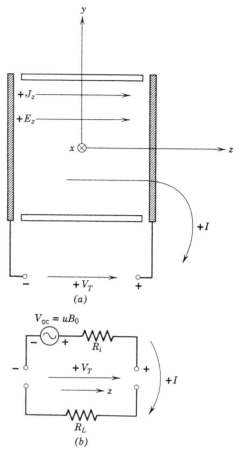

(a)

(b)

Figure 11.2-2 Diagram of sign conventions. (*a*) Cross section of channel, (*b*) equivalent circuit.

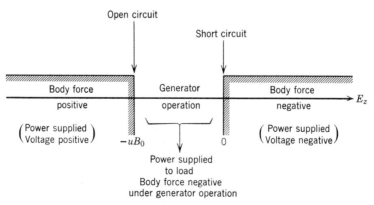

Figure 11.2-3 A one-dimensional plot of E_z showing the various regions of operations.

11.3 NEGATIVE E_z PUMP-GENERATOR MODE

The case of most practical interest and the one that is more complex to analyze is that of negative E_z. As long as the channel is operating as a generator or accelerator (pump), E_z will be negative.

We will follow Sears and Resler (1958) and define three critical speeds as follows:

$$u_1 = -\frac{\gamma - 1}{\gamma} \frac{E_z}{B_0} = \frac{\gamma - 1}{\gamma} u_3 \qquad (11.3\text{-}1)$$

$$u_2 = \frac{1 + \gamma M^2}{2 + (\gamma - 1)M^2} \cdot u_1 \qquad (11.3\text{-}2)$$

$$u_3 = -\frac{E_z}{B_0} = \frac{V_T}{B_0 l} \qquad (11.3\text{-}3)$$

These critical values for u appear in Equations (11.2-11) and (11.2-12), which can now be written as follows:

$$\frac{du}{dx} = \frac{\dfrac{u}{A}\left(\dfrac{dA}{dx}\right) - \dfrac{\gamma - 1}{\gamma}\dfrac{Q}{P} - \dfrac{\sigma B_0^2}{P}(u - u_3)(u - u_1)}{(M^2 - 1)} \qquad (11.3\text{-}4)$$

$$\frac{dM}{dx} = \frac{1}{(M^2 - 1)}\left[\left(1 + \frac{\gamma - 1}{2}M^2\right)\frac{M}{A}\frac{dA}{dx} - \frac{\gamma - 1}{\gamma}\cdot\frac{1 + \gamma M^2}{2}\cdot\frac{Q}{aP}\right.$$
$$\left. - \left(1 + \frac{\gamma - 1}{2}M^2\right)\frac{\sigma B_0^2}{aP}(u - u_3)(u - u_2)\right] \qquad (11.3\text{-}5)$$

From (11.3-4) we see that for $u < u_3$ the body force accelerates the flow and for $u > u_3$ the body force decelerates the flow. The speed u_1 is just that speed at which the electromagnetic body force is compensated for by the Joule heat. The net MGD effect on the flow can be stated then as: if $M > 1$, the flow is accelerated if u lies between u_3 and u_1 and decelerated if u lies outside that region. If $M < 1$, the flow is decelerated if u lies between u_3 and u_1 and accelerated if u lies outside this region. These results are shown graphically in Fig. 11.3-1.

The net MGD effect on M can be seen from Equation (11.3-5) as follows:

1. If $M > 1$ (supersonic), M increases with x $(dM/dx > 0)$ if u lies between u_2 and u_3 and decreases with x if M lies outside this interval.

2. For $M < 1$ (subsonic), the reverse is true. Figure 11.3-2 shows these regions graphically.

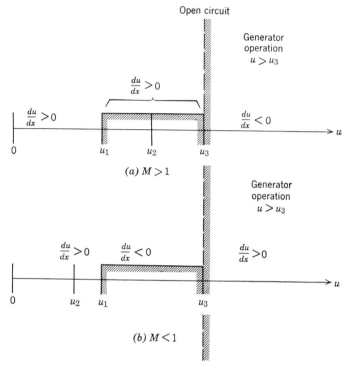

Figure 11.3-1   A one-dimensional plot of u (taken positive) showing the behavior of du/dx due to net electromagnetic effects in various regions. E_z is a fixed negative value in this plot.

In Figs. 11.3-1 and 11.3-2 the region corresponding to local generator operation is $u > u_3$. Physically u must become larger and larger as the generator is loaded down toward short-circuit conditions if u_3 is held constant. Under short-circuit conditions, of course, $u_3 = 0$ and u must be finite throughout the channel. Under local open-circuit conditions, of course, $u = u_3$. This observation can easily be verified by equating the voltage drop through the external load resistor to the terminal potential (see Fig. 11.2-2):

$$-E_z l = V_T = IR_L = \int_0^L h\sigma(E_z + uB_0)R_L\, dx$$

$$V_T = h\sigma\left(-\frac{V_T}{l} + \bar{u}B_0\right)R_L L \tag{11.3-6}$$

$$\bar{u} = \frac{V_T}{lB_0}\left[1 + \frac{l}{\sigma h R_L L}\right]$$

where R_L and I are the load resistance and total current. $\bar{u}$ is the mean value of u along the channel. As $R_L \to \infty$ (open circuit), $\bar{u} \to u_3$ and as $R_L \to 0$, $u_3 \to 0$ for finite $\bar{u}$.

The ratio $u_2/u_1 = (1 + \gamma M^2)/[2 + (\gamma - 1)M^2]$ is a monotonic function of M. The behavior of u_2 as a function of M can be represented as follows:

$$\begin{aligned} u_2 &= \frac{u_1}{2} & \text{at} & \quad M = 0 \\ u_2 &< u_1 & \text{for} & \quad M < 1 \\ u_2 &= u_1 & \text{at} & \quad M = 1 \\ u_2 &> u_1 & \text{for} & \quad M > 1 \\ u_2 &\to u_3 & \text{as} & \quad M \to \infty \end{aligned} \qquad (11.3\text{-}7)$$

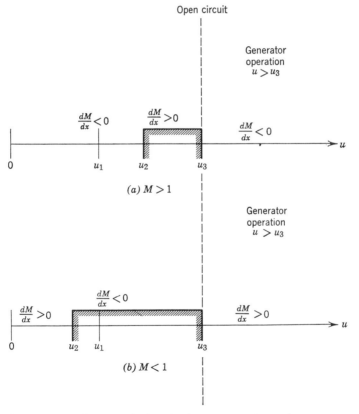

Figure 11.3-2 A one-dimensional plot of u (taken positive) showing the behavior of dM/dx due to net electromagnetic effects in various regions. E_z is a fixed negative value in this plot, so that u_3 is a fixed positive value.

Table 11.3-1

Classification of flow types according to initial conditions and type of channel.

	A = constant		$dA/dx > 0$		$dA/dx < 0$	
	1	2	1	2	1	2
	$M_0 > 1$	$M_0 < 1$	$M_0 > 1$	$M_0 < 1$	$M_0 > 1$	$M_0 < 1$
A	*$u_1 < u_2 < u_3 < u_0$	*$u_2 < u_1 < u_3 < u_0$	$u_1 < u_2 < u_3 < u_0$	$u_2 < u_1 < u_3 < u_0$	$u_1 < u_2 < u_3 < u_0$	$u_2 < u_1 < u_3 < u_0$
B	$u_1 < u_2 < u_0 < u_3$	$u_2 < u_1 < u_0 < u_3$	$u_1 < u_2 < u_0 < u_3$	$u_2 < u_1 < u_0 < u_3$	$u_1 < u_2 < u_0 < u_3$	$u_2 < u_1 < u_0 < u_3$
C	$u_1 < u_0 < u_2 < u_3$	$u_2 < u_0 < u_1 < u_3$	$u_1 < u_0 < u_2 < u_3$	$u_2 < u_0 < u_1 < u_3$	$u_1 < u_0 < u_2 < u_3$	$u_2 < u_0 < u_1 < u_3$
D	$u_0 < u_1 < u_2 < u_3$	$u_0 < u_2 < u_1 < u_3$	$u_0 < u_1 < u_2 < u_3$	$u_0 < u_2 < u_1 < u_3$	$u_0 < u_1 < u_2 < u_3$	$u_0 < u_2 < u_1 < u_3$

* Generator mode for constant area channel.

We see that for $M > 1$, the speeds are ordered as $u_1 < u_2 < u_3$ and for $M < 1$, $u_2 < u_1 < u_3$.

The observations in this section may now be used to discuss, qualitatively, the flow under various initial conditions in various types of channels. In general, remember, the basic equations cannot be integrated except under a few, rather artificial cases, such as constant density or constant temperature. However, a great deal of useful information can be gained by examining the behavior of du/dx and dM/dx functions of x for various initial values of u (which we denote as u_0) and various initial Mach numbers M_0, and for a given $A(x)$ and V_T/B_0. In general, the flow may be divided into distinct regions where its behavior is different. The regions are shown in Table 11.3-1. Each region of flow is classified accordingly as:

1. $dA/dx = 0$, $dA/dx < 0$, or $dA/dx > 0$.
2. $M_0 < 1$ or $M_0 > 1$.
3. u_0 in a given range, relative to u_1, u_2, and u_3.
4. Q may be zero or a given function of x, as may be E_z and σ.

In the next section we begin by examining the simplest case, that of constant area and constant V_T/B_0 with $Q = 0$ (Sears and Resler, 1958).

11.4   CONSTANT AREA FLOW, $Q = 0$, E_z/B_0 NEGATIVE, (u_3 POSITIVE)

The flow in a straight channel of constant area may be divided into eight distinct classes characterized by u_0 and M_0. These regions are tabulated in Table 11.3-1. Actual integration for $M(u)$ has been carried out by Rosa (1956) but the results are difficult to interpret physically. A simple physical picture can be had by showing how u and M develop with x (downstream) according to the class of flow.

Let us consider the eight possibilities now in order (since $Q = 0$ and $dA/dx = 0$, we are really looking at just the MGD effect). We will see that the flow may choke, approach an asymptotic state, or in two special cases act as a nozzle and reversed nozzle with smooth acceleration or deceleration through $M = 1$.

1A. $M_0 > 1$ and $u_1 < u_2 < u_3 < u_0$ (Generator Mode)

The flow is decelerated in this case. Here du/dx and dM/dx are initially negative. There are actually three subcases: If M_0 is sufficiently close to unity, the deceleration may be large enough to choke the flow. The

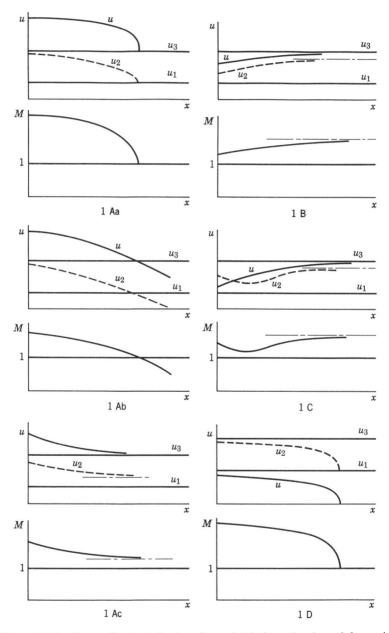

Figure 11.4-1 The qualitative behavior of u and M along the channel for various supersonic initial conditions. 1Aa, 1Ab, 1Ac are the three possibilities when $u_1 < u_2 < u_3 < u_0$; 1B. $u_1 < u_2 < u_0 < u_3$; 1C. $u_1 < u_0 < u_2 < u_3$; and 1D. $u_0 < u_1 < u_2 < u_3$.

qualitative development is shown in Fig. 11.4-1(1Aa). Also, there is a set of initial conditions u_0 and M_0 such that u reaches u_3 just as M reaches 1. In this case it is possible for the flow to decelerate smoothly through sonic conditions, as is shown in Fig. 11.4-1(1Ab). After passing through $M = 1$, the flow becomes that of case 2B, where $M \to 0$, $u \to u_1$, and the temperature increases indefinitely. Case 1Ab is like a reversed gas dynamic nozzle in which flow is unstable. For this reason 1Ab may be an unstable situation and impossible to achieve in practice. For a third set of initial conditions, u may decrease monotonically toward u_3, and M decreases asymptotically to a value greater than 1 (see Fig. 11.4-1(1Ac)).

Questions of stability arise in the smoothly decelerated flow 1Ab and whether the flow is actually possible or not is unanswered.

1B. $M_0 > 1$ and $u_1 < u_2 < u_0 < u_3$

Here du/dx and dM/dx are both positive and must remain so, approaching zero asymptotically as u increases. u_2 approaches u but must remain below u because dM/dx must be zero at $u = u_2$ but du/dx is positive for $u = u_2$ which is contradictory. Hence u_2 can only approach u from below. Similarly, u must remain below u_3 because as u approaches u_3, du/dx and dM/dx approach zero. This behavior is shown in Fig. 11.4-1(1B). The asymptotic condition is an ordinary gas dynamic one with no MGD effects.

1C. $M_0 > 1$ and $u_1 < u_0 < u_2 \lesssim u_3$

Initially $du/dx > 0$ and $dM/dx < 0$. u increases while u_2 decreases until they coincide where $dM/dx = 0$. Then dM/dx reverses sign, becoming positive, and u_2 becomes less than u. After this crossing of u and u_2 the case becomes 1B above. Case 1C is shown in Fig. 11.4-1(1C).

1D. $M_0 > 1$ and $u_0 < u_1 < u_2 < u_3$

Initially both $du/dx < 0$ and $dM/dx < 0$. As M approaches unity, the deceleration must increase towards infinity (dM/dx and $du/dx \to -\infty$). The flow must choke because it cannot pass through sonic conditions. The only subsonic condition where $u_0 < u_1$ is case 2D and clearly the flow cannot pass through sonic to this case because, there, du/dx and dM/dx are both positive. Figure 11.4-1(1D) shows this behavior.

2A. $M_0 < 1$ and $u_2 < u_1 < u_3 < u_0$ (Generator Mode)

Here the flow is choked in a manner similar to 1D. du/dx and dM/dx are initially positive and $du/dx \to \infty$ as $M \to 1$. Figure 11.4-2(2A) shows the curves.

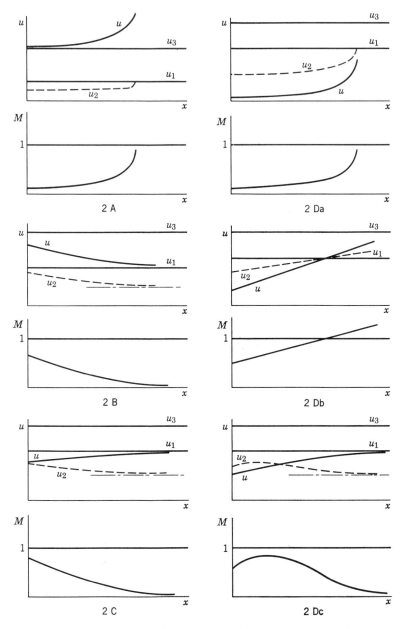

Figure 11.4-2 The qualitative behavior of u and M along the channel for various subsonic initial conditions.   2A. $u_2 < u_1 < u_3 < u_0$;   2B. $u_2 < u_1 < u_0 < u_3$;   2C. $u_2 < u_0 < u_1 < u_3$;   2Da, 2Db, 2Dc. $u_0 < u_2 < u_1 < u_3$.

2B. $M_0 < 1$ *and* $u_2 < u_1 < u_0 < u_3$

Here $dM/dx < 0$ and $du/dx < 0$. u approaches u_1 asymptotically while M approaches zero. As $M \to 0$, u_2 approaches the value of $u_1/2$ so that u and u_2 never coincide. The fact that u remains finite while $M \to 0$ means that the temperature must increase indefinitely downstream. See Fig. 11.4-2(2B).

2C. $M_0 < 1$ *and* $u_2 < u_0 < u_1 < u_3$

The behavior is the same as case 2B except that u approaches u_1 from below instead of from above. See Fig. 11.4-2(2C).

2D. $M_0 < 1$ *and* $u_0 < u_2 < u_1 < u_3$

There are three distinct possibilities here, as in case 1A; 2D is actually the subsonic counterpart of 1A. Just as in 1A, the flow can choke, smoothly accelerate, or approach an asymptotic state. The three types of behavior are shown in Fig. 11.4-2(2Da), (2Db), and (2Dc). If M_0 is sufficiently close to unity, the acceleration du/dx approaches infinity and the flow chokes. As in case 1A, there is one precise set of initial values of u_0 and M_0 that make u reach u_1 just as $M = 1$ and smooth acceleration through sonic conditions occurs. The flow then becomes case 1B with acceleration toward u_3. This case, 2Db, is effectively a nozzle produced by electromagnetic effects. Case 2Dc occurs when u_0 is close to u_2 and the u and u_2 curves cross. At the point of crossing, dM/dx changes sign and u approaches u_1 and M approaches zero asymptotically. This asymptotic behavior (after u and u_2 cross) is the same as in case 2C, with the temperature increasing indefinitely downstream.

The u–M Plot

Another informative way of looking at the behavior of the flow, other than u and M versus x plots, is a u–M plot. Following Culick (1964), we can combine Equations (11.3-4) and (11.3-5) to give an expression for dM/du as follows (for $dA/dx = 0$):

$$\frac{u}{M}\frac{dM}{du} = \left(1 + \frac{\gamma - 1}{2} M^2\right)\frac{u - u_2}{u - u_1} \qquad (11.4\text{-}1)$$

which may be integrated to give

$$M^2 = \frac{(u/u_3)(u/u_1 - 1)}{C + (\gamma - 1)(u/u_1)(1 - u/2u_3)} \qquad (11.4\text{-}2)$$

where C is the constant of integration. C may be written in terms of u_0 and M_0 as:

$$C = \frac{(u_0/u_3)(u_0/u_1 - 1)}{M_0^2} - (\gamma - 1)\frac{u_0}{u_1}\left(1 - \frac{u_0}{2u_3}\right) \qquad (11.4\text{-}3)$$

It is convenient to plot u/u_3 versus M for various values of C as shown in Fig. 11.4-3. The direction of increasing x is indicated by the arrows (which can be inferred from the u and M versus x plots already constructed). At $M = 1$ and $u/u_3 = (\gamma - 1)/\gamma$ (which is $u = u_1$) or $u/u_3 = 1$, nodal points occur through which all transitions through sonic conditions must pass. Opposing arrows on the same path which occur (for some values of C)

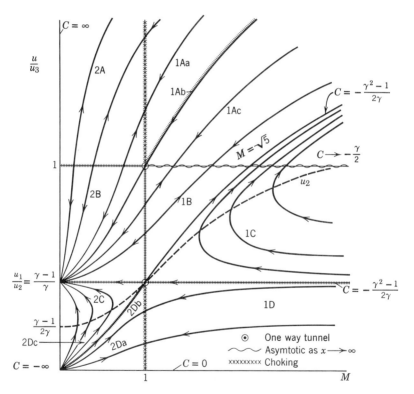

Figure 11.4-3 u-M plot for a channel with A constant, $Q = 0$, and E_z a negative constant. Note that the regions defined by Figs. 11.4-1 and 11.4-2 are shown in this plot. The flow cases 1Ab and 2Db are lines on the u-M plot, and the other cases are regions. The line 1Ab separates the regions 1Aa and 1Ac, and the line 2Db separates the regions 2Da and 2Dc. The region of generator operation is the area lying above the $u/u_3 = 1$ line.

on $u/u_3 = 1$ and on $M = 1$ indicate choking. The regions of flow already delineated in the u and M versus x plots are identified on the u–M plot, which shows the whole picture all at once.

We see that the generator region is the area that lies above the $u/u_3 = 1$ line. This area is inaccessible from below. Remember, Fig. 11.4-3 is based on the assumptions that the area is constant, Q is zero, and E_z is negative.

Generator Operation

For the channel to act as a generator, that is, deliver power to an external load, u must be greater than u_3. However, portions of the channel may be operating with $u < u_3$ even though the net overall effect is that of a generator. It is the overall effect that counts, of course. Hence it is convenient to speak of local conditions, as we have been doing throughout this analysis, and we can say that in a local sense the channel acts as a generator if $u > u_3$.

If we examine each of the preceding types of flow, we see that only in cases 1A and 2A is $u > u_3$. In 2A, u is always greater than u_3. In 1A, u remains greater than u_3 for 1Aa and 1Ac. In case 1Ab, it is possible for u to drop below u_3 and for the channel to stop acting as a generator.

We see then, in summary, that for a channel to act as a generator the inlet velocity u_0 must be greater than u_3. If $M_0 < 1$, the flow will choke if the channel is long enough. If $M_0 > 1$, there are three possibilities: choking, asymptotic approach to an ordinary gas dynamic state, or smooth deceleration to a nongenerator-type subsonic flow.' Figure 11.4-3 shows this behavior in a single picture.

It must be remembered, however, that any inlet velocity can be used under generator conditions—the value of E_z will adjust itself so that $u_0 > u_3$. We have been treating E_z as an independent variable defining u_1, u_2, and u_3. In practice, of course, E_z is a dependent variable under generator operation.

11.5 CHANNELS OF VARYING AREA

The equations for varying area channel flow cannot be integrated exactly for a prescribed $A(x)$, but we can, as before for constant channels, examine some of the qualitative features of the flow. Certain special solutions for channels with flows of constant density, temperature, and pressure can be obtained, but a rather peculiar area variation is required. Such solutions seem somewhat artificial and of more academic than practical value. Because of the rather cumbersome algebra these solutions are not presented here. The reader is referred to the references and to the problems for a discussion of such solutions.

In the Section 11.4 we found a total of eight possible types of flow in a constant area channel with zero heat transfer. In a variable area channel, the possibilities are greatly increased. For each of these eight cases, the dA/dx term can have either sign and dominate the electromagnetic term in one or both the du/dx or dM/dx expressions. The electromagnetic term can either augment the ordinary gas dynamic converging or diverging channel effect or completely reverse it. There is little point in classifying all the possibilities here, but for a given $A(x)$ and set of initial conditions we can determine qualitatively how the flow will develop downstream by using Equations (11.3-4) and (11.3-5).

For generator operation, $u > u_3$, and we know that for a constant area channel there is only one case where u can drop below u_3 (if $u_0 > u_3$), namely, the MGD nozzle case in which the flow smoothly decelerates through $M = 1$ at $u = u_3$. (The question of stability is unanswered and such flow may not occur in reality.) Generally, the flow would choke and u remain greater than u_3. The flow would remain subsonic or supersonic (with $u > u_3$) except for the one case just mentioned. However, if the area varies along the channel, the ordinary gas dynamic effect may combine with the electromagnetic effect to give rise to an effective throat in the channel. The varying area nozzle effects in ordinary gas dynamics may be enhanced or completely counterbalanced by the MGD effects. The flow could pass through sonic conditions at the throat and consequently pass smoothly through u_3 (from above or below) which is of course not necessarily the sonic speed in this case. Hence a variable area channel may operate as a generator only over part of its length when $u > u_3$.

To add to the complication, shock waves may occur in a divergent channel, just as in ordinary gas dynamics. The range of the critical exit pressure is then modified by the MGD effects, as are the shock jump relationships. The MHD normal shock relationships (including effects of finite conductivity) must be used.

For reference we will list the basic $x \to u$ transformed channel equations. They will be useful later on and lend insight into the qualitative behavior of the flow. A u–M plot will not be given here for varying area since the precise shape depends on the sign and magnitude of dA/du. (Culick (1964) shows a general plot for u–M under the assumption that $\{1 + (u_1/2A) \, dA/du + (\gamma - 1)M^2/2\} > 0$, which is not always the case.)

By suitably manipulating the basic expressions (11.2-7) through (11.2-10), we arrive at the following equations in terms of u as the independent variable:

$$\frac{dP}{du} = -\frac{(1/A)(d/du)(Au)}{(u - u_1)} P - \frac{m}{A}\left(\frac{\gamma - 1}{\gamma}\right)\left(\frac{u - u_3}{u - u_1}\right) \quad (11.5\text{-}1)$$

$$\frac{dx}{du} = \frac{m/A + dP/du}{\sigma B_0^2(u_3 - u)} = \frac{P}{\sigma B_0^2}\frac{1 + (u/A)(dA/du) - M^2}{(u - u_1)(u - u_3)} \quad (11.5\text{-}2)$$

$$\frac{u}{M}\frac{dM}{du} = \left[1 + \frac{u_1}{2A}\frac{dA}{du} + \frac{(\gamma - 1)}{2}M^2\right] \cdot \frac{u - u'_2}{u - u_1} \quad (11.5\text{-}3)$$

where

$$u'_2 = \frac{(1 + \gamma M^2)u_1}{2 + (u_1/A)(dA/du) + (\gamma - 1)M^2}$$

which $\rightarrow u_2$ as $dA/du \rightarrow 0$. The energy equation becomes

$$c_P\frac{dT}{du} = \frac{(u_1/Au)(d/du)(Au)}{(u_1 - u)}c_PT - u\left(\frac{u - u_3}{u - u_1}\right) \quad (11.5\text{-}4)$$

An expression for the entropy change along the channel can be obtained from Equation (5.7-1). If $Q = 0$, we have

$$\rho u T\frac{ds}{dx} = \mathbf{E}' \cdot \mathbf{J}' = \frac{J^2}{\sigma} = (u - u_3)^2\sigma B_0^2 \quad (11.5\text{-}5)$$

which when combined with (11.5-2) yields

$$\frac{ds}{du} = \frac{R(u - u_3)}{u(u - u_1)}\left(1 + \frac{u}{A}\frac{dA}{du} - M^2\right) \quad (11.5\text{-}6)$$

where R is the gas constant.

Usually A is specified as a function of x, not u, so that the actual integration of the above equations may be no easier than the original ones in terms of x. However, for constant area flow, with $dA = 0$, the u transformed equations are rather useful, as we will see in the next section.

11.6   THE CONSTANT AREA GENERATOR

In this section we will examine the constant area generator in some detail and discuss its optimization. A simpler model, the constant velocity generator, is left as an exercise for the student (see problems 1d, 6, and 7 at the end of the chapter). Recent work (Swift-Hook and Wright, 1963, and Medin 1965) seems to indicate that a constant velocity generator is the most efficient type.

In Section 11.4 we saw that for generator operation u must be greater than u_3. Another way to say this is: under generator operation, that is, an external load of from 0 to ∞ ohms across the electrodes, u_3 and hence the terminal voltage will adjust so that $u_3 < u$. The trajectories in Fig. 11.4-3 show the flow development as x increases (in the direction of the arrows) for various initial conditions. The initial values u_0 and M_0 define a point on the plot, and the contour through that point is the development trajectory.

As we have mentioned, the generator flow will generally choke and u remain u_3 except for two special cases. One case is initially supersonic flow which decelerates smoothly through sonic conditions to where $u < u_3$. In such a case, part of the channel may be fed power by the generator action of the part in which $u > u_3$.

If the flow is initially subsonic, it will remain subsonic with $u > u_3$ throughout the channel, with the possibility of choking (at $M = 1$) if the channel is long enough or if the outlet conditions are appropriately adjusted. (This region is 2A in Fig. 11.4-3.) There are three possibilities for initially supersonic flow: choking may occur at $M = 1$ (case 1Aa, Fig. 11.4-3), the flow may smoothly decelerate to subsonic conditions with $u < u_3$ (case 1Ab), or it may asymptotically approach a state where $u > u_3$ and $M > 1$. Hence there is a wide range of initial conditions where the flow may choke at $M = 1$.

In order to completely determine the behavior of a given generator channel, we need specify the channel area and length, the initial Mach number M_0, the initial velocity u_0, one exit parameter (say P_e or u_e), and the external resistive load or, equivalently, V_T or u_3. However, under choking conditions, the exit Mach number may remain constant (for fixed inlet conditions) while the other outlet parameters may be varied. For given inlet values of u_0 and M_0, a wide range of exit conditions can be satisfied by varying u_3 even without choking; this observation can be inferred directly from the u–M plot (Fig. 11.4-3) which is a plot u/u_3 versus M, remember.

In this section we will explicitly integrate some of the channel equations so that the inlet and outlet conditions and electrical parameters may be related and some of the generator characteristics determined. For example, we might ask: for a given generator configuration and given set of inlet conditions, u_0, M_0 (hence T_0), and m (hence P_0 and ρ_0), and for electrical load resistance R_L (or V_T), what are the exit conditions, what power will be generated, and will the flow choke or not?

Next we will consider how the performance of a constant area generator may be optimized. It might seem convenient in such calculations to derive an equivalent circuit of the generator—an open-circuit voltage in series with an internal resistance—and, indeed, such a circuit is useful. However, a complication arises in deciding how to calculate the internal resistance. Remember that when we studied (incompressible) Hartmann flow in Chapter 7, we found the internal resistance R_i by keeping the pressure gradient in the channel constant (as we varied R_L to find V_{oc} and I_{sc}). We saw, however, that a different value of R_i was obtained if we imposed a condition of constant flow rate. Here, with the generator, the choice of the parameter that should be kept constant as R_L varies is somewhat arbitrary. We are faced with several possibilities. Perhaps the easiest and most meaningful way is to fix the inlet conditions, mass flow rate, and channel size and then allow the exit conditions to vary to accommodate the load resistance R_L as it is varied. This is the way optimization calculations have generally been made (Neuringer, 1960) and we will use this method here. Internal resistances calculated in this manner can be matched to the load R_L to give optimum operating conditions.

Let us now look at the power calculation by more direct means and later we will consider the circuit approach. We can now explicitly integrate some of the basic equations for the constant area channel. The total current I is

$$I = \int_0^L J_z h \, dx$$

$$= \int_0^L \sigma B_0 (u - u_3) h \, dx \tag{11.6-1}$$

which is zero under open-circuit conditions although under open-circuit conditions $J_z(x)$ is not generally zero but may change sign to make $I = 0$. The total power p fed to the load R_L can be expressed as

$$p = IV_T = \int_0^L \sigma B_0^2 u_3 (u - u_3) A \, dx \tag{11.6-2}$$

A positive value of p represents power fed to the external load and a negative p represents power fed into the channel by an external generator. (V_T is a signed quantity and hence so is u_3.) For positive V_T and u_3, E_z is negative, $u > u_3$, and the integrand is positive throughout; M remains above or below unity throughout for generator action, except in the one case 1Ab. Now, by using (11.5-2) (with $dA/du = 0$), we can transform for $x \to u$ to give

$$p = \int_{u_0}^{u_e} \frac{P u_3 (1 - M^2) A}{(u - u_1)} \, du \tag{11.6-3}$$

where the subscripts 0 and e denote inlet and exit values. From $M = u/a = u/\sqrt{\gamma RT}$ we have

$$\frac{M^2}{M_0^2} = \frac{P_0 u}{u_0 P} \tag{11.6-4}$$

which may be combined with (11.5-1) and inserted into (11.6-3) to give

$$p = -\frac{P_0 M_0^2 A u_3}{u_0} \int_{u_0}^{u_e} \frac{u}{(u - u_1)} du - u_3 A \int_{P_0}^{P_e} dP$$

$$- m u_3 \left(\frac{\gamma - 1}{\gamma}\right) \int_{u_0}^{u_e} \left(\frac{u - u_3}{u - u_1}\right) du \tag{11.6-5}$$

which integrates to give the following expression for p in terms of inlet conditions, m, u_3, and P_e:

$$p = (u_0 - u_e)\left[\frac{u_3 P_0 M_0^2}{u_0} + \frac{u_3 m(\gamma - 1)}{A\gamma}\right] A + u_3 A(P_0 - P_e)$$

$$+ u_3 A \ln\left(\frac{u_e - u_1}{u_0 - u_1}\right) \cdot \left[\frac{m(\gamma - 1)}{A\gamma}(u_3 - u_1) - \frac{u_1 P_0 M_0^2}{u_0}\right] \tag{11.6-6}$$

Now, P_e is not independent and may be found in terms of m, the load (or, equivalently, u_3), and the inlet conditions. We can integrate (11.5-1) to find $P(u)$ and express P_e in terms of inlet conditions and flow rate or in terms of u_0 and u_e. Then P_e can be eliminated from (11.6-6) to give p in terms of m, u_3, inlet conditions, and one outlet parameter: u_e or M_e. Then m can be found in terms of u_3, u_e or M_e, and inlet conditions. Hence p can be found as a function of u_3, inlet conditions, and either m or one outlet parameter: P_e, u_e, or M_e.

Equation (11.5-1) integrates to give

$$\frac{P}{P_0} = \frac{M_0^2}{M^2} \cdot \xi = \frac{\gamma M_0^2}{1 - \xi/\xi_1}\left[\alpha - \frac{u_0}{u_3}\frac{1}{2}\left(\frac{\gamma + 1}{\gamma - 1}\right)\zeta - \xi - \frac{1}{2}\frac{u_0}{u_3}\xi^2\right] \tag{11.6-7}$$

where $\xi = u/u_0$, $\xi_1 = u_1/u_0$, $\alpha = 1 + 1/\gamma M_0^2$, and

$$\zeta = \frac{2}{\gamma + 1}\left[\frac{1}{M_0^2} + \frac{\gamma - 1}{2}\right] \tag{11.6-8}$$

Then u_e can be found explicitly by evaluating (11.6-7) at the exit to give

$$\xi_e = \frac{u_e}{u_0} = \frac{u_{2e}}{u_0} \pm \left\{\left(\frac{u_{2e}}{u_0}\right)^2 + \frac{M_e^2}{1 + \frac{\gamma - 1}{2}M_e^2}\left[\frac{\gamma + 1}{2}\xi - \frac{\xi_1}{M_0^2}(\gamma M_0^2 + 1)\right]\right\}^{1/2}$$

$$\tag{11.6-9}$$

where u_{2e} is u_2 evaluated at the exit. The positive sign in the above equation must be used for $u > u_3$ (generator operation).

By using (11.6-9), we can write the power fed to the load as

$$p = \frac{mAu_3\xi_1}{2\left(\dfrac{\gamma - 1}{\gamma + 1}\right)} \cdot \frac{(\xi_e - 1)(\zeta - \xi_e)}{(\xi_e - \xi_1)} \tag{11.6-10}$$

Now, m can be related to u_e, (ξ_e), by integrating (11.5-2) so that implicitly, at least, p is known as a function of inlet conditions and u_3 and either P_e, u_e, M_e, or m. By integrating (11.5-2) and combining with (11.6-7), we obtain $u(x)$ implicitly.

$$\frac{xN}{L} = \left[\frac{\gamma(\gamma - 1)}{2} - 1 - \gamma(\gamma - 1)\frac{u_0}{u_3}\left(\alpha - \frac{\gamma + 1}{\gamma - 1} \cdot \frac{u_0}{u_3} \cdot \frac{\zeta}{2}\right)\right]\ln\left(\frac{1 - u/u_3}{1 - u_0/u_3}\right)$$

$$+ \left[\frac{\gamma - 1}{\gamma} - \frac{(\gamma^2 + 1)(\gamma - 1)}{2\gamma} + \gamma(\gamma - 1)\frac{u_0}{u_3}\left(\alpha - \frac{\gamma + 1}{\gamma - 1} \cdot \frac{u_0}{u_3} \cdot \frac{\zeta}{2}\right)\right]$$

$$\times \ln\left(\frac{1 - \dfrac{\gamma u}{(\gamma - 1)u_3}}{1 - \dfrac{\gamma u_0}{(\gamma - 1)u_3}}\right)$$

$$+ \left[\frac{\gamma^2}{\gamma - 1}\left(\frac{u_0}{u_3}\right)^2\left(\alpha - \frac{\gamma + 1}{\gamma - 1} \cdot \frac{\zeta}{2}\right) + \frac{\gamma + 1}{2}\frac{u_0}{u_3}\right]$$

$$\times \left[\frac{\dfrac{u}{u_0} - 1}{\left(1 - \dfrac{\gamma u}{(\gamma - 1)u_3}\right)\left(1 - \dfrac{\gamma u_0}{(\gamma - 1)u_3}\right)}\right] \tag{11.6-11}$$

Evaluation at $x = L$ gives $u(L) = u_e$ in terms of inlet parameters and u_3. N is the product of the interaction parameter N_1 (defined in Chapter 6) and the ratio L/h.

$$N = N_1\frac{L}{h} = \frac{\sigma B_0^2 h}{\rho_0 u_0} \cdot \frac{L}{h} = \frac{\sigma B_0^2 L}{\rho_0 u_0} \tag{11.6-12}$$

Another useful way to express the power p is a direct application of an overall energy balance. If we treat the channel as a control volume, p is just the difference between the inlet and outlet values of total enthalpy flux. Hence, by denoting the specific total enthalpy as h_0, we have

$$p = (h_{00} - h_{0e})m = m[c_P(T_0 - T_e) + \tfrac{1}{2}(u_0^2 - u_e^2)]$$

$$= m\left[\frac{\gamma}{\gamma - 1}\left(\frac{P_0}{\rho_0} - \frac{P_e}{\rho_e}\right) + \tfrac{1}{2}(u_0^2 - u_e^2)\right] \tag{11.6-13}$$

One way to look at the optimization problem is to find the conditions under which the exit total enthalpy is a minimum for a fixed inlet total enthalpy flux. Furthermore, a generator effectiveness η may be defined

$$\eta = \frac{\text{Electric power generated}}{\text{total enthalpy flux}}$$

$$= \frac{h_{00} - h_{0e}}{h_{00}} \qquad (11.6\text{-}14)$$

which is the quantity to be maximized. For a given h_{00} and m, h_{0e} must be minimized (by varying u_3 and the outlet parameter). This viewpoint is identical, mathematically, to the optimization of Equation (11.6-10) in the manner already discussed.

In proceeding with optimization, we have several choices, all equivalent. Perhaps the easiest to carry out is the minimization of the flux of total enthalpy at the outlet of the channel. The quantity

$$m\left(\frac{\gamma}{\gamma - 1}\frac{P_e u_e}{\rho_0 u_0} + \frac{1}{2}u_0{}^2\right) \qquad (11.6\text{-}15)$$

must be minimized (with respect to u_3 and outlet conditions) under the constraint that the inlet conditions and m (or N) are fixed. (Alternatively, (11.6-10) could be maximized under the same constraints.) However, ξ_e is a function of N (or m) from (11.6-11). Hence we can differentiate (11.6-14) with respect to u_3. We must use (11.6-7) to express P_e in terms of u_e and u_3 and (11.6-11) to express u_e implicitly in terms of u_3. The algebra is a bit cumbersome but has been carried out by Neuringer (1960), who made numerical calculations for $M_0 = 0.3$ and $\gamma = 5/3$. His results are shown in dimensionless form in Table 11.6-1. Here p^*, the dimensionless power, is defined as

$$p^* = \frac{p}{u_3{}^2 B_0{}^2 \sigma L l} = \frac{pl}{\sigma L V_T}$$

For any given value of N and M_0 there is a corresponding value of u_0/u_3 and $p^*_{\max}$ and appropriate values of the outlet conditions ξ_e and M_e and the dimensionless pressure $P_e{}^* = P_e/\rho_0 u_0{}^2$.

A plot from these results may be made of $p^*_{\max}$ (the maximum dimensionless power for a given set of inlet conditions) versus ξ_e and u_3/u_0 (the reciprocal of u_0/u_3 in the table). This plot is shown in Fig. 11.6-1. The variables are dimensionless, but in terms of dimensional parameters the plot gives a great deal of information. For example, for a fixed N, we can pick a value of u_0, then find u_3 (or V_T) for a given B_0 and l. u_e is found, and for a given value of σ and L, the power generated is determined. The table also gives values for P_e and M_e. R_L can be found from $p = V_T{}^2/R_L$.

For any value of N there is an optimum operating point as shown by the curve. However, there are no stationary points on the $p^*(u_3/u_0, N)$ surface, so that it is always possible to extract more power by properly increasing B_0. But, as $B_0 \to \infty$, there is an absolute maximum value of

Table 11.6-1

Table of dimensionless variables at optimum generator performance. $M_0 = 0.3$, $\gamma = 5/3$. For a fixed given value of N the other parameters are computed for the maximum power operating point.

N	u_0/u_3	p^*_{max}	$\eta \%$	ξ_e	$P_e^* = \dfrac{P_e}{\rho_0 u_0^2}$	M_e
0.1	2.0017	0.99166	0.1466	1.0067	6.6096	0.30230
0.2	2.0035	0.98321	0.29519	1.0136	6.5515	0.30468
0.4	2.0076	0.96585	0.59858	1.0283	6.4321	0.30976
0.6	2.0122	0.94781	0.91076	1.0441	6.3080	0.31514
0.8	2.0175	0.92901	1.2324	1.0612	6.1786	0.32101
1.0	2.0236	0.90942	1.5642	1.0799	6.0434	0.32745
2.0	2.0736	0.79390	3.4129	1.2093	5.2425	0.37296
4.0	2.0077	0.62218	9.2909	2.7903	1.6742	1.0000
6.0	1.4202	1.2769	13.572	2.7237	1.6342	1.0000
8.0	1.2407	1.9160	15.801	2.6882	1.6130	1.0000
10.0	1.1562	2.5444	17.127	2.6671	1.6002	1.0000
12.0	1.1083	3.1645	17.983	2.6533	1.5920	1.0000
14.0	1.0783	3.7780	18.565	2.6438	1.5863	1.0000
16.0	1.0582	4.3865	18.976	2.6372	1.5823	1.0000
18.0	1.0442	4.9893	19.274	2.6323	1.5794	1.0000
20.0	1.0340	5.5887	19.496	2.6287	1.5772	1.0000
25.0	1.0186	7.0735	19.845	2.6230	1.5738	1.0000
30.0	1.0105	8.5437	20.358	2.6146	1.5687	1.0000

* Data taken from J. L. Neuringer, Optimum Power Generation from a Moving Plasma, *J. Fluid Mech.*, **7**, p. 287, 1960.

power. As $B_0 \to \infty$, $u_0/u_3 \to 1$, $N \to \infty$ (but m remains finite, of course), $V_{oc} \to \infty$, but then the internal resistance $R_i \to \infty$ so that p remains finite and bounded. This fact is obvious when we realize that the power must be extracted from the gas, which has a finite value of h_{00}. (Note that the flow in this particular case chokes at $M = 1$ and u_0/u_3 reaches a maximum value at the onset of choking.)

One possible use of the MHD generator is as a topping device. The hot gases would be fed through the generator into a conventional power plant,

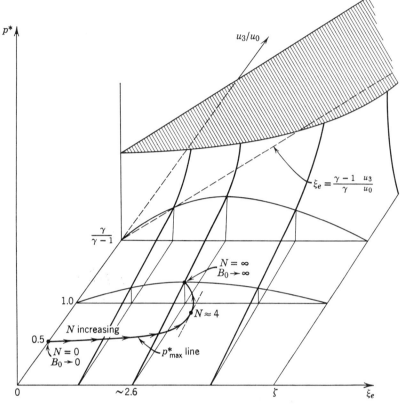

Figure 11.6-1 A qualitative plot of the optimum power line for various N (from $0 \to \infty$) on the p^* $(\xi_e, u_3/u_0)$ surface. $M_0 = 0.3$, $\gamma = \frac{5}{3}$, for the line shown on the surface. The region of the surface between $u_3/u_0 = 1$ and $u_3/u_0 = [\gamma/(\gamma - 1)]\xi_e$ is the surface for pumping (power being fed into the generator) for negative E_z. The form of the surface can be inferred from Equations (11.6-9) and (11.6-10).

the MHD generator being used to increase the overall efficiency. Figure 11.6-2 shows a possible scheme of such a device. Because of the rather low thermal efficiency of the generator, the temperature must remain high in order to keep the gases ionized. In order to increase the efficiency, other means of MHD power generation have been investigated. Such ideas as two-phase flow have been considered where a liquid metal vapor is used to entrain and propel the liquid phase through the channel.

We have made many simplifying assumptions in order to treat the generator in a tractable manner. In practice, the device is somewhat less efficient than our analysis would indicate. Among the complications that we have neglected are: (1) The finite conductivity of the electrodes, which causes current to flow axially and allows axial electric fields. (Split electrodes have been used to partially overcome this difficulty.) (2) An ion sheath that may develop on the electrode surfaces and cause a resistive layer to form. (3) Hall currents and nonuniform gas conductivity. (In Problem 7 a simple Hall current model is mentioned and the analysis

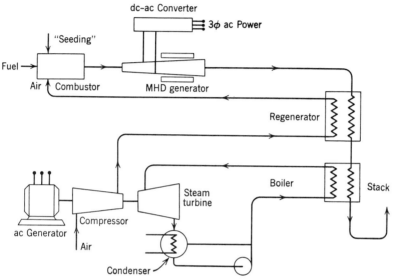

Figure 11.6-2   An open cycle MHD generator.

of the constant velocity device with Hall currents is left as an exercise for the student.) (4) Materials problems: The high temperatures necessary to maintain high conductivity cause rapid erosion of the wall and electrode materials. Temperatures of the order of $5000°R$ are required. In order to increase the electrical conductivity and maintain lower temperatures the gases are usually seeded with a low ionizing potential metal such as cesium or potassium. It is difficult to predict the future of the MHD generator, but the interactions in channel flow provide a vastly increased number of flow possibilities even for simple constant area channels.

In the next section we will look at some other types of MHD generators using vortex flow of an ionized gas.

11.7   THE VORTEX GENERATOR

We will now discuss some concepts of MHD vortices and apply them to the MHD vortex generator. In the vortex generator the ionized gas is made to spiral inward and is exhausted along the axis of the machine. The physical arrangement is shown in Fig. 11.7-1, where we see that a magnetic field may be applied either axially or radially in order to provide a **V** × **B** interaction since the primary velocity component is in the tangential (θ) direction. The electrode arrangement is either two concentric

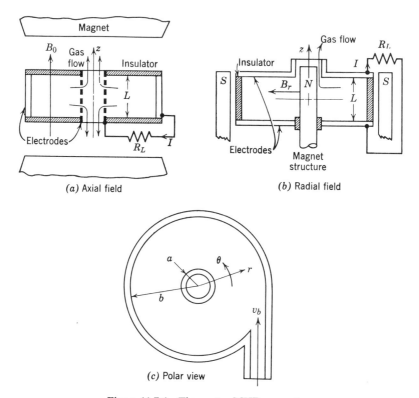

(a) Axial field   (b) Radial field

(c) Polar view

Figure 11.7-1   The vortex MHD generator.

slotted or screen cylinders with two disc insulators, or two disc electrodes with slotted or screened insulating coaxial cylinders, respectively.

There has been considerable interest in vortex generators because of their compact, efficient design. Results, theoretical and experimental, have shown that this design gives a higher power output per unit weight than the channel-type generator discussed in Section 11.6.

As an example, we will go through the analysis of the vortex generator for a radial field (Elco et al., 1962, and Weber and Marston, 1964). The axial field vortex, which is probably a better configuration to use for a generator because of increased efficiency at high power outputs, has been examined by McCune and Donaldson (1960) and Coerdt et al. (1960). We will leave the detailed calculations of the axial field generator as a problem for the student. As an example of the characteristics of a vortex generator, Table 11.7-1 shows some results taken from the work of Coerdt et al. (1960).

Table 11.7-1

Performance parameters for an open cycle axial field vortex generator
(Coerdt et al., 1960).

Net electrical power, kw	1000	50	3
Output voltage, volts	108	35	26
Duration of power, sec	60	60	60
Mean plasma conductivity, mho/cm	0.41	0.41	0.41
T_{max}/T_{min}, °K	3300/2000	3300/2000	3300/2000
Propellant flow rate, gm/sec	830	120	1.5
Total generator envelope (cylinder, including magnet, coils, diameter × depth), in.	29 × 17	12 × 7	6 × 3.5

The Radial Field Vortex Generator

The configuration and cylindrical coordinate system to be used is shown in Fig. 11.7-1, and the gas flow is idealized to the extent given by the following assumptions:

1.   The gas is assumed to be inviscid and boundary layer effects are confined to a thin layer along the generator surface.
2.   The gas is electrically neutral and has a uniform isotropic conductivity σ and a constant permeability μ_0.
3.   The radial and tangential velocities are independent of the axial position z, and the axial velocity is assumed zero.
4.   The radial velocity u is assumed to be much smaller than the tangential velocity v.
5.   All quantities are assumed to be independent of θ, that is, the flow is axially symmetric.
6.   The flow is in steady state.

The only additional assumptions that must be made to solve this system of equations are that the induced magnetic field is much smaller than the applied magnetic field and that the conductivity of the electrodes is much greater than that of the gas so that the electric field tangent to the electrode surfaces is approximately zero.

Specifically then

$$B_r \gg B_z \text{ and } B_\theta$$

$$E_r \text{ and } E_\theta \text{ at } z = \pm \frac{L}{2} \text{ are zero}$$

$$v \gg u$$

The boundary condition on the flow is that the tangential velocity at $r = b$, v_b, is equal to the injection velocity determined by the combustion chamber pressure and the injection nozzle design. The mass rate of flow is taken as m, which is positive for outward flow and negative for inward flow since $m = (2\pi r \rho u L)$ and u is positive in the outward positive direction.

An examination of $\nabla \times \mathbf{E} = 0$, which has the components

$$-\frac{\partial E_\theta}{\partial z} = 0 \qquad \frac{\partial E_r}{\partial z} = \frac{\partial E_z}{\partial r} \qquad \frac{1}{r} E_\theta + \frac{\partial E_\theta}{\partial r} = 0 \qquad (11.7\text{-}1)$$

indicates that E_θ is only a function of r, but since E_θ at the electrodes must be zero, $E_\theta = 0$. Also, since the electrodes constitute a parallel plate geometry, E_z must be independent of r and therefore, from the boundary condition at the electrodes, E_z is a constant and E_r is zero. The applied magnetic field B_r can be found from $\nabla \cdot \mathbf{B} = 0$ as

$$B_r = \frac{B_0 b}{r} \qquad (11.7\text{-}2)$$

where B_0 is the value of B_r at $r = b$. This kind of field can be obtained in practice by using a coaxial pole structure as shown in Fig. 11.7-1.

The continuity equation is

$$\frac{\partial}{\partial r}(\rho u) + \frac{\rho u}{r} = 0 \qquad (11.7\text{-}3)$$

and the radial mass rate of flow per unit area, ρu, is

$$\rho u = \frac{m}{2\pi r L} \qquad (11.7\text{-}4)$$

where m is the total mass flow rate and L is the separation between electrodes. Next, the components of the equation of motion are

$$r: \quad \rho\left(u \frac{\partial u}{\partial r} - \frac{v^2}{r}\right) = -\frac{\partial P}{\partial r} + J_\theta B_z - J_z B_\theta$$

$$\theta: \quad \rho u\left(\frac{\partial v}{\partial r} + \frac{v}{r}\right) = -J_r B_z + J_z B_r \qquad (11.7\text{-}5)$$

$$z: \qquad\qquad 0 = -\frac{\partial P}{\partial r} + J_r B_\theta - J_\theta B_r$$

and from Ohm's law the components of $\mathbf{J}$ are

$$r: J_r = \sigma(E_r + vB_z)$$
$$\theta: J_\theta = \sigma(E_\theta - uB_z) \quad \quad (11.7\text{-}6)$$
$$z: J_z = \sigma(E_z + uB_\theta - vB_r)$$

If $B_r \gg B_z$, then $J_z B_r \gg J_r B_z$ even if J_r is of the same order of magnitude as J_z. Also, since $v \gg u$ and $B_r \gg B_\theta$, J_z can be given by

$$J_z = \sigma(E_z - vB_r) \quad \quad (11.7\text{-}7)$$

By neglecting $J_r B_z$ in (11.7-5θ) and substituting (11.7-7) for J_z, (11.7-2) for B_r, and (11.7-4) for ρ_u, we can write Equation (11.7-5θ) as

$$\frac{\partial v}{\partial r} + \frac{v}{r}(1 + N) = \frac{NE_z}{B_0 b} \quad \quad (11.7\text{-}8)$$

where E_z is a constant and N, the interaction parameter, is defined as $N = 2\pi\sigma B_0{}^2 b^2 L/m$. The solution for v (using the boundary condition that $v = v_b$ at $r = b$) is

$$v = \frac{NE_z}{B_0(N+2)}\left[\frac{r}{b} - \left(\frac{b}{r}\right)^{N+1}\right] + v_b\left(\frac{b}{r}\right)^{N+1} \quad N \neq -2$$

$$\quad (11.7\text{-}9)$$

$$v = \left[\frac{2E_z}{B_0}\ln\frac{b}{r} + v_b\right]\frac{r}{b} \quad N = -2$$

For inward flow, N is negative and for outward flow, N is positive.

The generated current will be in the z direction and from (11.7-7) and (11.7-9)

$$J_z = \sigma\left\{E_z\left[1 - \frac{N}{N+2}\left(1 - \left(\frac{b}{r}\right)^{N+2}\right)\right] - v_b B_0\left(\frac{b}{b}\right)^{N+2}\right\} \quad N \neq -2$$

$$\quad (11.7\text{-}10)$$

$$J_z = \sigma\left\{E_z\left[1 - 2\ln\frac{b}{r}\right] - v_b B_0\right\} \quad N = -2$$

The axial electric field can be found in terms of the terminal voltage V_T of the generator from

$$V_T = -\int_{-L/2}^{+L/2} E_z \, dz \quad \quad (11.7\text{-}11)$$

If we take the electrode at $z = -L/2$ to be at zero potential, E_z is given by

$$E_z = -\frac{V_T}{L} \quad \quad (11.7\text{-}12)$$

The velocity profiles and current density distribution $(N = -2)$ as functions of the radius are shown in Fig. 11.7-2 and 11.7-3 for selected electrical load conditions (which will be determined later).

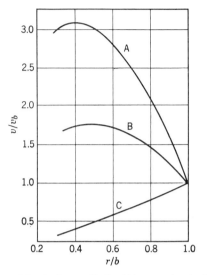

Figure 11.7-2   Tangential velocity profile for (A) open circuit, $V_T = V_{oc}$, (B) optimum load condition, $V_T = V_{oc}/2$, and (C) short circuit, $V_T = 0$, where $N = -2$ and $b/a = 3$.

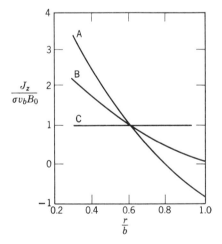

Figure 11.7-3   Axial current density J_z, distribution for (A) $V_T = V_{oc}$, (B) $V_T = V_{oc}/2$, and (C) $V_T = 0$, where $N = -2$ and $b/a = 3$.

The induced magnetic fields can be found from the components of $\nabla \times \mathbf{H} = \mathbf{J}$ which are

$$r: \qquad -\frac{\partial B_\theta}{\partial z} = \mu_0 J_r$$

$$\theta: \quad -\frac{\partial B_z}{\partial r} + \frac{\partial B_r}{\partial z} = \mu_0 J_\theta \qquad (11.7\text{-}13)$$

$$z: \qquad \frac{\partial B_\theta}{\partial r} + \frac{B_\theta}{r} = \mu_0 J_z$$

The induced B_θ can be obtained directly by integrating 11.7-13:

$$B_\theta = \frac{\mu_0}{r} \int J_r r \, dr + \frac{C_1}{r} \qquad (11.7\text{-}14)$$

If B_θ is to have any dependence on z, this dependence must be contained in C_1. The boundary condition at $r = a$ that $B_\theta = 0$ can be used since J_z for $r < a$ is zero because the electrodes extend only from $r = a$ to $r = b$, This indicates that C_1 cannot have any dependence on z. Therefore, B_θ is only a function of r and from (11.7-13r) it can be concluded that $J_r = 0$. Then from (11.7-6r) and (11.7-6θ) the remaining induced terms are found to be: $B_z = 0$ and $J_\theta = 0$ since E_r and E_θ are zero. The current densities J_z and J_r also satisfy $\nabla \cdot \mathbf{J} = 0$ and therefore the electromagnetic equations of the system are satisfied. By integrating Equation (11.7-14) and evaluating C_1, we find B_θ explicitly:

$$B_\theta = \mu_0 \sigma \left\{ E_z \left[\frac{1}{2}\left(1 - \frac{N}{N+2}\right)\left(r - \frac{a^2}{r}\right) - \frac{b}{N+2}\left(\left(\frac{b}{r}\right)^{N+1} - \frac{a}{r}\left(\frac{b}{a}\right)^{q+1}\right)\right] \right.$$

$$\left. + \frac{v_b B_0 b}{N}\left[\left(\frac{b}{r}\right)^{N+1} - \frac{a}{r}\left(\frac{b}{a}\right)^{N+1}\right] \right\} \qquad N \neq -2$$

$$B_\theta = \mu_0 \sigma \left[E_z\left(\frac{a^2}{r}\ln\frac{b}{a} - r\ln\frac{b}{r}\right) + \frac{v_b B_0}{2}\left(\frac{a^2}{r} - r\right)\right] \qquad N = -2$$

$$(11.7\text{-}15)$$

However, since B_θ is of order of magnitude $\mu_0 J_z$, it will be much smaller than the applied field B_r and the effects of B_θ can safely be neglected.

The terminal electrical characteristics of the generator can now be determined. The open-circuit voltage V_{oc} is obtained by first finding the total current I and evaluating V_T for $I = 0$. The total current I is:

$$I = 2\pi \int_a^b J_z r \, dr \qquad (11.7\text{-}16)$$

Integrating gives us

$$I = 2\pi\sigma\left\{-\frac{V_T}{L}\left[\frac{b^2 - a^2}{2}\left(1 - \frac{N}{N+2}\right) - \frac{b^2}{N+2}\left(1 - \left(\frac{b}{a}\right)^N\right)\right]\right.$$
$$\left. + \frac{v_bB_0b^2}{N}\left(1 - \left(\frac{b}{a}\right)^N\right)\right\} \qquad N \neq -2$$

$$I = -2\pi\sigma\left[\frac{V_T}{L}a^2\ln\frac{b}{a} + \frac{v_bB_0}{2}(b^2 - a^2)\right] \qquad N = -2 \qquad (11.7\text{-}17)$$

Then the open-circuit voltage is

$$V_{\text{oc}} = \frac{v_bB_0b^2L[1 - (b/a)^N]}{N\left\{\left(\frac{b^2 - a^2}{2}\right)\left(1 - \frac{N}{N+2}\right) - \left(\frac{b^2}{N+2}\right)\left[1 - \left(\frac{b}{a}\right)^N\right]\right\}}$$

$$N \neq -2 \quad (11.7\text{-}18)$$

$$V_{\text{oc}} = -\frac{v_bB_0L[(b/a)^2 - 1]}{2\ln(b/a)} \qquad N = -2$$

The short-circuit current I_{sc} is obtained from (11.7-17), for $V_T = 0$, as

$$I_{\text{sc}} = 2\pi\sigma\frac{v_bB_0b^2}{N}\left[1 - \left(\frac{b}{a}\right)^N\right] \qquad (11.7\text{-}19)$$

and the internal resistance of the generator, $R_i = V_{\text{oc}}I_{\text{sc}}$, is

$$R_i = \frac{L}{2\pi\sigma}\left\{\left(\frac{b^2 - a^2}{2}\right)\left(1 - \frac{N}{N+2}\right) - \frac{b^2}{N+2}\left[1 - \left(\frac{b}{a}\right)^N\right]\right\}^{-1} \qquad N \neq -2,$$

$$R_i = \frac{L}{2\pi\sigma} \cdot \frac{1}{a^2\ln(b/a)} \qquad N = -2 \qquad (11.7\text{-}20)$$

The maximum power output is then $V_{\text{oc}} \cdot I_{\text{sc}}/4$.

The electrical characteristics of the generator are dependent on the interaction parameter N. To visualize this dependence, the open-circuit voltage V_{oc}, the internal resistance R_i, and the normalized maximum electrical power output for a matched load (that is, $R_L = R_i$) are shown in Fig. 11.7-4 as functions of N. These curves are normalized with respect to v_bB_0, which is held constant, and N then is inversely proportional to the flow rate. When the flow is an inward spiral ($N < 0$), the internal resistance increases rapidly with increasing magnitude of N and maximum power output decreases, which indicates that for $N < 0$ a very low efficiency would be expected. This can also be seen from Fig. 11.7-3, where, for open-circuit conditions, circulating currents exist and the current density at the inside radius is very large compared to J_z at the outer radius. It is this extremely nonuniform current density that contributes to the large internal resistance and low output power occurring with the inflow case.

For the outward spiral flow ($N > 0$), which in practice would be difficult to realize, the internal resistance decreases rapidly and the maximum power increases with increasing N, indicating that as the mass

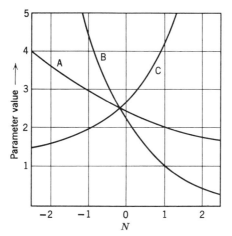

Figure 11.7-4 Normalized parameter values for (A) the open-circuit voltage $V_{oc}/v_b B_0 L$, (B) the internal resistance $2\pi\sigma b^2 R_i/L$, and (C) the maximum power output $2V_{oc}I_{sc}/\pi\sigma v_b^2 B_0^2 L$ as functions of the interaction parameter N.

flow rate is decreased the output power is increased. However, since the conductivity of the gas is dependent on the density, the power output curve will peak at some $N > 0$ and then decrease as the conductivity drops.

The energy equation becomes

$$\rho u \frac{\partial h_0}{\partial r} = \mathbf{E} \cdot \mathbf{J} \qquad (11.7\text{-}21)$$

The temperature can now be found, assuming a perfect gas, from

$$\frac{\partial T}{\partial r} = \frac{1}{c_P}\left[\left(\frac{1}{\rho u}\right)(J_r E_r + J_\theta E_\theta + J_z E_z) - v\frac{\partial v}{\partial r} - u\frac{\partial u}{\partial r}\right] \quad (11.7\text{-}22)$$

If the term $u(\partial u/\partial r)$ is neglected (because $v \gg u$), this equation can be integrated since E_r and E_θ are zero and $J_z E_z$ is only a function of r. Therefore, by using the boundary condition that $T = T_b$ at $r = b$, we can write the temperature as

$$T - T_b = \frac{1}{c_P}\left\{\frac{2\pi\sigma}{m}\left[\frac{V_T^2}{L}\left\{\frac{r^2 - b^2}{2}\left(1 - \frac{N}{N+2}\right)\right.\right.\right.$$
$$\left.\left.+ \frac{b^2}{N+2}\left(1 - \left(\frac{b}{r}\right)^N\right)\right\} + \frac{V_T v_b B_0 b^2}{N}\left\{1 - \left(\frac{b}{r}\right)^N\right\}\right] \qquad \text{(11.7-23)}$$
$$\left.+ \frac{v_b^2 - v^2}{2}\right\}$$

It is important in any generator using an ionized gas that the lowest temperature in the device be greater than the minimum temperature necessary for maintenance of ionization.

The efficiency of the generator may be defined in terms of the "turbine" or adiabatic efficiency, which is the ratio of the actual change in the specific total enthalpy through the device to the change in specific total enthalpy through an engine operating isentropically between the same pressures. The turbine or isentropic efficiency is usually defined as

$$\eta_i = \frac{h_{0b} - h_{0a}}{h_{0b} - h'_{0a}} \qquad \text{(11.7-24)}$$

where h'_{0a} is the value of h_{0a} that would exist if the flow were expanded isentropically to the same final exit pressure as that in the actual machine. Ideally it would seem desirable to use a diffuser on the gas exhaust channel since this would keep the pressure at $r = a$ below the exhaust or atmospheric pressure, thus diffusing the gas to stagnation at the outlet and increasing the efficiency. Such a means of recovery is not possible, however, because of the high angular velocity of the exhausting gases and it seems consistent to charge this loss of kinetic energy to the adiabatic efficiency. Hence

$$\eta_i = \frac{h_{0b} - h_{0a}}{h_{0b} - h'_{0e}} \qquad \text{(11.7-25)}$$

In terms of pressure then

$$\eta'_i = \frac{h_{0b} - h_{0a}}{h_{0b}\left[1 - \left(\frac{P_{0e}}{P_{0b}}\right)^{\frac{\gamma-1}{\gamma}}\right]} \qquad \text{(11.7-26)}$$

where γ is the ratio of specific heats and P_0 is stagnation pressure, and the subscript e indicates final exit properties.

Now from Equation (11.7-21) the numerator can be evaluated explicitly:

$$\eta_i = \frac{\int_a^b (\mathbf{E} \cdot \mathbf{J})\left(\dfrac{1}{\rho u}\right) dr}{h_{0b}\left[1 - \left(\dfrac{P_{0e}}{P_{0b}}\right)^{\frac{\gamma-1}{\gamma}}\right]} \qquad (11.7\text{-}27)$$

where $N < 0$. If $N > 0$, the limits of integration must be reversed. Then

$$\eta_i = \frac{V_T I}{m|h_{0b}\left[1 - \left(\dfrac{P_{0e}}{P_{0b}}\right)^{\frac{\gamma-1}{\gamma}}\right]} \qquad (11.7\text{-}28)$$

A more realistic measure of efficiency is the effectiveness, that is, the ratio of the total enthalpy converted to electrical energy to the total enthalpy input into the generator. The effectiveness η is then

$$\eta = \frac{h_{0b} - h_{0a}}{h_{0b}} \qquad (11.7\text{-}29)$$

The numerator is the same as Equation (11.7-26) so that

$$\eta = \frac{V_i I}{h_{0b}} \qquad (11.7\text{-}30)$$

In order to complete the description of this type of generator, we must find the mass density ρ, radial velocity u, and pressure P as functions of r. Taking the derivative of the equation of state with respect to r gives

$$\rho R \frac{dT}{dr} + RT \frac{d\rho}{dr} = \frac{dP}{dr} \qquad (11.7\text{-}31)$$

Substituting (11.7-5r) for $\partial \rho / \partial r$ where the induced effects and radial velocity terms are neglected gives

$$\frac{d\rho}{\rho} = \frac{v^2}{RTr} dr - \frac{dT}{T} \qquad (11.7\text{-}32)$$

which can be integrated for ρ. Then u can be found from (11.7-4) and P from (11.7-5r). We will not carry out these calculations here.

The relatively large internal resistance and the large current densities at small radii which exist for open circuit and normal loading make the use of this type of generator impractical at high power levels. The possible advantage of this configuration is that the secondary induced effects are very small, thus making this type of generator useful in low power applications.

11.8 – MHD THERMAL CONVECTION

Introduction

The effect of viscous and Joule dissipations on MHD free convection between two plates was first investigated by Osterle and Young (1961), Poots (1961), and Young and Huang (1964). The former authors considered the case in which the loading condition corresponds to a short circuit and the latter treated the open-circuit case and also the entrance flow. This section will deal with the general-circuit case, where the

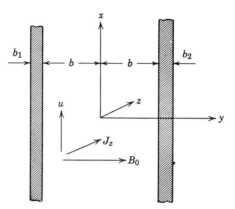

Figure 11.8-1   Configuration of flow.

vertical channel is connected through electrodes to an external circuit containing a finite load resistance R_L and an emf source V_{app} and where the two vertical plates are electrically conducting and of finite thickness. The electrical loading is assumed to be symmetrical. An iteration scheme is employed to solve the nonlinear system of integro-differential equations governing this flow.

The forms of the vertical channel and the external circuit are shown in Figs. 11.8-1 and 11.8-2. Fully developed MHD free convection is considered in a viscous, electrically conducting fluid flowing within this channel, and the resulting electromagnetic interaction is treated. The properties of the fluid are: mass density ρ, kinematic viscosity v, magnetic permeability μ, electric conductivity σ, and thermal conductivity κ_T. The fluid temperature is denoted by T. The flow with velocity u is in the x direction, a uniform applied magnetic field B_0 is in the y direction, and there is an induced magnetic field B_x in the x direction. The two conducting plates are maintained at a uniform temperature T_1, which exceeds the ambient temperature T_0, and are separated by a distance $2b$; their electrical conductivities and thickness are σ_1, b_1, and σ_2, b_2, respectively. The channel is assumed to be sufficiently long to insure a fully developed flow. The electrodes are assumed to be perfect conductors so that the voltage drops across them can be neglected; and the distance a separating them is also taken sufficiently large to allow a one-dimensional approach, that is, all quantities except the pressure P in the fluid depend on y only.

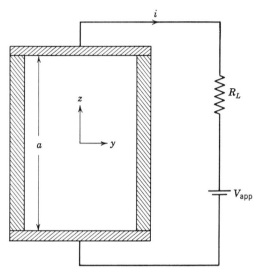

Figure 11.8-2 External circuit.

The MHD Convection Equations

In this problem the gravitational force must be included. The x component of the Navier-Stokes equations is then given by

$$\mu_f \frac{d^2 u}{dy^2} - J_z B_0 - \rho g - \frac{\partial P}{\partial x} = 0 \qquad (11.8\text{-}1a)$$

where ρg is the gravitational force and J_z is the current density in the z direction. The heating of the walls produces a temperature rise (above the reservoir temperature T_0) in the fluid, which will be warmest along the center surface of the channel and will be least dense there. Hence the fluid rises in the x direction. The temperature difference between the walls and the fluid in the center of the channel must be small or the flow will not be laminar. The derivation of the critical Grashof number ($G = \beta g b^3 (T_1 - T_0) \nu^{-2}$), which is considered in the literature (Gershuni and

Zhukhovitskii, 1958, and Damaskos and Young, 1965), indicates that ΔT is less than a few tenths of a degree centigrade in laminar flow regimes. Therefore, it is assumed that the difference in temperature is small compared to the wall temperature. Thus $\Delta T = T - T_0 \ll T_0$. Corresponding to the temperature rise in the fluid is a density change $\Delta\rho$. Therefore, Equation (11.8-1a) can be expressed as

$$\mu_f \frac{d^2u}{dy^2} - J_z B_0 - \frac{\partial P}{\partial x} - g(\rho_0 + \Delta\rho) = 0 \qquad (11.8\text{-}1b)$$

where ρ_0 is fluid density in the reservoir at temperature T_0. If there were no heating and no electric generator connected to the electrodes the fluid would be at rest. Hence $\partial P/\partial x + \rho_0 g = 0$. The remaining term $-g\Delta\rho$ is the buoyancy force and is easily expressed in terms of the expansivity of the fluid. The expansivity is defined as

$$\beta = -\frac{1}{\rho}\left(\frac{\partial \rho}{\partial T}\right)_P \qquad (11.8\text{-}1c)$$

Hence the buoyancy force term becomes

$$-g\Delta\rho = \rho g \beta \Delta T = \rho g \beta(T - T_0) \qquad (11.8\text{-}1d)$$

and the x component of the Navier-Stokes equation becomes

$$\mu_f \frac{d^2u}{dy^2} - J_z B_0 + \rho g \beta(T - T_0) = 0 \qquad (11.8\text{-}1e)$$

which can be simplified by dividing through by ρ_0 and neglecting second-order terms. The law of conservation of momentum given by (11.8-1e) becomes

$$\nu \frac{d^2u}{dy^2} + \beta g(T - T_0) - \frac{\sigma}{\rho_0}(E_z + uB_0)B_0 = 0 \qquad (11.8\text{-}2)$$

when Ohm's law is used to express the current density in terms of E_z and u. Under the assumption of fully developed flow the energy equation obtained from (5.10-7) and (5.11-1) is given by

$$\kappa_T \frac{d^2T}{dy^2} + \frac{J_z^2}{\sigma} + \rho_0 \nu \left(\frac{du}{dy}\right)^2 = 0 \qquad (11.8\text{-}3)$$

The pressure is given by the y component of the Navier-Stokes equations as

$$\frac{dP}{dy} = \sigma(E_z + uB_0)B_x \qquad (11.8\text{-}4)$$

where E_z is the z component of the electric field.

The current density J_z is given by Ohm's law

$$J_z = \sigma(E_z + uB_0) \tag{11.8-5}$$

and the induced magnetic field is given by Ampere's law

$$\frac{dB_x}{dy} = -\mu J_z \tag{11.8-6}$$

Faraday's law

$$\nabla \times \mathbf{E} = 0 \tag{11.8-7}$$

shows that E_z is equal to a constant and has the same value everywhere; hence $-E_za$ obviously equals the voltage drop V_T between the electrodes. We have then the following relation:

$$E_z = -\frac{V_T}{a} = \frac{V_{\text{app}} - iR_L}{a} \tag{11.8-8}$$

where i is the total current flowing through the circuit and is given by

$$i = (\sigma_1 b_1 + \sigma_2 b_2)LE + \sigma B_0 L \int_{-b}^{b} u \, dy \tag{11.8-9}$$

and L is the length of the channel. Now by introducing the dimensionless quantities

$$Y = \frac{y}{b} \qquad U = \nu u[g\beta b^2(T_1 - T_0)]^{-1}, \qquad \Theta = \frac{T - T_0}{T_1 - T_0}$$

$$\psi = E_z\nu[B_0 g\beta b^2(T_1 - T_0)]^{-1} \qquad \Pi = V_{\text{app}}\nu[B_0 ag\beta b^2(T_1 - T_0)]^{-1}$$

$$I = i\nu[B_0 g\beta b^2(T_1 - T_0)2b\sigma] \qquad K = \frac{2b\sigma R}{a}$$

and

$$C = \frac{\sigma_1 b_1 + \sigma_2 b_2}{2b\sigma} \tag{11.8-10}$$

into Equations (11.8-2), (11.8-3), and (11.8-8), we have the following dimensionless equations:

$$\frac{d^2U}{dY^2} + \Theta - M^2U - M^2\psi = 0 \tag{11.8-11}$$

$$\frac{d^2\Theta}{dY^2} + NM^2\psi^2 + 2NM^2\psi U + NM^2U^2 + N\left(\frac{dU}{dY}\right)^2 = 0 \tag{11.8-12}$$

$$\psi = \Pi - IK \tag{11.8-13}$$

$$I = (1 + C)\psi + \frac{1}{2}\int_{-1}^{1} U \, dY \tag{11.8-14}$$

where

$$M = B_0 b\sqrt{\frac{\sigma}{\rho\nu}} = \text{the Hartmann number} \tag{11.8-15}$$

and

$$N = \rho b^4 g^2 \beta^3 \frac{T_1 - T_0}{\kappa_T \nu} = \frac{\mu_J bg\beta G}{\kappa_T} \qquad (11.8\text{-}16)$$

is the dimensionless parameter measuring the buoyancy force. The primes denote differentiation with respect to Y. The boundary conditions for U and Θ are

$$U(1) = 0 \qquad \Theta(1) = 1 \qquad U'(0) = 0 \qquad \Theta'(0) = 0 \qquad (11.8\text{-}17)$$

Solution

The fact that N is small in most practical problems allows us to employ a perturbation technique to solve the nonlinear system of integro-differential equations (11.8-11), (11.8-12), (11.8-13), (11.8-14), and (11.8-17). We can write

$$U = U_0 + NU_1 \qquad \Theta = \Theta_0 + N\Theta_1$$
$$\psi = \psi_0 + N\psi_1 \qquad I = I_0 + NI_1 \qquad (11.8\text{-}18)$$

where the zero-subscript quantities are solutions for the special case in which N is equal to zero (this is equivalent to neglecting the viscous and Joule heating), and where U_1, Θ_1, ψ_1, and I_1 are perturbed quantities relative to U_0, Θ_0, ψ_0, and I_0, respectively. The zero-subscript quantities are governed by the following system of linear integro-differential equations:

$$U''_0 + \Theta_0 - M^2 U_0 - M^2 \psi_0 = 0 \qquad (11.8\text{-}19)$$

$$\Theta''_0 = 0 \qquad (11.8\text{-}20)$$

$$\psi_0 = \Pi - I_0 K \qquad (11.8\text{-}21)$$

$$I_0 = (1 + C)\psi_0 + \frac{1}{2}\int_{-1}^{1} U_0 \, dY \qquad (11.8\text{-}22)$$

$$U_0(1) = 0 \qquad \Theta_0(1) = 1 \qquad U'_0(0) = 0 \qquad \Theta'_0(0) = 0 \qquad (11.8\text{-}23)$$

The solutions of Equations (11.8-19) through (11.8-23) are

$$\Theta_0 = 1 \qquad (11.8\text{-}24)$$

$$U_0 = \frac{1/M^2 - \psi_0}{1 - \text{ch } MY/\text{ch } M} \qquad (11.8\text{-}25)$$

$$\psi_0 = \frac{\pi/k - (1 - \text{th } M/M)/M^2}{C + 1/K + \text{th } M/M} \qquad (11.8\text{-}26)$$

$$I_0 = \frac{\pi(C + \text{th } M/M) + (1 - \text{th } M/M)/M^2}{1 + K(C + \text{th } M/M)} \qquad (11.8\text{-}27)$$

By putting (11.8-18) and (11.8-24) through (11.8-27) back in (11.8.11) through (11.8-14) and (11.8-17) and neglecting the products of the perturbed quantities, we obtain the following system of linear perturbation integro-differential equations:

$$U''_1 + \Theta_1 - M^2 U_1 - M^2 \psi_1 = 0 \tag{11.8-28}$$

$$\Theta''_1 + M^2 \psi_0{}^2 + 2M^2 \psi_0 U_0 + M^2 U_0{}^2 + (U'_0)^2 = 0 \tag{11.8-29}$$

$$\psi_1 = -K I_1 \tag{11.8-30}$$

$$I_1 = (1 + C)\psi_1 + \frac{1}{2}\int_{-1}^{1} U_1 \, dY \tag{11.8-31}$$

and

$$U_1(1) = 0 \qquad \Theta_1(1) = 0 \qquad U'_1(0) = 0 \qquad \Theta'_1(0) = 0 \tag{11.8-32}$$

Equations (11.8-28) through (11.8-32) can be integrated easily to give the following solutions:

$$\Theta_1 = \frac{1 - Y^2}{2M^2} - \frac{2}{M^2}\left(\frac{1}{M^2} - \psi_0\right)\left(1 - \frac{\mathrm{ch}\ MY}{\mathrm{ch}\ M}\right)$$
$$+ \frac{1}{4}\left(\frac{1}{M^2} - \psi_0\right)^2 \frac{(\mathrm{ch}\ 2M - \mathrm{ch}\ 2MY)}{\mathrm{ch}^2\ M} \tag{11.8-33}$$

$$U_1 = \left[\frac{1}{2M^4} - \frac{3}{M^6} - \psi_1 + \frac{2\psi_0}{M^4} + \left(\frac{1}{M^2} - \psi_0\right)^2 \frac{\mathrm{ch}\ 2M}{4M^2\ \mathrm{ch}^2\ M}\right]$$
$$+ \left[\psi_1 + \frac{3}{M^6} - \frac{2\psi_0}{M^4} - \left(\frac{1}{M^2} - \psi_0\right)^2 \frac{\mathrm{ch}\ 2M}{3M^2\ \mathrm{ch}^2\ M}\right.$$
$$+ \left(\frac{1}{M^2} - \psi_0\right)\frac{\mathrm{th}\ M}{M^3}\bigg]\frac{\mathrm{ch}\ MY}{\mathrm{ch}\ M} - \frac{Y^2}{2M^4} + \left(\frac{1}{M^2} - \psi_0\right)^2$$
$$\times \frac{\mathrm{ch}\ 2MY}{12M^2\ \mathrm{ch}^2\ M} - \left(\frac{1}{M^2} - \psi_0\right)\frac{Y\ \mathrm{sh}\ MY}{M^3\ \mathrm{ch}\ M} \tag{11.8-34}$$

$$\psi_1 = \frac{K}{1 + CK + K\dfrac{\mathrm{th}\ M}{M}}\left[\frac{3}{M^6}\left(1 - \frac{\mathrm{th}\ M}{M}\right) - \frac{1}{3M^4} - \frac{2\psi_0}{M^4}\left(1 - \frac{\mathrm{th}\ M}{M}\right)\right.$$
$$+ \left(\frac{1}{M^2} - \psi_0\right)^2\left(\frac{\mathrm{ch}\ 2M\ \mathrm{th}\ M}{3M^3\ \mathrm{ch}^2\ M} - \frac{\mathrm{ch}\ 2M}{4M^2\ \mathrm{ch}^2\ M} - \frac{\mathrm{sh}\ 2M}{24M^2\ \mathrm{ch}^2\ M}\right)$$
$$- \left(\frac{1}{M^2} - \psi_0\right)\frac{\mathrm{th}^2\ M}{M^4} + \left(\frac{1}{M^2} - \psi_0\right)\frac{1}{M^5}\left(1 - \frac{\mathrm{th}\ M}{M}\right)\bigg] \tag{11.8-35}$$

$$I_1 = \frac{-1}{1 + CK + K\dfrac{\text{th } M}{M}}\left[\frac{3}{M^6}\left(1 - \frac{\text{th } M}{M}\right) - \frac{1}{3M^4} - \frac{2\psi_0}{M^4}\left(1 - \frac{\text{th } M}{M}\right)\right.$$

$$+ \left(\frac{1}{M^2} - \psi_0\right)^2\left(\frac{\text{ch } 2M \text{ th } M}{3M^3 \text{ ch}^2 M} - \frac{\text{ch } 2M}{4M^2 \text{ ch}^2 M} - \frac{\text{sh } 2M}{24M^2 \text{ ch}^2 M}\right)$$

$$\left. - \left(\frac{1}{M^2} - \psi_0\right)\frac{\text{th}^2 M}{M^4} + \left(\frac{1}{M^2} - \psi_0\right)\frac{1}{M^5}\left(1 - \frac{\text{th } M}{M}\right)\right] \qquad (11.8\text{-}36)$$

By taking $K = 0$ and $\Pi = 0$ in the preceding solutions, we obtain the short-circuit solutions:

$$\Theta_0 = 1 \qquad U_0 = \frac{1}{M^2}\left(1 - \frac{\text{ch } MY}{\text{ch } M}\right)$$

$$U_1 = \frac{1}{M^6}\left(\frac{M^2}{2} - 3 + \frac{\text{ch } 2M \text{ sech}^2 M}{4}\right)$$

$$+ \left(3 - \frac{\text{ch } 2M \text{ sech}^2 M}{3} + M \text{ th } M\right)\frac{\text{sech } M \text{ ch } MY}{M^6}$$

$$- \frac{Y^2}{2M^4} + \frac{\text{ch } 2MY}{12M^6 \text{ ch}^2 M} - \frac{Y \text{ sech } M \text{ sh } MY}{M^6}$$

$$\Theta_1 = \frac{1}{M^2}\left(\frac{2 \text{ sech } M \text{ ch } MY}{M^2} - \frac{\text{ch } 2MY \text{ sech}^2 M}{4M^2}\right.$$

$$\left. - \frac{Y^2}{2} + \frac{1}{2} - \frac{2}{M^2} + \frac{\text{sech}^2 M \text{ ch } 2M}{4M^2}\right)$$

$$\psi_0 = \psi_1 = 0 \qquad\qquad (11.8\text{-}37)$$

which are exactly the same as the solutions given by Osterle and Young (1961). Likewise, by putting K equal to ∞, we can obtain the open-circuit solutions.

Discussion of the Results

The first-order electric field ψ_0 given by (11.8-26) is a function of Π, K, C, and M. For the case without the applied emf, ψ_0 increases with an increase of the load K and/or with a decrease of the wall conductances C. Then ψ_0 has maximum value for insulated walls ($C = 0$) and open circuit ($K = \infty$). The applied voltage Π plays an important role in changing the value of ψ_0. If it is of such magnitude that it gives rise to an electromagnetic body force that is very large compared with the buoyancy force, it dominates the other factors and controls the flow; the problem then becomes a hydromagnetic pump problem, which will not be discussed here. We shall confine ourself to the MHD free convection problem in which the applied emf is either zero or is of such a strength that it causes an electromagnetic body force of the same order of magnitude as the buoyancy force. A change of Π will alter ψ_0, and this, again, will affect the velocity and temperature. It is found that when

$$\Pi = \frac{1 + K(1 + C)}{M^2}$$

the free convection is suppressed so that

$$U_0 = 0$$

and

$$\Theta_1 = \frac{1 - Y^2}{2M^2}$$

Equation (11.8-25) shows that U_0 (and therefore the flow rate) is a linear function of ψ_0. Figures 11.8-3 and 11.8-4 show that when $\Pi = 0$, U_0

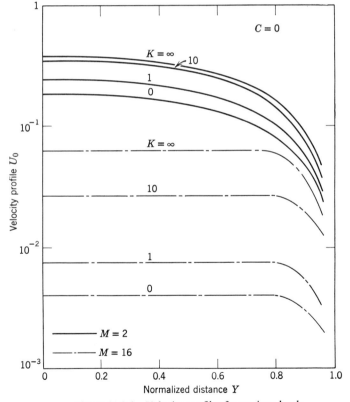

Figure 11.8-3 Velocity profiles for various loads.

increases with an increase in K and/or with a decrease in C, that is, U_0 increases with the magnitude of ψ_0. U_0 has maximum value when $K = \infty$ and $C = 0$ since in this situation there is no energy extracted from the channel and there is no loss in the walls.

The effects of small N on the velocity, temperature, electric field, and current are indicated by Equations (11.8-33) through (11.8-36), which

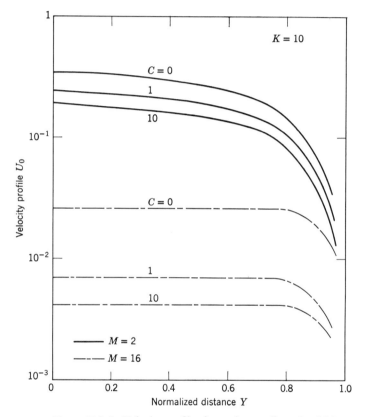

Figure 11.8-4 Velocity profiles for various wall conductivities.

show that the perturbed quantities Θ_1, U_1, ψ_1, and I_1 are nonlinear functions of the parameters that characterize ψ_0 and the external circuit and wall conditions. It is interesting to study the temperature profile Θ_1. In general, this profile becomes flattened in the center and steepened near the walls and hence the heat transfer rate through the walls is increased as K is increased or C is decreased; in other words, as ψ_0 is increased. Figures 11.8-5 and 11.8-6 illustrate the above statement. For any value of Y there is a critical value of ψ_0 that gives minimum local temperature for a fixed value of M. The critical ψ_0 for minimum midchannel temperature is found by differentiating (11.8-33) with respect to ψ_0 and setting the derivative equal to zero:

$$\psi_{0_{\mathrm{crit}}} = \frac{1}{M^2}\left[1 - \frac{4\ \mathrm{ch}\ 2M(\mathrm{ch}\ 2M - 1)}{\mathrm{ch}\ M(\mathrm{ch}\ M - 1)}\right]$$

This channel has the same current generation characteristics as the Hartmann flow except that the generated current i_0 is directly proportional to the temperature difference $(T_1 - T_0)$, as indicated by Equation (11.8-27). The generated power $i_0 V_T$ is proportional to the square of $(T_1 - T_0)$.

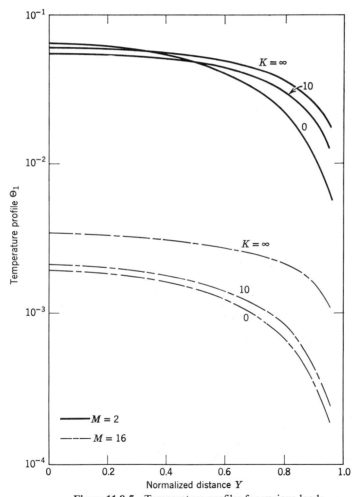

Figure 11.8-5   Temperature profiles for various loads.

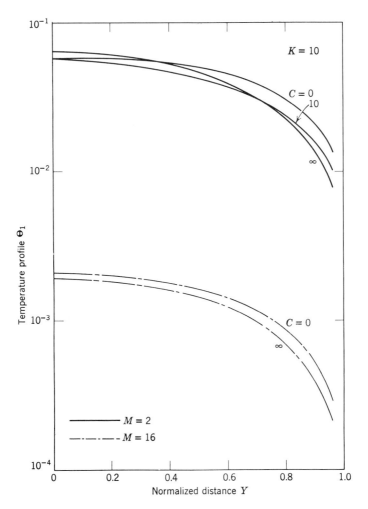

Figure 11.8-6 Temperature profiles for various wall conductivities.

PROBLEMS

1. Determine the characteristics of a channel operating at (*a*) constant density, (*b*) constant temperature, (*c*) constant pressure, and (*d*) constant velocity. The area variation $A(x)$ must be such as to insure the particular flow in each case. Some results are as follows (electrodes assumed parallel): (*a*) Constant density:

$$x = \frac{\rho}{\sigma E_z B_0}\left[(u_3 - u_0)(u_0 - u) + u_3{}^2\left(\frac{\gamma - 1}{\gamma}\ln\left|\frac{u - u_1}{u_0 - u_1}\right| - \ln\left|\frac{u - u_3}{u_0 - u_3}\right|\right)\right]$$

(b) Constant temperature:

$$\frac{P}{P_0} = \exp\left[\left(\frac{u - u_3}{u_3 RT}\right)\left(\frac{u^2 - u_0^2}{2}\right)\right]$$

(c) Constant pressure:

$$\frac{T}{T_0} = 1 + \frac{\gamma - 1}{2}M_0^2\left[1 - \left(\frac{u}{u_0}\right)^2 - \frac{u_3}{u_0}\left(1 - \frac{u}{u_0}\right)\right]$$

$u(x)$ is given by

$$x = \frac{\rho_0 u_0}{\sigma B_0^2}\left\{-\frac{u_3}{2u_0 K}\ln\left[\left(\frac{u - u_3}{u_0 - u_3}\right)^2 \cdot \frac{1}{1 + \frac{\gamma - 1}{2}\frac{M_0^2}{u_0^2}\{(u_0 - u_3)^2 - (u - u_3)^2\}}\right]\right.$$

$$-\frac{1}{2M_0\sqrt{K\frac{\gamma - 1}{2}}}\ln\left[\frac{\sqrt{Ku_0^2\left/\frac{\gamma - 1}{2}\right. M_0^2} + (u - u_3)}{\sqrt{Ku_0^2\left/\frac{\gamma - 1}{2}\right. M_0^2} + (u - u_3)}\right.$$

$$\left.\left.\cdot\frac{\sqrt{Ku_0^2\left/\frac{\gamma - 1}{2}\right. M_0^2} + (u_3 - u)}{\sqrt{Ku_0^2\left/\frac{\gamma - 1}{2}\right. M_0^2} + (u_3 - u)}\right]\right\}$$

where

$$K = 1 + \frac{\gamma - 1}{2u_0}M_0^2(u_0 - u_3)$$

(d) Constant velocity:

$$P_0 - P = xB_0^2\sigma(u_0 - u_3)$$

$$\frac{T}{T_0} = \left(\frac{P}{P_0}\right)^{\frac{(\gamma - 1)u_3}{\gamma u_0}}$$

The area change is given by

$$\frac{A}{A_0} = \left(\frac{P_0}{P}\right)^{1 - (\gamma - 1)u_3/\gamma u_0}$$

2. In a converging diverging nozzle (in terms of area), does $M = 1$ necessarily occur at the geometric throat as in ordinary gas dynamics? Is $u = u_3$ at the throat? Is $u = u_3$ at the place where $M = 1$? Explain.

3. For the constant area MHD generator, find the internal resistance R_i (under the constraint of constant inlet conditions and mass flow rate), V_{oc}, and $\mathcal{I}_{sc}$, and compare matched load conditions with Table 11.6-1.

4. Is there an upper limit to the power that can be fed into a channel as there is for the power extracted? What happens in a channel in which power is being fed as B_0 is increased without limit?

5. Analyze the uniform axial field vortex magnetogasdynamic generator. The outer and inner cylinders are the screen or slotted electrodes. See Fig. 11.7-1.

Some results are:

$$\frac{v}{v_b} = \frac{b}{r} + \frac{IB_0 r}{2mv_b}\left(\frac{b^2}{r^2} - 1\right)$$

$$V_{\rm oc} = v_b b B_0 \ln\left(\frac{b}{a}\right)$$

$$I_{\rm sc} = 2\pi L \sigma v_b b B_0 \left[1 - \frac{N}{2}\left(1 - \frac{(b/a)^2 - 1}{2(b/a)^2 \ln (b/a)}\right)\right]^{-1}$$

where

$$N = \frac{2\pi\sigma B_0^2 b^2 L}{m} \quad (m \text{ is mass flow rate})$$

6. Consider a constant velocity generator (see Problem 1d). Assuming that the electric field is uniform (parallel electrodes), find the electrical power output in terms of relevant parameters. What is the nature of the internal resistance that could be matched to an external load for optimum operation? Answer

$$p = \frac{A_0 P_0 \gamma u_0}{(\gamma - 1)}\left[1 - \left\{\frac{1 - B_0^2 \sigma}{P_0}(u_0 - u_3)L\right\}^{\frac{(\gamma-1)u_3}{\gamma u_0}}\right]$$

Then optimize with respect to u_3 for a given L.

7. The effect of Hall current may be taken into account approximately by the following form of Ohm's law:

$$\mathbf{J} = \sigma(\mathbf{E} + \mathbf{V} \times \mathbf{B}) + \frac{\omega\tau}{|\mathbf{B}|}(\mathbf{J} \times \mathbf{B})$$

where ω is the electron cyclotron frequency and τ the mean time between electron collisions with other types of particles (neutrals and ions). For a fixed value of $\omega\tau$, determine the effect of Hall current on the performance of the generator in Problem 6. For a given set of operating conditions, the efficiency is reduced by the Hall current, and split or segmented electrodes have been used to partially overcome the adverse effects of the Hall currents. However, the value of u_3 will vary from electrode section to electrode section since each set of electrodes may be loaded separately. Complete optimization of the constant velocity generator would require electrode specification and loading while considering a variable $\omega\tau$ and σ (as a function of temperature and density) along the channel.

REFERENCES

Coerdt, R. J., W. C. Davis, R. T. Craig, and J. E. McCune, A Vortex MHD Power Generator, paper presented at American Rocket Society Meeting, Santa Monica, Calif., September 1960.

Culick, F. E. C., Compressible Magnetogasdynamic Channel Flow, Z.A.M.P., **15**, p. 129, 1964.

Dahlberg, E., On the One-Dimensional Flow of a Conducting Gas in Crossed Fields, Quart. Appl. Math., **XIX**, No. 3, p. 177, 1961.

Damaskos, N. J., and F. J. Young, The Stability of Thermally Induced Flow in the Coreless Induction Furnace, Int. J. Heat Mass Transfer, **8**, pp. 721–728, 1965.

Deissler, R. G., A One-Dimensional Analysis of Magnetohydrodynamic Energy Conversion, NASA Technical Note D-680, March 1961.

Elco, R. A., W. F. Hughes, and F. J. Young, Theoretical Analysis of the Radial Field Vortex Magneto-Gas Dynamic Generator, Z.A.M.P., **13**, p. 1, 1962.

Gershuni, G. Z., and E. M. Zhukhovitskii, Stability of the Stationary Convective Flow of an Electrically Conducting Liquid between Parallel Vertical Plates in a Magnetic Field, *Soviet Phys. JETP*, **34**, No. 7, pp. 465–470, 1958.

Gunderson, R., Quasi-One-Dimensional Magnetohydrodynamic Flow with Heat Addition, Z.A.M.P., **14**, p. 294, 1963.

Gunderson, R., Quasi-One-Dimensional Magnetohydrodynamic Flow with Heat Addition-Oblique Field, Z.A.M.P., **15**, p. 210, 1964.

McCune, J. E., and C. DuP. Donaldson, On the Magneto-Gas Dynamics of Compressible Vortices, paper presented at American Rocket Society Meeting, Los Angeles, Calif., May 1960.

Medin, S. A. (Inst. of High Temperature, Moscow), Variational Calculus Problem of MHD Generator Flow, Sixth Symposium on Engineering Aspects of MHD, Pittsburgh, Pa., U.S.A., 1965.

Neuringer, J. L., Optimum Power Generation from a Moving Plasma, *J. Fluid Mech.*, **7**, p. 287, 1960.

Osterle, J. F., and F. J. Young, Natural Convection between Heated Vertical Plates in a Horizontal Magnetic Field, *J. Fluid Mech.*, **11**, Part 4, pp. 512–518, 1961.

Poots, G., Laminar Natural Convection Flow in Magneto-Hydrodynamics, *Int. J. Heat Mass Transfer*, **3**, p. 1, 1961.

Resler, E. L. Jr., and W. R. Sears, Magneto-Gasdynamic Channel Flow, Z.A.M.P., **IXb**, p. 509, 1958.

Resler, E. L. Jr., and W. R. Sears, The Prospects for Magneto-Aerodynamics, *J. Aeronaut. Sci.*, **25**, p. 235, 1958.

Rosa, R. J., Engineering Magnetohydrodynamics, Ph.D. Thesis, Cornell University, 1956.

Rosa, R. J., and A. R. Kantrowitz, Magnetohydrodynamic Energy Conversion Techniques, Res. Rept. No. 86, Avco-Everett Res. Lab., April 1959.

Slepian, J., The Ionic Centrifuge and Fusion Nuclear Power, *Proceedings of the National Academy of Sciences*, **47**, p. 313, 1961.

Sutton, G. W., Magnetohydrodynamic Channel Flow of a Perfect Gas for the Generation of Electrical Power, General Electric Co. Res. Rept. No. R59SD473, December 1959.

Swift-Hook, D. T., and J. K. Wright, The Constant-Mach-Number MHD Generator, *J. Fluid Mech.*, **15**, Part 1, pp. 97–110, 1963.

Way, S., Design Considerations in MHD Generators, paper presented at the First Symposium on Engineering Aspects of MHD, Philadelphia, Pa., 1960.

Way, S., Magnetohydrodynamic Power Generation, Westinghouse Res. Lab. Scientific Paper 6-40509-2-P2, April 1960.

Weber, H. E., and D. H. Marston, MHD with Liquid Metal, *Mech. Eng.*, **86**, No. 8, p. 34, 1964.

Young, F. J., and H. Huang, Effects of External Circuit and Wall Conditions on Magnetohydrodynamic Free Convection between Two Heated Walls, Z.A.M.P., **15**, No. 4, pp. 419–425, 1964.

See also the following publications:

Symposium on Magnetoplasmadynamic Electrical Power Generation, sponsored by the Inst. of Elect. Eng., King's College, University of Durham, Newcastle-upon-Tyne, September 1962.

Yearly Symposia on Engineering Applications of Magnetohydrodynamics, sponsored by ASME, AIEE, and AIAA since 1960.

12

Magnetoaerodynamics

12.1 INTRODUCTION

We are now prepared to discuss flow past bodies. As in conventional fluid mechanics, there are two broad aspects of such flow—the main stream or potential flow analogue, and the boundary layer flow near the body. However, in general, in conducting fluids the definition of the boundary layer is not simple and it sometimes becomes difficult to distinguish it from the main flow. The problems of separation and the analogue of the Kutta-Joukowsky condition are still not well understood. Many new and unexpected phenomena occur in magnetoaerodynamics. For example, vortical wakes and wavelike disturbances may extend not only downstream but upstream as well under certain conditions.

We will begin our discussion with a qualitative description of the behavior and methods of classifying magneto-fluid dynamic flow past bodies and of the appropriate analogues in conventional fluid mechanics. There are many ways to classify the flow in conventional fluid dynamics: incompressible or compressible, subsonic or supersonic, viscous or inviscid, etc. Flow is usually classified according to whether the Reynolds number $Re >$ or < 1. If $Re \ll 1$, the viscous forces dominate and no distinct boundary layer is present. Linearizations of the Oseen or Stokes type are often employed. However, if $Re \gg 1$, the inertia forces dominate and viscosity is neglected except in the boundary layer. In the inviscid case, a gas is further classified as incompressible or compressible according to whether the Mach number M is small or large, respectively. For a gas, small M usually means $M < 0.3$ but this division is arbitrary and depends on the accuracy desired. Furthermore, according to whether $M < 1$ or > 1 the basic linearized equations for the compressible fluid are elliptic and hyperbolic, respectively.

Essentially there are only two basic parameters in conventional aerodynamic flow: the Reynolds number Re and the Mach number M. However, in a conducting fluid several additional parameters are necessary to characterize the flow. We have already examined the parameters in Chapter 6, but let us quickly review the important ones.

$$M = \frac{U_0}{a} = \frac{\text{fluid speed}}{\text{sonic speed}} = \text{Mach number} \qquad (12.1\text{-}1)$$

$$Re = \frac{U_0 L}{\nu} = \frac{\text{inertia force}}{\text{viscous force}} = \text{Reynolds number} \qquad (12.1\text{-}2)$$

The Reynolds number may also be interpreted as the ratio of vorticity convection to vorticity diffusion.

$$Mm = \frac{U_0}{A} = \frac{U_0}{\sqrt{\dfrac{B_0^2}{\mu \rho_0}}} = \frac{\text{fluid speed}}{\text{Alfvén speed}} = \text{Magnetic Mach number,}$$
$$\text{or Alfvén number.*} \qquad (12.1\text{-}3)$$

Small values of Mm correspond to small values of fluid speed or large values of magnetic field. We can also write Mm^2 as: $Mm^2 = U_0^2 \rho_0 / \mathbf{H_0} \cdot \mathbf{B_0}$, which is the ratio of dynamic pressure to magnetic pressure. This interpretation is often useful.

The magnetic Reynolds number is defined as:

$$Rm = \frac{U_0 L}{\eta} = \frac{\text{magnetic convection}}{\text{magnetic diffusion}} \qquad (12.1\text{-}4)$$

If electrodes are provided in the flow field, the terminal voltage may be controlled by an external circuit and the new parameter $E_0/\mu H_0$ or V_T/LB_0 would be of importance, as it was in Chapter 11.

These two basic new parameters Rm and Mm, along with Re and M, characterize the flow of a conducting fluid. However, the following combinations of these four parameters may be physically meaningful and useful in any practical situation.

$$Pm = \frac{\nu}{\eta} = \frac{Rm}{Re} = \text{the magnetic Prandtl number} \qquad (12.1\text{-}5)$$

As we saw in Chapter 9, this number is usually small so that the magnetic field usually diffuses faster than the vorticity. (For mercury, $Pm \approx 10^{-7}$ and for ionized air at $5400°K$, $Pm \approx 10^{-6}$, so that $\lim Pm \to 0$ is appropriate for many physical situations.)

---

* Some authors refer to $1/Mm$ as the Alfvén number.

The Hartmann number is sometimes useful in discussing viscous flow (that is, Oseen type and boundary layers). We will use M_H to represent Hartmann number here since M is now reserved for Mach number.

$$M_H = \mu H_0 L \sqrt{\frac{\sigma}{\rho\nu}} = \frac{\sqrt{Re\,Rm}}{Mm} \qquad (12.1\text{-}6)$$

M_H is the ratio of ponderomotive to viscous force. Remember that this interpretation is based on the assumption that the current is of order $(\sigma\mu U_0 H_0)$ so that the preceding form of M_H should not be used if $\sigma \to \infty$. In that case, $J \approx 0$ (H_0/L) and the appropriate form for M_H would be Re/Mm. However, in practice only the former form seems useful.

The interaction parameter, the ratio of ponderomotive to viscous force, is also important. As we mentioned in Chapter 6, this parameter may be written in two forms, depending on whether the current is given by $\sigma\mu U_0 H_0$ or H_0/L. When the current is given by Ohm's law, which is certainly the case for $Rm \ll 1$, we have

$$N = \frac{\text{ponderomotive force}}{\text{inertia force}} = \frac{(\sigma\mu U_0 H_0)(\mu H_0)}{\rho U_0^2/L} = \frac{Rm}{Mm^2} \qquad (12.1\text{-}7)$$

Rm will usually be small $(Rm \ll 1)$ for most practical aerodynamic situations so that N will usually be small $(N \ll 1)$. However, if the magnetic field is very strong, N may be large $(N \gg 1)$ even for small Rm. If Rm is large $(Rm \gg 1;\ \sigma$ large, effectively $\infty)$, then J is given by H_0/L and N becomes

$$N = \frac{(H_0/L)(\mu H_0)}{(\rho U_0^2/L)} = \frac{1}{Mm^2} \qquad (12.1\text{-}8)$$

Hence, for $Rm \gg 1$, N is not a descriptive parameter and is redundant with Mm.

It seems convenient to divide the aerodynamic flow into two broad categories: Rm small and Rm large. If Rm is small $(Rm \ll 1)$, the applied magnetic field is only slightly distorted by the flow (and induced currents), and to a first approximation the applied magnetic field may be considered as known. However, if Rm is large, the magnetic field is distorted by the flow and as $Rm \to \infty$ the field becomes "frozen" into the fluid. Only the two limits $Rm \ll 1$ and $Rm \gg 1$ (frozen-field case) have been investigated with any degree of thoroughness. Intermediate values of Rm entail calculation of the field distortion, and only approximate methods have been developed (perturbation for thin airfoils, for example), and the results are rather complex compared to some of the rather simple and beautiful results for the limiting cases of Rm.

Before we look at some of the solutions in detail let us briefly examine the qualitative behavior of compressible aerodynamic flow in magneto-fluiddynamics.

12.2 QUALITATIVE DESCRIPTION OF MAGNETOAERODYNAMICS

Since there are at least four basic parameters involved, it is difficult to make generalizations about the possible types of flow. Nevertheless, certain broad features are evident and lend a great deal of insight into what sort of analytical solutions to expect. These basic features seem to distinguish flows of low Rm from those of high Rm. In fact there appears to be an analogy between Rm and Re of conventional flow and their influences on the flow patterns. Let us look at these basic features in terms of the magnetic Reynolds number.

Small Magnetic Reynolds Number ($Rm \ll 1$)

Here the diffusion of vorticity by electrical resistance is much more rapid than the convection. This situation is analogous to the classical Stokes or Oseen flow, where the diffusion of vorticity by viscosity dominates the convection. We would expect then a real analogy between the two types of flow for $Rm \ll 1$ and $Re \ll 1$, which is indeed the case for small N. If $\mathbf{B}_0$ is small (N small), the result is a large wake of vorticity and current which diffuses outward from the body and is convected downstream if the free stream velocity $\mathbf{U}_0$ and $\mathbf{B}_0$ are generally aligned. The viscous wake, which is still present but perhaps weaker than the magneto-aerodynamic wake, is more or less aligned. ($\mathbf{B}_0$ is essentially undisturbed by the flow, remember, for Rm small.) The magnetic Prandtl number is usually small (particularly if $Rm \ll 1$) and the diffusion may be accomplished mainly by resistance effects and not necessarily by viscosity. We would expect then that the wake would lie generally in the direction of $\mathbf{B}_0$ if $\mathbf{U}_0$ and $\mathbf{B}_0$ are slightly skewed (see Fig. 12.2-1).

However, for a given flow speed, as $\mathbf{B}_0$ is increased (N becomes large), an entirely new phenomenon occurs which has no analogue in conventional aerodynamics. If $\mathbf{B}_0$ is sufficiently large, two wakes occur. The wake develops downstream, but a new wake of vorticity and current will extend *upstream* and dominate the downstream wake as either v or $\eta \to 0$. If v or $\eta = 0$, the downstream wake is completely absent (see Fig. 12.2-2).

The magnetoaerodynamical effect appears to have been completely reversed; the direction of the wake is now generally upstream in the

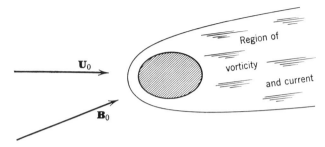

Figure 12.2-1 Flow past a body at low *Rm* showing a downstream vortical wake (**B**$_0$ small).

negative **B**$_0$ direction. (Actually the sense of **B**$_0$ is unimportant and **B**$_0 \rightarrow$ $-$**B**$_0$ only changes the sense of the current and vorticity in the wake.) The mechanism for this wake reversal is readily understood. The Alfvén wave disturbances propagate upstream along the **B**$_0$ lines, along with or dominating the downstream convection and Alfvén propagation. The speed of the Alfvén disturbances must be greater than the fluid speed U_0 for upstream wakes to appear. **B**$_0$ must be large enough to make $A > U_0$ (for an incompressible fluid) if the upstream wake is to exist. Hasimoto (1960) has given an elegant discussion of the wake phenomena in an incompressible fluid and has calculated the relative strengths of the upstream and downstream wakes for various orientations of the magnetic field. He finds that the upstream wake dominates (for **U**$_0$ and **B**$_0$ aligned) if $A > U_0$ except for $A/U_0 \gg (Pm)^{\pm 1/2}$ in which case both wakes have equal strength. Ahlstrom (1963) has recently confirmed the existence of these upstream wakes by experiments in liquid mercury.

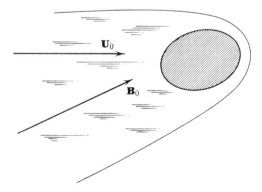

Figure 12.2-2 Same as Fig. 12.2-1 except that **B**$_0$ is large. The upstream wake may dominate even in a viscous flow if $\sigma \rightarrow \infty$.

For *Rm* small, the diffusion process dominates and consequent wakes of vorticity and current (in addition to viscous wakes) occur, and except for the Alfvén disturbances (and ordinary sonic waves if the flow is supersonic), magnetohydrodynamic wave effects damp rapidly and are unimportant.

Large Magnetic Reynolds Number ($Rm \gg 1$)

As *Rm* becomes large, the vortical wakes become narrower and less diffuse. In aligned flows ($\mathbf{U}_0$ and $\mathbf{B}_0$ parallel) narrow Alfvénic disturbances propagate upstream or downstream and appear as narrow wakes rather

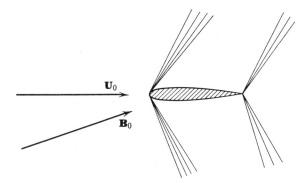

Figure 12.2-3   Flow past a body at high *Rm*, showing diffuse standing Alfvén waves ($U_0 > A$).

than wide diffuse regions of vorticity and current. Because, as $Rm \to \infty$, the stream lines and magnetic field lines are parallel throughout the flow (for aligned flows at infinity), the Alfvén disturbances generated on the body surface propagate along the surface, joining the wakes at the ends of the body, but creating a boundary layer of rotational flow (even in an inviscid fluid).

If the $\mathbf{B}_0$ field is not aligned but is skewed to the free stream flow, diffuse Alfvén standing waves extending from the body are generated (as the skewed vortical wakes contract with increasing *Rm*) at angles to the body. The directions of these waves are determined by the direction of the free stream $\mathbf{B}_0$ and the convection effects of the fluid velocity. Figure 12.2-3 shows such a pattern.

In general, the width of these waves depends on *Rm*, that is, the ratio of diffusion to convection of the magnetic disturbances. As *Rm* becomes large ($\sigma \to \infty$), the diffusion becomes negligible and the waves are surfaces (approximately conical for a three-dimensional body). In practice, the conductivity is usually such a value that the Alfvén waves diffuse and damp out a few body lengths away.

If the fluid is incompressible, the Alfvén waves or disturbances tell the story and describe the flow. (If viscosity is important, the viscous wake may also have to be considered, in the absence of stream-lining, say. Such a wake could alter the flow pattern and the orientation of the Alfvén disturbances, but the simultaneous consideration of these problems along with separation, etc., is extremely complex and not very well understood at present.) If the fluid is compressible, not only do the Alfvén waves appear, but new waves, called magnetosonic waves make their appearance and affect the flow. These are the analogues of the ordinary sonic waves in gas dynamics and we expect, by analogy to subsonic and supersonic flow, that these waves can completely change the character of the flow. If the body is slender, the pattern around the body is wavelike, but if the body is thick, the waves become strong and may eventually steepen into magnetohydrodynamic shock waves.

In Chapter 8 we studied waves in conducting gases and discussed the Friedrichs diagram for a sound pulse in a perfectly conducting, inviscid, nonheat-conducting gas. Let us now apply these results of ideal magnetosonic waves to the aerodynamics problem of the flow of an ideal (in the above sense) gas over an object. Each of the three waves, slow, intermediate (Alfvén), and fast, will generate a disturbance on a body and form a standing wave pattern analogous to the Mach cone in ordinary gas dynamics, and the disturbances travel along the characteristics, analogous to the Mach line. The form of the rather complex wave pattern depends on the orientation of the free stream velocity to the magnetic field. For the two simple cases of aligned and crossed fields we can sketch the resultant wave pattern for a slender body.

As we will see, the differential equations for large Rm can be hyperbolic, elliptic, doubly hyperbolic, or sometimes elliptic-hyperbolic, depending on the relative magnitudes of the flow speed, Alfvén speed, slow and fast magnetosonic speeds, and the relative orientation of the U_0 and B_0 vectors. The sketches (Figs. 12.2-4, 12.2-5, and 12.2-6) illustrate how this complexity comes about.

The Alfvén disturbances appear as thin wakes in the aligned field case and are exactly the waves discussed earlier for incompressible flow. These Alfvén waves are purely transverse and are not affected by compressibility.

Let us examine these diagrams to see what information they reveal. In the aligned case (Fig. 12.2-5) we see that two sets of symmetric waves occur (a and c) or no waves at all (b and d). In the latter case the characteristics degenerate into the horizontal axis and coincide with stream lines.

For incompressible flow we are always in case (*b*) or (*d*) with only an Alfvén disturbance; the flow equations are purely elliptic. (For incompressible flow for other than aligned flow the equations are always elliptic-hyperbolic.) A current layer similar to a boundary layer is formed around the body and grows along its length toward the rear for the downstream wake and toward the front for the upstream wake, joining the wake

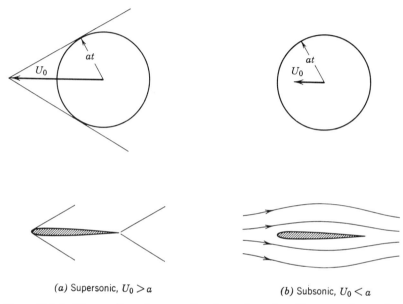

(*a*) Supersonic, $U_0 > a$ (*b*) Subsonic, $U_0 < a$

Figure 12.2-4   Wave patterns in conventional aerodynamics. The upper figures show the sonic sphere and the velocity vectors of the airfoil (*a* is the ordinary sonic speed).

at the extremity of the body. It is interesting to note that the speed for changeover from a downstream to an upstream wake can be seen for the diagram. When both of the degenerate (horizontal) tangents must be drawn downstream (*a* and *c*), the wake lies behind the body. When one degenerate wave extends forward (as in case *d*), the wake is found to lie upstream or in front of the body. It follows then that the changeover speed is that of point *P* in the Friedrichs diagram. Hence the wake is downstream if

$$U_0 > \sqrt{\frac{a^2 A^2}{a^2 + A^2}}$$
(12.2-1)

and upstream if

$$U_0 < \sqrt{\frac{a^2 A^2}{a^2 + A^2}}$$
(12.2-2)

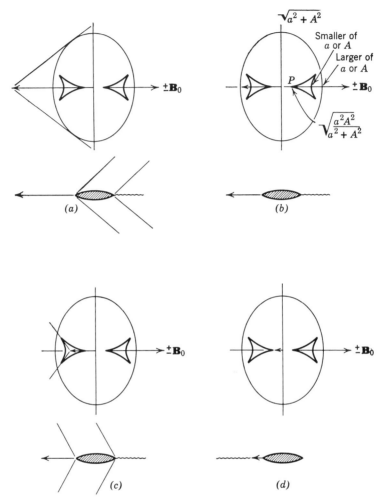

Figure 12.2-5   The wave pattern inferred from the Friedrichs diagrams. Aligned flow, infinite conductivity. The wavy lines indicate magnetohydrodynamic "wakes" of vorticity and current. The magnetic field is horizontal.

(where a is the ordinary sonic speed) which checks in the incompressible limit (as $a \to \infty$) where the changeover speed is simply A. In (b) of Fig. 12.2-5 the flow is elliptic, even though it may be supersonic, and, as we will see later, can give rise to negative lift for a positive angle of attack, another rather surprising result with no analogue in conventional aerodynamics.

In the case of crossed fields the pattern is more complex, but Fig. 12.2-6 gives some idea of what to expect. We will not discuss the arbitrary

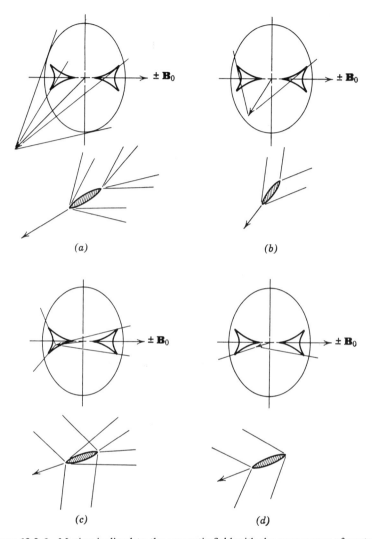

Figure 12.2-6 Motion inclined to the magnetic field with the appearance of upstream waves. (*a*) and (*c*) are doubly hyperbolic and (*b*) and (*d*) are "hyper-liptic." The magnetic field is horizontal. These cases are the same as those in Fig. 12.2-5, but now the velocity vectors are rotated away from the aligned field direction. As the velocity vector is rotated into alignment with the magnetic field, one set of waves degenerates into a wake. (The Friedrichs diagrams must be rotated about the **B** vector and continually generated along the velocity vector in order to visualize the true shape of the wave pattern.)

orientation of the field at this time, but later we will return to a discussion of perturbation techniques for thin airfoil theory for large Rm.

In summary, then, for a viscous fluid of finite or infinite conductivity, upstream wakes may appear (in addition to downstream wakes) for certain speeds below a critical value. As the viscosity approaches zero, even for finite conductivity, the downstream wake disappears completely, but the upstream wake remains (if the speed is below the critical value). Similarly, as the conductivity goes to infinity, regardless of the value of viscosity, the downstream wake disappears when the upstream wake comes into being. Compressibility introduces additional standing wavelike disturbances that are analogous to sonic disturbances and that may point upstream or downstream. These waves give rise to the complex multiplicity of flow patterns which we examined briefly by means of the Friedrichs diagram. As the body becomes thick, the wave disturbances become strong and magnetohydrodynamic shock waves of the fast, slow, or intermediate type may occur.

Boundary Layer Theory

We have mentioned the boundary layer only briefly in connection with a current sheet that grows along a body in an aligned field. Let us confine ourselves to flow over bodies for the moment and see what role the boundary layer plays.

If the viscosity is zero, there still may be magnetoaerodynamic wakes of thickness of order $(Rm^{-\frac{1}{2}})$, which may be forward- or backward-facing, as we have mentioned. These wakes are formed as current sheets around the body and grow in the direction in which the wake extends. Hence we may have a situation where the inviscid current boundary layer begins at the trailing edge and undergoes a reversed growth to the leading edge, where it separates and forms the vortical-current upstream wake. Hence we have the concept of separation even in absolutely inviscid flow. As $\eta \to 0 (\sigma \to \infty)$, separation does not occur and only a thin wake extends from the body.

For finite η and ν there exists both the inviscid layer just mentioned and a viscous boundary layer. For small Pm the viscous layer is a sublayer of the order $\sqrt{Pm}$ as thick as the inviscid layer. The viscous layer increases in thickness downstream along the body, giving rise to a viscous separation and downstream wake, but the inviscid layer may grow either way depending on the direction of the vortical-current wake. We might have a situation, then, with separation on both the leading and the trailing ends of a body.

In the limit of infinite σ ($\eta \to 0$), regardless of the value of viscosity, there is no downstream wake or trailing edge separation if the speed is below the critical value (A for incompressible flow and $\sqrt{a^2A^2/(a^2 + A^2)}$) for compressible flow). The viscous boundary layer is then always contained by the inviscid layer, which completely dominates the direction of the wake.

We can say a few words about actual calculations in aligned fields. For Rm and Re very small, an Oseen or Stokes type of linearization may be made and no definite boundary layer appears; viscosity dominates the entire picture.

For aerodynamic flow about thin bodies, the viscous boundary layer may be neglected altogether, just as in conventional aerodynamics.

For flow of a perfectly conducting fluid, where $Pm \gg 1$ or where viscosity is negligible so that $Pm \ll 1$, the magnetoaerodynamic inviscid boundary layer dominates and determines separation so that the effect of viscosity may not be important.

For intermediate cases of finite v and η, both types of boundary layers are formed, possibly causing separation into two (forward and backward) wakes. Such calculations are difficult and little progress has been made in matching the boundary layer solutions to the main flow field outside the layer.

For arbitrary orientations of the magnetic field, the description is generally the same except that the separation points and consequent directions of the wakes are shifted toward alignment with the magnetic field lines and away from the free stream velocity direction. In a field not aligned with the free stream flow, Alfvén disturbances can originate at both the leading and trailing edge of a body and, in addition to the viscous layer and wake, magnetic wakes of vorticity and current lie in diffuse surfaces which form conelike regions from the leading and trailing edge (Fig. 12.2-3). The inviscid boundary layer growth direction is somewhat ill-defined in such a case.

Later we will examine the structure of some of these boundary layers in detail. Of particular interest is the growth of the boundary layer over a semi-infinite flat plate in an aligned or crossed field (in which $\mathbf{B_0}$ is perpendicular to the plate and free stream flow). The solution to the Rayleigh problem may be used to construct an approximate solution to the boundary layer development from the leading edge along the plate.

For the crossed field case ($\mathbf{B_0}$ perpendicular to the plate and to $\mathbf{U_0}$) a diffuse Alfvén wave, generated at the leading edge, carries a region of vorticity and current out along an inclined direction analogous to the Mach line of a supersonic plate. At the same time, a viscous boundary layer (also with current) is generated along the surface of the plate. Figure 12.2-7a shows this development. If the field is aligned along the plate in incompressible flow, the vortical-current-viscous layer builds up along the plate (downstream) if $U_0 > A$, but if $U_0 < A$, the reversed boundary layer effect fills all of space and blocks the flow. This latter result is easy to understand since the plate extends to infinity downstream and the layer has had sufficient time to build up its size. In practice, of course, the plate

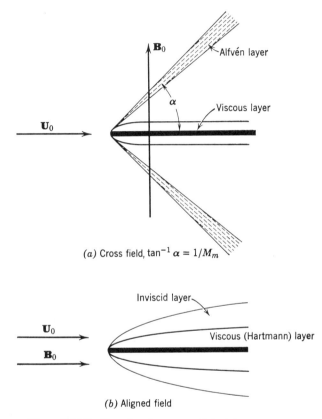

(a) Cross field, $\tan^{-1} \alpha = 1/M_m$

(b) Aligned field

Figure 12.2-7   Boundary layer on a flat plate.

would have finite length and the upstream wake, although perhaps wide, would diffuse and damp out sufficiently far from the plate (Fig. 12.2-7b).

One other point should be mentioned at this time: the electric field and its boundary conditions. For the flow over an immersed body in a fluid, there are no external electrodes (unless provided by a power source within the body, say), and current must flow in loops in the fluid. At infinity, $\mathbf{E}'_\infty = 0$ in the frame of the free stream fluid or ground (for aerodynamic motion through an ionospheric gas). Thus, with respect to a frame of reference fixed to the body, $\mathbf{E}_\infty = -\mathbf{U}_0 \times \mathbf{B}_0$, where $\mathbf{U}_0$ and $\mathbf{B}_0$ are the free stream velocity and applied magnetic field, respectively. For aligned flow, of course, $\mathbf{U}_0 \times \mathbf{B}_0 = 0$ and $\mathbf{E}'_\infty = \mathbf{E}_\infty = 0$. The boundary condition on $\mathbf{E}$ at the surface of the body depends on the particular problem. In an axially symmetric aligned flow, for example, $E_\theta = 0$, but E_r and E_z may depend on the conductivity of the body and fluid. If $\sigma = \infty$ in the fluid, $\mathbf{V} \times \mathbf{B} = 0$ and $\mathbf{E}' = \mathbf{E} = 0$ everywhere. In a crossed field configuration, however, $\mathbf{E}_\infty = -\mathbf{U}_0 \times \mathbf{B}_0 \neq 0$ and the value of $\mathbf{E}$ at the surface of the body may be different from $\mathbf{E}_\infty$. It becomes particularly important to establish the boundary conditions correctly when analyzing the structure of the boundary layer. We defer further discussion until we analyze in detail some of the boundary layer problems.

12.3   SMALL CONDUCTIVITY, $Rm \ll 1$

Having reviewed qualitatively the type of flow to be expected in magneto-aerodynamics, we will now consider in detail some specific problems. Perhaps the simplest flow around a solid body is that under the condition that the conductivity is low and hence the magnetic Reynolds number Rm is very small. Then at least to a first approximation, to order Rm, the applied magnetic field is undistorted by the flow and may be taken as known. There are several problems under the assumption of $Rm \ll 1$ that yield rather simple and informative results.

Slow Viscous Flow Past a Sphere

The Stokes drag on a sphere slowly moving through a viscous liquid is given by the well-known formula

$$D_S = 6\pi \rho \nu a U_0 \qquad (12.3\text{-}1)$$

where a is the radius of the sphere and U_0 its speed relative to the un-disturbed liquid. For an aligned field configuration (Fig. 12.3-1) Chester

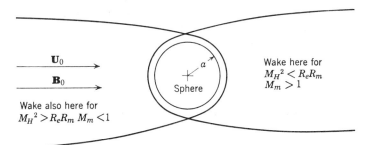

Figure 12.3-1   Wake pattern around a sphere for aligned viscous flow.

(1957) has given a Stokes approximation and Ludford (1960) has given an Oseen-type analysis valid for small Re and Rm with the following rather surprising results. Defining the magnetic Mach number Mm as $\sqrt{\rho_0 U_0^2/\mu H_0^2}$, which is also the ratio of dynamic pressure to magnetic pressure, we can write $M_H^2 = ReRm/Mm^2$, where M_H is the Hartmann number and Re is the Reynolds number. $Re = U_0 a/\nu$, $Rm = U_0 a\mu\sigma$, and $M_H = \mu H_0 a\sqrt{\sigma/\rho\nu}$. As we recall, for $Mm > 1$ $(M_H^2 < ReRm)$, the wakes lie downstream but for $Mm < 1$ $(M_H^2 > ReRm)$ one wake (the magnetic wake of vorticity and current) lies upstream. Hence we would expect the value of drag to change drastically, depending on whether $Mm < 1$ or > 1. Such is indeed the case. Correct to first order in M_H, Re, and Rm (so that the interaction parameter N is also small), the drag is

$$\frac{D}{D_S} = 1 + \tfrac{3}{8}KRe \qquad (12.3\text{-}2)$$

where (in terms of magnetic Prandtl number Pm)

$$K = \begin{cases} 1 & Mm > 1 \\ \dfrac{Mm^2 - PmMm^2 + 2Pm}{Mm\sqrt{(Pm - 1)^2 Mm^2 + 4Pm}} & Mm < 1 \end{cases} \qquad (12.3\text{-}3)$$

which may be written in terms of M_H as

$$K = \begin{cases} 1 & M_H^2 < ReRm \\ \dfrac{2M_H^2 + Re^2 - ReRm}{\sqrt{(Re - Rm)^2 + 4M_H^2}} & M_H^2 > ReRm \end{cases} \qquad (12.3\text{-}4)$$

Since $Pm = Rm/Re$, it may be any value for Re and Rm both small in the present approximation. For $Mm > 1$ we see that to the first order (Oseen accuracy) there is no magnetic influence on the drag.

An extension of the work of Ludford was made by Imai (1960) for an arbitrary orientation of the magnetic field. Imai used a Stokes approximation to discuss motion over insulating spheres and his discussion checks (for aligned fields) with Ludford's results (12.3-4) and Chester's result as $Re = Rm = 0$. Imai found for motion parallel to the field (x axis)

$$\frac{D_x}{D_S} = \left(1 + \frac{3}{8}M_H\right) \qquad (12.3\text{-}5)$$

and for motion at right angles to the field (y axis)

$$\frac{D_y}{D_S} = \left(1 + \frac{9}{16}M_H\right) \qquad (12.3\text{-}6)$$

For rotation about the x axis the drag moment is

$$M_x = -8\pi\rho\nu\Omega_x a_3\left(1 + \frac{1}{15}M_H{}^2\right)$$ (12.3-7)

and for rotation about the y axis

$$M_y = -8\pi\rho\nu\Omega_y a^3\left(1 + \frac{1}{45}M_H{}^2\right)$$ (12.3-8)

Here Ω is the angular velocity. If the sphere is given some arbitrary initial translation and rotation, it will move in a curved path with its axis of rotation constantly changing until it finally comes to rest.

We will not go into the calculations in detail but the nature of the electric field should be mentioned. If the motion is aligned with the field, at infinity $\mathbf{U}_0 \times \mathbf{B}_0 = 0$ and $\mathbf{E}'_\infty = \mathbf{E}_\infty = 0$. That is, in the frame of reference of the sphere and of the free stream fluid, the electric field is zero very far from the sphere. Since the flow is axially symmetric, $\mathbf{V}$ relative to the sphere and $\mathbf{H}$ at any point both lie in a meridian plane so that on the sphere the $\mathbf{V} \times \mathbf{H}$ vector forms concentric circles. Hence, from $\nabla \times \mathbf{E} = 0$, $\mathbf{E}$ must be zero on the sphere (relative to the sphere) and the current lines are circles (of constant latitude) given by $\mathbf{J} = \sigma\,(\mathbf{V} \times \mathbf{B})$. In the frame of the sphere, $\mathbf{E}$ is then everywhere zero.

In contrast to the aligned field motion, for the motion of the sphere across the magnetic field, the electric field (in the frame of the sphere) at infinity is $-\mathbf{U}_0 \times \mathbf{B}_0$, which has a finite value. Hence the electric field $\mathbf{E}$ varies over the surface of the sphere and the problem is rather different from the preceding one. In the aligned field motion $\mathbf{E}$ was zero on the sphere regardless of the conductivity of the sphere. The conductivity there played no part in the analysis. However, for the cross field motion, the conductivity of the sphere is, obviously, important. Only the insulator case has been treated in the above discussion.

Motion through an Inviscid Fluid with a Cross Field for $Rm \ll 1$, but N Large

Another problem for $Rm \ll 1$ is the motion of a nonmagnetic body through an inviscid fluid with a very strong magnetic field. Even though the magnetic field is essentially undistorted, the influence on the potential flow can be very great because the interaction parameter N is now large. Certainly the flow is now rotational, even though inviscid. The incompressible flow around insulating cylindrical bodies (at right angles to the free stream flow and the magnetic field) has been investigated in a rather clever manner by Ludford (1961), and at least near the body the flow pattern can be visualized at once.

The fluid may slip freely along magnetic lines of force but change in the motion at right angles to the lines is strongly inhibited. This fact is easily understood, for only motion perpendicular to the field lines can produce currents (from $\mathbf{V} \times \mathbf{B}$) and these currents in turn retard this particular motion. As shown in Fig. 12.3-2, the net result is that the fluid is displaced above and below the object so that the stream lines form curves congruent

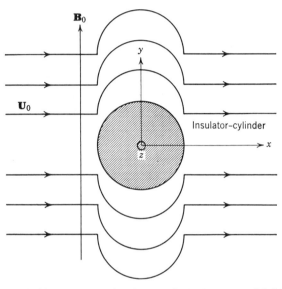

Figure 12.3-2 Inviscid flow over an insulating cylinder in a crossed field. The flow is incompressible, $Rm \ll 1$ and $N \gg 1$.

to the body surface. However, at distances from the body of order $\sqrt{N}$ times the characteristic length of the body, the inertia of the fluid becomes more dominant and the stream lines eventually straighten out. If the cylinder (or two-dimensional body) is not symmetrical about the flow direction, the inertia also distorts the flow upstream even near the body, but no distortion occurs downstream (Figs. 12.3-3). We will not go through the complete analysis here, but we will show how the congruent flow pattern comes about.

If we assume that in the frame of the free stream far from the body the electric field is zero, then the electric field (in the frame of the body) at infinity is $-\mathbf{U}_0 \times \mathbf{B}_0 = -U_0 B_0 \hat{z}$. From $\nabla \times \mathbf{E} = 0$ and the assumption that no electrodes are provided in the flow and that the body is an insulator, $J_z = 0$, and $\mathbf{E}$ must be constant $(-U_0 B_0 \hat{z})$ everywhere throughout the flow (in the frame of the body). The relevant equations can be written

$$\rho(\mathbf{V} \cdot \nabla)\mathbf{V} = -\nabla P + \sigma(\mathbf{E} + \mathbf{V} \times \mathbf{B_0}) \times \mathbf{B_0}$$

$$\nabla \cdot \mathbf{V} = 0$$

$$\mathbf{E} = -U_0 B_0 \hat{z} \qquad (12.3\text{-}9)$$

$$w = 0$$

$$\mathbf{B_0} = B_0 \hat{y} = \text{constant}$$

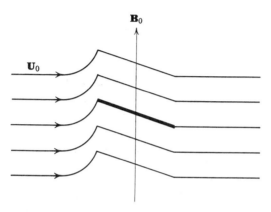

Figure 12.3-3 Flow over an insulating flat plate at incidence to the free stream, in a crossed field, $Rm \ll 1$, $N \gg 1$.

By normalizing as follows (where a is a characteristic length)

$$\mathbf{V}^* = \frac{\mathbf{V}}{U_0} \qquad P^* = \rho U_0^2 P$$

$$\mathbf{v}^* = \frac{\mathbf{v}}{a} \qquad \mathbf{U_0}^* = \hat{x}$$

$$\mathbf{H_0}^* = \frac{\mathbf{H_0}}{H_0} = \hat{y} \qquad N = \frac{a\mu^2 H_0^2 \sigma}{\rho U_0}$$

$$x^* = \frac{x}{a} \qquad y^* = \frac{y}{a}$$

we have

$$(\mathbf{V}^* \cdot \nabla^*)\mathbf{V}^* = -\nabla^* P^* - N(V^* - 1)\hat{x}^* \qquad (12.3\text{-}10)$$

N characterizes the ponderomotive force in relationship to the inertia force and we see that such a force is exerted on the fluid only in the x direction, at right angles to the magnetic field. For very large N ($N \gg 1$)

(12.3-10) reduces to

$$u^* = 1 - \frac{\partial}{\partial x^*}\left(\frac{P^*}{N}\right)$$

$$\frac{\partial}{\partial y^*}\left(\frac{P^*}{N}\right) = 0 \tag{12.3-11}$$

where it is supposed that P^* may become large as N does. By integrating, we find

$$P^* = Nf(x^*)$$

$$u^* = -\frac{df(x^*)}{dx^*} + 1 \tag{12.3-12}$$

and from continuity

$$v^* = y\frac{d^2f(x^*)}{dx^{*2}} + g(x^*) \tag{12.3-13}$$

where f and g are arbitrary functions to be determined by the boundary conditions. This solution will not completely satisfy the boundary conditions exactly but at least to the order of accuracy of the approximate solutions we can determine $f(x^*)$ and $g(x^*)$. At infinity, $u^* = 1$, but d^2f/dx^{*2} must be zero so that df/dx^* is a constant, zero. Hence $f(x^*)$ must be zero since it is zero at infinity. $g(x^*)$ is determined by the boundary condition on the cylinder, $y^* = F_{\pm}(x^*)$. Since $u^* = 1$ everywhere, v^* must be given on the surface of the cylinder as

$$v^* = g(x^*) = \begin{array}{ll} \dfrac{dF_+(x^*)}{dx^*} & |x^*| \leq 1 \quad \text{and} \quad y^* \geq F_+(x^*) \\[3mm] \dfrac{dF_-(x^*)}{dx^*} & |x^*| \leq 1 \quad \text{and} \quad y^* \leq F_-(x^*) \end{array} \tag{12.3-14}$$

For $|x^*| > 1$ we can set $v = g(x^*) = 0$. The solution is shown in Fig. 12.3-2. But at infinity $v^* \neq 0$ for $|x^*| < 1$. Only by considering the inertia terms can the stream lines be shown to straighten out. Furthermore, in the upstream direction there is an influence if the body is asymmetrical about the x axis. Figure 12.3-3 shows such a pattern over a flat plate at incidence.

Since u^* is constant at the value U_0, it may seem from Ohm's law that the current is everywhere zero and no interaction takes place. However, although the current may be a second-order effect and not show up in this analysis, the fact that the force is proportional to $\sigma(U_0 - u)H_0^2$ allows it to be finite even though $\sigma(U_0 - u)H_0$ is neglected. This comparison comes about because N is considered large and even though $\sigma(U_0 - u)H_0$

is second order, $\sigma(U_0 - u)H_0{}^2$ is not. Admittedly, the solution for moderate values of N is of a more practical interest, but the beautiful simplicity of this result sheds light on an otherwise exceedingly complex problem.

Further Considerations of Motion of an Inviscid Fluid, $Rm \ll 1$

In $N \ll 1$ or if the field is not oriented as in the preceding case, other flow configurations result. The possibilities are many and we will mention only a few.

Ludford and Murray (1960) found that if the field originates inside a sphere (that is, a dipole), the flow at $N \ll 1$ is clearly potential but the fluid acquires vorticity near the body. Vortical-magnetic wakes are generated.

The precise effect on the boundary layer and separation in this type of flow, and, in fact, most flows considered in magnetohydrodynamics, is an open problem in 1966.

Flow over thin bodies for $Rm \ll 1$ has been treated by a perturbation technique by Pai (1959) and will be mentioned later.

Let us now turn our attention to the somewhat more intriguing, if perhaps less realistic, problem of large magnetic Reynolds number.

12.4 LARGE CONDUCTIVITY, $Rm \ll 1$

As the conductivity becomes very large and $Rm \gg 1$, the magnetic field becomes more convected than diffused and approaches a "frozen-in" state. In aerodynamic problems the limit of large Rm is perhaps unrealistic, but on an astronomical scale such a limit is quite reasonable. Consideration of large Rm flow may be more than just a mathematician's game when we think of such problems as the solar wind flow over the planets and the like.

The first work along these lines was concerned with linearized theory for thin airfoils for fluid of essentially infinite conductivity. This problem of infinite conductivity has led to problems involving the precise definitions of the conditions at infinity, but if we consider the fluid to have slight, but negligible to the order of calculation, conductivity, the difficulty is removed. If disturbances created by the body could propagate indefinitely without attenuation, we would have the problem, discussed in Chapter 9, of a true steady state not existing. Alfvén disturbances would propagate outward and eventually interact with the source of the applied magnetic field. In a truly infinite geometry the waves continue to propagate and clearly no

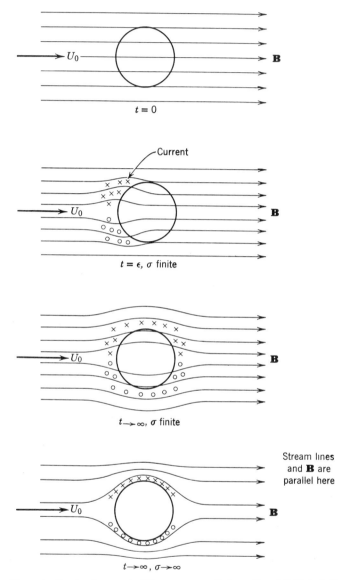

Figure 12.4-1   Stages in the development of flow over a cylinder, aligned field, infinite conductivity. The **B** lines are shown. The current is shown normal to the page.

limit solution, as time $t \to \infty$, is meaningful. Such considerations have given rise to some controversy. Two schools of thought, those of Sears and Resler (1959) and Stewartson (1960, 1961, 1963), have grown around the study of flow in infinitely conducting fluids. As pointed out by Stewartson, the true ultimate state solution (that is, as $t \to \infty$) requires disturbances at infinity. But if we consider a solution for large finite times, it would appear from our transient analyses in Chapter 9 that a wavelike solution (with the waves becoming damped and dispersed sufficiently far from the body) is adequate and corresponds to a real physical situation in which Rm is very large (but certainly not quite equal to infinity) so that the flow can be described, at least in the vicinity of the body, by the equations for a fluid of infinite conductivity. This is the approach of Sears and Resler.

The main difficulty in this controversy seems to be that the final steady-state solution for flow through an infinitely conducting fluid depends on the order or the limiting process if one starts with a real fluid. That is, the order in which the limits of $t \to \infty$, $\sigma \to \infty$, and $\nu \to 0$ are taken gives rise to completely different answers. The solution which we adopt here, the Sears-Resler version, is based on the fluid velocity vector and magnetic field vectors being parallel throughout the flow (for the aligned flow at infinity case) with, consequently, no magnetic field in the body, which is assumed to have finite or zero conductivity. It seems reasonable that as the fluid starts up, it will convect the field lines, which are initially all parallel, away from the body and the lines will slip readily through the body by diffusion until the field lines are parallel to the stream lines. A current sheet forms on the surface of the body and allows the tangential discontinuity in **B** at the surface of the body. If we assume a start-up from test, with σ of the fluid finite, and then imagine that σ increases, we would expect the field inside the body to become less and less and a current layer to build up in strength and become thinner in size until finally the field lines are entirely outside the body and the current layer becomes a sheet (see Fig. 12.4-1).

In this section we will discuss some of the features of general flow about three-dimensional bodies and point out certain analogies with classical aerodynamics. In Section 12.5 we will take up in detail the theory of thin airfoils, following the method of Sears and Resler.

The Magnetogasdynamic Analogy for Aligned, Compressible, Inviscid Flow

A rather clever analogy between aligned flow of an inviscid fluid and conventional gas dynamics has been made by Cowley (1960) and Imai

(1960). This analogy allows us to interpret immediately a general magneto-gas-dynamic flow of an ideal fluid around a body of finite or zero conductivity in terms of the corresponding gas-dynamic flow.

We assume steady flow of an ideal fluid with infinite conductivity and negligible heat conductivity (Fig. 12.4-1). From $\sigma = \infty$ it follows that

$$\mathbf{E} + \mathbf{V} \times \mathbf{B} = 0 \tag{12.4-1}$$

(in the frame of the body), and the current is given by

$$\mathbf{J} = \nabla \times \mathbf{H} \tag{12.4-2}$$

At infinity $\mathbf{V} \times \mathbf{B} = 0$ and hence $\mathbf{E}_\infty = 0$. In fact $\mathbf{V} \times \mathbf{B} = 0$ everywhere since $\sigma = \infty$ and hence $\mathbf{E} = 0$ everywhere in the flow field ($\mathbf{E}$ measured in the frame of the body). Hence $\mathbf{E} \cdot \mathbf{J} = 0$ and from the energy equation

$$\rho \frac{Dh_0}{Dt} = \rho(\mathbf{V} \cdot \nabla)h_0 = 0$$
$$h_0 = \text{constant} \tag{12.4-3}$$
$$s = \text{constant}$$

where h_0 is the specific total enthalpy ($h + V^2/2$) and s is the specific entropy. There is no dissipation so that the flow is isentropic and the entropy must be conserved throughout the flow. Furthermore, from the magnetic transport equation and the fact that $\mathbf{V} \times \mathbf{B} = 0$ it follows that

$$\mathbf{B} = K\rho\mathbf{V} \tag{12.4-4}$$

throughout the flow, where K is a constant. (We have no magnetic field in the body and $\mathbf{B}$ is parallel to $\mathbf{V}$.) Along with the above equations the equations of continuity and motion specify the system

$$\nabla \cdot (\rho\mathbf{V}) = 0 \tag{12.4-5}$$
$$(\mathbf{V} \cdot \nabla)\mathbf{V} + \frac{\nabla P}{\rho} = (\nabla \times \mathbf{V}) \times \mathbf{V} + \nabla\tfrac{1}{2}V^2 + \frac{\nabla P}{\rho} = \frac{(\nabla \times \mathbf{B}) \times \mathbf{B}}{\mu\rho} \tag{12.4-6}$$

From (12.4-3) and the fact that the flow is isentropic, Bernoulli's equation holds between points in the flow:

$$\nabla\tfrac{1}{2}V^2 + \frac{\nabla P}{\rho} = 0 \tag{12.4-7}$$

even though the flow is rotational because of the rotational body force. The validity of Bernoulli's equation in a rotational flow is perhaps somewhat unusual and does not occur in ordinary gas-dynamics. Equation

(12.4-6) becomes

$$(\nabla \times \mathbf{V}) \times \mathbf{V} = \frac{(\nabla \times \mathbf{B}) \times \mathbf{B}}{\mu \rho} \qquad (12.4\text{-}8)$$

From (12.4-4) and (12.4-8) then

$$\nabla \times \mathbf{V} = \pm \frac{B}{\mu \rho V} \nabla \times \mathbf{B} = K\mathbf{J} \qquad (12.4\text{-}9)$$

so that the vorticity is proportional to the current density. The positive and negative signs refer to $\mathbf{B}$ parallel and antiparallel to $\mathbf{V}$, respectively.

Now from (12.4-9) a new irrotational vector may be constructed using condition (12.4-4). Equation (12.4-9) can be expressed as

$$\nabla \times \left[\mathbf{V} \left(1 - \frac{B^2}{\mu \rho V^2} \right) \right] = 0 \qquad (12.4\text{-}10)$$

We can define the new irrotational vector $\tilde{\mathbf{V}}$ by

$$\tilde{\mathbf{V}} = \mathbf{V} \left(1 - \frac{A^2}{V^2} \right) = \mathbf{V} \left(1 - \frac{1}{Mm^2} \right) \qquad (12.4\text{-}11)$$

where A is the Alfvén speed $B/\sqrt{\mu \rho}$ and Mm is the magnetic Mach number. $\tilde{\mathbf{V}}$ is then parallel to $\mathbf{V}$ and the boundary conditions at the surface of the body are the same for $\tilde{\mathbf{V}}$ and $\mathbf{V}$. Further, we define

$$\tilde{\rho} = \frac{\rho}{1 - \dfrac{1}{Mm^2}} \qquad (12.4\text{-}12)$$

so that

$$\nabla \cdot (\tilde{\rho} \tilde{\mathbf{V}}) = 0 \qquad (12.4\text{-}13)$$

If we define $\tilde{P}$ as

$$\tilde{P} = P + \frac{B^2}{2\mu} \qquad (12.4\text{-}14)$$

the equation of motion (12.4-6) can be written

$$\tilde{\rho}(\tilde{\mathbf{V}} \cdot \nabla)\tilde{\mathbf{V}} + \nabla \tilde{P} = 0 \qquad (12.4\text{-}15)$$

Equations (12.4-13) and (12.4-15) have the same form as the equations for an appropriate inviscid, compressible fluid in conventional gas dynamics. The only necessary equation remaining is a relationship between $\tilde{P}$ and $\tilde{\rho}$ which must be determined in order to satisfy the equation of state and conditions (12.4-3) and (12.4-4).

In the new system of $\tilde{P}$, $\tilde{\rho}$, and $\tilde{\mathbf{V}}$, the sonic speed $\tilde{a}$ can be written as

$$\tilde{a}^2 = \frac{d\tilde{P}}{d\tilde{\rho}} = \tilde{V}^2 \left(\frac{1}{M^2} + \frac{1}{Mm^2} - \frac{1}{M^2 Mm^2} \right) \qquad (12.4\text{-}16)$$

where M is the ordinary Mach number. The analogous Mach number in the new system is then

$$\tilde{M}^2 = \left(\frac{\tilde{V}}{\tilde{a}}\right)^2 = \frac{M^2 M m^2}{M^2 + M m^2 - 1} \qquad (12.4\text{-}17)$$

The values of $\tilde{M}$ may now be plotted on a M versus Mm graph, thus providing us with insight into the various flow regimes (see Fig. 12.4-2)

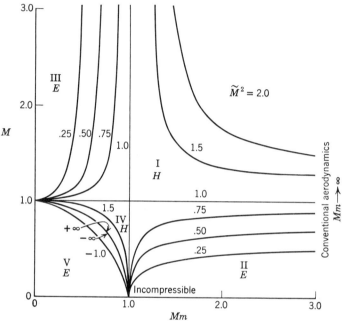

Figure 12.4-2   Regions of aligned flow, infinite conductivity, $\tilde{M}^2$ for various values of M and Mm. Various regions are numbered and E and H indicate that the equations are elliptic or hyperbolic. The incompressible limit is the abscissa, $M = 0$, and conventional aerodynamics is $\lim Mm \to \infty$.

The lines $\tilde{M}^2 = 0$, $\tilde{M}^2 = 1$, and $\tilde{M}^2 = \pm \infty$ divide the graph into the five following regions and may be compared with the results shown in Figs. 12.2-5 and 12.2-6.

1. $Mm > 1$; $M > 1$; $\tilde{M}^2 > 1$. The equations are hyperbolic and the gas dynamic analogy is supersonic flow. Mach waves, at an angle $\sin^{-1} 1/\tilde{M}$ to the stream lines, are generated by disturbances and are inclined downstream. These waves, as was indicated in Section 12.2, are fast magnetosonic disturbances. (Fig. 12.2-5a.)

2. $Mm > 1$; $M < 1$; $0 < \tilde{M}^2 < 1$. The equations are elliptic, and the analogue is subsonic flow. No waves are generated but a thin wake can exist downstream. (Fig. 12.2-5b.)

3. $Mm < 1$; $M > 1$; $0 < \tilde{M}^2 < 1$. The equations are again elliptic and the thin wake extends downstream. Here $\tilde{V}$ is anti-parallel to V and $\tilde{\rho}$ is a negative quantity. We may redefine $\tilde{V}$ and $\tilde{\rho}$ so that $\tilde{\rho}$ is positive and $\tilde{V}$ is parallel to V so that the analogue is subsonic flow. (Fig. 12.2-5b.)

4. $Mm < 1$; $M < 1$; $(M^2 + Mm^2) > 1$; $\tilde{M}^2 > 1$. The equations are hyperbolic and Mach waves corresponding to slow magnetosonic waves are inclined upstream from a disturbance. The analogue is super-sonic flow in the *reverse* direction. (Fig. 12.2-5c.)

5. $(Mm^2 + M^2) < 1$; $\tilde{M}^2 < 0$. $\tilde{M}^2$ here is a negative quantity so there is no analogue in conventional gas dynamics. The equations are elliptic but the thin wake extends upstream. (Fig. 12.2-5d.)

The changeover from downstream to upstream wakes (cases 4 and 5) checks with Equations (12.2-9) and (12.2-10), which were inferred directly from the Friedrichs diagram.

We have thus been able to obtain a qualitative picture of what the flow looks like under various conditions. To carry out the calculations com-pletely requires specification of a $\tilde{P}(\tilde{\rho})$ relationship, which will not, in general, be the same as an ordinary gas. The flow may be treated by the method of ordinary gas dynamics applied to an arbitrary nonconducting gas with an appropriate but artificial $\tilde{P}(\tilde{\rho})$ relationship. $\tilde{P}(\tilde{\rho})$ must be determined from the equation of state of the real gas and the conditions (12.4-3) and (12.4-4). This determination is not simple and generally requires numerical computation. We will not pursue the problem in further detail but will go on (in Section 12.5) to a special case of pertur-bation theory where the same results may be obtained by a different method. Before we do this, let us consider another similar analogy for viscous, incompressible, aligned flow.

The Analogy for the Incompressible, Viscous, Aligned Flow of a Perfectly Conducting Fluid

A particularly simple and important result was obtained by Hasimoto (1959) for viscous, incompressible flow of a perfectly conducting fluid around bodies. The magnetic field and free stream velocity are aligned as in the preceding discussion (Fig. 12.4-1). The limit as viscosity goes to zero would, of course, be the same as the limit in the preceding section if ρ is taken constant there. The abscissa ($M = 0$) in Fig. 12.4-2 represents the flow for incompressible, inviscid flow.

By the method of the preceding discussion, $E = 0$ (in the frame of the body) everywhere and we can impose the condition

$$\frac{B}{V} = K\rho = \text{constant} \tag{12.4-18}$$

where K and ρ are both constant throughout the flow. It follows then that $Mm = V/A = V\sqrt{\mu\rho}/B$ is constant throughout the flow. By using condition (12.4-18) we can write the equations of motion and continuity as

$$\left(1 - \frac{1}{Mm^2}\right)(\mathbf{V} \cdot \nabla)\mathbf{V} = -\frac{\nabla \tilde{P}}{\rho} + \nu \nabla^2 \mathbf{V} \qquad (12.4\text{-}19)$$

$$\nabla \cdot \mathbf{V} = 0 \qquad (12.4\text{-}20)$$

where $\tilde{P}$ is the total pressure $(P + B^2/2\mu)$ and the boundary conditions are $\mathbf{V} = 0$ on the body and $\mathbf{V} = U_0\hat{x}$ far from the body. The equations may be normalized as in Section 12.3 to give

$$\left(1 - \frac{1}{Mm^2}\right)(\mathbf{V}^* \cdot \nabla^*)\mathbf{V}^* = -\nabla^*\tilde{P}^* + \frac{1}{Re}\nabla^{*2}\mathbf{V}^* \qquad (12.4\text{-}21)$$

$$\nabla^* \cdot \mathbf{V}^* = 0$$

For $Mm = 1$ the equations are the classical Stokes equations for very viscous flow ($Re \ll 1$ but $Rm \gg 1$). For $Mm > 1$ the flow is the same as ordinary viscous flow with the density reduced by a factor of $(1 - 1/Mm^2)$. For $Mm < 1$ the effective density is negative in the ordinary flow sense; this difficulty can be removed by defining a new velocity and pressure as the negative of the actual velocity and pressure. The reversed $\tilde{P}$ and $\mathbf{V}$ satisfy the equation of motion then with the reduced density $[(1/Mm^2 - 1)\rho]$ and with the fluid flowing at infinity in the reversed direction. Hence this case of sub-Alfvénic flow gives rise to upstream wakes, as we learned earlier.

The body actually "feels" the total pressure $\tilde{P}$, $(P + B^2/2\mu)$, so that in determining the force on the body we must consider the total pressure. There is no magnetic field inside the body since the fluid is a perfect conductor and does not allow the field lines to diffuse out of it into the body. The $B^2/2\mu$ pressure then is actually due to a current sheet on the surface of the body which interacts with the magnetic field to squeeze the body. The net force then is due to the mechanical pressure P plus the magnetic pressure $B^2/2\mu$. These results may also be seen by considering the electromagnetic stress tensor at the surface of the body.

Hence the force (lift, drag) or moment on the body is obtained by suitably integrating $\tilde{P}$ over the body. In terms of the ordinary fluid dynamic vector force coefficient $\mathbf{C}_0$, which is a function of Reynolds number Re and normalized with respect to $\rho U_0^2/2$, we can express the force coefficients $\mathbf{C}$ in the conducting fluid as follows (as a function of Re):

$$\mathbf{C}(Re) = \left(1 - \frac{1}{Mm^2}\right)\mathbf{C}_0\left[\left(1 - \frac{1}{Mm^2}\right)Re\right] \qquad Mm > 1 \quad (12.4\text{-}22)$$

$$\mathbf{C}(Re) = \left(1 - \frac{1}{Mm^2}\right)\mathbf{C}_0^-\left[\left|1 - \frac{1}{Mm^2}\right|Re\right] \qquad Mm < 1 \quad (12.4\text{-}23)$$

C_0 denotes the ordinary coefficient of a nonconducting fluid in the absence of a magnetic field and is considered a function of the bracketed quantity, which is the effective Reynolds number. This coefficient must be multiplied by $(1 - 1/Mm^2)$ to get the desired $\mathbf{C}$ (Re) in the conducting fluid. $\mathbf{C}_0^-$ is the coefficient for the corresponding reversed flow.

It is possible for a force, that is $\mathbf{C}$ (Re), to reverse sign for $Mm < 1$, a phenomenon unknown in conventional flow. For example, consider the free stream flow and $\mathbf{B}$ at infinity aligned in the x direction, and a body symmetric about the yz plane (such as a cambered body at zero angle of attack). Then

$$C_{0x} = -C_{0x}^- \qquad C_{0y} = C_{0y}^- \qquad C_{0z} = C_{0z}^- \qquad (12.4\text{-}24)$$

The coefficient $(1 - 1/Mm^2)$ changes sign in (12.4-22) and (12.4-23) depending on Mm. If $Mm > 1$, all forces are the same sign as in the nonconducting fluid case, but if $Mm < 1$, the sense of C_y and C_z is reversed. C_x does not change sign. We see here that the lift in the y or z direction reverses sign for $Mm < 1$. It is interesting to note that an inclined flat plate does not undergo any change of sign of lift because it is antisymmetric about the yz plane. (However, there is an inversion of moment, which we will not show here.)

As we will see later, these observations about lift inversion hold for compressible, inviscid flow.

Incompressible, Inviscid, Aligned Flow of a Perfectly Conducting Fluid

It is a simple matter to take the limit of the preceding discussion as $Re \rightarrow \infty$ (inviscid) to obtain the results for subsonic incompressible aerodynamics, where $M \ll 1$ and the flow may be considered incompressible. The potential flow of subsonic aerodynamics becomes modified by the effective density change and the total pressure plays the role of ordinary pressure. For $Mm < 1$ the analogous flow is reversed. Equations (12.4-22) and (12.4-23) become simply

$$\mathbf{C} = \left(1 - \frac{1}{Mm^2}\right)\mathbf{C}_0 \qquad Mm > 1 \qquad (12.4\text{-}25)$$

and

$$\mathbf{C} = \left(1 - \frac{1}{Mm^2}\right)\mathbf{C}_0^- \qquad Mm < 1 \qquad (12.4\text{-}26)$$

where $\mathbf{C}_0$ is the force coefficient for potential flow and $\mathbf{C}_0^-$, as before, is the corresponding ordinary potential flow coefficient for reversed flow. The phenomenon of reversed lift occurs here as in the viscous case. These equations will appear again in linearized perturbation theory for incompressible flow but our analysis here shows that they are valid for general three-dimensional motion. The Kutta-Joukowsky condition here is the same as for ordinary aerodynamics, but if the magnetic field is not aligned additional conditions on magnetic parameters are necessary.

Arbitrary Re and Rm

Only a few other solutions of general two- and three-dimensional motion are available. Limiting solutions for large Hartmann numbers but arbitrary Re and Rm were given by Chester (1961) for flow over bodies of revolution and by Childress (1963) for two-dimensional flow.

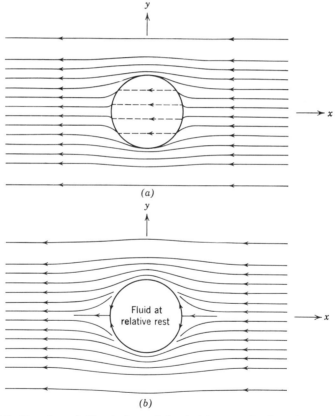

Figure 12.4-3 Top view of ultimate flow relative to (*a*) nonconducting sphere and (*b*) perfectly conducting sphere. —— Horizontal part of stream line, – – – – projection of remainder of stream line. From G. S. S. Ludford and M. P. Singh, *Proc. Camb. Phil. Soc.*, **59**, p. 615, 1963.

The flow over a sphere for aligned and crossed fields at arbitrary Rm for incompressible, inviscid flow is discussed by Ludford and Singh (1963). Their analysis will not be reproduced here, but some of their results are rather striking and unexpected. Part of the Stewartson controversy is avoided since the disturbances go to zero at infinity, although large slugs

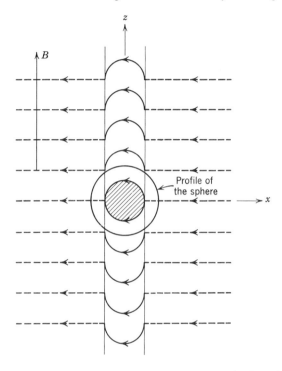

Figure 12.4-4 Side view of ultimate flow relative to a nonconducting sphere. ——— part of stream line in plane y = const., – – – – projection of remainder of stream line. From G. S. S. Ludford and M. P. Singh, *Proc. Camb. Phil. Soc.*, **59**, p. 615, 1963.

of fluid do move with the sphere. However, the wave-like character of the flow is not present and the solutions do represent different ones from the Sears-Resler theory. The general stream line patterns are shown in Figs. 12.4-3 and 12.4-4 for flow over both an insulating and perfectly conducting sphere for cross field configuration. The insulating case is similar to the flow over a cylinder treated in Section 12.3 for small Rm and large N. The side view of the central stream line flow shows a cylindrical disturbance with stream lines displaced congruently over an imaginary sphere somewhat smaller than the actual one; and from the top, looking down, the flow tends to divide around the column.

The perfectly conducting sphere carries with it a rigid column of fluid (a cylinder of the same radius as the sphere) that behaves like a solid cylinder parallel to the magnetic field lines. All these disturbances actually damp out along the column and the figures show only flow in the vicinity of the sphere. These column flows are similar to the classical Taylor columns in rotating fluids. Whether flow such as that described by Ludford and Singh is physically possible is not clear and remains a point of controversy.

Two-Dimensional Transverse Field Analogues

The particular flow considered is one in which the applied magnetic field is at right angles to the free stream flow direction and at right angles to the plane of the flow. If U_0 is $U_0\hat{x}$, then B_0 is $B_0\hat{z}$ and the flow is two-dimensional in the xy plane. Under certain conditions the flow reduces to a classical fluid dynamical problem which can be easily solved.

Consider incompressible flow over an insulating cylinder (whose generators lie in the $\hat{z}$ direction. Assume that in the laboratory (at rest with respect to fluid at infinity) frame $\mathbf{E}_\infty = 0$ so that $\mathbf{E}_{c\infty} = -\mathbf{U}_0 \times \mathbf{B}_0 = U_0 B_0 \hat{y}$ and $\mathbf{E}_0$ everywhere must be the same for small Rm. $\mathbf{E}_c$ is the electric field in the frame of the cylinder.

The equation of motion is

$$\rho\left[\frac{\partial \mathbf{V}}{\partial t} + (\mathbf{V} \cdot \nabla)\mathbf{V}\right] = -\nabla P + \mathbf{J} \times \mathbf{B}$$

$$= -\nabla\left(P + \frac{B^2}{2\mu}\right) + \frac{1}{\mu}(\mathbf{B} \cdot \nabla)\mathbf{B} \quad (12.4\text{-}27)$$

We form the circulation Γ and obtain

$$\frac{D\Gamma}{Dt} = 0 \quad (12.4\text{-}28)$$

where we have used the fact that all current is confined to the xy plane and the induced magnetic field must have only a z component. Hence $(\mathbf{B} \cdot \nabla)\mathbf{B}$ is identically zero since there can be no variations in the z direction. So that if one starts from an irrotational flow, the flow must remain irrotational about a fluid line. At infinity $\Gamma = 0$ so that we conclude that the flow must be irrotational throughout and the flow pattern is exactly the same as classical potential flow. The $\mathbf{V}$ vector and the streamlines are then determined. However, in order to find the pressure we must integrate the equation of motion. This is not simple except for small Rm, in which case we have

$$\nabla\left(\frac{V^2}{2} + \frac{P}{\rho}\right) = \frac{\sigma B_0^2}{\rho}(\mathbf{U}_0 - \mathbf{V}) \qquad (12.4\text{-}29)$$

which may be integrated to find P explicitly. Integration between any points in the fluid gives

$$\frac{V^2}{2} + \frac{P}{\rho} - \frac{\sigma B_0^2}{\rho}(\Phi + U_0 x) = \text{constant} \qquad (12.4\text{-}30)$$

where Φ is the velocity potential so that $\mathbf{V} = -\nabla\Phi$. The appearance of x is not startling; the origin is arbitrary and Φ is a function of x and y. At infinity $xU_0 + \Phi = 0$. Since $\mathbf{V}$ is now known, (12.4-30) allows immediate determination of P.

12.5 PERTURBATION THEORY OF THIN AIRFOILS

In the preceding section we discussed the character of aligned flow in a fluid of very large conductivity. In this section we will discuss some approximate methods which will allow us to calculate the inviscid flow over thin bodies. We saw in the last section that for aligned field flow certain analogies with conventional gas dynamics can be made. These results may be checked against the perturbation methods of the present section. Now we will not only be able to discuss aligned flow with $\sigma = \infty$ but we will be able to extend explicit calculations to account for arbitrary orientation of the field and arbitrary conductivity. Sears and Resler (1959) analyze flow over thin bodies for aligned and crossed field configurations assuming the fluid to be inviscid, perfectly conducting $Rm \to \infty$, and incompressible. Compressibility effects are considered by McCune and Resler (1960) and the extension to large but finite conductivity has been made by McCune (1960) for incompressible flow. Further work by Lary (1962) and Dragos (1963) considers arbitrary conductivity but the fluid incompressible. An analysis for an arbitrarily oriented field for a compressible but infinitely conducting fluid is given by Cumberbatch et al. (1963), and the works of Pai (1959) contains a perturbation theory for small conductivity ($Rm \ll 1$).

We will not consider in detail all the general problems, but will present the analysis for a compressible fluid of infinite conductivity in an aligned and crossed field. (The incompressible limit for an aligned field will check the results of the third part of Section 12.4 and for the compressible flow the results could well have been obtained using the analogy in the first part of Section 12.4.)

General Equations for Perturbation Theory for Thin Airfoils

In Fig. 12.5-1, we assume that the free stream flow is in the x direction so that $\mathbf{U}_0 = U_0\hat{x}$. Then the velocity at any point in the flow field can be written as $\mathbf{U} = \mathbf{U}_0 + \mathbf{v}$ where $v \ll U_0$. Similarly, the magnetic field is $(\mathbf{B}_0 + \mathbf{b})$ where $b \ll B_0$. The other variables can be represented as $(\rho_0 + \rho)$, $(P_0 + P)$, and $(T_0 + T)$, where $\rho \ll \rho_0$, $P \ll P_0$, and $T \ll T_0$.

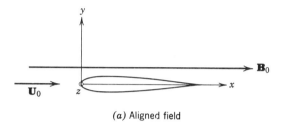

(a) Aligned field

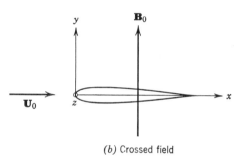

(b) Crossed field

Figure 12.5-1   Thin airfoil in a flow U_0 in the x direction.

By linearizing, we obtain the first-order equations as follows:

Continuity

$$\frac{\partial \rho}{\partial t} + U_0 \frac{\partial \rho}{\partial x} + \rho_0 \nabla \cdot \mathbf{v} = 0 \qquad (12.5\text{-}1)$$

Motion

$$\frac{\partial \mathbf{v}}{\partial t} + U_0 \frac{\partial \mathbf{v}}{\partial x} = -\frac{\nabla P}{\rho_0} + \frac{1}{\rho_0}(\nabla \times \mathbf{h}) \times \mathbf{B}_0 \qquad (12.5\text{-}2)$$

Energy

$$c_V\left(\frac{\partial T}{\partial t} + U_0 \frac{\partial T}{\partial t}\right) - \frac{P_0}{\rho_0{}^2}\left(\frac{\partial \rho}{\partial t} + U_0 \frac{\partial \rho}{\partial x}\right) = 0 \qquad (12.5\text{-}3)$$

Magnetic transport

$$\frac{\partial \mathbf{h}}{\partial t} = \eta\, \nabla^2 \mathbf{h} + \nabla \times (\mathbf{U}_0 \times \mathbf{h} + \mathbf{v} \times \mathbf{H}_0) \qquad (12.5\text{-}4)$$

Perfect gas law

$$\frac{P}{P_0} = \frac{T}{T_0} + \frac{\rho}{\rho_0} \qquad (12.5\text{-}5)$$

Equations (12.5-1) through (12.5-5) can be combined to give a single equation in terms of the current density $\mathbf{J} = \nabla \times \mathbf{h}$:

$$\left(\nabla^2 - \frac{1}{a_0^2}\frac{D^2}{Dt^2}\right)\left[\eta\,\nabla^2\!\left(\frac{D\mathbf{J}}{Dt}\right) + \frac{\mu}{\rho_0}(\mathbf{H}_0 \cdot \nabla)^2\mathbf{J} - \frac{D^2\mathbf{J}}{Dt^2}\right]$$
$$= \frac{\mu}{\rho_0 a_0^2}\left(\frac{D^2}{Dt^2}\right)(\mathbf{H}_0 \times \nabla)(\mathbf{H}_0 \cdot \nabla \times \mathbf{J}) \quad (12.5\text{-}6)$$

where $D/Dt = \partial/\partial t + \mathbf{U}_0 \cdot \nabla$ and $a_0 =$ the ordinary sonic speed in the free stream, $\gamma P_0/\rho_0 = \sqrt{\gamma R T_0}$.

For two-dimensional motion in the xy plane and $\mathbf{H}_0$ in that plane the perturbation equation simplifies to the following. $\mathbf{J}$ then has only a z component and the basic equation becomes

$$\left\{\left[\beta^2\!\left(1 - \frac{1}{Mm_x^2}\right) + \frac{M^2}{Mm_y^2}\right]\frac{\partial^4 J_z}{\partial x^4}\right.$$
$$+ \left[1 - \beta^2\!\left(\frac{1}{Mm_x^2} + \frac{1}{Mm_y^2}\right)\right]\frac{\partial^4 J_z}{\partial x^2\,\partial y^2}$$
$$\left.- \frac{1}{Mm_y^2}\frac{\partial^4 J_z}{\partial y^4} - \frac{2}{Mm_x Mm_y}\cdot\frac{\partial^2}{\partial x\,\partial y}\nabla^2 J_z\right\}$$
$$= \eta U_0\!\left(\beta\frac{\partial^2}{\partial x^2} + \frac{\partial^2}{\partial y^2}\right)\nabla^2\frac{\partial J_z}{\partial x} \quad (12.5\text{-}7)$$

where $M = U_0/a_0$, $\beta^2 = (1 - M^2)$, $Mm_x = U_0/A_x$, and $Mm_y = U_0/A_y$.

It is interesting to note that this set of equations is almost identical to the perturbation equations for plane waves in a gas that were discussed in Chapter 8, and, indeed, wave-type solutions will emerge under certain conditions. After J_z is known, the other fundamental quantities may be found from Ohm's law and the other equations. The continuity, momentum, and energy equations combine to give

$$\beta^2\frac{\partial u}{\partial x} + \frac{\partial v}{\partial y} = \frac{U_0 B_{0y} J_z}{\rho_0 a_0^2} \qquad (12.5\text{-}8)$$

Aligned Magnetic Field, Infinite Conductivity

For aligned field flow ($\mathbf{U}_0$ and $\mathbf{B}_0$ parallel in the x direction), $A_y \to 0$ and $1/Mm_y \to 0$ and we also let $\sigma \to \infty$ so that (12.5-7) becomes

$$(1 - \tilde{M}^2)\frac{\partial^2 J_z}{\partial x^2} + \frac{\partial^2 J_z}{\partial y^2} = 0 \tag{12.5-9}$$

where $\tilde{M}^2$ is, as before, $M^2 Mm_x^2/(M^2 + Mm_x^2 - 1)$. This equation is purely elliptic or hyperbolic depending on the sign of the coefficient of $\partial^2 J_z/\partial x^2$.

We may proceed with (12.5-7) but a simpler approach for this special case of aligned flow is possible if we define a small perturbation stream function. Equation (12.5-8) becomes

$$\beta^2 \frac{\partial u}{\partial x} + \frac{\partial v}{\partial y} = 0 \tag{12.5-10}$$

so that the equation is satisfied by a perturbation stream function $\psi(x, y)$ such that

$$u = \frac{1}{\beta^2}\frac{\partial \psi}{\partial y} \qquad v = -\frac{\partial \psi}{\partial x} \tag{12.5-11}$$

Then the x and y components of the linearized momentum equation for this case give

$$P - P_0 = -\rho_0 U_0 u \tag{12.5-12}$$

$$\frac{B_0 U_0}{\rho_0} \nabla \times \mathbf{h} = \nabla \times \mathbf{v} \qquad \frac{B_0 U_0 J_z}{\rho_0} = \left(\frac{\partial v}{\partial x} - \frac{\partial u}{\partial y}\right) \tag{12.5-13}$$

For infinite conductivity, $\mathbf{E} = -\mathbf{V} \times \mathbf{B}$ (in the frame of the airfoil). But as we have discussed earlier $\mathbf{V}$ and $\mathbf{B}$ are parallel so that $\mathbf{E} = -\mathbf{V} \times \mathbf{B} = 0$ everywhere. It follows then that in linearized form $\mathbf{V} \times \mathbf{B} = 0$ provides

$$h_y U_0 = H_{0x} v \tag{12.5-14}$$

Then (12.5-14) and (12.5-10) together with $\nabla \cdot \mathbf{h} = 0$ yield

$$h_x U_0 = H_{0x} \beta^2 u \tag{12.5-15}$$

By using (12.5-14) and (12.5-15), we can write (12.5-13) entirely in terms of u and v. Introducing the stream functions gives us

$$(1 - \tilde{M}^2)\frac{\partial^2 \psi}{\partial x^2} + \frac{\partial^2 \psi}{\partial y^2} = 0 \tag{12.5-16}$$

The flow is then elliptic or hyperbolic depending on the sign of $(1 - \tilde{M}^2)$, that is, whether $\tilde{M}^2$ is less than or greater than one, respectively. The regimes of flow have been shown in Fig. 12.4-2. Equation (12.5-16) is completely analogous to conventional aerodynamics with the effective Mach number $\tilde{M}$ and the stream function as defined in Equation (12.5-11). The significance of each type of flow has been discussed in Section 12.4. As mentioned earlier in 12.4, the loading on the airfoil depends on the total pressure $\tilde{P} = (P + \mu/2\mathbf{H} \cdot \mathbf{H})$, which in the linearized aligned theory is $P + B_{0x}h_x$.

The loading $l(x)$ per unit length in the z direction on a thin airfoil can now be written in terms of perturbation velocity as

$$l(x) = \rho_0 U_0 \left(1 - \frac{\beta^2}{Mm_x^2}\right)[u(x, 0^+) - u(x, 0^-)] \qquad (12.5\text{-}17)$$

Elliptic Regime. In the elliptic regime ($\tilde{M}^2 < 1$) the compressible flow may be related to the equivalent incompressible flow with the same U_0, Mm, and physical shape by the Prandtl-Glauert rule. Then the velocities are related

$$u_{\text{comp}} = \frac{u_{\text{inc}}}{\sqrt{1 - \tilde{M}^2}} \qquad v_{\text{comp}} = v_{\text{inc}} \qquad (12.5\text{-}18)$$

and from (12.5-17) the loading is

$$l(x) = \frac{1 - M^2}{(1 - \tilde{M}^2)^{3/2}} \cdot l_{\text{inc}}(x) \qquad (12.5\text{-}19)$$

where $l_{\text{inc}}(x)$ is the loading in the equivalent incompressible MHD flow (at the same Mm_x). In Section 12.4 we discussed the solution to the incompressible flow problem. By using those results (12.4-22 and 12.4-23), we finally have $l_0(x)$ in terms of the ordinary gas dynamic loading.

$$l(x) = \frac{(1 - M^2)(1 - 1/Mm_x^2)}{(1 - \tilde{M}^2)^{3/2}} \cdot l_0(x) \qquad Mm > 1$$

$$(12.5\text{-}20)$$

$$l(x) = \frac{(1 - M^2)(1 - 1/Mm_x^2)}{(1 - \tilde{M}^2)^{3/2}} \cdot l_0^-(x) \qquad Mm < 1$$

where $l_0^-(x)$ is the loading for reversed flow (that is, flow under the same conditions but in the negative x direction). In terms of the lift coefficient C_L,

$$C_L = \frac{1 - M^2}{(1 - \tilde{M}^2)^{3/2}} C_{L\,\text{inc}} = \frac{(1 - M^2)(1 - 1/Mm_x^2)}{(1 - \tilde{M}^2)^{3/2}} C_{L0} \qquad Mm > 1$$

$$(12.5\text{-}21)$$

$$C_L = \frac{1 - M^2}{(1 - \tilde{M}^2)^{3/2}} C_{L\,\text{inc}} = \frac{(1 - M^2)(1 - 1/Mm_x^2)}{(1 - \tilde{M}^2)^{3/2}} C_{L0}^- \qquad Mm < 1$$

In the limit of incompressible flow, M is taken as zero and we have $\tilde{M}^2 \to 0$ and we get

$$C_{L\,\mathrm{inc}} = \left(1 - \frac{1}{Mm_x^2}\right) \cdot C_{L0} \qquad Mm > 1$$

$$C_{L\,\mathrm{inc}} = \left(1 - \frac{1}{Mm_x^2}\right) \cdot C_{L0}^- \qquad Mm < 1 \tag{12.5-22}$$

where C_{L0}^- refers to the reversed flow.

From (12.5-20) or (12.5-21) we see that in the region where $M^2 > 1$ (and consequently $Mm^2 < 1$ since $\tilde{M}^2 < 1$ for the elliptic regime) the lift is of opposite sign to that of the incompressible case. Remember, the incompressible lift itself was for this condition ($Mm < 1$) of opposite sign to the classical aerodynamic lift. This lift reversal is caused by the surface currents (that is, magnetic pressure), which generate an opposite effect to the mechanical pressure, and in this region the current effect dominates. However, in the compressible case for $M^2 > 1$ (supersonic flow) the current effect is reversed and enhances the pressure lift so that it is larger than the classical aerodynamic lift.

Hyperbolic Regime. In the hyperbolic regime, $\tilde{M}^2 > 1$ and wave-type solutions occur corresponding to the magnetosonic disturbances. The characteristics are inclined at angles $\pm \tan^{-1} 1/\sqrt{\tilde{M}^2 - 1}$ to the x axis. In region I of Fig. 12.4-2 the flow is similar to ordinary supersonic flow, the characteristics slanting further back as the speed increases. The waves slant downstream. However, in region IV the wave angle increases as the Mach number M increases toward unity so that the correct family of characteristics slant forward or upstream, as we saw earlier in Section 12.4 by considering the analogous flow. The flow pattern is then determined from the characteristic pattern. This condition is the same as (12.2-9) and (12.2-10).

For a flat plate at a small angle of attack ϵ, the lift and drag coefficients are

$$C_L = \frac{4\epsilon \left| 1 - \dfrac{1}{Mm_x^2} \right|}{\tilde{M}} \tag{12.5-23}$$

$$C_D = C_L \epsilon$$

which are valid in both regimes of hyperbolic flow.

Crossed Field—Infinite Conductivity

When $\mathbf{B}_0$ and $\mathbf{U}_0$ are perpendicular ($\mathbf{B}_0 = B_0 \hat{y}$ and $\mathbf{U}_0 = U_0 \hat{x}$), no perturbation stream function exists and we must use the equation for J_z.

In general the flow may be divided into two regimes—purely hyperbolic, and a superposition of a hyperbolic and elliptic flow, which is referred to as "hyper-liptic" flow. The transition from one region to the other occurs at $U_0^2 = a_0^2 + A_y^2$. For $U_0^2 < a_0^2 + A_y^2$ the flow is hyper-liptic and for $U_0^2 > a_0^2 + A_y^2$ the flow is hyperbolic. The wave pattern of the

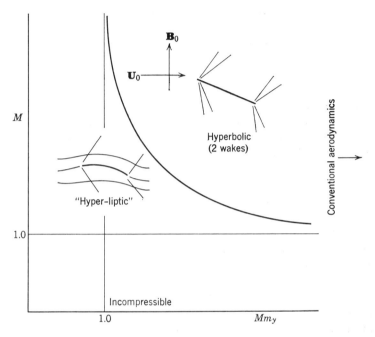

Figure 12.5-2 Regimes of flow for compressible flow in a crossed field with infinite conductivity. The dividing line is given by the condition $U_0^2 = a^2 + A^2$. The abscissa, $M = 0$, is the incompressible limit. Conventional aerodynamics lies out at $Mm_y \to \infty$.

characteristics may be inferred from the Friedrichs diagram. A curve of $1/Mm_y$ versus M (Fig. 12.5-2) may be constructed in a manner similar to Fig. 12.4-2.

In the purely hyperbolic flow there are two characteristics corresponding to fast and slow waves. In the hyper-liptic regime only the slow wave exists. We will not go into detail here, but we will show how the forms of the equation come about.

Equation (12.5-7) becomes, for $1/Mm_x \to 0$ and $\sigma \to \infty$ ($\eta \to 0$),

$$\left(\beta^2 + \frac{M^2}{Mm_y^2}\right)\frac{\partial^4 J_z}{\partial x^4} + \left(1 - \frac{\beta^2}{Mm_y^2}\right)\frac{\partial^4 J_z}{\partial x^2\,\partial y^2} - \frac{1}{Mm_y^2}\frac{\partial^4 J_z}{\partial y^4} = 0 \quad (12.5\text{-}24)$$

which may be factored into two operators:

$$\left(\frac{\partial^2}{\partial x^2} - \alpha^2 \frac{\partial^2}{\partial y^2}\right) \cdot \left(\xi^2 \frac{\partial^2}{\partial x^2} + \gamma^2 \frac{\partial^2}{\partial y^2}\right) \cdot J_z = 0 \qquad (12.5\text{-}25)$$

where

$$\alpha^2 = \frac{\dfrac{\beta^2}{Mm_y^2} - 1 + [4M/Mm_y^4 + (1 + \beta^2/Mm_y^2)^2]^{1/2}}{2(\beta^2 + M^2/Mm_y^2)}$$

$$\gamma^2 = (Mm_y\alpha)^{-2}$$

$$\xi^2 = 1 - M^2\left(1 - \frac{1}{Mm_y^2}\right)$$

For values of M and Mm_y other than zero, α^2 and hence γ^2 are always positive. However, ξ^2 may be positive or negative. For $\xi^2 > 0$ ($U_0^2 < a_0^2 + A_y^2$), the flow is the superposition of a hyperbolic and elliptic flow. For $\xi^2 < 0$ ($U_0^2 > a_0^2 + A_y^2$), the flow is doubly hyperbolic.

12.6. BOUNDARY LAYER THEORY

In magnetoaerodynamic flow the boundary layer is generally comprised of two distinct types of layers, a viscous layer and a current-vortical layer. The layers may be superimposed but if one dominates, the other will appear as a sublayer. The relative size of the two layers depends on the parameters of the particular problem. The size of the inviscid boundary layer, in which current and vorticity are large, is determined by the magnetic Reynolds number Rm, and the size of viscous layer is determined by the ordinary Reynolds number Re. The larger the value of Re the thinner the viscous boundary layer, and the larger the value of Rm the thinner the inviscid layer of order $0 \, (Rm^{-1/2})$. As was discussed earlier, as $\sigma \to \infty$, $Rm \to \infty$ and the inviscid layer is a current sheet (with a sheet of vorticity) along the body. From a practical standpoint the magnetic Prandtl number $Pm = Rm/Re$ will generally be small. For a liquid metal $Pm \approx 10^{-6}$ and for ionized air $Pm \approx 10^{-6}$ to 10^{-8}. We would thus expect the viscous layer to be much thinner than the inviscid layer and to behave as a thin sublayer somewhat as the viscous boundary layer appears as a sublayer in a thermal boundary layer for small ordinary Prandtl numbers.

We will consider two basic configurations—the aligned field and crossed field. The aligned field flow can give rise to both forward and backward facing wakes, so that the boundary layers can grow from front to back as in ordinary flow, or from back to front, or a combination of both. The forward-facing wake dominates, remember, (1) if Pm is very small

(ν small, Re large) so that the viscous layer is subdued in comparison and (2) if $\sigma \to \infty$ so that $Rm \to \infty$ and $Pm \to \infty$, regardless of the value of ν. The criterion for the existence of the upstream wake has been discussed. For an incompressible fluid, an upstream wake exists and the inviscid layer grows from rear to front if the speed of the body is less than the Alfvén speed (Hasimoto, 1960).

In a cross field configuration the same general remarks apply for the boundary layer sizes, but upstream wakes cannot exist, and both layers grow from the front to rear as do ordinary boundary layers.

There are also the problems of separation, particularly of the inviscid layer, and an equivalent Kutta-Joukowsky condition. We will not consider these problems here, but some progress has been made along these lines, particularly by Sears (1961) and Cumberbatch et al. (1962, 1963).

The Crossed Field Boundary Layer

In a flat plate cross field geometry a viscous boundary layer is formed as well as an Alfvén layer. Figure 12.6-1 shows two types of flat plate

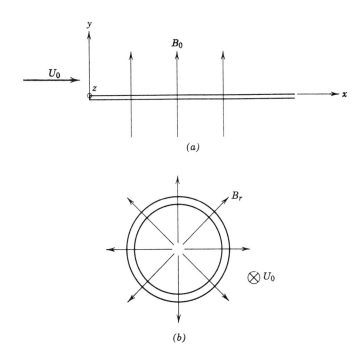

(a)

(b)

Figure 12.6-1 The crossed field boundary layer over a flat plate. (a) True flat plate, (b) axisymmetric with B_r (in this case B_r is assumed to originate in the body).

flow. We assume the plate to be moving with a velocity U_0 through a still fluid. For convenience, we can assume that the plate is fixed and the free stream fluid is moving with speed U_0 in the x direction past the plate. However, the boundary conditions on the electric field are determined by which of these choices represents the true physical picture. If we assume

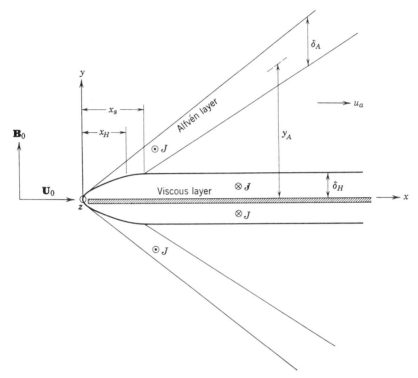

Figure 12.6-2   Boundary layer over a flat plate with a crossed field. The field fills all space. The region between the viscous (Hartmann) layer and the diffused Alfvén layer flows with constant velocity u_a which is less than U_0.

that the fluid is at rest, in the frame of the plate the electric field at infinity $\mathbf{E}_{p\infty}$ must be

$$\mathbf{E}_{p\infty} = -\mathbf{U}_0 \times \mathbf{B}_0 = U_0 B_0 \hat{z} \qquad (12.6\text{-}1)$$

so that currents there are zero. $\mathbf{E}'_{\infty}$ (in the frame of the fluid) is zero. We assume this approach here since it corresponds to a true aerodynamic system. The boundary condition on $\mathbf{E}_p$ at the surface of the plate depends on the conductivity of the plate. For an infinitely conducting plate, $\mathbf{E}_p$ on the plate is zero. For an insulating plate this is not so and $\mathbf{E}_p$ on the plate has a definite value which we will determine.

The qualitative picture of the flow over the flat plate is shown in Figs. 12.6-2 and 12.6-3. The viscous layer builds up to a constant thickness at which point the Alfvén layer has shed. The current in the viscous (or Hartmann) layer is in the z direction, and the return circuit is completed through the Alfvén layer. This layer is produced at the frontal region where the viscous (or Hartmann) layer is developing. A look at the figure shows that the Alfvén layer diffuses downstream. In Chapter 9 the nature of such a layer was discussed in detail. If both v and η are zero, the layer does not diffuse, but if either v or η, or both, are nonzero, the layer will diffuse. A qualitative order-of-magnitude study shows the critical dimensions in Fig. 12.6-2 to be as follows (D is the larger of v or η, and A is the Alfvén velocity):

$$x_H \sim \frac{\rho U_0}{\sigma B_0^2} \sim \quad \text{characteristic development distance for the Hartmann (viscous) layer}$$

$$\delta_H \sim \left(\frac{\rho v}{\sigma}\right)^{1/2} B_0 \sim \quad \text{thickness of the Hartmann (viscous) layer}$$

$$y_A \sim \frac{Ax}{U_0} \sim \quad \text{distance of the Alfvén layer from the plate} \quad (12.6\text{-}2)$$

$$\delta_A \sim \left(\frac{Dx}{U_0}\right)^{1/2} \sim \quad \text{thickness of the Alfvén layer}$$

$$x_s \sim \frac{\mu_0 \rho U_0 D}{B_0^2} \sim \quad \text{the distance required for the Alfvén and Hartmann layers to separate}$$

If there is no interaction, that is, $\sigma = 0$ or $\mathbf{B}_0 = 0$, then there is no Alfvén layer and the viscous layer continues to grow without stabilizing at a fixed thickness.

Now we want to confine our attention to the viscous sublayer. A study of the entire problem under transient conditions has been made by Dix (1963). For an infinitely conducting fluid the effect of viscosity is suppressed and only a current-vortex sheet exists on the surface of the plate. The velocity is zero (that is, the fluid is attached to the plate) from the surface of the plate out to the Alfvén line. Figure 9.6-8 illustrates how this comes about.

In a viscous layer of finite conductivity we expect the electric field to be uniform from the surface of the plate out to the Alfvén line where it jumps to its free stream value. At the ends of the plate there is some question about just how the current completes its path or how the electric field varies. In an axisymmetric geometry this question does not arise. We denote the values of parameters between the viscous and Alfvén layers with a subscript a. They may be determined approximately from Chapter 9 (by replacing t there by x/U_0). In the viscous layer then Ohm's law is

$$J_z = \sigma(-u_a B_0 + u B_0) \tag{12.6-3}$$

In the axisymmetric case $\mathbf{E}_{p\infty} = 0 = \mathbf{E}'_\infty$ since $B_r \to 0$ as $r \to \infty$. Also $\mathbf{E}_{ps} = 0$ from $\nabla \times \mathbf{E}_p = 0$. And also $E_{p\theta} = 0$ and $E_{pr} = 0$. We expect

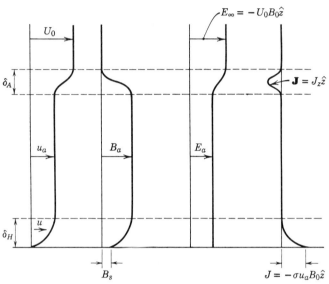

Figure 12.6-3 Profiles in the flat plate boundary layer shown in Fig. 12.6-2. For an insulating plate, B_s at the plate is zero and $E_a = -u_a B_0 z$. For a perfectly conducting plate $E_a = 0$, $B_s = B_a$, and the Hartmann layer thickness δ_H is zero. Also, then, u at the plate and u_a are $\frac{1}{2} U_0$. For finite plate conductivity, u is zero at the plate.

then that here $\mathbf{E}'_a = 0$ and from Ohm's law:

$$J_\theta = \sigma u B_r \tag{12.6-4}$$

and current would flow in concentric rings out as far as B_r extends (until $\mathbf{B}_0$ begins its return path and eventually runs parallel to $\mathbf{U}_0$). The subscript s denotes values on the surface of the plate.

In a real situation there is a distinct difference between the flat plate and the axisymmetric body. We have discussed only the flat plate in detail in Chapter 9. (In the fluid rest frame the E'_θ comes about because of a $\partial \mathbf{B}/\partial t$ which the fluid sees as it flows past the magnetic field of the body. In the axisymmetric geometry we assume the magnetic field to originate within the body that is magnetized.) Figures 12.6-2 and 12.6-3 refer only to a flat plate.

For the flat plate the viscous boundary layer in an incompressible fluid is approximately governed by the equation of motion:

$$u \frac{\partial u}{\partial x} + v \frac{\partial u}{\partial y} = - \frac{1}{\rho} \frac{\partial P}{\partial x} + v \frac{\partial^2 u}{\partial y^2} - \frac{\sigma B_0^2 (u - u_a)}{\rho} \tag{12.6-5}$$

where the effective free stream velocity is u_a. The transverse pressure gradient may be neglected and the usual boundary layer assumptions have been made. The exact treatment by Dix requires the inclusion of the Alfvén or inviscid layer and its interaction with the viscous layer.

For an axisymmetric body the equation of motion is

$$u \frac{\partial u}{\partial x} + v \frac{\partial u}{\partial y} = - \frac{1}{\rho} \frac{\partial P}{\partial x} + v \frac{\partial^2 u}{\partial y^2} - \frac{\sigma B_0^2 u}{\rho} \tag{12.6-6}$$

with U_0 the free stream velocity which is used as the boundary condition.

Equations of the form of (12.6-5) and (12.6-6) have been solved with a Blasius-type solution by Rossow for zero pressure gradient, although a constant value of $\partial P / \partial x$ could be included in the constant $(-\sigma B_0^2 u_a)$ without difficulty. The thermal boundary layer has also been solved under the preceding conditions for Prandtl number unity by Rossow (1958) and by Bush (1960). The energy equation for incompressible flow for the flat plate is

$$\rho c_V \left(u \frac{\partial T}{\partial x} + v \frac{\partial T}{\partial y} \right) = \kappa_T \frac{\partial^2 T}{\partial y^2} + v\rho \left(\frac{\partial u}{\partial y} \right)^2 + \sigma B_0^2 (u - u_a)^2 \tag{12.6-7}$$

and for the axisymmetric body

$$\rho c_V \left(u \frac{\partial T}{\partial x} + v \frac{\partial T}{\partial y} \right) = \kappa_T \frac{\partial^2 T}{\partial y^2} + v\rho \left(\frac{\partial u}{\partial y} \right)^2 + \sigma B_0^2 u^2 \tag{12.6-8}$$

One other geometry is of interest here, namely, the flat plate carrying its own magnetic field. In this case the flux lines must return to the bottom of the plate or to another portion of the plate. In any case, the plate will behave differently than the one just considered, and we would have to be careful to set the proper values of the boundary conditions on $\mathbf{E}'$ and $\mathbf{E}_p$.

Returning to the preceding problems, we can find solutions to Equations (12.6-5) and (12.6-6) for zero pressure gradient in a manner analogous to the classical Blasius solution.

Consider first the flow over an axisymmetric body. We introduce the dimensionless variables as

$$\eta = y \sqrt{\frac{U_0}{vx}} \tag{12.6-9}$$

$$\xi = x$$

just as in the Blasius solution. The stream function is defined as

$$\psi = \sqrt{U_0 \nu x} \, [f_0 + \sqrt{mx} \, f_1 + mx f_2 + (mx)^{3/2} f_3 + \cdots] \quad (12.6\text{-}10)$$

where $f_0, f_1, f_2, \ldots$ are functions of η only, and mx is

$$mx = \frac{\sigma B_0^2 x}{\rho U_0} = N \quad (12.6\text{-}11)$$

the interaction parameter based on the length x. Then the velocity components are

$$u = \frac{\partial \psi}{\partial y} = \frac{\partial \psi}{\partial \xi} \cdot \frac{\partial \xi}{\partial y} + \frac{\partial \psi}{\partial \eta} \cdot \frac{\partial \eta}{\partial y} \quad (12.6\text{-}12)$$

and

$$v = -\frac{\partial \psi}{\partial x} = -\frac{\partial \psi}{\partial \xi} \cdot \frac{\partial \xi}{\partial x} - \frac{\partial \psi}{\partial \eta} \cdot \frac{\partial \eta}{\partial x} \quad (12.6\text{-}13)$$

$$u = U_0[f'_0 + \sqrt{mx} \, f'_1 + mx f'_2 + (mx)^{3/2} f'_3 + \cdots] \quad (12.6\text{-}14)$$

$$v = \frac{\eta}{2} \sqrt{\frac{U_0 \nu}{x}} \, [f'_0 + \sqrt{mx} f_1' + mx f'_2 + (mx)^{3/2} f'_3 + \cdots]$$

$$- \frac{1}{2} \sqrt{\frac{U_0 \nu}{x}} \, [f_0 + 2\sqrt{mx} f_1 + 3mx f_2 + 4(mx)^{3/2} f_3 + \cdots] \quad (12.6\text{-}15)$$

We use the boundary conditions that at $y = 0$, $u = 0$, and at $y = \infty$, $\partial u/\partial y = v = 0$ and $\partial u/\partial x = -\sigma B_0^2/\rho$. Infinity here is far from the plate but still within the region of essentially uniform $\mathbf{B_0}$. The resulting ordinary differential equations for the f functions have been discussed by Rossow. $f_1 = f_3 = 0$ and f_0 is known; f_2 was found by a Runge-Kutta method and tabulated. An abbreviated table of f_2 is shown here (Table 12.6-1 a). The skin-friction coefficient and displacement thickness are found as

$$C_f = \frac{0.664 - 1.788 mx + \cdots}{\sqrt{Re_x}} \quad (12.6\text{-}16)$$

$$\delta^* = mxy + (1.73 + 0.54 mx)\sqrt{\frac{\nu x}{U_0}} \quad (12.6\text{-}17)$$

It is interesting to note that the effect of the magnetic field here is similar to that of a pressure gradient, and reversed flow can occur even on a flat plate with zero pressure gradient. The question of what this means in terms of separation is not clear, especially since the inviscid layer and inhomogeneities necessary in this configuration have been neglected.

For the flat plate flow, Equation (12.6-5) can be solved in a similar manner. η and ψ are the same, but based on u_a instead of U_0.

$$\eta = y\sqrt{\frac{u_a}{\nu x}} \qquad mx = \frac{\sigma B_0^2 x}{\rho u_a} \qquad (12.6\text{-}18)$$

As before $f_1 = f_3 = 0$ and f_0 is the classical Blasius solution. The appropriate equation for f_2 has been integrated by Rossow and some data

Table 12.6-1

Table of the f_2 functions for the boundary layer solutions

η	f_2	f'_2	f''_2	η	f_2	f'_2	f''_2
0	0	0	−0.894	0	0	0	1.147
1.0	−0.433	−0.839	−0.730	1.0	0.420	0.702	0.312
2.0	−1.573	−1.367	−0.296	2.0	1.181	0.737	−0.184
3.0	−3.010	−1.435	0.121	3.0	1.788	−0.324	−0.324
4.0	−4.354	−1.239	0.216	4.0	2.093	−0.208	−0.208
5.0	−5.501	−1.073	0.107	5.0	2.191	−0.071	−0.071
6.0	−6.537	−1.013	0.026	6.0	2.210	−0.013	−0.013
7.0	−7.542	−1.001	0.003	7.0	2.213	0	−0.002
8.0	−8.543	−1.000	0	8.0	2.213	0	0

(a)	(b)
Solution for axisymmetric flow.	Solution for the flat plate.
$\mathbf{B}_0$ originates in body.	Homogeneous $\mathbf{B}_0$ throughout fluid.

is presented in Table 12.6-1 *b*. Here no reversed flow occurs, because as y becomes large the current goes to zero. The skin-friction coefficient is

$$C_f = \frac{0.664 + 2.293mx + \cdots}{\sqrt{Re_x}} \qquad (12.6\text{-}19)$$

and the displacement thickness is

$$\delta^* = (1.73 - 2.21mx - \cdots + \cdots)\sqrt{\frac{\nu x}{u_a}} \qquad (12.6\text{-}20)$$

Sample velocity profiles for both cases are shown in Fig. 12.6-4.

Aligned Field Boundary Layer

As we have pointed out, in the aligned field geometry the wakes may point upstream or downstream, or both, and the two types of boundary layers may grow from front to rear or rear to front. One interesting consequence of this observation is pointed out by Greenspan and Carrier

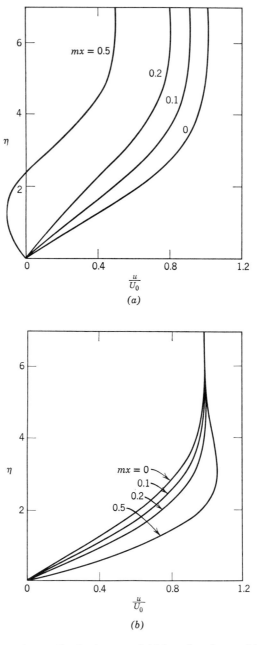

Figure 12.6-4 Velocity profiles in the cross field boundary layer. (*a*) Axisymmetric, B_r originates within the plate, (*b*) flat plate with $\mathbf{B_0}$ throughout all space.

(1959). If we consider a semi-infinite plate with incompressible flow at velocities less than the Alfvén velocity (that is, $Mm < 1$), upstream wakes appear and grow from the downstream end of the plate located at infinity. Consequently, the boundary layer, having had an infinite distance in which to grow, completely covers and plugs or blocks the flow.

An analysis of the boundary layer for small Pm has been made by Sears (1961). For Pm small, the viscous layer is a thin sublayer in the inviscid

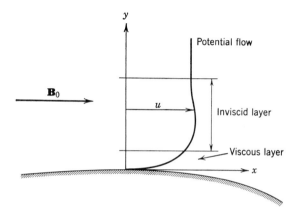

Figure 12.6-5   The viscous and inviscid boundary layer in aligned flow.

layer. Under this condition of small Pm the equations of the viscous layer take the following form

$$u \frac{\partial u}{\partial x} + v \frac{\partial u}{\partial y} + \frac{1}{\rho} \frac{\partial P}{\partial x} = v \frac{\partial^2 u}{\partial y^2} - \frac{\sigma}{\rho} u [B_y(x, 0)]^2 \qquad (12.6\text{-}21)$$

$B_y(x, 0)$ is the value of the magnetic field at the inner edge of the inviscid layer (see Fig. 12.6-5).

The inviscid layer, because of its large current density, reduces the free stream $\mathbf{B}_0$ to a small value so that the low Rm interaction equations apply in the viscous layer. Equation (12.6-19) is identical to (12.6-6) and that solution applies here with the appropriate value for u at the outer value of the viscous layer. (As the conductivity approaches infinity ($Rm \rightarrow \infty$), the inviscid layer becomes a current sheet on the body and includes a layer of vorticity. Then the sublayer has no meaning.) In the viscous layer $P(x)$ is equal to the value of $[P(x) + B^2/2\mu]$ in the inviscid layer. As we have pointed out before, the pressure close to the body is the free stream pressure plus the magnetic pressure which varies but little through the inviscid layer if $Rm \gg 1$. As $Rm \rightarrow \infty$, the total pressure felt by the body is the free stream static pressure plus the magnetic pressure of the free stream (which, in other words, is the surface force generated by the static pressure plus the $\mathbf{J} \times \mathbf{B}$ force of the current sheet).

The values of H_y and u at the outer edge of the viscous layer (inner edge of the inviscid layer) must be found by solving the inviscid boundary layer equations. These can be solved (for $Pm \ll 1$) by assuming that the outer edge of the viscous layer is effectively at $y = 0$ and that there $H_x = v = 0$; then H_y and u may be found from the inviscid solution. For details the reader is referred to the original work of Sears.

12.7   HYPERSONIC FLOW

One of the most important applications of magnetoaerodynamics is to the hypersonic flow around a missile or reentry vehicle in the atmosphere. Because of the high speed, the air may be shock heated or heated by the boundary layer to a temperature at which the gas is ionized. Generally, the magnetic field of the Earth is negligibly small, but a magnetic field may be generated inside the body and carried along with it. Such interactions can affect the skin-friction. Detailed calculations of hypersonic boundary layer flow have been made by Bush (1958) and Meyer (1958). The problem of an ionizing hypersonic shock has been considered by Levy et al. (1964). They found that under certain cases the gas can be substantially pushed away from the surface of the body, thereby reducing the skin-friction.

Another similar class of problems is that of the flow of the "solar wind" over bodies in the solar system. The solar wind, which is a rarefied neutral gas of charged particles with a high conductivity, as it flows distorts the dipole magnetic field of the Earth and drags it into a "tail". This concept of a magnetosphere about the Earth has received considerable attention and its existence has been verified by recent satellite measurements. Although the magnetosphere problem is one of the most striking examples of the success of theoretical predictions in magnetofluidmechanics, we cannot pursue problems of this type here. Unfortunately, they require a more sophisticated model of the gas than the continuum model we use here and such problems are the realm of plasma physics. A rather good review of these problems is given by Bachynski (1964) along with a bibliography of recent theoretical and experimental work.

PROBLEMS

1. In the example treated in the second part of Section 12.3, what are the shapes of the current profiles, qualitatively?
2. Derive Equations (12.4-22) and (12.4-23) in detail.

3. Derive expressions for the moment for the viscous flow of a perfectly conducting fluid discussed in the second part of Section 12.4.

4. For compressible thin airfoil theory, derive an expression for the current sheet. Sketch the flow lines around a thin flat airfoil.

5. In Problem 4, does it matter what the conductivity of the airfoil is if in the fluid $\sigma \rightarrow \infty$?

6. In aligned flow does the sense of $\mathbf{B}_0$ affect the wake pattern? Explain.

7. An infinitely long, circular insulating cylinder is oriented so that the free stream velocity $U_0\hat{x}$ is at right angles to its axis. A homogeneous, magnetic field $B_0\hat{z}$ is parallel to the axis of the cylinder. Discuss this flow, particularly for $Rm \ll 1$. What is the current distribution? Can you make a quantitative study of the boundary layer? What about separation? Show that the flow is potential and the velocity and stream lines are the same as classical potential flow, but with the pressure given by the following equation, which is the analogue of the Bernoulli equation:

$$\rho \frac{V^2}{2} + P - \sigma\Phi B_0{}^2 - \sigma U_0 B_0{}^2 x = \text{constant}$$

(Φ is the velocity potential and the value of E relative to the cylinder is everywhere $-\mathbf{U}_0 \times \mathbf{B}_0$).

REFERENCES

Ahlstrom, H., Experiments on the Upstream Wake in Magneto-fluid Dynamics, *J. Fluid Mech.*, **15**, p. 205, 1963.

Bachynski, M. P., Simulation of Geophysical Phenomena in the Laboratory, AIAA, **2**, No. 11, p. 1873, 1964.

Bush, W. B., Magnetohydrodynamic-Hypersonic Flow Past a Blunt Body, *J. Aerospace Sciences*, **25**, No. 11, p. 685, 1958.

Bush, W. B., Compressible Flat-Plate Boundary-Layer Flow with an Applied Magnetic Field, *J. Aerospace Sciences*, **27**, No. 1, p. 49, 1960.

Carrier, G. F., and H. P. Greenspan, The Time-Dependent Magnetohydrodynamic Flow Past a Flat Plate, *J. Fluid Mech.*, **7**, p. 22, 1960.

Chester, W., The Effect of a Magnetic Field on Stokes Flow in a Conducting Fluid, *J. Fluid Mech.*, **3**, p. 304, 1957.

Chester, W., The Effect of a Magnetic Field on the Flow of a Conducting Fluid Past a Body of Revolution, *J. Fluid Mech.*, **10**, p. 459, 1961.

Childress, S., The Effect of a Strong Magnetic Field on Two-Dimensional Flows of a Conducting Fluid, *J. Fluid Mech.*, **15**, p. 429, 1963.

Cowley, M. D., A Magnetogasdynamic Analogy, *J. Am. Rocket Soc.*, **30**, p. 271, 1960.

Cumberbatch, E., L. Sarason, and H. Weitzner, A Magnetofluid-Dynamic Kutta-Joukowsky Condition, *J. Aerospace Sciences*, **29**, No. 2, p. 244, 1962.

Cumberbatch, E., L. Sarason, and H. Weitzner, Magnetohydrodynamic Flow Past a Thin Airfoil, AIAA, **1**, No. 3, p. 679, 1963.

Dix, D. M., The Magnetohydrodynamic Flow Past a Non-Conducting Flat Plate in the Presence of a Transverse Magnetic Field, *J. Fluid Mech.*, **15**, p. 449, 1963.

Dragos, L., Theory of Thin Airfoils in Magnetohydrodynamics, *Arch. Ratl. Mech. Anal.*, **13**, No. 4, p. 262, 1963.

Fan, D. N., Aligned-fields Magnetogasdynamic Wakes, *J. Fluid Mech.*, **20**, p. 433, 1964.

Grad, H., Reducible Problems in Steady Flow, *Rev. Mod. Phys.*, **32**, No. 4, p. 828, 1960.

Greenspan, H. P., and G. F. Carrier, The Magnetohydrodynamic Flow Past a Flat Plate, *J. Fluid Mech.*, **6**, p. 77, 1959.

Hasimoto, H., Viscous Flow of a Perfectly Conducting Fluid with a Frozen Magnetic Field, *Phys. Fluids*, **2**, p. 337, 1959.

Hasimoto, H., Magnetohydrodynamic Wakes in a Viscous Conducting Fluid, *Rev. Mod. Phys.*, **32**, No. 4, p. 860, 1960.

Hasimoto, H., Steady Longitudinal Motion of a Cylinder in a Conducting Fluid, *J. Fluid Mech.*, **8**, p. 61, 1960.

Imai, I., On Flows of Conducting Fluids Past Bodies, *Rev. Mod. Phys.*, **32**, No. 4, p. 992, 1960.

Jungclaus, G., Two-Dimensional Boundary Layers and Jets in Magneto-Fluid Dynamics, *Rev. Mod. Phys.*, **32**, No. 4, p. 823, 1960.

Lary, E. C., A Theory of Thin Airfoils and Slender Bodies in Fluids of Finite Electrical Conductivity with Aligned Fields, *J. Fluid Mech.*, **12**, p. 209, 1962.

Levy, R. H., P. J. Gierasch, and D. B. Henderson, Hypersonic Magnetohydrodynamics with or without a Blunt Body, AIAA, **2**, No. 12, p. 2091, 1964.

Ludford, G. S. S., Inviscid Flow Past a Body at Low Magnetic Reynolds Number, *Rev. Mod. Phys.*, **32**, No. 4, p. 1000, 1960.

Ludford, G. S. S., The Effect of an Aligned Magnetic Field on Oseen Flow of a Conducting Fluid, *Arch. Ratl. Mech. Anal.*, **4**, p. 405, 1960.

Ludford, G. S. S., The Effect of a Very Strong Magnetic Cross-Field on Steady Motion Through a Slightly Conducting Fluid, *J. Fluid Mech.*, **10**, p. 141, 1961.

Ludford, G. S. S., and J. D. Murray, On the Flow of a Conducting Fluid Past a Magnetized Sphere, *J. Fluid Mech.*, **7**, p. 516, 1960.

Ludford, G. S. S., and M. P. Singh, On the Motion of a Sphere through a Conducting Fluid in the Presence of a Magnetic Field, *Proc. Camb. Phil. Soc.*, **59**, p. 625, 1963.

Ludford, G. S. S., and M. P. Singh, The Motion of a Non-Conducting Sphere through a Conducting Fluid in a Magnetic Cross-Field, *Proc. Camb. Phil. Soc.*, **59**, p. 615, 1963.

McCune, J. E., On the Motion of Thin Airfoils in Fluids of Finite Electrical Conductivity, *J. Fluid Mech.*, **7**, p. 449, 1960.

McCune, J. E., and E. L. Resler, Jr., Compressibility Effects in Magnetoaerodynamic Flows Past Thin Bodies, *J. of the Aerospace Sciences*, **27**, No. 7, p. 493, 1960.

Meyer, R. X., Rate of Heat-Transfer Near the Stagnation Point of a Blunt Body of Revolution, in the Presence of a Magnetic Field, Space Technology Laboratories Report GM-TR-0127-00016, 1958.

Pai, S. I., Linearized Theory of Airfoils in Fluids of Low Electrical Conductivity, Tech. Inf. Series R60SD311, Space Sciences Lab., General Electric Co., December 1959.

Rossow, V. J., On Magneto-Aerodynamic Boundary Layers, Z.A.M.P., **9b**, p. 519, 1958.

Sears, W. R., Some Remarks about Flow Past Bodies, *Rev. Mod. Phys.*, **32**, No. 4, p. 701, 1960.

Sears, W. R., On a Boundary-Layer Phenomenon in Magneto-Fluid Dynamics, *Astronautica Acta*, **12**, p. 223, 1961.

Sears, W. R., and E. L. Resler, Theory of Thin Airfoils in Fluids of High Electrical Conductivity, *J. Fluid Mech.*, **5**, p. 257, 1959.

Sears, W. R., and E. L. Resler, Jr., Sub- and Super-Alfvénic Flows Past Bodies, *Advances in Aeronautical Sciences*, Vols. 3 and 4, Pergamon Press, London, p. 657, 1962.

Stewartson, K., Motion of a Sphere Through a Conducting Fluid in the Presence of a Strong Magnetic Field, *Proc. Cambridge Phil. Soc.*, **52**, No. 2, p. 301, 1956.

Stewartson, K., Motion of Bodies Through Conducting Fluids, *Rev. Mod. Phys.*, **32**, No. 4, p. 855, 1960.

Stewartson, K., On the Motion of a Non-Conducting Body Through a Perfectly Conducting Fluid, *J. Fluid Mech.*, **8**, p. 82, 1960.

Stewartson, K., Magneto-Fluid-Dynamics of Thin Bodies in Oblique Fields, Z.A.M.P., **12**, p. 261, 1961.

Stewartson, K., Magneto-Fluid Dynamics of Bodies in Aligned Fields, *Proc. Roy. Soc.* (London), Series A, **275**, p. 70, 1963.

Tamada, K., Flow of a Slightly Conducting Fluid Past a Circular Cylinder with Strong, Aligned Magnetic Field, *Phys. Fluids*, **5**, No. 7, p. 817, 1962.

Yosinobu, H., A Linearized Theory of Magnetohydrodynamic Flow Past a Fixed Body in a Parallel Magnetic Field, *J. Phys. Soc. Japan*, **15**, No. 1, p. 175, 1960.

13

Waves in Bounded Media

13.1 INTRODUCTION

The effect of insulating or ideally conducting boundaries on the propagation of magnetohydrodynamic waves is studied in this chapter. Throughout this investigation we regard the fluid medium as bounded by parallel infinite planes which allow certain simplifications to occur. Displacement currents are neglected and the fluid is assumed to be slightly compressible.

Transverse wave propagation between parallel conducting and insulating planes is considered. This is done first for an inviscid, ideally conducting fluid and subsequently the influence of conductivity and viscosity is examined. This investigation is executed when the parallel planes are in an axial direct-current magnetic field and when they are in a transverse direct-current magnetic field.

After considering the transverse modes, more general equations for wave propagation in bounded media are derived. The application of these equations, although they are valid in rectangular tubes, is made to a parallel plane geometry in which there are pressure variations.

A "slug" flow analysis of the traveling wave electromagnetic pump is discussed. The laminar case is not discussed because it is not likely to exist in a practical device. In the "slug" flow analysis, the relationship between the slip and the excitation frequency for optimum performance is discussed.

The last section of this chapter contains an investigation of the laminar traveling wave induction stirring of a liquid. The problem arises in the industrial induction stirring of molten iron and is a good example of one of the diverse applications of the principles presented in this textbook.

13.2 TRANSVERSE WAVE PROPAGATION BETWEEN PARALLEL PLATES

(a) Introduction

In classical electromagnetics the simplest form of propagation taking place in a bounded structure occurs between infinite parallel conducting plates. Energy propagates axially and all the fields are perpendicular to the direction of propagation. Furthermore, the solutions are identical to the plane wave solutions existing in an unbounded space. In conducting

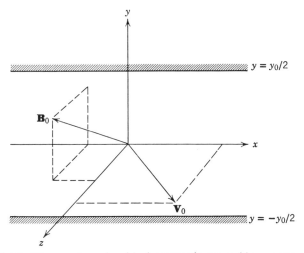

Figure 13.2-1 The one-dimensional hydromagnetic waveguide geometry.

liquids and gases a plane wave solution exists in an unbounded medium and is characterized by the absence of alternating fields and velocities in the direction of propagation. These waves were referred to as transverse modes in Chapter 8 and, more specifically, can be called Transverse Electro Magnetic Velocity or TEMV modes. However, when waves propagate between infinite plates, TEMV modes cannot exist because they require energy flow in the direction of propagation only. Unless the conducting fluid is an inviscid, ideal electrical conductor and the parallel plates are lossless, energy must flow perpendicular to the direction of propagation in order to supply energy for viscous and Joulean losses. Hence Transverse Magnetic Velocity or TMV modes are expected to exist in the conducting liquid contained between two infinite plates. In the geometry of Fig. 13.2-1, a steady magnetic induction is applied in an arbitrary direction. It is also interesting to include steady streaming velocities in this problem. However, in general, the streaming velocities cause variable coefficients in the Navier-Stokes equations. Streaming in the xz plane is included at first to illustrate the difficulties caused by the interaction of the streaming fluid and the applied magnetic induction. A general solution to the streaming problem is not included in this chapter.

The general formulation of this problem is most easily obtained by requiring that the only alternating, propagating velocity component is in the z direction. In addition, it is clear that $\partial/\partial z$ of all electromagnetic field components and velocities is zero. In order to linearize the problem all quantities are assumed to vary as $\mathbf{Q}(x, y, t) = \mathbf{Q}_0(y) + \mathbf{q}(y)e^{j(\omega t - kx)}$, where $\mathbf{Q}_0(y)$ is the steady direct-current value of the quantity involved and $\mathbf{q}(y)$ is a small perturbation in the form of a traveling wave. For an incompressible fluid the Navier-Stokes and the magnetic diffusion equations completely describe the problem. They are given in a convenient form for this analysis as

$$\left(\nu\nabla^2 - \frac{\partial}{\partial t} - \mathbf{V}\cdot\nabla\right)\mathbf{V} = \frac{\nabla}{\rho}\left(P + \mu\frac{\mathbf{H}^2}{2}\right) - \frac{\mu}{\rho}(\mathbf{H}\cdot\nabla)\mathbf{H} \quad (13.2\text{-}1a)$$

and

$$\left(\eta\nabla^2 - \frac{\partial}{\partial t} - \mathbf{V}\cdot\nabla\right)\mathbf{H} = -(\mathbf{H}\cdot\nabla)\mathbf{V} \quad (13.2\text{-}1b)$$

The x components of (13.2-1a) and (13.2-1b) are given by

$$\nu\frac{\partial^2 U_0}{\partial y^2} = \frac{1}{\rho}\frac{\partial P_0}{\partial x} - \frac{\mu}{\rho}H_{0y}\frac{\partial H_{0x}}{\partial y} \quad (13.2\text{-}2a)$$

$$\frac{1}{\mu}\frac{\partial p}{\partial x} = jk(H_{0y}h_y + H_{0z}h_z) + H_{0y}\frac{\partial h_x}{\partial y} + \frac{\partial H_{0x}}{\partial y}h_y \quad (13.2\text{-}2b)$$

$$\eta\frac{\partial^2 H_{0x}}{\partial y^2} = -H_{0y}\frac{\partial U_0}{\partial y} \quad (13.2\text{-}3a)$$

$$\left(\eta\frac{\partial^2}{\partial y^2} - \eta k^2 + jkU_0 - j\omega\right)h_x = -\frac{\partial U_0}{\partial y}h_y \quad (13.2\text{-}3b)$$

the y components by

$$\frac{1}{\mu}\frac{\partial P_0}{\partial y} = H_{0x}\frac{\partial H_{0x}}{\partial y} + H_{0z}\frac{\partial H_{0z}}{\partial y} \quad (13.2\text{-}4a)$$

$$-\frac{1}{\mu}\frac{\partial p}{\partial y} = \frac{\partial H_{0x}}{\partial y}h_x + H_{0x}\frac{\partial h_x}{\partial y} + \frac{\partial H_{0z}}{\partial y}h_z + H_{0z}\frac{\partial h_z}{\partial y} + jkH_{0x}h_y \quad (13.2\text{-}4b)$$

$$\eta\frac{\partial^2 H_{0y}}{\partial y^2} = 0 \quad (13.2\text{-}5a)$$

$$\left(\eta\frac{\partial^2}{\partial y^2} - \eta k^2 - j\omega + jkU_0\right)h_y = 0 \quad (13.2\text{-}5b)$$

and the z components as

$$\nu \frac{\partial^2 W_0}{\partial y^2} = \frac{1}{\rho} \frac{\partial P_0}{\partial z} - \frac{\mu}{\rho} H_{0y} \frac{\partial H_{0z}}{\partial y} \qquad (13.2\text{-}6a)$$

$$\left(\nu \frac{\partial^2}{\partial y^2} - \nu k^2 - j\omega + jkU_0 \right) w = \frac{1}{\rho} \frac{\partial p}{\partial z} - \frac{\mu}{\rho} \left(-jkH_{0x}h_z + \frac{\partial H_{0z}}{\partial y} h_y \right)$$

$$+ H_{0y} \frac{\partial h_z}{\partial y} \qquad (13.2\text{-}6b)$$

$$\eta \frac{\partial^2 H_{0z}}{\partial y} = -H_{0y} \frac{\partial W_0}{\partial y} \qquad (13.2\text{-}7a)$$

$$\left(\eta \frac{\partial^2}{\partial y^2} - \eta k^2 - j\omega + jkU_0 \right) h_z = jkH_{0x}w - H_{0y} \frac{\partial w}{\partial y} - \frac{\partial W_0}{\partial y} h_y \qquad (13.2\text{-}7b)$$

The equations just obtained are linear and have, in general, coefficients which are functions of y. For example, U_0 depends upon y because of viscous and/or electromagnetic body forces. Physically, the streaming of the fluid modifies the dispersion of the waves.

(b) An Inviscid, Ideally Conducting Fluid Streaming Along an Axial Magnetic Field

Let $\partial P_0/\partial z = \partial P_0/\partial x = 0$, $H_{0y} = 0$, and $W_0 = 0$ which implies that the fluid flows in the x direction at a steady velocity U_0, provided $\nu = 0$ and $\eta = 0$. In this case, zero $\partial P_0/\partial x$ is needed to sustain a steady flow of fluid since there are no losses. Superposed upon the steady flow are propagating waves. Under these assumptions, Equations (13.2-1a and b) to (13.2-7a and b) yield $\partial p/\partial x = 0$, U_0 is independent of y, $h_x = 0$, $\partial P_0/\partial y = 0$, $\partial p/\partial x = \partial p/\partial z = 0$, $h_y = 0$, and

$$(-\omega + kU_0)w = \frac{\mu}{\rho} kH_{0x}h_z \qquad (13.2\text{-}8a)$$

$$(-\omega + kU_0)h_z = kH_{0x}w \qquad (13.2\text{-}8b)$$

When (13.2-8a and b) are combined, the dispersion equation for k results. It is given by

$$\left(U_0^2 - \frac{\mu}{\rho} H_{0x}^2 \right) k^2 - 2\omega U_0 k + \omega^2 = 0 \qquad (13.2\text{-}9a)$$

which has the solutions

$$k_{1,2} = \frac{\omega}{U_0 \mp A_x} \qquad (13.2\text{-}9b)$$

where A_x is the Alfvén speed in the x direction. The solutions k_1 and k_2 represent backward and forward waves having phase velocities of $U_0 - A_x$ and $U_0 + A_x$, respectively. It is easy to show that

$$e_y = \frac{\mu \omega h_z}{k} \tag{13.2-9c}$$

and that the wave impedance is given by

$$\frac{e_y}{h_z} = \mu(U_0 \pm A_x) \tag{13.2-9d}$$

This is the simplest possible mode since all the propagating fields and propagating velocity waves are perpendicular to the direction of propagation. It is called the TEMV mode and is not influenced by the parallel planes. When there is no steady streaming of fluid along the steady magnetic field, the waves propagate at the Alfvén speed along the applied steady magnetic field.

(c) A Viscous, Conducting Fluid in an Axial, Steady Magnetic Field

Because problems involving finite viscosity and conductivity become complicated, it is essential to study limiting cases. Let the steady pressure gradients and fluid velocities (except for U_0) be zero and assume $H_{0y} = 0$. The equations describing this physical problem are (13.2-3b), (13.2-5b), (13.2-6b), and (13.2-7b). The first of these indicates that an h_x can exist and is coupled to h_z because $\partial U_0 / \partial y \neq 0$. For that reason we set U_0 to zero and h_x decouples from the equations. Since the applied magnetic field is H_{0x} and no streaming is allowed, h_y need not be considered. Then (13.2-6b) and (13.2-7b) become

$$\left(\nu \frac{d^2}{dy^2} - \nu k^2 - j\omega \right) w = j A_x^2 k h_z^* \tag{13.2-10a}$$

$$\left(\eta \frac{d^2}{dy^2} - \eta k^2 - j\omega \right) h_z^* = jkw \tag{13.2-10b}$$

where $h_z^* = h_z / H_{0x}$. These are combined to yield an equation in w which is is given by

$$\nu\eta \frac{d^4 w}{dy^4} - [\eta(\nu k^2 + j\omega) + \nu(\eta k^2 + j\omega)] \frac{d^2 w}{dy^2}$$
$$+ [(\eta k^2 + j\omega)(\nu k^2 + j\omega) + k^2 A_x^2] w = 0 \tag{13.2-10c}$$

This equation reduces to the dispersion equation given by (8.2-14) when $d^4/dy^4 = d^2/dy^2 = 0$. Before we obtain a general solution to (13.2-10c), it is interesting to consider limiting cases where either ν or $\eta = 0$. If ν is taken as zero, (13.2-10c) becomes

$$-j\eta\omega\frac{d^2w}{dy^2} + [(\eta k^2 + j\omega)j\omega + k^2A_x^2]w = 0 \qquad (13.2\text{-}11)$$

In order to obtain this equation for $\nu \neq 0$ and $\eta = 0$ it is sufficient to replace η by ν in (13.2-11). The solution for the z component of velocity obtained from (13.2-11) is

$$w = A \sin my + B \cos my \qquad (13.2\text{-}12a)$$

and the solution for the dimensionless magnetic field $h_z{}^*$ is easily found from (13.2-10a) by setting ν to zero. The same result can be obtained from (13.2-10b). It is given by

$$h_z{}^* = -\frac{\omega A}{kA_x^2}\sin my - \frac{\omega B}{kA_x^2}\cos my \qquad (13.2\text{-}12b)$$

where

$$m^2 = \frac{\omega^2 - j\omega\eta k^2 - A_x^2 k^2}{j\omega\eta} \qquad (13.2\text{-}12c)$$

There are three quantities (A, B, and k) which are undetermined. A and B depend upon the method of excitation of the waves. For example, if the excitation were oppositely directed currents in the bounding conductors (that is, current flow in the x direction in the top plate and in the $-x$ direction in the bottom), A would be zero, as it is in the classical electromagnetic case. It would also be possible, if an excitation method were used, to force B to be zero while maintaining a nonzero A. When $A = 0$ and $B \neq 0$, we have the symmetrical case (the other would be the antisymmetrical case). All other possibilities can be handled by the superposition of the antisymmetric and symmetric solutions.

(d) An Inviscid, Conducting Fluid in an Axial Magnetic Field Confined between Ideally Conducting Walls

In this case the boundary condition $(dh_z/dy)\,|_{y=\pm y_0} = 0$ allows k to be determined. This condition is given by

$$A \cos\frac{m_a y_0}{2} = 0$$

or $\qquad\qquad\qquad\qquad\qquad\qquad\qquad (13.2\text{-}13a)$

$$-B \sin\frac{m_s y_0}{2} = 0$$

where the subscripts a and s denote the antisymmetric and the symmetric cases, respectively. The result is

$$k_{a,s}^2 = \frac{\omega\{\omega(A_x^2 - \eta^2\alpha_{a,s}^2/y_0^2) - j\eta[(\alpha_{a,s}^2/y_0^2)A_x^2 + \omega^2]\}}{A_x^4 + \omega^2\eta^2} \qquad (13.2\text{-}13b)$$

where

$$\alpha_a = (2n + 1)\pi \qquad \text{and} \qquad \alpha_s = 2n\pi \qquad (13.2\text{-}13c)$$

and $n = 0, 1, 2, \ldots$ It is convenient to write (13.2-13b) in the following

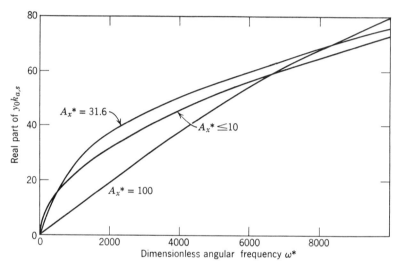

Figure 13.2-2 The real part of the propagation constant versus frequency for various Alfvén speeds when $\alpha_{s,a} = 2\pi$.

dimensionless form

$$y_0^2 k_{a,s}^2 = \frac{\omega^*[\omega^*(A_x^{*2} - \alpha_{a,s}^2) - j(\alpha_{a,s}^2 A_x^{*2} + \omega^{*2})]}{A_x^{*4} + \omega^{*2}} \qquad (13.2\text{-}13d)$$

where $\omega^* = \omega y_0^2/\eta$ and $A_x^* = A_x y_0/\eta$. It is easy to show that

$$\text{Re}\,(y_0 k_{a,s}) =$$

$$\sqrt{\frac{\omega^*}{2}}\left[\frac{\sqrt{\omega^{*2}(A_x^{*2} - \alpha_{a,s}^2)^2 + (\alpha_{a,s}^2 A_x^{*2} + \omega^{*2})^2} + \omega^*(A_x^{*2} - \alpha_{a,s}^2)}{A_x^{*4} + \omega^{*2}}\right]^{\frac{1}{2}}$$

$$(13.2\text{-}13e)$$

$$\text{Im}\,(y_0 k_{a,s}) =$$

$$-\sqrt{\frac{\omega^*}{2}}\left[\frac{\sqrt{\omega^{*2}(A_x^{*2} - \alpha_{a,s}^2)^2 + (\alpha_{a,s}^2 A_x^{*2} + \omega^{*2})^2} - \omega^*(A_x^{*2} - \alpha_{a,s}^2)}{A_x^{*4} + \omega^{*2}}\right]^{\frac{1}{2}}$$

$$(13.2\text{-}13f)$$

which are given in Figs. 13.2-2 and 13.2-3. It is useful to study limiting values of $\mathrm{Re}\,(y_0 k_{a,s})$ and $\mathrm{Im}\,(y_0 k_{a,s})$. When the dimensionless frequency is small compared to the dimensionless Alfvén speed (for the lowest mode),

$$\mathrm{Re}_{\omega^* \ll A_x^*}\,(y_0 k_{a,s}) \simeq \frac{\omega^*}{A_x^*} \qquad (13.2\text{-}13\mathrm{g})$$

and

$$\mathrm{Im}_{\omega^* \ll A_x^*}\,(y_0 k_{a,s}) \simeq -\frac{\omega^{*3}}{2\sqrt{2}A_x^{*3}} \qquad (13.2\text{-}13\mathrm{h})$$

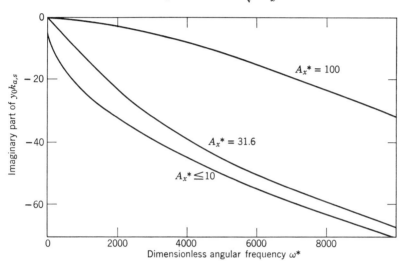

Figure 13.2-3 The imaginary part of the propagation constant versus frequency for various Alfvén speeds when $\alpha_{s,a} = 2\pi$.

which indicates that low-frequency waves travel at the Alfvén speed and that the attenuation of these is greatly influenced by the Alfvén speed. Where $\omega^* \gg A_x^*$

$$\mathrm{Re}\,(y_0 k_{a,s}) \simeq \sqrt{\frac{\omega^*}{2}} \qquad (13.2\text{-}13\mathrm{i})$$

$$\mathrm{Im}\,(y_0 k_{a,s}) \simeq -\sqrt{\frac{\omega^*}{2}} \qquad (13.2\text{-}13\mathrm{j})$$

whence the phase velocity is inversely proportional to the square root of the dimensionless frequency, and the attenuation increases with the square root of the dimensionless frequency regardless of the Alfvén speed. For both the symmetric and antisymmetric cases the velocity is an extremum at the conducting walls. Where the viscosity is not zero, similar solutions result and a boundary layer near the walls allows the no-slip condition to be satisfied.

(e) An Inviscid, Conducting Fluid in an Axial Magnetic Field Confined between Insulating Walls

In this case the current generated in the conducting fluid by the interaction of the fluid flow with the direct-current axial magnetic field flows entirely in the fluid. Hence the magnetic field at the fluid-insulator interface must be zero. This condition, which yields k, is given by

$$A \sin \frac{m_a y_0}{2} = 0$$

or   (13.2-14)

$$B \cos \frac{m_s y_0}{2} = 0$$

Thus for insulating walls, $m_a = 2n\pi/y_0$ and $m_s = (2n + 1)\pi/2$ which is the reverse of the conducting-wall case. Therefore, the propagation constants for the symmetric and the antisymmetric cases with insulating walls are the same as they are for the antisymmetric and symmetric cases with ideal conducting walls. Equations (13.2-13b through f) are valid for the insulating-wall case provided the subscripts a and s are interchanged. The velocities go to zero at both walls, as dictated by Ampere's law for the magnetic fields. Hence it is expected that viscosity exerts very little influence on the solutions when the guide walls are insulators. The influence of viscosity is considered by Blue (1957).

(f) The Effect of Viscosity in the Conducting-Wall Case

The antisymmetric solution to (13.2-10c) is

$$w = A_1 \sin m_1 y + A_2 \sin m_2 y \qquad (13.2\text{-}15a)$$

where

$$m_{1,2}^2 = -\left[k^2 + \frac{j\omega(\nu + \eta)}{2\eta\nu}\right] \pm \sqrt{\left[\frac{j\omega(\eta - \nu)}{2\eta\nu}\right]^2 - \frac{k^2 A_x^2}{\nu\eta}} \qquad (13.2\text{-}15b)$$

In the laboratory $\nu \ll \eta$ for most liquid metals and (13.2-15b) assumes a much simpler form. (See Appendix 1, Table 1 for values of ν and η.) It is given by

$$m_1^2 = \frac{\omega^2 - j\omega\eta k^2 - k^2 A_x^2}{j\omega\eta} \qquad (13.2\text{-}15c)$$

$$m_2^2 = -\frac{j\omega}{\nu} \qquad (13.2\text{-}15d)$$

where the m_1 solution is the same as that obtained when no viscosity was present. The normalized magnetic field h_z^* is easily found by substituting

(13.2-15a) into (13.2-10a). The result, valid for $v \ll \eta$, is given by

$$h_z^* = -\frac{\omega A_1}{k A_x^2} \sin m_1 y + \frac{jkv A_2}{A_x^2} \sin m_2 y \qquad (13.2\text{-}16)$$

If the walls are insulators rather than conductors, the boundary conditions on both w and h_z^* are satisfied by setting A_2 to zero and using the value of k obtained in the preceding discussion. Hence the effect of viscosity for the insulating-wall case is completely negligible when $v \ll \eta$. In the conducting-wall case the boundary conditions are $w(\pm y_0/2) = 0$ and $(dh_z^*/dy)|_{\pm y_0/2} = 0$. The application of these conditions yields

$$m_1 y_0 \simeq (2n + 1)\pi \qquad (13.2\text{-}17a)$$

and

$$A_2 \simeq \frac{-A_1(-1)^n}{\sin (m_2 y_0/2)} \qquad (13.2\text{-}17b)$$

which indicates that the viscosity does not influence the propagation constant provided $v \ll \eta$. Hence the real and imaginary parts of k are given by

$$\mathrm{Re}\,(y_0 k) = \sqrt{\frac{\omega^*}{2}} \left[\frac{\sqrt{\omega^{*2}(A_x^{*2} - \alpha^2)^2 + (\alpha^2 A_x^{*2} + \omega^{*2})^2} + \omega^*(A_x^{*2} - \alpha^2)}{A_x^{*4} + \omega^{*2}} \right]^{1/2}$$

$$(13.2\text{-}17c)$$

$$\mathrm{Im}\,(y_0 k) = \sqrt{\frac{\omega^*}{2}} \left[\frac{\sqrt{\omega^{*2}(A_x^{*2} - \alpha^2)^2 + (\alpha^2 A_x^{*2} + \omega^{*2})^2} - \omega^*(A_x^{*2} - \alpha^2)}{A_x^{*4} + \omega^{*2}} \right]^{1/2}$$

$$(13.2\text{-}17d)$$

where

$$\alpha = (2n + 1)\pi \qquad (13.2\text{-}17e)$$

Provided $Pm \ll 1$, $\sin m_2 y \simeq \exp [(1 + j)y/\delta_f]$, where δ_f is the viscous skin depth in the fluid and $\delta_f = \sqrt{2v/\omega}$. The velocity and the dimensionless magnetic field in the z direction become

$$w = A \left\{ \sin m_1 y - (-1)^n \exp\left[-\left(\frac{1+j}{\delta_f}\right)\left(\frac{y_0}{2} - y\right)\right] \right\} \qquad (13.2\text{-}18a)$$

and

$$h_z^* = -\frac{\omega A_1}{k A_x^2} \left\{ \sin m_1 y + \frac{jk^2 \delta_f^2}{2}(-1)^n \exp\left[-\left(\frac{1+j}{\delta_f}\right)\left(\frac{y_0}{2} - y\right)\right] \right\}$$

$$(13.2\text{-}18b)$$

In mercury at a frequency of 100 cps, $\delta_f \simeq 2.5 \times 10^{-5}$ meters and decreases with increasing frequency. Hence the velocity profile is not influenced by the viscosity except in the vicinity of the conducting wall. A viscous boundary layer starts to form at a distance of about four skin depths from the conducting walls and this reduces the fluid velocity to zero at the wall. This effect is seen in the second term of (13.2-18a). The magnetic field is not influenced by the viscosity (when $v \ll \eta$) since the magnitude of the second term of (13.2-18b) is much less than unity. Hence the solutions given here are good approximations for most liquid metals.

A similar solution can be obtained when a symmetrical velocity profile is assumed to exist. This problem is left as an exercise for the reader (see Problem 4).

(g) Wave Propagation in an Inviscid, Conducting Fluid in a Steady, Transverse Magnetic Field

We assume that the conducting fluid is not streaming and the only steady magnetic field present is H_{0y}. Propagation of the TMV modes in the x direction is investigated under these assumptions. The transverse velocity and magnetic field are given by

$$j\omega w = A_y^2 \frac{dh_z^*}{dy} \tag{13.2-19a}$$

$$\left(\eta \frac{d^2}{dy^2} - \eta k^2 - j\omega\right) h_z^* = -\frac{dw}{dy} \tag{13.2-19b}$$

where $h_z^* = h_z/H_{0y}$. The z component of the velocity is obtained from (13.2-19a) and substituted into (13.2-19b) to yield

$$(A_y^2 + j\omega\eta) \frac{d^2 h_z^*}{dy^2} + (\omega^2 - j\omega\eta k^2) h_z^* = 0 \tag{13.2-19c}$$

which has the solution

$$h_z^* = A \sin my + B \cos my \tag{13.2-19d}$$

where

$$m^2 = \frac{\omega^2 - j\omega\eta k^2}{A_y^2 + j\omega\eta} \tag{13.2-19e}$$

The corresponding velocity w given by (13.2-19a) is

$$w = \frac{A_y^2 m}{j\omega} (A \cos my - B \sin my) \tag{13.2-20}$$

Two forms of solution exist, the symmetric and the antisymmetric, as is the case for a steady axial field.

When the walls are ideal conductors, $(dh_z{}^*/dy)|_{y=\pm y_0/2} = 0$, which implies that $w(\pm y_0/2) = 0$. Hence the magnetic field boundary condition makes the fluid velocity zero at the walls regardless of the viscosity. Then

$$m_s y_0 = (2n + 1)\pi \quad \text{and} \quad m_a y_0 = 2n\pi \qquad (13.2\text{-}21a)$$

which is the reverse of the condition obtained in Section d. Then the square of the propagation constant is given by

$$k_{s,a}^2 y_0{}^2 = -\alpha_{s,a}^2 + \frac{j}{\omega^*}(\alpha_{s,a}^2 A_y{}^{*2} - \omega^{*2}) \qquad (13.2\text{-}21b)$$

where $\omega^* = \omega y_0{}^2/\eta$ and $A_y{}^* = A_y y_0/\eta$. It is interesting to observe the possibility of the real part of k going to zero at some value of frequency, which would imply the existence of a frequency at which propagation fails to occur. It is easy to show that $\operatorname{Re} k_{s,a} = 0$ when $\omega^* = \alpha_{s,a} A_y{}^*$ and that $\operatorname{Im} k_{s,a} = -\alpha_{s,a}/y_0$, where $\alpha_s = (2n + 1)\pi$ and $\alpha_a = 2n\pi$. The real and the imaginary parts of $k_{s,a} y_0$ are given by

$$\operatorname{Re} k_{s,a} y_0 = \pm \sqrt{\frac{1}{2}\left[\sqrt{\alpha_{s,a}^4 + \frac{(\omega^{*2} - \alpha_{s,a}^2 A_y{}^{*2})^2}{\omega^{*2}}} - \alpha_{s,a}^2\right]}^{\,1/2} \qquad (13.2\text{-}21c)$$

$$\operatorname{Im} k_{s,a} y_0 = \mp \sqrt{\frac{1}{2}\left[\sqrt{\alpha_{s,a}^4 + \frac{(\omega^{*2} - \alpha_{s,a}^2 A_y{}^{*2})^2}{\omega^{*2}}} + \alpha_{s,a}^2\right]}^{\,1/2} \qquad (13.2\text{-}21d)$$

for $\alpha_{s,a} A_y{}^{*2} < \omega^{*2}$. The positive and negative signs are associated with the forward and backward traveling waves. When $\alpha_{s,a}^2 A_y{}^{*2} > \omega^{*2}$, the real and imaginary parts of $k_{s,a} y_0$ are given by

$$\operatorname{Re} k_{s,a} y_0 = \pm \sqrt{\frac{1}{2}\left[\sqrt{\alpha_{s,a}^4 + \frac{(\omega^{*2} - \alpha_{s,a}^2 A_y{}^{*2})^2}{\omega^{*2}}} - \alpha_{s,a}^2\right]}^{\,1/2} \qquad (13.2\text{-}21e)$$

$$\operatorname{Im} k_{s,a} y_0 = \pm \sqrt{\frac{1}{2}\left[\sqrt{\alpha_{s,a}^4 + \frac{(\omega^{*2} - \alpha_{s,a}^2 A_y{}^{*2})^2}{\omega^{*2}}} + \alpha_{s,a}^2\right]}^{\,1/2} \qquad (13.2\text{-}21f)$$

When $\alpha_{s,a}^2 A_y{}^{*2} < \omega^{*2}$, the forward traveling wave is attenuated as it travels for $\operatorname{Im} k_{s,a} y_0 < 0$, whereas for $\alpha_{s,a}^2 A_y{}^{*2} > \omega^{*2}$ the wave which appears to be a forward traveling wave [obtained from (13.2-21e) and (13.2-21f) using the positive sign] grows larger as x increases. If the negative sign is chosen in (13.2-21f) to eliminate growing waves on a physical basis, the negative sign must be used in (13.2-21e). If the resulting wave is interpreted as a forward traveling wave, it must have a negative phase velocity. If this wave is interpreted as a backward traveling wave, it is clearly one which grows as it travels in the negative x direction. This effect is present in the work of Kliman (1964). The interpretation of waves for $\omega^{*2} < \alpha_{s,a}^2 A_y^{*2}$ is best made by inspecting the x component of the Poynting vector. When energy flows in the positive x direction, the waves carrying the energy are forward traveling waves, regardless of their phase velocities. From the y component of $\nabla \times \mathbf{H} = \mathbf{J}$ we obtain

$$E_y = \frac{jk}{\sigma} h_z \tag{13.2-22}$$

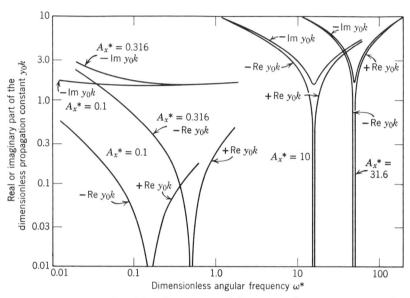

Figure 13.2-4 The real and imaginary parts of the propagation constant versus frequency for various Alfvén speeds for $\alpha = \pi/2$.

When h_z from (13.2-19d) is substituted into (13.2-22) there results

$$E_y(x, y) = \frac{jkH_{0y}}{\sigma} [Ae^{-(j\,\mathrm{Re}\,k_s - \mathrm{Im}\,k_s)} \sin my + Be^{-(j\,\mathrm{Re}\,k_a - \mathrm{Im}\,k_a)} \cos my]$$

$$\tag{13.2-23a}$$

and $h_z(x, y)$ is given by

$$h_z(x, y) = H_{0y}Ae^{-(j\,\mathrm{Re}\,k_s - \mathrm{Im}\,k_s)} \sin my + BH_{0y}e^{-(j\,\mathrm{Re}\,k_a - \mathrm{Im}\,k_a)} \cos my$$

$$\tag{13.2-23b}$$

For the symmetrical solutions the real part of the x component of the Poynting vector is given by

$$\mathrm{Re}\, E_y \bar{h}_z = -\mathrm{Im}\, k_s H_{0y}^2 A^2 e^{2\mathrm{Im}\,k_s x} \sin^2 my \tag{13.2-23c}$$

from which it is seen that the direction of the flow of energy depends upon the sign of $\text{Im }k_s$. Here the bar denotes the complex conjugate. When $\text{Im }k_s < 0$, energy flows in the positive x direction and the x component of the real part of the Poynting vector decreases exponentially as x increases because some of the energy is being used for Joulean losses in the conducting fluid. Hence the solution to the dispersion equation which applies when energy propagates in the positive x direction is the one which yields $\text{Im }k < 0$. At the critical frequency $\omega_c{}^* = \alpha_{s,a}A_y{}^*$ energy is carried by electromagnetic diffusion. Below the critical frequency energy propagates with a negative phase velocity and above with a positive phase velocity. The attenuation passes through a minimum in the vicinity of the critical frequency. The curves for $\text{Re }k$ and $\text{Im }k$ are given in Fig. 13.2-4.

(h) The Effect of Viscosity in a Steady, Transverse Magnetic Field

When viscosity is included, (13.2-6b) and (13.2-7b) become

$$\left(\nu\frac{d^2}{dy^2} - \nu k^2 - j\omega\right)w = -A_y{}^2\frac{dh_z{}^*}{dy} \qquad (13.2\text{-}24a)$$

and

$$\left(\eta\frac{d^2}{dy^2} - \eta k^2 - j\omega\right)h_z{}^* = -\frac{dw}{dy} \qquad (13.2\text{-}24b)$$

which are combined to yield

$$\eta\nu\frac{d^4h_z{}^*}{dy^4} - [A_y{}^2 + \nu(\eta k^2 + j\omega) + \eta(\nu k^2 + j\omega)]\frac{d^2h_z{}^*}{dy^2}$$

$$+ (\eta k^2 + j\omega)(\nu k^2 + j\omega)h_z{}^* = 0 \quad (13.2\text{-}24c)$$

The solution for the magnetic field is assumed to be

$$h_z{}^* = A_1\sin m_1 y + A_2\sin m_2 y + B_1\cos m_1 y + B_2\cos m_2 y \quad (13.2\text{-}25a)$$

which is substituted into (13.2-24c) to obtain

$$m_{1,2}^2 = \frac{-(A_y{}^2 + 2\nu\eta k^2 + j\omega\eta)}{} \\ \frac{\pm\sqrt{A_y{}^4 + 2A_y{}^2[2\nu\eta k^2 + j\omega(\eta + \nu)] + [j\omega(\eta - \nu)]^2}}{2\nu\eta}$$

which simplifies when $\nu \ll \eta$. In that case

$$m_1{}^2 = \frac{\omega^2 - j\omega\eta k^2}{A_y{}^2 + j\omega\eta} \qquad (13.2\text{-}25b)$$

and

$$m_2{}^2 = \frac{A_y{}^2 + j\omega\eta}{-\eta\nu} \qquad (13.2\text{-}25c)$$

It is easy to show that

$$w = \frac{m_1}{j\omega} (A_1 \cos m_1 y - B_1 \sin m_1 y) - \eta m_2 (A_2 \cos m_2 y - B_2 \sin m_2 y)$$

$$(13.2\text{-}25d)$$

As an example of a solution to this problem, we work the case where the channel walls are insulators and the velocity profile is symmetrical. Under these assumptions the boundary conditions are $w(\pm y_0/2) = 0$ and $h_z{}^*(\pm y_0/2) = 0$. It is easy to show that under these conditions

$$\frac{m_1 y_0}{2} = n\pi \qquad (13.2\text{-}26a)$$

and

$$A_2 = \frac{m_1 A_1 (-1)^n}{j\omega \eta m_2 \cos (m_2 y_0/2)} \qquad (13.2\text{-}26b)$$

When the constants just found are substituted into the velocity and magnetic field solutions of (13.2-25d) and (13.2-25a), there results

$$w = \frac{2n\pi}{j\omega y_0} A_1 \left[\cos \frac{2n\pi y}{y_0} - (-1)^n e^{-(y_0/2-y)(\text{Im } m_2 - j \text{ Re } m_2)} \right] \qquad (13.2\text{-}27a)$$

and

$$h_z{}^* = A_1 \left[\sin \frac{2n\pi y}{y_0} - \frac{2n\pi\sqrt{\eta\nu}(-1)^n}{\omega\eta\sqrt{A_y{}^2 + j\omega\eta}} e^{-(y_0/2-y)(\text{Im } m_2 - j \text{ Re } m_2)} \right] \qquad (13.2\text{-}27b)$$

which indicates the presence of a boundary layer in which the fluid goes from its peak to zero at the wall in order to satisfy the no-slip condition dictated by the presence of viscosity. In this case, however, the boundary layer thickness depends not only upon frequency and viscosity but also is a function of the magnetic diffusivity and the transverse Alfvén speed. The real and imaginary parts of m_2 are given by

$$\text{Re } m_2 = -\frac{1}{\sqrt{2\eta\nu}} \left(\sqrt{A_y{}^4 + \omega^2\eta^2} - A_y{}^2 \right)^{\frac{1}{2}} \qquad (13.2\text{-}28a)$$

and

$$\text{Im } m_2 = \frac{1}{\sqrt{2\eta\nu}} \left(\sqrt{A_y{}^4 + \omega^2\eta^2} + A_y{}^2 \right) \qquad (13.2\text{-}28b)$$

and the skin depth of the boundary layer is given by the reciprocal of $\text{Im } m_2$. Hence the greater the Alfvén speed and/or frequency the smaller is the skin depth.

13.3 PRESSURE WAVE PROPAGATION BETWEEN PARALLEL PLANES

(a) Introduction

In addition to the transverse hydromagnetic waves studied in Section 13.2, it has been theoretically shown by Alfvén (1950), Herlofson (1950), and Lundquist (1951) that pressure or longitudinal hydromagnetic waves may exist in conducting liquids and plasmas. According to Osterbrock (1961), longitudinal hydromagnetic waves are very important factors in the consideration of energy transport in the chromosphere of the sun. In the laboratory, pressure waves were produced by Westphal (1962) to test the dispersion theory of Anderson (1953). Pressure waves in magnetoacoustic waveguides have been observed by Murphy (1966).

(b) The General Equations

In pressure modes the fluid is compressed and the equation of state for the fluid is given by (8.3-1). In this section the fluid is assumed to be slightly compressible and to have the magnetic properties of free space. Heat flow and the effect of temperature variations upon density are neglected. Under these assumptions, the system is described by the Navier-Stokes, continuity, state, and the magnetic diffusion equations. In this section fluid streaming is neglected and a constant uniform magnetic field is applied. All quantities are assumed to vary as

$$\mathbf{Q}(x, y, z, t) = \mathbf{Q}_0 + \mathbf{q}(y, z)e^{j(\omega t - kx)} \tag{13.3-1}$$

where $\mathbf{Q}_0$ is the steady value of the variable and is not a function of position. The approach used here differs from the treatment of Section 13.2 in order to make it easier to identify the normal modes of propagation. In this section diffusion equations in the electric and magnetic fields, pressure, vorticity, and velocity are obtained, although it is possible to reduce the MHD equations for this case into a single pair of coupled equations in the velocity and magnetic field at the expense of hiding certain aspects of the problem. The magnetic diffusion equation contains one more term than (13.2-1b) because the fluid is compressible. It is given by

$$\eta \nabla^2 \mathbf{h} - j\omega \mathbf{h} = \mathbf{H}_0 \nabla \cdot \mathbf{V} - (\mathbf{H}_0 \cdot \nabla)\mathbf{V} \tag{13.3-2}$$

where $\mathbf{H}_0$ is the arbitrarily directed, direct-current magnetic field which is applied to the configuration. By combining Maxwell's curl equations of the electric and magnetic field, we obtain

$$\eta \nabla^2 \mathbf{e} - j\omega \mathbf{e} = \eta \nabla \nabla \cdot \mathbf{e} + j\omega \mathbf{V} \times \mathbf{B}_0 \qquad (13.3\text{-}3a)$$

which can be simplified by taking the divergence of the curl of the magnetic field. This yields $\nabla \cdot \mathbf{E} = -\nabla \cdot (\mathbf{V} \times \mathbf{B}_0)$, which does not violate $\nabla \cdot \mathbf{D} = \rho_e$. The charge density may be zero in the rest frame of the fluid but is not necessarily zero in the laboratory frame. By the vector identity, $\nabla \cdot (\mathbf{A} \times \mathbf{B}) = \mathbf{B} \cdot \nabla \times \mathbf{A} - \mathbf{A} \cdot \nabla \times \mathbf{B}$ and since the vorticity (although the vorticity is a perturbed quantity, a capital omega is used) $\boldsymbol{\Omega} = \nabla \times \mathbf{V}$, $\nabla \cdot \mathbf{e}$ becomes $\nabla \cdot \mathbf{e} = -\mathbf{B}_0 \cdot \boldsymbol{\Omega}$. Hence (13.3-3a) can be written as

$$\eta \nabla^2 \mathbf{e} - j\omega \mathbf{e} = j\omega \mathbf{V} \times \mathbf{B}_0 - \eta \nabla (\mathbf{B}_0 \cdot \boldsymbol{\Omega}) \qquad (13.3\text{-}3b)$$

In order to obtain a diffusion equation in vorticity, the curl of all members of (6.4-9) is taken. Because $\nabla \times \nabla P = 0$, the result is

$$\nu \nabla^2 \boldsymbol{\Omega} - j\omega \boldsymbol{\Omega} = \frac{-\mu_0}{\rho_0} \nabla \times [(\mathbf{H}_0 \cdot \nabla)\mathbf{h}] = -\frac{\mathbf{H}_0 \cdot \nabla}{\rho_0 \eta} (\mathbf{e} + \mathbf{V} \times \mathbf{B}_0) \qquad (13.3\text{-}4)$$

The equation for the pressure is obtained by taking the divergence of all members of (6.4-9). When this operation is done, the equations of state and continuity are used to simplify the results. The continuity equation is given by

$$j\omega \rho + \rho_0 \nabla \cdot \mathbf{V} = 0 \qquad (13.3\text{-}5a)$$

where ρ_0 is the steady density. The equation of state is $\partial \rho / \partial P = \rho / \beta$, where β is the compressibility. Then $(1/\beta)(\partial p / \partial t) = (1/\rho_0)(\partial \rho / \partial t)$ or $j\omega \rho = (\rho_0 / \beta) \nabla \cdot \mathbf{V}$. This is substituted into (13.3-5a) to yield

$$p = \frac{-\beta}{j\omega} \nabla \cdot \mathbf{V} \qquad (13.3\text{-}5b)$$

By using (13.3-5b) and the divergence of (6.4-9), we obtain

$$\left[1 + \frac{j\omega}{\beta} \left(\tfrac{4}{3} \nu \rho_0 + \zeta \right) \right] \nabla^2 p - \frac{\omega^2 \rho_0}{\beta} p = -\mu_0 \nabla^2 (\mathbf{H}_0 \cdot \mathbf{h}) \qquad (13.3\text{-}5c)$$

The perturbation in pressure is coupled to the rest of the perturbed quantities through the magnetic pressure. If there is no perturbation of magnetic field in the direction of the applied magnetic field, there will be no interaction between the perturbed pressure and any other perturbed quantities. In Section 13.2, $\mathbf{H}_0 \cdot \mathbf{h}$ was always zero and the pressure equation was decoupled from the rest of the equations describing the propagation of the hydromagnetic waves. It is also useful to have (6.4-9) in terms of the velocity and magnetic field. It is easy to obtain

$$\nu \, \nabla^2 \mathbf{V} + \left[\left(\frac{\zeta}{\rho_0} + \frac{\nu}{3} \right) - \frac{j\beta}{\rho_0 \omega} \right] \nabla\nabla \cdot \mathbf{V} - j\omega \mathbf{V} =$$

$$- \frac{\mu_0}{\rho_0} [(\mathbf{H}_0 \cdot \nabla)\mathbf{h} - \nabla(\mathbf{H}_0 \cdot \mathbf{h})] \quad (13.3\text{-}6)$$

(c) The Pressure Mode in an Inviscid, Ideally Conducting Fluid between Parallel Insulating Planes

The simplest mode is characterized by vorticity in only the z direction which implies $\mathbf{V} = \hat{x}u + \hat{y}v$. In order to investigate the existence of such a solution, we must inspect the various diffusion equations. If $\mathbf{\Omega} = \hat{z}\Omega_z$, it is clear from (13.3-4) that $\mathbf{e} = \hat{z}e_z$ and that the applied magnetic field has no z component. The quantity B_{0z} must be zero for it leads to a y component of the vorticity and for simplicity B_{0x} is taken as zero. These observations agree with (13.3-3b) and from (13.3-2) we see that x and y components of $\mathbf{h}$ exist. From (13.3-2) we obtain

$$j\omega h_x{}^* = \frac{du}{dy} \quad (13.3\text{-}7a)$$

$$\omega h_y{}^* = ku \quad (13.3\text{-}7b)$$

and from (13.3-3b) we get

$$e_z = -B_{0y}u \quad (13.3\text{-}7c)$$

where $h^* = h/H_{0y}$. The x component of the equation of motion given by (13.3-6) yields

$$j(\omega^2 - a_0{}^2k^2)u + a_0{}^2k \frac{dv}{dy} = \omega A_y{}^2 \left(\frac{dh_x{}^*}{dy} + jkh_y{}^* \right) \quad (13.3\text{-}8a)$$

where the acoustic velocity $a_0 = \sqrt{\beta/\rho_0}$ and A_y is the Alfvén speed. The y component of (13.3-6) yields

$$-a_0{}^2k \frac{du}{dy} - j\left(a_0{}^2 \frac{d^2}{dy^2} + \omega^2 \right)v = 0 \quad (13.3\text{-}8b)$$

and the z component indicates that $w = 0$ by virtue of the infinite z dimensions of the configuration. When (13.3-7a), (13.3-7b), (13.3-8a), and (13.3-8b) are combined, we obtain

$$\left\{ A_y{}^2 a_0{}^2 \frac{d^4}{dy^4} - [a_0{}^2 A_y{}^2 k^2 - (a_0{}^2 + A_y{}^2)\omega^2] \frac{d^2}{dy^2} \right.$$

$$\left. + \omega^2[\omega^2 - (A_y{}^2 + a_0{}^2)k^2] \right\}u = 0 \quad (13.3\text{-}8c)$$

provided $H_{0x} = 0$. If $H_{0x} \neq 0$, the equation for u is more complicated. When $H_{0x} = 0$, the most obvious cause of the transverse velocity, v, is eliminated. However, v remains because of the presence of the boundaries. The solution to (13.3-8c) is

$$u = C_1 \cos m_1 y + C_2 \cos m_2 y + C_3 \sin m_1 y + C_4 \sin m_2 y$$

$$\tag{13.3-8d}$$

where

$$m_{1,2}^2 = \frac{-[k^2 - \omega^2(A_y^{-2} + a_0^{-2})] \pm \sqrt{[k^2 + \omega^2(A_y^{-2} + a_0^{-2})]^2 - 4\omega^4/a_0^2 A_y^2}}{2}$$

$$\tag{13.3-8e}$$

The expression for the velocity v is obtained by solving (13.3-8a) for v and is given by

$$v = C_5 \cos m_1 y + C_6 \cos m_2 y + C_7 \sin m_1 y + C_8 \sin m_2 y$$

$$\tag{13.3-8f}$$

where

$$C_{5,6} = -\frac{j}{a_0^2 k m_{1,2}} [A_y^2 m_{1,2}^2 + (a_0^2 + A_y^2)k^2 - \omega^2] C_{3,4}$$

and

$$C_{7,8} = \frac{j}{a_0^2 k m_{1,2}} [A_y^2 m_{1,2}^2 + (a_0^2 + A_y^2)k^2 - \omega^2] C_{1,2}$$

The x component of the magnetic field is given by

$$h_x^* = \frac{1}{j\omega} (-m_1 C_1 \sin m_1 y - m_2 C_2 \sin m_2 y$$

$$+ m_1 C_3 \cos m_1 y + m_2 C_4 \cos m_2 y) \quad \text{(13.3-8g)}$$

The solutions can be separated into symmetric and antisymmetric solutions, as they were in Section 13.2. The boundary conditions used are $h_x^*(y = \pm y_0/2) = 0$ and $v(y = \pm y_0/2) = 0$. Here we choose (as a special case of the general solution) the solutions which are antisymmetrical in u and symmetrical in v and h_x^*. Applying the boundary conditions yields

$$C_4 = -\frac{m_1 \cos m_1 y_0/2}{m_2 \cos m_2 y_0/2} C_3 \tag{13.3-9a}$$

$$(m_2^2 - m_1^2)[(a_0^2 + A_y^2)k^2 - \omega^2] = 0 \tag{13.3-9b}$$

where C_3 depends upon the strength of the excitation. Two different values of k are obtained from (13.3-9b). These are

$$k = \frac{\pm \omega}{\sqrt{a_0^2 + A_y^2}} \tag{13.3-9c}$$

and

$$k = \pm\omega\sqrt{\frac{2}{a_0 A_y} - \frac{1}{A_y^{\,2}} - \frac{1}{a_0^{\,2}}} \qquad (13.3\text{-}9\text{d})$$

However, the k given by (13.3-9d) is imaginary for all Alfvén speeds, excluding the acoustic velocity. Hence, the value of k given by (13.3-9c) is the only one that represents propagation. Since the phase velocity in this case is $v_P = \sqrt{A_y^{\,2} + a_0^{\,2}}$, the wave is called a fast wave. This wave propagates unattenuated, as is expected, for no losses occur in an inviscid, ideally conducting fluid.

(d) Conclusions

In this section the general equations for wave propagation in an electrically conducting, viscous, compressible liquid are presented. In these equations streaming of the fluid, nonuniform applied magnetic fields, and thermal effects are not considered. If needed, these effects can be included in a similar but more complicated derivation. The equations presented here exhibit a very important feature. The wave equation in the perturbed pressure, (13.3-5c), is coupled to the rest of the equations only when the perturbed magnetic field has a component parallel to the applied magnetic field. Thus in Section 13.2 the pressure did not enter into the problem, regardless of the magnitude of the compressibility of the fluid, because **h** was perpendicular to $\mathbf{H}_0$.

The exact solution to the transient problem of Section 9.5 could be found using the approach taken in this section. In the analysis given in Section 9.5, the transients traveling at the magnetoacoustic speed are neglected compared to those occurring by diffusion processes. The transients of Chapter 9 diffuse at the Alfvén speed and are therefore very slow compared to the magnetoacoustic waves which propagate at a speed greater than the acoustic velocity. Hence the approximations of Section 9.5 are valid after the pressure waves have passed.

13.4 ELECTROMAGNETIC INDUCTION PUMPING

(a) Introduction

The induction pump is closely related to the ordinary induction motor. Its greatest advantage over other types of magnetohydrodynamic pumps arises from the fact that no electrodes are necessary. In this pump a traveling magnetic field interacts with the current it induces in the fluid, and a body force results which has a component in the direction of the desired motion of the fluid. Induction pumps have been used to pump coolants in nuclear reactors. In the study by Blake (1957) several geometries are considered and some experimental data are presented.

Lyons and Turcotte (1962) make a detailed study based on the equations derived by Harris (1960) which treat the effect of magnetic field fringing caused by pole piece separation. It is concluded that fringing reduces the efficiency as much as laminar skin-friction losses. However, it is assumed that flux penetration is complete and later it is concluded that electrical skin effects are negligible. Clearly, induction devices will not work at zero frequency because no fields or currents can be induced. At very high frequencies all the induced fields and currents will be restricted to regions in the fluid where no motion can take place because of the no-slip boundary condition. Since at both ends of the frequency spectrum no force exists to do pumping, there must exist an optimum frequency for induction pumping.

It is the purpose of this section to investigate the optimum operating frequency for an electromagnetic induction pump.

(b) The Slug Flow Model

Since the flow is turbulent, the simplest model of the induction pump assumes a flat velocity profile. Furthermore, skin friction between the container walls and fluid is neglected. The geometry used in this investigation is shown in Fig. 13.4-1. The polyphase windings are arranged so that at $x = \pm x_0$, H_y, the magnetic field in the y direction, is given by

$$H_y(\pm x_0, y, z, t) = H_0 \cos(\omega t - ky) \qquad (13.4\text{-}1)$$

With heating effects neglected, the motion of the slug of fluid is given by the Maxwell equations and Newton's laws of motion. The Maxwell equations are

$$\nabla \times \mathbf{E} = -\mu_0 \frac{\partial \mathbf{H}}{\partial t} \qquad (13.4\text{-}2)$$

$$\nabla \times \mathbf{H} = \mathbf{J} \qquad (13.4\text{-}3)$$

$$\nabla \cdot \mathbf{H} = 0 \qquad (13.4\text{-}4)$$

where

$$\mathbf{J} = \sigma(\mathbf{E} + \mu_0 \mathbf{V} \times \mathbf{H}) \qquad (13.4\text{-}5)$$

and $\mathbf{E}$, $\mathbf{H}$, $\mathbf{J}$, μ_0, σ, and $\mathbf{V}$ are the electric field, magnetic field, current density, permeability of free space, conductivity, and velocity of the metal, respectively. Newton's law of motion is

$$\rho \frac{dV_y}{\partial t} = -\frac{\partial P}{\partial y} + \frac{\mu_0}{2x_0} \int_{-x_0}^{x_0} (\mathbf{J} \times \mathbf{H})_y \, dx \qquad (13.4\text{-}6)$$

Here ρ is fluid density, P is pressure, and $(\mathbf{J} \times \mathbf{H})_y$ is the y component of the electromagnetic body force. By combining (13.4-2), (13.4-3), and (13.4-5), there results the transport equation in magnetic field:

$$\nabla^2 \mathbf{H} + \mu_0 \sigma \nabla \times (\mathbf{V} \times \mathbf{H}) = \mu_0 \sigma \frac{\partial \mathbf{H}}{\partial t} \tag{13.4-7}$$

Since the mechanical relaxation time for liquid metals is of the order of $\rho x_0 / 2\pi \mu_f$, we see that this relaxation time is much greater than the electrical

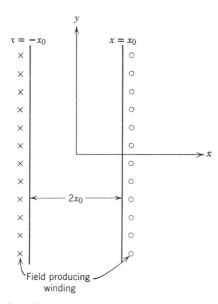

Figure 13.4-1   Coordinate system for the induction pump.

period of the lowest frequency used in the polyphase coil. Thus we are interested only in the time averages of velocity and pressure. Then, for steady pumping, (13.4-6) becomes

$$\frac{\partial P}{\partial y} = \frac{\mu_0}{2 x_0 T} \int_0^T \int_{-x_0}^{x_0} (\mathbf{J} \times \mathbf{H})_y \, dx \, dt \tag{13.4-8}$$

where P is the time averaged pressure and T is the electrical period. The magnetic transport equation becomes

$$\nabla^2 \mathbf{H} + \mu_0 \sigma \nabla \times (V_y \hat{y} \times \mathbf{H}) = \mu_0 \sigma \frac{\partial \mathbf{H}}{\partial t} \tag{13.4-9}$$

If, in the alternating-current steady state, it is assumed that the time variation is sinusoidal, a phasor solution is possible in which $j\omega$ replaces

$\partial/\partial t$. Also, since the excitation is of the form $H_0 \operatorname{Re} e^{j(\omega t - ky)}$, where H_0 is the linear current density per unit y dimension of the exciting winding,

$$\mathbf{H} = [\hat{x}H_x(x) + \hat{y}H_y(x)]e^{j(\omega t - ky)} \tag{13.4-10}$$

Upon substituting the phasor quantities into Maxwell's equations, we obtain

$$\left(\frac{d^2}{dx^2} - k^2 - j\omega\mu_0\sigma\right)(\hat{x}H_x + \hat{y}H_y) + \mu_0\sigma\left(\hat{x}jk + \hat{y}\frac{d}{dx}\right)V_yH_x = 0 \tag{13.4-11}$$

$$J_z = \frac{dH_y}{dx} + jkH_x \tag{13.4-12}$$

and

$$\frac{dH_x}{dx} - jkH_y = 0 \tag{13.4-13}$$

Equation (13.4-8) becomes

$$\frac{\partial P}{\partial y} = \frac{\mu_0}{2x_0}\operatorname{Re}\int_{-x_0}^{x_0} J_z\bar{H}_x\,dx \tag{13.4-14}$$

where Re denotes the real part and $\bar{H}_x$ is the complex conjugate of H_x. The y component of (13.4-11) must be combined with (13.4-13) in order to eliminate dH_x/dx. There results

$$\left(\frac{d^2}{dx^2} - \beta^2\right)H_y = 0 \tag{13.4-15}$$

where

$$\beta^2 = k^2 + j\omega\mu_0\sigma\left(1 - \frac{kV_y}{\omega}\right)$$

The solution to (13.4-15) that satisfies the boundary condition on H_y at $x = \pm x_0$ is

$$H_y = \frac{H_0 \operatorname{ch} \beta x}{\operatorname{ch} \beta x_0} \tag{13.4-16}$$

H_x is obtained directly from (13.4-13) and is

$$H_x = \frac{jk H_0 \operatorname{sh} \beta x}{\beta \operatorname{ch} \beta x_0} \tag{13.4-17}$$

From (13.4-12)

$$J_z = \frac{H_0(\beta^2 - k^2) \operatorname{sh} \beta x}{\beta \operatorname{ch} \beta x_0} \tag{13.4-18}$$

From (13.4-17), (13.4-18), and suitable hyperbolic identities,

$$\text{Re } J_z \bar{H}_x = \frac{\mu_0^2 H_0^2 \omega \sigma k (1 - kV_y/\omega)}{\sqrt{k^4 + [\mu_0 \sigma \omega (1 - kV_y/\omega)]^2}} \frac{\text{ch } 2\beta_r x - \cos 2\beta_i x}{\text{ch } 2\beta_r x_0 + \cos 2\beta_i x_0} \quad (13.4\text{-}19)$$

where β_r and β_i are the real and imaginary parts of β, respectively. Integrating (13.4-19) yields

$$\int_{-x_0}^{x_0} \text{Re } J_z \bar{H}_x \, dx = \frac{\mu_0^2 H_0^2 \omega \sigma k (1 - kV_y/\omega)}{\sqrt{k^4 + [\mu_0 \sigma \omega (1 - kV_y/\omega)]^2}}$$

$$\cdot \frac{(1/\beta_r) \text{ sh } 2\beta_r x_0 - (1/\beta_i) \sin 2\beta_i x_0}{\text{ch } 2\beta_r x_0 + \cos 2\beta_i x_0} \quad (13.4\text{-}20)$$

Table 13.4-1

Optimum values for induction pump

π_4	π_2	π_1	π_3	$(2\pi_1\pi_3)^{-\frac{1}{2}}$
0.714	0.1	0.025	0.45	6.67
0.714	0.3	0.075	0.45	3.85
0.714	0.5	0.125	0.45	2.98
0.714	0.7	0.175	0.45	2.52
0.711	0.9	0.195	0.40	2.54

Here

$$\beta = \frac{1}{x_0 \pi_3 \sqrt{2\pi_1}} \left\{ \sqrt{\sqrt{\pi_1^2 + (\pi_2\pi_3)^2} + \pi_1} + j \sqrt{\sqrt{\pi_1^2 + (\pi_2\pi_3)^2} - \pi_1} \right\}$$

$$(13.4\text{-}21)$$

Let $b = x_0 \pi_3 \sqrt{2\pi_1} \beta$ and rearrange (13.4-20), which becomes

$$\pi_4 = \frac{2x_0(\partial P/\partial y)}{\mu_0 H_0^2} = \frac{\pi_3 \pi_2 \sqrt{2\pi_1}}{\sqrt{\pi_1^2 + \pi_2^2 \pi_3^2}}$$

$$\cdot \frac{(1/b_r) \text{ sh } 2\beta_r x_0 - (1/b_i) \sin 2\beta_i x_0}{\text{ch } 2\beta_r x_0 + \cos 2\beta_i x_0} \quad (13.4\text{-}22)$$

where $\pi_1 = (x_0 v_P \mu_0 \sigma)^{-1}$, $v_P = \omega/k$, $\pi_2 = 1 - V_y/v_P$, and $\pi_3 = v_P/\omega x_0$. In (13.4-22) we have expressed the ratio of driving or retarding pressure gradient to maximum magnetic force as a function of slip (π_2) and frequency. Frequency is contained in all the parameters. If the phase velocity is fixed at a certain value, varying π_1 is equivalent to adjusting x_0 or σ, π_2 to V_y and π_3 to frequency.

The ratio π_4 has been maximized for various values of π_2. The necessary values of π_1 and π_3 are given in Table 13.4-1.

The electrical skin depth δ is defined as $\delta = \sqrt{2/\omega\mu_0\sigma}$. Under this definition

$$\frac{x_0}{\delta} = (2\pi_1\pi_3)^{-\frac{1}{2}} \tag{13.4-23}$$

and Table 13.4-1 shows that for optimum ratio of pressure gradient to applied magnetic force, the ratio of pump width ($2x_0$) to skin depth (δ) is not zero. Instead, it varies from about 13.3 at 0.1 slip to 5 at 0.7 slip.

(c) Conclusion

It has been shown for a slug flow model of induction driven flow that the skin effect cannot be neglected. This result is reasonable because the x component of the magnetic field and the z component of the current density produce the body force which propels the slug. Both of these quantities are induced effects that gain strength when the skin effect begins to develop. Hence the electromagnetic field quantities are not uniformly distributed in an optimum electromagnetic pump. It is interesting to note that the maximum driving force π_4 is obtained when $v_P/\omega x_0 = 0.45$, regardless of the slip. On the other hand, the maximum driving force cannot be obtained at the various values of slip without making large adjustments of the magnetic Reynolds number π_1^{-1}. Hence, for a given value of slip, $x_0^2\omega\mu_0\sigma = (\pi_1\pi_3)^{-1}$, with π_1 and π_3 as given by Table 13.4-1. Thus, for maximum driving force, the quantity $x_0^2\omega\sigma$ must be adjusted at each different value of slip.

The work presented here is but a brief introduction to a well explored subject. For details concerning traveling wave converters and pumps, the work of Messerle (1964) and Penhune (1961) should be consulted.

13.5   INDUCTION STIRRING IN FURNACES

Introduction and Description of the Model

In some industrial furnaces stirring is achieved by exciting traveling flux waves in the molten charge. The action resulting in motion is similar to that in the induction motor in which the traveling flux wave in the stator pulls the rotor along. It is the purpose of this section to study the influence of the furnace parameters on flow induced by this means, called induction stirring. This problem has a great deal in common with the induction pumping of liquid metals.

Although most induction furnaces are cylindrical (see Fig. 13.5-1a), it is much simpler to analyze a parallel-planes model. The geometry of the model treated here is given in Fig. 13.5-1*b* where the furnace walls are infinite yz planes. The fluid flows in the y direction and the end effects at $y = \pm\infty$ are taken into account by requiring no net flow past any xz plane. Further, it is assumed that nothing is a function of the z coordinate. The exciting coil of such a furnace consists of polyphase windings that induce a space periodic magnetic field traveling in the axial direction. The space period of the field is given by the wavelength λ, or reciprocal wavenumber $1/k$.

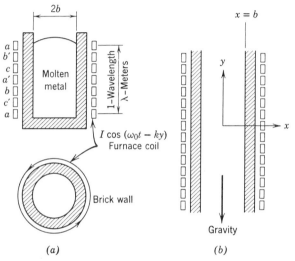

(a)   (b)

Figure 13.5-1 Geometry of idealized model for induction-driven flow illustrated for a 3ϕ exciting coil of wavelength approximately equal to a diameter. For phase a, b, and c, currents flow out of the paper if unprimed, into paper if primed. $I =$ linear current density of coil in amps/unit y dimension, $\omega_0 =$ frequency in radians/sec, $k =$ propagation constant in radians/m.

If the metal flows in the axial direction only, with velocity v, only a z component of the eddy current density, J_z, exists. This interacts with the applied magnetic field to produce both a "radial" pinch (contributing to the magnetic pressure only) and the "axial" stirring force. The use of an infinite geometry allows the induction stirring action to be examined without the complication of stirring effects that arise because of the finite height of the coil and/or charge. The fluid near the walls moves in the direction of propagation of the traveling wave and that in the middle is oppositely directed so that the net flow is zero, as required by the conservation of mass. The model does not include thermo-mechanical coupling so that the density ρ_0 is independent of temperature, and motion is independent of the gravitational force.

Equations

The excitation is assumed to travel in the y direction and is of the form $Ie^{j(\omega_0 t - ky)}$. Then, in terms of their complex components, the magnetic field and eddy current density are $\mathbf{H} = [H_x(x)\hat{x} + H_y(x)\hat{y}]e^{j(\omega_0 t - ky)}$ and $J_z = J_z(x)e^{j(\omega_0 t - ky)}$. The Maxwell and Navier-Stokes equations become

$$\left(\frac{d^2}{dx^2} - k^2 - j\omega_0\mu_0\sigma\right)(\hat{x}H_x + \hat{y}H_y) + \mu_0\sigma\left(jk\hat{x} + \frac{d}{dx}\hat{y}\right)vH_x = 0 \quad (13.5\text{-}1)$$

$$J_z = \frac{dH_y}{dx} + jkH_x \quad (13.5\text{-}2)$$

$$\frac{dH_x}{dx} - jkH_y = 0 \quad (13.5\text{-}3)$$

$$0 = -\frac{\partial P}{\partial x} - \frac{\mu_0}{2}\mathrm{Re}\,(J_z\bar{H}_y) \quad (13.5\text{-}4)$$

$$0 = -\frac{\partial P}{\partial y} + \mu_f\frac{d^2v}{dx^2} + \frac{\mu_0}{2}\mathrm{Re}\,(J_z\bar{H}_x) - \rho_0 g \quad (13.5\text{-}5)$$

where v and P are not phasors but steady quantities. Differentiating Equation (13.5-4) with respect to y results in $\partial^2 P/\partial x\,\partial y = 0$ which when integrated with respect to x yields $\partial P/\partial y = $ a function of y. But Equation (13.5-5) states that this same derivative of the pressure is a function of x. Hence this derivative must be a constant L. If we let $L' = L + \rho_0 g$, the equation of motion (13.5-5) becomes

$$L' = \mu_f\frac{d^2v}{dx^2} + \frac{\mu_0}{2}\mathrm{Re}\,(J_z\bar{H}_x) \quad (13.5\text{-}6)$$

It is now possible to identify the pinch and induction stirring forces from Equations (13.5-4) and (13.5-6), respectively. For a furnace excited from a single phase source and without end effects there is no radial field, hence no forcing function for (13.5-6). Thus under these assumptions the fluid is motionless, but pinched.

Before proceeding to the solution, we note that Equation (13.5-6) may also be written as

$$L' = \mu_f\frac{d^2v}{dx^2} + \frac{\mu_0}{2}\mathrm{Re}\left(\frac{H_x}{jk}\frac{d^2\bar{H}_x}{dx^2}\right) \quad (13.5\text{-}7)$$

where (13.5-2) and (13.5-3) have been used. This equation, along with the first of the pair (13.5-1), that is,

$$\left(\frac{d^2}{dx^2} - k^2 - j\omega_0\mu_0\sigma\right)H_x + jk\mu_0\sigma v H_x = 0 \tag{13.5-8}$$

reduces the problem to the solution of a pair of nonlinear equations in v and H_x—a somewhat formidable task.

Solution

However, a solution to (13.5-1) and (13.5-6) is readily obtained by neglecting the nonlinear terms in Equation (13.5-1). This implies that the transport term is small compared to the diffusion term of Equation (13.5-1) or, equivalently, that the magnetic Reynolds number $Rm = bV_0\mu_0\sigma$ is small (b and V_0 are characteristic dimensions and velocities, respectively). If we proceed in this manner and introduce the new dimensionless parameter $\mathcal{K} = \sqrt{2}b/\lambda$ and the new dimensionless variables $H_{x,y}^* = H_{x,y}/I$ and $J_z^* = bJ_z/I$, equations (13.5-1), (13.5-2), (13.5-3), and (13.5-6) become

$$\left[\frac{d^2}{dX^2} - \frac{\mathcal{K}^2}{2}\right]\begin{bmatrix} H_x^* \\ H_y^* \end{bmatrix} = \frac{jb'^2}{2}\begin{bmatrix} H_x^* \\ H_y^* \end{bmatrix} \tag{13.5-9}$$

$$J_z^* = \frac{dH_y^*}{dX} + \frac{j\mathcal{K}}{\sqrt{2}}H_x^* \tag{13.5-10}$$

$$\frac{dH_x^*}{dX} - \frac{j\mathcal{K}}{\sqrt{2}}H_y^* = 0 \tag{13.5-11}$$

$$L' = \frac{\mu_f}{b^2}\frac{d^2v(X)}{dX^2} + \frac{\mu_0 I^2}{2b}\text{Re}\,(J_z^*\bar{H}_x^*) \tag{13.5-12}$$

where $\delta = \sqrt{2/\omega\mu_0\sigma}$, $X = x/\delta$, and $b' = 2b/\delta$.
From Equation (13.5-9) it is seen that

$$H_y^* = C_1 \text{ch}\,\frac{X}{\sqrt{2}}\sqrt{\mathcal{K}^2 + jb'^2} + C_2 \text{ sh}\,\frac{X}{\sqrt{2}}\sqrt{\mathcal{K}^2 + jb'^2}$$

where $C_2 = 0$ because of symmetry. Applying the boundary condition $H_y^*(1) = 1$ yields the solution

$$H_y^* = \frac{\text{ch}\,(X/\sqrt{2})\sqrt{\mathcal{K}^2 + jb'^2}}{\text{ch}\,(1/\sqrt{2})\sqrt{\mathcal{K}^2 + jb'^2}} \tag{13.5-13}$$

From Equations (13.5-11) and (13.5-10)

$$H_x^* = \frac{j\mathcal{K}}{\sqrt{\mathcal{K}^2 + jb'^2}} \cdot \frac{\text{sh } (X/\sqrt{2})\sqrt{\mathcal{K}^2 + jb'^2}}{\text{ch } (1/\sqrt{2})\sqrt{\mathcal{K}^2 + jb'^2}} \tag{13.5-14}$$

$$J_z^* = \frac{jb'^2}{\sqrt{2}\sqrt{\mathcal{K}^2 + jb'^2}} \frac{\text{sh } (X/\sqrt{2})\sqrt{\mathcal{K}^2 + jb'^2}}{\text{ch } (1/\sqrt{2})\sqrt{\mathcal{K}^2 + jb'^2}} \tag{13.5-15}$$

which when substituted into (13.5-12) result in

$$L' = \frac{\mu_f}{b^2} \frac{d^2v}{dX^2} + \frac{\mu_0 I^2 \mathcal{K} b'^2}{2\sqrt{2}b\sqrt{\mathcal{K}^4 + b'^4}}$$

$$\cdot \frac{\text{ch } X\sqrt{\sqrt{\mathcal{K}^4 + b'^4} + \mathcal{K}^2} - \cos X\sqrt{\sqrt{\mathcal{K}^4 + b'^4} - \mathcal{K}^2}}{\text{ch } \sqrt{\sqrt{\mathcal{K}^4 + b'^4} + \mathcal{K}^2} + \cos \sqrt{\sqrt{\mathcal{K}^4 + b'^4} - \mathcal{K}^2}} \tag{13.5-16}$$

Before rewriting this equation more compactly, we will examine the forcing function (the constant L' is not really a forcing function since without the induction stirring force the solution is trivial, that is, $v = 0$). For a fixed diameter, material, and applied field, we can see that as $\mathcal{K}$ is varied, the forcing function goes to zero both for a very small and very large $\mathcal{K}$. Between these extremes, therefore, there is some wavelength of the exciting coil for which the induction stirring force and, consequently, the velocity are maximum. Now, if we allow b' to vary and fix the other parameters, we see that at very low frequencies the induction stirring force vanishes and at very high frequencies this force is proportional to $e^{b'(X-1)}$. Doubly integrating this indicates that velocity falls off at very large frequencies so that we again expect to find an optimum frequency which maximizes velocity.

By substituting as follows,

$$\alpha = \sqrt{\mathcal{K}^4 + b'^4}$$

$$D = \text{ch } \sqrt{\alpha + \mathcal{K}^2} + \cos \sqrt{\alpha - \mathcal{K}^2}$$

$$L'' = \frac{2\sqrt{2}b\alpha L' D}{\mu_0 I^2 \mathcal{K} b'^2}$$

$$C_3 = \frac{2\sqrt{2}\mu_f \alpha D}{b\mu_0 I^2 \mathcal{K} b'^2}$$

and (13.5-16) simplifies to

$$L'' = C_3 \frac{d^2v}{dX^2} + \text{ch } X\sqrt{\alpha + \mathcal{K}^2} - \cos X\sqrt{\alpha - \mathcal{K}^2}$$

By integrating, retaining even functions because of symmetry, and imposing the no-slip boundary condition $v(1) = 0$, we obtain

$$C_3 v = \frac{L''(X^2 - 1)}{2} + \frac{1}{b'^4}[(\alpha - \mathcal{K}^2)(\mathrm{ch}\sqrt{\alpha + \mathcal{K}^2} - \mathrm{ch}\, X\sqrt{\alpha + \mathcal{K}^2})$$
$$+ (\alpha + \mathcal{K}^2)(\cos\sqrt{\alpha - \mathcal{K}^2} - \cos X\sqrt{\alpha - \mathcal{K}^2})]$$

Finally, the constant L'' is computed by noting that, in a furnace, as much fluid flows up as down. Hence $\int_0^1 v\, dX = 0$. The result is

$$L'' = \frac{3}{b'^4}[(\alpha - \mathcal{K}^2)\, \mathrm{ch}\sqrt{\alpha + \mathcal{K}^2} + (\alpha + \mathcal{K}^2)\cos\sqrt{\alpha - \mathcal{K}^2}]$$
$$- \frac{3}{b'^6}[(\alpha - \mathcal{K}^2)^{3/2}\, \mathrm{sh}\sqrt{\alpha + \mathcal{K}^2} + (\alpha + \mathcal{K}^2)^{3/2}\sin\sqrt{\alpha - \mathcal{K}^2}]$$

which when substituted into the last expression for velocity yields

$$\frac{\sqrt{2}\mu_f\alpha D b'^2}{b\mu_0 I^2 \mathcal{K}}v$$

$$= \tfrac{3}{2}(X^2 - 1)\left\{[(\alpha - \mathcal{K}^2)\, \mathrm{ch}\sqrt{\alpha + \mathcal{K}^2} + (\alpha + \mathcal{K}^2)\cos\sqrt{\alpha - \mathcal{K}^2}]\right.$$
$$\left. - \frac{1}{b'^2}[(\alpha - \mathcal{K}^2)^{3/2}\, \mathrm{sh}\sqrt{\alpha + \mathcal{K}^2} + (\alpha + \mathcal{K}^2)^{3/2}\sin\sqrt{\alpha - \mathcal{K}^2}]\right\}$$
$$+ (\alpha - \mathcal{K}^2)(\mathrm{ch}\sqrt{\alpha + \mathcal{K}^2} - \mathrm{ch}\, X\sqrt{\alpha + \mathcal{K}^2})$$
$$+ (\alpha + \mathcal{K}^2)(\cos\sqrt{\alpha - \mathcal{K}^2} - \cos X\sqrt{\alpha - \mathcal{K}^2}) \qquad (13.5\text{-}17)$$

Results

Velocity profiles, calculated from Equation (13.5-17), are shown in Figs. 13.5-2 and 13.5-3. The profiles are normalized with respect to the center velocity, and the parameter $K = \sqrt{2}\mathcal{K} = 2b/\lambda$ is introduced so that wavelength and skin depth may be similarly treated. The figures show that b' and K are almost interchangeable. We see that as either frequency increases or wavelength decreases, the magnitude of the peak velocity near the wall increases relative to the magnitude of the center velocity.

Figure 13.5-4 gives the center velocity as a function of b' or K for the special cases $b' = 4$ and $K = 4$ and demonstrates the existence of an optimum frequency and wavelength. The curves were made using the values given in Table 13.5-1 and indicate that the combination of wavelength and skin depth that produces maximum induction stirring at

constant applied field occurs when both are half a radius. For higher
frequencies the optimum results when the wavelength and skin depth are
equal. Also shown in Fig. 13.5-4 is the average of the body force per unit
volume in the axial direction. This correlates with the center velocity and
peaks at the same values of wavelength and skin depth. For molten iron

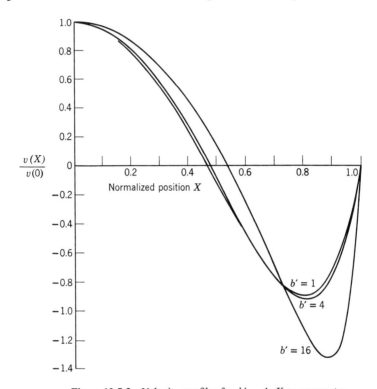

Figure 13.5-2   Velocity profiles for $b' = 4$, K as parameter.

the maximum center velocity corresponding to $b' = K = 4$ is

$$v(0)_{max} = 2.57 \times 10^{-6} bI^2 \qquad (13.5\text{-}18)$$

An important point to consider is that neglecting the transport term
becomes quite serious as the furnace size and exciting current increase. In
fact, when either b or I becomes too large, the flow is no longer laminar,
as in this model, but turbulent and (13.5-18) must be used with additional
reservation. Further, the approximation neglects the induced electric
field $\mu_0 \mathbf{V} \times \mathbf{H}$ which serves to limit the fluid velocity to values below the
phase velocity of the traveling wave. The limitations of the approximation
made can be seen by comparing the size of the diffusion term and the

neglected transport term in the H_x component of Equation (13.5-1) using the solution obtained. If this is done and if the center velocity given in the table is used as a measure of the term v, the criterion that the approximation be a good one is the inequality

$$\frac{M^2 K v^*(b', K)}{2\sqrt{2}} \ll b'^2 \qquad (13.5\text{-}19)$$

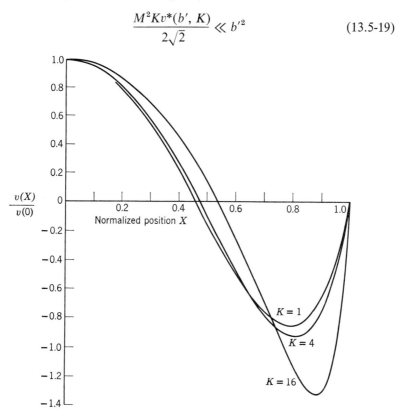

Figure 13.5-3   Velocity profiles for $K = 4$, b' as parameter.

where $M^2 = \sigma \mu_0^2 I^2 b^2 / \mu_f$ is the square of the Hartmann number and v^* is the dimensionless velocity. For a furnace diameter of half a meter and $b' = K = 4$, inequality (13.5-19) becomes $I \ll 5260$ amps/m, which is below industrial practice.

Conclusions

Although the analysis is restrictive because the coupling between the magnetic field and velocity has been neglected, it does serve to indicate that induction stirring in a furnace can be maximized by properly selecting the frequency and wavelength of the exciting coil. That an optimum

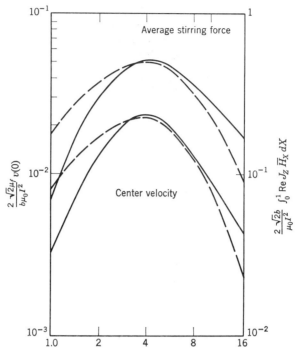

Figure 13.5-4 Center velocity and average stirring force: —— versus b', $K = 4$; – – – – versus K, $b' = 4$.

frequency should exist may be seen from the limiting cases. Thus at zero frequency there are no body forces because of the absence of induced eddy currents and at extremely high frequencies the body forces are concentrated at the wall, leaving the bulk of the fluid unaffected. As for wavelength, there is no radial field at very long wavelengths and hence no induction stirring, and at very small wavelengths the phase velocity goes to

Table 13.5-1

Values for $v^*(b', K) = \dfrac{2\sqrt{2}\mu_f}{b\mu_0 I^2}\, v(0)$

K	$b' = 1.0$	2.0	4.0	8.0	16.0
1.0	0.004702	0.01268	0.008738	0.003447	0.001120
2.0	0.005855	0.01803	0.01633	0.006775	0.00229
4.0	0.003431	0.01265	0.02313	0.01257	0.004364
8.0	0.0008639	0.03423	0.01192	0.01724	0.007973
16.0	0.0001403	0.0005607	0.002219	0.007631	0.01041

zero so that the flux wave moves very slowly. It has been shown that when the applied field is held constant, the optimum skin depth and wavelength correspond to half a radius. At frequencies above those that correspond to this optimum, maximum induction stirring occurs when the wavelength equals the skin depth. Lastly, the motion of the charge correlates with the average of the axial component of the stirring force. An analysis that enters into greater detail is warranted only if the nonlinear terms are included.

PROBLEMS

1. Investigate the problem of 13.2c when the parallel planes have finite nonzero conductivity.

2. A circular cylindrical pipe is filled with an electrically conducting fluid and is situated in an axial magnetic field. At one end of the pipe a transducer moves in the angular direction in simple harmonic motion. What is the simplest mode that can exist? Find the attenuation and propagation constants when the pipe is an ideal conductor.

3. Rework the problem of Section 13.2f for the case of $v = \eta$.

4. In Section 13.2f it is mentioned that the effect of the viscosity on the antisymmetric solution to the insulating wall case is negligible. The symmetric solution is greatly modified by the viscosity in the insulating-wall case. Show that the effect results in

$$w = B_1[\cos m_1 y - (-1)^n e^{-(1+j)(y_0/2-y)/\delta_f}]$$

and

$$h_z{}^* = \frac{-B_1\omega}{k_s A_x{}^2}\left[\cos m_1 y + \frac{jk_s{}^2\delta_f{}^2}{2}(-1)^n e^{-(1+j)(y_0/2-y)/\delta_f}\right]$$

where $m_1 y_0/2 = n\pi$, $n = 1, 2, 3 \ldots$, and k_s is given by (13.2-13d and e).

5. Consider the propagation of waves in a rectangular tube filled with inviscid conducting liquid having (a) ideally conducting walls in an axial magnetic field, (b) ideally conducting walls in a transverse magnetic field, (c) insulating walls in an axial magnetic field, and (d) insulating walls in a transverse magnetic field.

6. Rework Section 13.4 for a circular cylindrical slug.

7. Rework Section 13.5 for a laminar induction pump. *Hint:* Adjust the pressure gradient so that a net flow exists.

8. Examine Section 13.3c for other modes. It is especially interesting to find the mode that reduces to the ordinary acoustic mode when $A_y \to 0$.

REFERENCES

Alfvén, H., *Cosmical Electrodynamics*, Oxford: Clarendon Press, 1950.

Anderson, N. S. Longitudinal Magneto-Hydrodynamic Waves, *J. Acoust. Soc. Am.,* **25**, p. 529, 1953.

Blake, L. R., Conduction and Induction Pumps for Liquid Metals, Proceedings of the I.E.E., **104A**, pp. 49–65, 1957.

Blue, E., Torsional MHD Waves in the Presence of Finite Viscosity, AFSOR TN-54-57, 1957.

Damaskos, N. J., and F. J. Young, The Stability of Thermally Induced Flow in the Coreless Induction Furnace, *Int. J. Heat Mass Transfer*, **8**, pp. 721–728, 1965.

Harris, L. P., *Hydromagnetic Channel Flow*, Technology Press of M.I.T., 1960.

Herlofson, N., Magneto-Hydrodynamic Waves in a Compressible Fluid Conductor, *Nature* (London), **165**, p. 1020, 1950.

Kliman, G. B., Effect of Some Imperfections on Liquid Metal Hydromagnetic Waveguide Performance, M.I.T. QPR No. 73, pp. 114–120, 1964.

Lundquist, S., On the Stability of Magneto-Hydrostatic Fields, *Phys. Rev.*, **83**, p. 307, 1951.

Lyons, J. M., and D. L. Turcotte, A Study of Magnetohydrodynamic Induction Devices, ASTIA AD272 082, 1962.

Messerle, H. K., The Travelling-Wave Plasma Converter, *J. Fluid Mech.*, **19**, Part 4, pp. 577–590, 1964.

Murphy, J. H., and W. F. Hughes, Observations on Magnetoacoustic Waves in Mercury, *Proc. I.E.E.E.*, **54**, p. 55, 1966.

Osterbrock, D. E., The Heating of the Solar Chromosphere, Plages, and Corona by Magnetohydrodynamic Waves, *Astrophys. J.*, **134**, No. 2, p. 347, 1961.

Penhune, J. P., Energy Conversion in Laminar Magnetohydrodynamic Channel Flow, ASD Technical Report 61-294, 1961.

Westphal, W., Magnetohydrodynamische Dispersion und Absorption von Ultraschall, *Z. Physik*, **168**, pp. 333–342, 1962.

Appendix 1

Tables of Properties and Constants

Properties of

	Viscosity, μ_f Nwt-sec/m²	Magnetic Diffusivity, η m²/sec	Kinematic Viscosity ν m²/sec	Electrical Conductivity, σ mho/m	Density, ρ kg/m³	Pressure, P Nwt/m²
Liquid mercury	1.55×10^{-3}	0.744	1.14×10^{-7}	1.07×10^6	1.355×10^4	10^5
Liquid sodium	0.705×10^{-3}	0.0765	7.6×10^{-7}	10.4×10^6	9.27×10^2	10^5
Na—K 22%–78%	0.5×10^{-3}	0.30	5.9×10^{-7}	2.66×10^6	8.5×10^2	10^5
Na—K 56%–44%	0.6×10^{-3}	0.266	6.75×10^{-7}	3×10^6	8.9×10^2	10^5
Wood's metal Pb Bi 50% 25% Sn Cd 12.5% 12.5%	2×10^{-3}	8.85	19×10^{-7}	0.9×10^6	1.05×10^3	10^5
Air (Sea level)	1.827×10^{-5}	–	1.827×10^{-5}	–	1	10^5
Air	–	8×10^5	–	1	8.4×10^{-2}	10^5
Air	–	2×10^4	–	40	5.9×10^{-2}	10^5
Air at 100 km	–	–	–	–	10^{-6}	3×10^{-2}
Interplanetary space (Solar wind)	10^{-5}	10	10^{16}	10^5	10^{-21}	2×10^{-13}
Interstellar space	10^{-5}	10^3?	10^{17}	10^3	10^{-22}	1.4×10^{-15}
Ionized hydrogen	10^{-6}	15	10	5.3×10^4	10^{-7}	42
Solar corona	10	1?	10^{16}	8×10^5	10^{-15}	–
Earth's interior	10^{-2}	1	10^{-6}	8×10^5	10^4	–
Sea water	10^{-3}†	2×10^5	9.8×10^{-7}†	4	1.025×10^3	10^5
Magnetic variable stars	3×10^{-4}?	1	3×10^{-7}	8×10^5	10^3?	–
Sunspots*	10^{-3}	20	10^{-2}	4×10^4	10^{-1}	–

* In the deep interior of the sun the density is about 30 times that of lead and the
† The viscosity depends slightly on salinity, but is approximately the same as ordinary

1

conducting fluids

Temperature, T °K	Thermal Conductivity, κ_T watts/m °K	Sonic Speed, a_0 m/sec	Magnetic Field, B Webers/m^2	Alfvén Speed, A m/sec	Magnetic Prandtl Number, Pm	
293	8.8	1450	1	7.7	1.53×10^{-7}	Liquid mercury
373	85	2525	1	29.4	10^{-5}	Liquid sodium
293	24.3	–	1	30.7	1.97×10^{-6}	Na—K 22%–78%
293	25.8	–	1	30.0	2.54×10^{-6}	Na—K 56%–44%
373	13.4	–	1	27.6	2.15×10^{-7}	Wood's metal Pb Bi 50% 25% Sn Cd 12.5% 12.5%
293	0.0238	340	–	–	–	Air (Sea level)
3500	–	1180	1	3.2×10^3	–	Air
5000	–	1400	1	3.7×10^3	–	Air
200	–	280	10^{-4}	25	–	Air at 100 km
10^5	–	2×10^5	4×10^{-10}	3×10^3	10^{16}	Interplanetary space (Solar wind)
10^4	–	–	10^{-11}	10^3	10^{14}	Interstellar space
10^5	–	–	10^{-1}	2×10^5	66	Ionized hydrogen
10^6	–	–	10^{-4}	10^6	10^{16}	Solar corona
10^4	–	–	10^{-3}	6×10^{-3}	10^{-6}	Earth's interior
293	0.6	1531	10^{-4}	7.8×10^{-4}	4.9×10^{-12}	Sea water
10^6	–	–	1	20	3×10^{-7}	Magnetic variable stars
4×10^3	–	–	0.2	360	5×10^{-4}	Sunspots

value of σ is indeed large, essentially ∞.
water.

Table 2
Properties of liquid metals
(M.K.S. units)

Liquid metals	Melting point °C	Boiling point °C	Density ρ Multiply the following number by 10^3 to get kg/m³	°C	Electrical conductivity σ Multiply the following number by 10^6 to get mho/m	°C	Viscosity μ_f Multiply the following number by 10^{-3} to get Nwt/sec/m²	°C	Surface tension Nwt/m	°C
Aluminum Al 13	660.2	2950	2.380 2.261	660 1100	5.1 4.31	657 870	2.9 1.4	700 800	0.520	750
Bismuth Bi 83	271.0	1477	10.03 9.20	300 962	0.775 0.651	300 750	1.662 0.996	304 600	0.376 0.363	300 500
Cadmium Cd 48	321	765	8.01 7.72	330 600	2.97 2.80	330 600	2.37 1.54	350 600	0.564 0.600	330 500
Cesium Cs 55	28.5	705	1.84	28	2.73	30	0.630 0.343	43.4 210.9	–	–
Gallium Ga 31	29.92	1983	6.093 5.445	32.38 1100	3.86 3.66	29.75 46.1	1.894 0.652	52.9 806	0.735	30 40
Indium In 49	156.4	2087	7.026	164	3.43	154	–	–	0.340	170 250
Lead Pb 82	327.4	1737	10.51 9.81	400 1000	1.084 0.816	327 1000	2.116 1.185	441 844	0.442 0.431	350 500
Lithium Li 3	179	2403	0.507 0.441	200 1000	2.21	230	0.592 0.455	183.4 285.5	–	–

Substance										
Mercury Hg 80	−38.37	357	13.55 / 12.88	20 / 300	1.016 / 0.737	50 / 350	1.55 / 1.01	20 / 200	0.465 / 0.394	20 / 354
Potassium K 19	63.7	760	0.819 / 0.676	100 / 700	7.6 / 3.18	64 / 350	0.515 / 0.136	69.6 / 700	0.086	100 / 150
Rubidium Rb 37	39.0	688	1.475	39.0	4.32 / 3.64	50 / 100	0.673 / 0.323	38 / 220.1	–	–
Silver Ag 47	960.5	2212	9.3 / 9.0	960.5 / 1300	6.04 / 4.76	1000 / 1340	2.98	1200	923	995
Sodium Na 11	97.8	1621	0.928 / 0.780	100 / 700	10.35 / 5.41	100 / 350	0.686 / 0.182	103.7 / 700	206.4 / 199.5	100 / 250
Tin Sn 50	231.9	2270	6.834 / 6.64	409 / 704	2.1 / 1.45	231.9 / 1000	1.91 / 1.05	240 / 600	526 / 510	300 / 500
Zinc Zn 30	419.5	1663	6.92 / 6.57	419.5 / 800	2.83 / 2.80	419.5 / 800	3.17 / 1.88	450 / 700	785 / 765	510 / 640
NaK Alloy 1 Na 22% K 78%	19	1518	0.886 / 0.742	100 / 700	3.03 / 2.44	50 / 200	0.546 / 0.161	103.7 / 700	100—110	m.p. 250
NaK Alloy 2 Na 56% K 44%	−11	784	0.847 / 0.703	100 / 700	2.66 / 2.13	50 / 200	0.468 / 0.146	103.7 / 700	110—120	m.p. 250
Wood's Metal	70	–	9.8 / 6.94	73 / 687	0.993 / 0.936	85.6 / 326.5	281 / 177	100 / 200	326	100
NaCl, Standard solution	–	–	1.201	18	0.226 / 0.277	20 / 30	108 / 112	18 / 60	80	20

Table 3

Some useful constants in MKS *units*

Permittivity in vacuum $\epsilon_0 =$ 8.85×10^{-12} farad/m
Permeability in vacuum $\mu_0 =$ $4\pi \times 10^{-7}$ henry/m
Velocity of light $c = 2.998 \times 10^8$ m/sec
Electronic charge $e = 1.602 \times 10^{-19}$ coulomb
Mass of electron $m_e = 9.108 \times 10^{-31}$ kg

Appendix 2

Relativistic Formulation
of Magnetohydrodynamics

Various approaches to a relativistic formulation of magnetohydrodynamics have been made. The most logical approach seems to be from
the energy-momentum tensor. The equations of energy and momentum
can be expressed by the single four-dimensional equation

$$T^{\mu\nu}{}_{,\nu} = 0 \tag{1}$$

where $T^{\mu\nu}$ is the complete energy-momentum tensor. For magnetohydrodynamics this tensor must include the fluid, the electromagnetic field, and
the effects of heat conduction. The tensor is considered to be made up of
three parts

$$T^{\mu\nu} = T_m{}^{\mu\nu} + T_e{}^{\mu\nu} + T_h{}^{\mu\nu} \tag{2}$$

where the three terms represent the parts due to the fluid, the electromagnetic field, and heat conduction, respectively. The notation is that
of the tensor calculus and a comma represents differentiation with respect
to the coordinate identified by the subscript following the comma.

The four-divergence of $T^{\mu\nu}$ represents the three momentum equations
and the energy equation, and these, along with Maxwell's equations and
covariant forms of the constitutive equations, Fourier's law, and the
equation of state, constitute the basic equations of relativistic magnetohydrodynamics.

A metric tensor $g^{\mu\nu}$ is assumed and can be used to raise and lower suffixes
as follows:

$$A_\mu = g_{\mu\nu}A^\nu \qquad A^\mu = g^{\mu\nu}A_\nu \tag{3}$$

A coordinate system (x^1, x^2, x^3, ct) is assumed and the metric tensor is supposed to take the form in a Galilean system:

$$g^{\mu\nu} = g_{\mu\nu} = \begin{bmatrix} -1 & 0 & 0 & 0 \\ 0 & -1 & 0 & 0 \\ 0 & 0 & -1 & 0 \\ 0 & 0 & 0 & 1 \end{bmatrix} \quad \begin{aligned} ds^2 &= -(dx^1)^2 - (dx^2)^2 - (dx^3)^2 \\ &\quad + c^2\,dt^2 \\ &= g_{\mu\nu}\,dx^\mu\,dx^\nu \end{aligned} \tag{4}$$

The expression for $T_m{}^{\mu\nu}$ can be written

$$T_m{}^{\mu\nu} = P^{\mu\nu} + \rho^0 U^\mu U^\nu \tag{5}$$

where U^μ is the four-velocity defined as

$$U^\mu = [\beta\mathbf{V};\ \beta c] = \frac{dx^\mu}{d\tau} = c\,\frac{dx^\mu}{ds} \tag{6}$$

τ is proper time, and $\mathbf{V}$ is the ordinary three-velocity $d\mathbf{x}/dt$. β is simply $(1 - V^2/c^2)^{-1/2}$. From the definition of U^μ it is seen that

$$U_\mu U^\mu = g_{\mu\nu} U^\nu U^\mu = c^2 \tag{7}$$

ρ^0 is the rest mass density and $P^{\mu\nu}$ is defined by its rest-frame value of $\tau_{ik}{}^0$. (Here the Latin suffixes have a range 1, 2, 3 and the Greek suffixes a range 1, 2, 3, 4. A superscript zero represents the rest-frame value as in the nonrelativistic formulation.) $\tau_{ik}{}^0$ is the negative of the ordinary mechanical stress tensor. In the special Galilean frame any four-vector A^μ and tensor $B^{\mu\nu}$ satisfy the following relationships:

$$A^i = -A_i \qquad A^4 = A_4 \tag{8}$$
$$B^{ij} = B_{ij} \qquad B^{i4} = -B_{i4}$$

The second term on the right side of (5) is called the kinetic energy-momentum tensor. A Lorentz transformation then gives the appropriate value of $P^{\mu\nu}$ in any frame other than S^0, and the tensor $T_m{}^{\mu\nu}$ is defined uniquely. In any arbitrary frame $P^{\mu\nu}$ does not represent the ordinary mechanical stress tensor directly and it is convenient to introduce the momentum density g^i and stress tensor τ_{ij}. ($P^{\mu\nu}$ does not transform into τ_{ij}.) The energy-momentum tensor can then be written

$$T_m{}^{\mu\nu} = \left[\begin{array}{c|c} \tau^{ij} + g^i V^j & \begin{array}{c} cg^1 \\ cg^2 \\ cg^3 \end{array} \\ \hline cg^1 cg^2 cg^3 & \rho c^2 \end{array} \right] \tag{9}$$

which is valid in any frame of reference. The three-space part ($\tau^{ij} + g^i V^j$) is called the absolute stress tensor and τ^{ij} the relative stress tensor. The explicit components can be written in terms of τ^{ij} and ρ^0 as

$$T_m{}^{ij} = T_m{}^{ji} = \rho^0 U^i U^j + \tau^{ij} - \frac{\tau_{lk} U^k U^j g^{li}}{c^2}$$

$$T_m{}^{i4} = T_m{}^{4i} = \rho^0 U^i U^4 - \frac{\tau_{lj} U^j U^4 g^{li}}{c^2} \tag{10}$$

$$T_m{}^{44} = \rho^0 U^4 U^4 + \frac{U^i \tau_{ij} U^j}{c^2} = h = \rho c^2$$

where h is the energy density. Density here refers to unit volume in the local frame of reference, and the changes of volume with Lorentz transformations must be taken into account. The divergence of (9) can then be written in the more familiar form that retains the difference between space and time. In the absence of electromagnetic and heat conduction effects then:

$$\frac{\partial h}{\partial t} + \frac{\partial}{\partial x^i}(h V^i - V_j \tau^{ji}) = 0$$

$$\frac{\partial g^i}{\partial t} + \frac{\partial}{\partial x^j}(g^i V^j + \tau^{ij}) = 0 \tag{11}$$

The Lorentz transformations for the quantities which appear in the energy momentum tensor are listed at the end of this appendix for Galilean frames that do not undergo spatial rotations. In particular

$$\rho^0 = \frac{\rho}{\beta^2} - \frac{1}{c^4}(V^i \tau_{ij} V^j)$$

$$= \frac{\rho}{\beta^2} - \frac{1}{c^4}(V^i \tau_{ij}{}^0 V^j) \tag{12}$$

The electromagnetic energy momentum tensor can be expressed as

$$T_e{}^{\mu\nu} = (\tfrac{1}{4} F^{\alpha\beta} H_{\alpha\beta}) g^{\mu\nu} - g^{\beta\nu} F^{\mu\alpha} H^{\beta\alpha} \tag{13}$$

where the field quantities $F^{\mu\nu}$ and $H^{\mu\nu}$ are antisymmetric and defined as

$$\mathbf{B} = \frac{1}{c}(F^{23}, F^{31}, F^{12})$$

$$\mathbf{E} = (F^{41}, F^{42}, F^{43})$$

$$\mathbf{H} = c(H^{23}, H^{31}, H^{12}) \tag{14}$$

$$\mathbf{D} = (H^{41}, H^{42}, H^{43})$$

where $\mathbf{B}$, $\mathbf{E}$, $\mathbf{H}$, and $\mathbf{D}$ are defined as identical with $\mathbf{B}^0$, $\mathbf{E}^0$, $\mathbf{H}^0$, and $\mathbf{D}^0$ when measured in the rest frame S^0. Striction effects are not considered and, in order to avoid questions of the form of the momentum and energy density, this energy momentum tensor is assumed to be valid only for media with μ_0 and ϵ_0. Maxwell's equations can then be written

$$F_{\mu\nu,\alpha} + F_{\nu\alpha,\mu} + F_{\alpha\mu,\nu} = 0$$
$$H^{\mu\nu}{}_{,\nu} = J^\mu \tag{15}$$

where the four current J^μ is defined as

$$J^\mu = [J^i/c;\ \rho_e] \tag{16}$$

Here ρ_e is the charge density and J^i the three current density. The electromagnetic energy momentum tensor cannot be defined in an unambiguous manner but there are arguments that lead us to believe that Equation (13) is correct.

If Equation (2) is expressed as

$$T_m{}^{\mu\nu}{}_{,\nu} + T_h{}^{\mu\nu}{}_{,\nu} = -T_e{}^{\mu\nu}{}_{,\nu} = f^\mu \tag{17}$$

where f^μ is the interaction between the electromagnetic field and the fluid and heat conduction fields, f^μ can be given a simplified form for an isotropic, homogeneous medium with a constant permeability and dielectric constant (ordinary vector notation is used for the three vector or space part of a four-vector):

$$f^\mu = -F^{\mu\nu}J_\nu = [(\rho_e\mathbf{E} + \mathbf{J} \times \mathbf{B});\ \mathbf{E} \cdot \mathbf{J}] \tag{18}$$

f^i is recognizable as the familiar Lorentz force and f^4 gives the Poynting theorem

$$\frac{1}{2}\frac{\partial}{\partial t}(\mathbf{E} \cdot \mathbf{D} + \mathbf{H} \cdot \mathbf{B}) + \nabla \cdot (\mathbf{E} \times \mathbf{H}) = -\mathbf{E} \cdot \mathbf{J} \tag{19}$$

The constitutive equations for the electromagnetic field can be written in the rest frame as

$$D_i{}^0 = \epsilon E_i{}^0$$
$$B_i{}^0 = \mu H_i{}^0 \tag{20}$$
$$J_i{}^0 = \sigma E_i{}^0$$

The last equation is the ordinary Ohm's law. These equations can be put into a covariant form:

$$H_{\mu\nu}U^\mu = \epsilon F_{\mu\nu}U^\mu$$

$$(g_{\alpha\beta}F_{\mu\nu} + g_{\alpha\mu}F_{\nu\beta} + g_{\alpha\nu}F_{\beta\mu})U^\alpha = \mu(g_{\alpha\beta}H_{\mu\nu} + g_{\alpha\mu}H_{\nu\beta} + g_{\alpha\nu}H_{\beta\mu})U^\alpha \tag{21}$$

$$J^\mu - \frac{J_\nu U^\nu U^\mu}{c^2} = \frac{\sigma}{c^2}g_{\nu\alpha}F^{\alpha\mu}U^\nu$$

A suitable form for the heat conduction part of the energy momentum tensor is

$$T_h^{\mu\nu} = \frac{q^\mu U^\nu + q^\nu U^\mu}{c^2} \tag{22}$$

where q^μ is the heat flux four-vector. In the rest frame the divergence of the heat conduction part of the energy momentum tensor reduces to the four vector

$$T_h^{0\mu\nu}{}_{,\nu} = \left[\frac{\partial}{\partial t}\left(\frac{\mathbf{q}^0}{c^2}\right); \ \frac{1}{c}\nabla\cdot\mathbf{q}^0\right] \tag{23}$$

We see that the momentum associated with the conduction of heat is $\mathbf{q}/c^2$. A covariant form of Fourier's law has been suggested

$$q^\mu = -\kappa_T S^{\mu\nu}\left(\theta^0{}_{,\nu} - \frac{\theta^0}{c^2}U^\alpha U_{\nu,\alpha}\right) \tag{24}$$

where θ is the temperature which transforms according to

$$\theta = \frac{\theta^0}{\beta} \tag{25}$$

and

$$S^{\mu\nu} = -g^{\mu\nu} + \frac{U^\mu U^\nu}{c^2} \tag{26}$$

so that $S^{\mu\nu}$ serves as a proper space projection operator. κ_T is an invariant scalar and equal to the ordinary thermal conductivity.

The expressions for the various parts of the energy-momentum tensor can now be combined to give one expression for momentum and energy balance:

$$\left[P^{\mu\nu} + \rho^0 U^\mu U^\nu + \tfrac{1}{4}(F^{\alpha\beta}H_{\alpha\beta})g^{\mu\nu} - g^{\beta\nu}F^{\mu\alpha}H_{\beta\alpha} + \frac{q^\mu U^\nu + q^\nu U^\mu}{c^2}\right]_{,\nu} = 0 \tag{27}$$

Now the first law formulation is obtained by multiplying through by U_μ and simplifying the resulting scalar equation. In order to introduce the internal energy, the following substitution is indicated:

$$h^0 = \rho^0 c^2 = n^0(m^0 c^2 + \mathscr{E}^0) \tag{28}$$

where n is the particle density (number of particles or molecules per unit volume) in the rest frame S^0, m^0 is the average rest mass per particle, and $\mathscr{E}^0$ is the average excess energy (in the rest frame) per particle over the rest mass and can be thought of as a measure of the ordinary internal energy. Then h^0 transforms as

$$\begin{aligned}
h &= \rho c^2 = (\rho^0 c^2 - c^{-2}V^i\tau_{ij}V^j)\beta^2 \\
&= [n^0(m^0 c^2 + \mathscr{E}^0) + c^{-2}V^i\tau_{ij}{}^0 V^j]\beta^2
\end{aligned} \tag{29}$$

The following relationships are needed

$$T_m{}^{\mu\nu}U_\nu = \rho^0 c^2 U^\mu = h^0 U^\mu$$

$$U^\mu U_\mu = c^2$$

$$P^{\mu\nu}U_\nu = 0 \tag{30}$$

$$q^\mu U_\mu = 0$$

$$U^\mu U_{\mu,\nu} = U_\mu U^\mu{}_{,\nu} = 0$$

The last three expressions can be verified by writing them in the rest frame. The first expression then follows from these directly. The fact that the number of particles is conserved is stated by

$$(n^0 U^\mu)_{,\mu} = 0 \tag{31}$$

which is the analogue of the classical continuity equation.

By combining Equations (28), (30), (31), and Equation (27) multiplied through by U_μ, we have

$$n^0 U^\mu \mathscr{E}^0{}_{,\mu} - P^{\mu\nu}U_{\mu,\nu} + T_e{}^{\mu\nu}{}_{,\nu}U_\mu + q^\mu{}_{,\mu} - \frac{q^\mu U^\nu U_{\mu,\nu}}{c^2} = 0 \tag{32}$$

which is the relativistic statement of the first law of thermodynamics. The $U^\mu \mathscr{E}^0{}_{,\mu}$ term is the analogue of the classical material derivative. The tensor $P^{\mu\nu}$ can be broken up into a viscous and pressure part as

$$P^{\mu\nu} = \hat{P}^{\mu\nu} + P S^{\mu\nu} \tag{33}$$

and the term $\hat{P}^{\mu\nu}U_{\mu,\nu}$ represents the relativistic dissipation function. (It must be remembered here that the stress tensor has been defined such that pressure is a positive stress.)

For isotropic, homogeneous media in which the permeability and dielectric constant are constants the electromagnetic part of Equation (32) can be simplified. From Equation (18)

$$T_e{}^{\mu\nu}{}_{,\nu} = -f^\mu = F^{\mu\nu}J_\nu = -[(\rho_e \mathbf{E} + \mathbf{J} \times \mathbf{B}); \; \mathbf{E} \cdot \mathbf{J}] \tag{34}$$

By using Ohm's law, we can show that

$$f^\mu U_\mu = -F^{\mu\nu}J_\nu U_\mu = -U_\mu{}^0 F^{\mu\nu}J_\nu{}^0 = \mathbf{E}^0 \cdot \mathbf{J}^0 = -E_i{}^0 J^{0i} \tag{35}$$

Hence Equation (32) takes the form using

$$n^0 U^\mu \mathscr{E}^0{}_{,\mu} - \hat{P}^{\mu\nu}U_{\mu,\nu} + P^0 U^\mu{}_{,\mu} - \mathbf{E}^0 \cdot \mathbf{J}^0 + q^\mu{}_{,\mu} - \frac{q^\mu U^\nu U_{\mu,\nu}}{c^2} = 0 \tag{36}$$

which is the first law statement for an isotropic, homogeneous fluid with constant μ and ϵ. Now, for a perfect fluid the rest frame value of $P^{0\mu\nu}$ takes the simple form

$$P^{0\mu\nu} \equiv \tau^{0ij} = -P^0 g^{ij} \tag{37}$$

and

$$P^{\mu\nu} = P^0 S^{\mu\nu} = P S^{\mu\nu} \tag{38}$$

since the isotropic pressure is an invariant scalar. The mechanical energy-momentum tensor then takes the form

$$T_m{}^{\mu\nu} = \rho^0 U^\mu U^\nu + \frac{P^0 U^\mu U^\nu}{c^2} - P^0 g^{\mu\nu}$$

$$= \rho^0 U^\mu U^\nu + P^0 S^{\mu\nu} \tag{39}$$

Hence the $\hat{P}^{\mu\nu}$ term drops out of the first law and we are left with the following expression:

$$n^0 U^\mu \mathcal{E}^0{}_{,\mu} + P^0 U^\mu{}_{,\mu} - \mathbf{E}^0 \cdot \mathbf{J}^0 + q^\mu{}_{,\mu} - \frac{q^\mu U^\nu U_{\mu,\nu}}{c^2} = 0 \tag{40}$$

The terms are completely analogous to the classical expressions except for the last term of the left side, which represents a heat conduction brought about by the acceleration of the fluid. The $(-\mathbf{E}^0 \cdot \mathbf{J}^0)$ term is simply $(E_i^0 J^{0i})$, which is exactly the same as the nonrelativistic value.

If we assume a simple fluid, the internal energy is a function of two variables, say P and the specific volume. A covariant form of Equation 5.7-1 can be stated

$$n^0 U^\mu \mathcal{E}^0{}_{,\mu} + P^0 U^\mu{}_{,\mu} = n^0 \theta^0 U^\mu s^0{}_{,\mu} \tag{41}$$

where s^0 is the entropy per particle. The entropy per particle is a scalar invariant, so that $s = s^0$. Equation (41) can be combined with the first law statement (36) to give a first law expression in terms of entropy

$$n^0 \theta^0 U^\mu s^0{}_{,\mu} - \hat{P}^{\mu\nu} U_{\mu,\nu} - \mathbf{E}^0 \cdot \mathbf{J}^0 + q^\mu{}_{,\mu} - \frac{q^\mu U^\nu U_{\mu,\nu}}{c^2} = 0 \tag{42}$$

and for a perfect fluid

$$n^0 \theta^0 U^\mu s^0{}_{,\mu} - \mathbf{E}^0 \cdot \mathbf{J}^0 + q^\mu{}_{,\mu} - \frac{q^\mu U^\nu U_{\mu,\nu}}{c^2} = 0 \tag{43}$$

A covariant expression for the second law of thermodynamics can be stated as

$$n^0 U^\mu s^0{}_{,\mu} = -\left(\frac{q^\mu}{\theta^0}\right)_{,\mu} + \Sigma \tag{44}$$

where Σ is the entropy production rate per unit volume. Now by combining Equations (42) and (44), we get, using the identity

$$\left(\frac{q^\mu}{\theta^0}\right)_{,\mu} = \frac{1}{\theta^0}q^\mu{}_{,\mu} - \frac{q^\mu\theta^0{}_{,\mu}}{\theta^{02}} \tag{45}$$

the expression for the entropy production rate:

$$\Sigma - \frac{\hat{P}^{\mu\nu}U_{\mu,\nu}}{\theta^0} - \frac{\mathbf{E}^0\cdot\mathbf{J}^0}{\theta^0} + \frac{q^\mu}{\theta^{02}}\left(\theta^0{}_{,\mu} - \frac{\theta^0 U^\alpha U_{\mu,\alpha}}{c^2}\right) = 0 \tag{46}$$

Fourier's law (Equation 24) can now be combined with Equation (46) to give

$$\Sigma - \frac{\hat{P}^{\mu\nu}U_{\mu,\nu}}{\theta^0} - \frac{\mathbf{E}^0\cdot\mathbf{J}^0}{\theta^0} - \frac{q^\nu(S^{\mu\nu})^{-1}q^\mu}{\kappa_T\theta^{02}} = 0 \tag{47}$$

where $(S^{\mu\nu})^{-1}$ is the inverse of $S^{\mu\nu}$ and can be written

$$(S^{\mu\nu})^{-1} = -g_{\mu\nu} + \frac{(U^\mu U^\nu)^{-1}}{c^2} \tag{48}$$

But

$$q^\nu(U^\mu U^\nu)^{-1}q^\mu = 0 \tag{49}$$

as can be seen by writing the expression in the rest frame. Hence we have the final expression for entropy production:

$$\Sigma = \frac{\hat{P}^{\mu\nu}U_{\mu,\nu}}{\theta^0} + \frac{\mathbf{E}^0\cdot\mathbf{J}^0}{\theta^0} - \frac{q^\mu q_\mu}{\kappa_T\theta^{02}} \tag{50}$$

The relativistic form of the entropy production equation is seen to be completely analogous to the nonrelativistic equation if the term $\hat{P}^{\mu\nu}U_{\mu,\nu}$ is interpreted as the dissipation function. In the nonrelativistic limit as $|V|^2 \ll c^2$ the two relationships become identical, of course.

It is important to remember that because of the uncertainty in the form of the electromagnetic energy-momentum tensor, the final results are reliable only for material that is nonmagnetic and nonpolarizable, that is μ is μ_0 and ϵ is ϵ_0. This is not a serious restriction since most liquids are nonmagnetic and in magnetohydrodynamics the electric terms are negligible compared to the magnetic terms.

A short list of the more useful Lorentz transformations is as follows. The frame S^0 is fixed with respect to the fluid which is moving with velocity V with respect to the frame S'. A Galilean system is assumed and the transformation is supposed to leave the spatial coordinate axes of S^0 and

S' parallel. β is $(1 - V^2/c^2)^{-\frac{1}{2}}$. The subscripts $\perp$ and $\parallel$ indicate the components perpendicular and parallel to the velocity vector $\mathbf{V}$, respectively. δV is a unit of volume.

$$\rho = \beta\left(\rho^0 + V^i \tau_{ij}{}^0 \frac{V^j}{c^4}\right)$$

$$P = P^0$$

$$\theta = \frac{1}{\beta} \theta^0$$

$$s = s^0$$

$$\delta V = \frac{1}{\beta} \delta V^0$$

$$n = \beta n^0$$

$$\rho_e = \beta\left(\rho_e{}^0 + \frac{1}{c^2}\, \mathbf{V} \cdot \mathbf{J}\right)$$

$$\mathbf{J} = \mathbf{J}^0 + \beta \frac{\mathbf{V}}{|\mathbf{V}|^2}\left[(\mathbf{V} \cdot \mathbf{J}^0)\left(1 - \frac{1}{\beta}\right) + \rho_e{}^0 |\mathbf{V}|^2\right]$$

$$\mathbf{g} = \frac{\mathbf{V}}{\beta^2 c^2}\left[h^0 + \frac{V^i \tau_{ik}{}^0 V^k}{|\mathbf{V}|^2}(1 - \beta)\right] - \frac{\tau^{0ij} V_j}{\beta c^2}$$

$$\tau^{ik} = \tau^{0ik} + \frac{V^i V_j \tau^{0jk}(1 - 1/\beta)}{|\mathbf{V}|^2} + \frac{\tau^{0ij} V_j V^k(1 - \beta)}{|\mathbf{V}|^2}$$
$$- \beta \frac{V^i V^k V^j \tau^0{}_{jl} V^l(1 - 1/\beta)^2}{|\mathbf{V}|^4}$$

$$\mathbf{E}_\perp{}^0 = \beta(\mathbf{E} + \mathbf{V} \times \mathbf{B})_\perp$$

$$\mathbf{E}_\parallel{}^0 = \mathbf{E}_\parallel$$

$$\mathbf{D}_\perp{}^0 = \beta\left(\mathbf{D} + \frac{\mathbf{V} \times \mathbf{H}}{c^2}\right)_\perp$$

$$\mathbf{D}_\parallel{}^0 = \mathbf{D}_\parallel$$

$$\mathbf{H}_\perp{}^0 = \beta(\mathbf{H} - \mathbf{V} \times \mathbf{D})_\perp$$

$$\mathbf{H}_\parallel{}^0 = \mathbf{H}_\parallel$$

$$\mathbf{B}_\perp{}^0 = \beta\left(\mathbf{B} - \frac{\mathbf{V} \times \mathbf{E}}{c^2}\right)_\perp$$

$$\mathbf{B}_\parallel{}^0 = \mathbf{B}_\parallel$$

The relationships between the stress tensor and rate of strain in the fluid are best expressed in the rest frame in one of the usual linearized theories of elasticity or hydrodynamics. However, a suitable relativistic formulation based on the usual linear relationship of the Navier-Stokes equation has been suggested by Eckart*:

$$-\hat{P}^{\mu\nu} = -P^{\mu\nu} + P^0 S^{\mu\nu} = -\lambda_1 S^{\mu\gamma} S^{\nu\delta}(U_{\gamma,\delta} + U_{\delta,\gamma}) - \lambda_2 S^{\mu\nu} S^{\gamma\delta} U_{\gamma,\delta}$$

Here $-\hat{P}^{\mu\nu}$ is the viscous stress tensor and equal to the classical value in the rest frame; λ_1 and λ_2 are the first and second coefficients of viscosity, respectively.

The equation of state for a gas takes the same form as the classical value and is covariant as it stands:

$$P^0 = \frac{Nk\theta}{V} = nk\theta = n^0 k\theta^0$$

V is the volume of the system, N the invariant number of particles contained in the system of volume V, k the Boltzmann constant, an invariant scalar, and θ is the temperature.

* C. Eckart, The Thermodynamics of Irreversible Processes, III; Relativistic Theory of the Simple Fluid, *Phys. Rev.* **58**, p. 919, 1940.

Author Index

Subject Index

637